Mathematics
Teacher's Guide

CONTENTS

Revision Editor: Alan Christopherson, M.S.

Alpha Omega Publications ®

300 North McKemy Avenue, Chandler, Arizona 85226-2618
© MM by Alpha Omega Publications, Inc.   All rights reserved.
LIFEPAC is a registered trademark of Alpha Omega Publications, Inc.

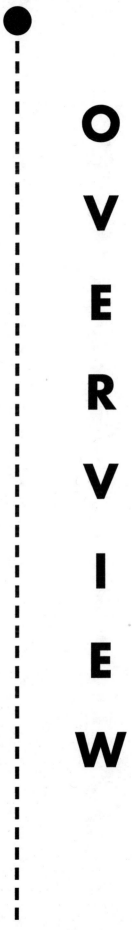

OVERVIEW

MATHEMATICS

Curriculum Overview
Grades K–12

Kindergarten

1-40	41-80	81-120	121-160
Directions-right, left, high, low, etc. **Comparisons**-big, little, alike, different **Matching** **Cardinal Numbers**-to 9 **Colors**-red, blue, green, yellow, brown ,purple **Shapes**-circle, square, rectangle, triangle **Number Order** **Before and After** **Ordinal Numbers**-to 9th **Problem Solving**	**Directions**-right, left, high, low, etc. **Comparisons**-big, little, alike, different **Matching** **Cardinal Numbers**-to 12 **Colors**-orange **Shapes**-circle, square, rectangle, triangle **Number Order** **Before and After** **Ordinal Numbers**-to 9th **Problem Solving** **Number Words**-to nine **Addition**-to 9	**Directions**-right, left, high, low ,etc. **Comparisons**-big, little, alike, different **Matching** **Cardinal Numbers**-to 19 **Colors**-black, white **Shapes**-circle, square, rectangle, triangle **Number Order** **Before and After** **Ordinal Numbers**-to 9th **Problem Solving** **Number Words**-to nine **Addition**-multiples of 10 **Subtraction**-to 9 **Place Value** **Time/Calendar**	**Directions**-right, left, high, low, etc. **Comparisons**-big, little, alike, different **Matching** **Cardinal Numbers**-to 100 **Colors**-pink **Shapes**-circle, square, rectangle, triangle **Number Order** **Before and After** **Ordinal Numbers**-to 9th **Problem Solving** **Number Words**-to nine **Addition**-to 10 and multiples of 10 **Subtraction**-to 10 **Place Value** **Time/Calendar** **Money** **Skip Counting**-2's, 5's, 10's **Greater/ Less than**

	Grade 1	Grade 2	Grade 3
LIFEPAC 1	**NUMBERS TO 99** • Number order, skip-count • Add, subtract to 9 • Story problems • Measurements, shapes	**NUMBERS TO 100** • Numbers and words to 100 • Operation symbols +, −, =, >, < • Add, subtract, story problems • Place value, fact families	**NUMBERS TO 999** • Digits, place value to 999 • Add, subtract, time • LInear measurements, dozen • Operation symbols +, −, =, ≠, >, <
LIFEPAC 2	**NUMBERS TO 99** • Add, subtract to 10 • Number words • Place value, shapes • Patterns, sequencing, estimation	**NUMBERS TO 200** • Numbers and words to 200 • Add, subtract, even and odd • Skip-count 2's, 5's, 10's, shapes • Ordinal numbers, fractions, money	**NUMBERS TO 999** • Fact families, patterns, fractions • Add, subtract - carry, borrow • Skip count 2's, 5's, 10's • Money, shapes, lines, even, odd
LIFEPAC 3	**NUMBERS TO 100** • Number sentences, • Fractions, oral directions • Story problems • Time, symbols =, ≠	**NUMBERS TO 200** • Add w/ carry to 10's place • Subtract, standard measurements • Flat shapes, money, AM/PM • Rounding to 10's place	**NUMBERS TO 999** • Add 3 numbers w/ carry • Coins, weight, volume, AM/PM • Fractions, oral instructions • Skip count 3's, subtract w/ borrow
LIFEPAC 4	**NUMBERS TO 100** • Add to 18, place value • Skip-count, even and odd • Money • Shapes, measurement	**NUMBERS TO 999** • Numbers and words to 999 • Add, subtract, place value • Calendar, making change • Measurements, solid shapes	**NUMBERS TO 9,999** • Place value to 9,999 • Rounding to 10's, estimation • Add and subtract fractions • Roman numerals, 1/4 inch
LIFEPAC 5	**NUMBERS TO 100** • Add 3 numbers - 1 digit • Ordinal numbers, fractions • Time, number line • Estimation, charts	**NUMBERS TO 999** • Data and bar graphs, shapes • Add, subtract to 100's • Skip-count 3's, place value to 100's • Add fractions, temperature	**NUMBERS TO 9,999** • Number sentences, temperature • Rounding to 100's, estimation • Perimeter, square inch • Bar graph, symmetry, even/odd rules
LIFEPAC 6	**NUMBERS TO 100** • Number words to 99 • Add 2 numbers - 2 digit • Symbols >, < • Fractions, shapes	**NUMBERS TO 999** • Measurements, perimeter • Time, money • Subtract w/ borrow from 10's place • Add, subtract fractions	**NUMBERS TO 9,999** • Add, subtract to 9,999 • Multiples, times facts for 2 • Area, equivalent fractions, money • Line graph, segments, angles
LIFEPAC 7	**NUMBERS TO 200** • Number order, place value • Subtract to 12 • Operation signs • Estimation, graphs, time	**NUMBERS TO 999** • Add w/ carry to 100's place • Fractions as words • Number order in books • Rounding and estimation	**NUMBERS TO 9,999** • Times facts for 5, missing numbers • Mixed numbers - add, subtract • Subtract with 0's in minuend • Circle graph, probability
LIFEPAC 8	**NUMBERS TO 200** • Addition, subtract to 18 • Group counting • Fractions, shapes • Time, measurements	**NUMBERS TO 999** • Add, subtract, measurements • Group count, 'think' answers • Convert coins, length, width • Directions-N, S, E, W	**NUMBERS TO 9,999** • Times facts for 3, 10 - multiples of 4 • Convert units of measurement • Decimals, directions, length, width • Picture graph, missing addend
LIFEPAC 9	**NUMBERS TO 200** • Add 3 numbers - 2 digit • Fact families • Sensible answers • Subtract 2 numbers - 2 digit	**NUMBERS TO 999** • Area and square measurement • Add 3 numbers - 20 digit w/ carry • Add coins and convert to cents • Fractions, quarter-inch	**NUMBERS TO 9,999** • Add, subtract whole numbers, fractions, mixed numbers • Standard measurements, metrics • Operation symbols, times facts for 4
LIFEPAC 10	**NUMBERS TO 200** • Add, subtract, place value • Directions - N, S, E, W • Fractions • Patterns	**NUMBERS TO 999** • Rules for even and odd • Round numbers to 100's place • Time - digital, sensible answers • Add 3 numbers - 3 digit	**NUMBERS TO 9,999** • Add, subtract, times facts 2,3,4,5,10 • Rounding to 1,000's, estimation • Probability, equations, parentheses • Perimeter, area

Grade 4	Grade 5	Grade 6	
WHOLE NUMBERS & FRACTIONS • Naming whole numbers • Naming Fractions • Sequencing patterns • Numbers to 1,000	**WHOLE NUMBERS & FRACTIONS** • Operations & symbols • Fraction language • Grouping, patterns, sequencing • Rounding & estimation	**FRACTIONS & DECIMALS** • Number to billions' place • Add & subtract fractions • Add & subtract decimals • Read and write Fractions	LIFEPAC 1
WHOLE NUMBERS & FRACTIONS • Operation symbols • Multiplication - 1 digit multiplier • Fractions - addition & subtraction • Numbers to 10,000	**WHOLE NUMBERS & FRACTIONS** • Multiplication & division • Fractions - +, –, simplify • Plane & solid shapes • Symbol language	**FINDING COMMON DENOMINATORS** • Prime factors • Fractions with unlike denominators • Exponential notation • Add & subtract mixed numbers	LIFEPAC 2
WHOLE NUMBERS & FRACTIONS • Multiplication with carrying • Rounding & estimation • Sequencing fractions • Numbers to 100,000	**WHOLE NUMBERS & FRACTIONS** • Short division • Lowest common multiple • Perimeter & area • Properties of addition	**MULTIPLYING MIXED NUMBERS** • Multiply mixed numbers • Divide decimals • Bar and line graphs • Converting fractions & decimals	LIFEPAC 3
LINES & SHAPES • Plane & solid shapes • Lines & line segments • Addition & subtraction • Multiplication with carrying	**WHOLE NUMBERS** • Lines - shapes - circles • Symmetric - congruent - similar • Decimal place value • Properties of multiplication	**DIVIDING MIXED NUMBERS** • Divide mixed numbers • Area and perimeter • Standard measurements	LIFEPAC 4
WHOLE NUMBERS • Division - 1 digit divisor • Families of facts • Standard measurements • Number grouping	**WHOLE NUMBERS & FRACTIONS** • Multiply & divide by 10, 100, 1,000 • Standard measurements • Rate problems • Whole number & fraction operations	**METRIC MEASURE** • Metric measures • Plane & solid shapes • Multi-operation problems • Roman Numerals	LIFEPAC 5
WHOLE NUMBERS & FRACTIONS • Division - 1 digit with remainder • Factors & multiples • Fractions - improper & mixed • Equivalent fractions	**FRACTIONS & DECIMALS** • Multiplication of fractions • Reading decimal numbers • Adding & subtracting decimals • Multiplication - decimals	**LCM & GCF** • LCM, GCF • Fraction and decimal equivalents • Percent • Variables, functions & formulas	LIFEPAC 6
WHOLE NUMBERS & FRACTIONS • Multiplication - 2 digit multiplier • Simplifying fractions • Averages • Decimals in money problems	**WHOLE NUMBERS & FRACTIONS** • Division - 2-digit divisor • Metric units • Multiplication - mixed numbers • Multiplication - decimals	**INTEGERS, RATIO & PROPORTION** • Positive and negative integers • Ratio & proportion • Fractions, decimals & percents • Statistics	LIFEPAC 7
WHOLE NUMBERS & FRACTIONS • Division 1 digit divisor • Fractions - unlike denominators • Metric units • Whole numbers - +, –, x, ÷	**WHOLE NUMBERS** • Calculators & whole numbers • Calculators & decimals • Estimation • Prime factors	**PROBABILITY & GRAPHING** • Probability • Graphs • Metric and standard units • Square root	LIFEPAC 8
DECIMALS & FRACTIONS • Reading and writing decimals • Mixed numbers - +, – • Cross multiplication • Estimation	**FRACTIONS & DECIMALS** • Division - fractions • Division - decimals • Ratios & ordered pairs • Converting fractions to decimals	**CALCULATORS & ESTIMATION** • Calculators • Estimation • Geometric symbols & shapes • Missing number problems	LIFEPAC 9
PROBLEM SOLVING • Estimation & data gathering • Charts & Graphs • Review numbers to 100,000 • Whole numbers - +, –, x, ÷	**PROBLEM SOLVING** • Probability & data gathering • Charts & graphs • Review numbers to 100 million • Fractions & decimals - +, –, x, ÷	**INTEGERS & OPERATIONS** • Mental arithmetic • Fraction operations • Variables & properties • Number lines	LIFEPAC 10

Mathematics LIFEPAC Overview

	Grade 7	Grade 8	Grade 9
LIFEPAC 1	**WHOLE NUMBERS** • Number concepts • Addition • Subtraction • Applications	**WHOLE NUMBERS** • The set of whole numbers • Graphs • Operations with whole numbers • Applications with whole numbers	**VARIABLES AND NUMBERS** • Variables • Distributive Property • Definition of signed numbers • Signed number operations
LIFEPAC 2	**MULTIPLICATION AND DIVISION** • Basic facts • Procedures • Practice • Applications	**NUMBERS AND FACTORS** • Numbers and bases • Sets • Factors and multiples • Least common multiples	**SOLVING EQUATIONS** • Sentences and formulas • Properties • Solving equations • Solving inequalities
LIFEPAC 3	**GEOMETRY** • Segments, lines, and angles • Triangles • Quadrilaterals • Circles and hexagons	**RATIONAL NUMBERS** • Proper and improper fractions • Mixed numbers • Decimal fractions • Per cent	**PROBLEM ANALYSIS AND SOLUTION** • Words and symbols • Simple verbal problems • Medium verbal problems • Challenging verbal problems
LIFEPAC 4	**RATIONAL NUMBERS** • Common fractions • Improper fractions • Mixed numbers • Decimal fractions	**FRACTIONS AND ROUNDING** • Common fraction addition • Common fraction subtraction • Decimal fractions • Rounding numbers	**POLYNOMIALS** • Addition of polynomials • Subtraction of polynomials • Multiplication of polynomials • Division of polynomials
LIFEPAC 5	**SETS AND NUMBERS** • Set concepts and operations • Early number systems • Decimal number system • Factors and multiples	**FRACTIONS AND PER CENT** • Multiplication of fractions • Division of fractions • Fractions as per cents • Per cent exercises	**ALGEBRAIC FACTORS** • Greatest common factor • Binomial factors • Complete factorization • Word problems
LIFEPAC 6	**FRACTIONS** • Like denominators • Unlike denominators • Decimal fractions • Equivalents	**STATISTICS, GRAPHS, & PROBABILITY** • Statistical measures • Types of graphs • Simple probability • And–Or statements	**ALGEBRAIC FRACTIONS** • Operations with fractions • Solving equations • Solving inequalities • Solving word problems
LIFEPAC 7	**FRACTIONS** • Common fractions • Decimal fractions • Per cent • Word problems	**INTEGERS** • Basic concepts • Addition and subtraction • Multiplication and division • Expressions and sentences	**RADICAL EXPRESSIONS** • Rational and irrational numbers • Operations with radicals • Irrational roots • Radical equations
LIFEPAC 8	**FORMULAS AND RATIOS** • Writing formulas • A function machine • Equations • Ratios and proportions	**FORMULAS AND GEOMETRY** • Square root • Perimeter, circumference, and area • Rectangular solid • Cylinder, cone, and sphere	**GRAPHING** • Equations of two variables • Graphing lines • Graphing inequalities • Equations of lines
LIFEPAC 9	**DATA, STATISTICS AND GRAPHS** • Gathering and organizing data • Central tendency and dispersion • Graphs of statistics • Graphs of points	**ALGEBRAIC EQUATIONS** • Variables in formulas • Addition and subtraction • Multiplication and division • Problem solving	**SYSTEMS** • Graphical solution • Algebraic solutions • Determinants • Word problems
LIFEPAC 10	**MATHEMATICS IN SPORTS** • Whole numbers • Geometry, sets, and systems • Fractions • Formulas, ratios, and statistics	**NUMBERS, FRACTIONS, ALGEBRA** • Whole numbers and fractions • Fractions and per cent • Statistics, graphs and probability • Integers and algebra	**QUADRATIC EQUATIONS AND REVIEW** • Solving quadratic equations • Equations and inequalities • Polynomials and factors • Radicals and graphing

Grade 10	Grade 11	Grade 12	
A MATHEMATICAL SYSTEM • Points, lines, and planes • Definition of definitions • Geometric terms • Postulates and theorems	**SETS, STRUCTURE, AND FUNCTION** • Properties and operations of sets • Axioms and applications • Relations and functions • Algebraic expressions	**RELATIONS AND FUNCTIONS** • Relations and functions • Rules of correspondence • Notation of functions • Types of functions	LIFEPAC 1
PROOFS • Logic • Reasoning • Two-column proof • Paragraph proof	**NUMBERS, SENTENCES, & PROBLEMS** • Order and absolute value • Sums and products • Algebraic sentences • Number and motion problems	**SPECIAL FUNCTIONS** • Linear functions • Second-degree functions • Polynomial functions • Other functions	LIFEPAC 2
ANGLES AND PARALLELS • Definitions and measurement • Relationships and theorems • Properties of parallels • Parallels and polygons	**LINEAR EQUATIONS & INEQUALITIES** • Graphs • Equations • Systems of equations • Inequalities	**TRIGONOMETRIC FUNCTIONS** • Definition • Evaluation of functions • Trigonometric tables • Special angles	LIFEPAC 3
CONGRUENCY • Congruent triangles • Corresponding parts • Inequalities • Quadrilaterals	**POLYNOMIALS** • Multiplying polynomials • Factoring • Operations with polynomials • Variations	**CIRCULAR FUNCTIONS & GRAPHS** • Circular functions & special angles • Graphs of sin and cos • Amplitude and period • Phase shifts	LIFEPAC 4
SIMILAR POLYGONS • Ratios and proportions • Definition of similarity • Similar polygons and triangles • Right triangle geometry	**RADICAL EXPRESSIONS** • Multiplying and dividing fractions • Adding and subtracting fractions • Equations with fractions • Applications of fractions	**IDENTITIES AND FUNCTIONS** • Reciprocal relations • Pythagorean relations • Trigonometric identities • Sum and difference formulas	LIFEPAC 5
CIRCLES • Circles and spheres • Tangents, arcs, and chords • Special angles in circles • Special segments in circles	**REAL NUMBERS** • Rational and irrational numbers • Laws of Radicals • Quadratic equations • Quadratic formula	**TRIGONOMETRIC FUNCTIONS** • Trigonometric functions • Law of cosines • Law of sines • Applied problems	LIFEPAC 6
CONSTRUCTION AND LOCUS • Basic constructions • Triangles and circles • Polygons • Locus meaning and use	**QUADRATIC RELATIONS & SYSTEMS** • Distance formulas • Conic sections • Systems of equations • Application of conic sections	**TRIGONOMETRIC FUNCTIONS** • Inverse functions • Graphing polar coordinates • Converting polar coordinates • Graphing polar equations	LIFEPAC 7
AREA AND VOLUME • Area of polygons • Area of circles • Surface area of solids • Volume of solids	**EXPONENTIAL FUNCTIONS** • Exponents • Exponential equations • Logarithmic functions • Matrices	**QUADRATIC EQUATIONS** • Conic sections • Circle and ellipse • Parabola and hyperbola • Transformations	LIFEPAC 8
COORDINATE GEOMETRY • Ordered pairs • Distance • Lines • Coordinate proofs	**COUNTING PRINCIPLES** • Progressions • Permutations • Combinations • Probability	**PROBABILITY** • Random experiments & probability • Permutations • Combinations • Applied problems	LIFEPAC 9
REVIEW • Proof and angles • Polygons and circles • Construction and measurement • Coordinate geometry	**REVIEW** • Integers and open sentences • Graphs and polynomials • Fractions and quadratics • Exponential functions	**CALCULUS** • Mathematical induction • Functions and limits • Slopes of functions • Review of 1200 mathematics	LIFEPAC 10

MANAGEMENT

STRUCTURE OF THE LIFEPAC CURRICULUM

The LIFEPAC curriculum is conveniently structured to provide one teacher handbook containing teacher support material with answer keys and ten student worktexts for each subject at grade levels two through twelve. The worktext format of the LIFEPACs allows the student to read the textual information and complete workbook activities all in the same booklet. The easy to follow LIFEPAC numbering system lists the grade as the first number(s) and the last two digits as the number of the series. For example, the Language Arts LIFEPAC at the 6th grade level, 5th book in the series would be LA 605.

Each LIFEPAC is divided into 3 to 5 sections and begins with an introduction or overview of the booklet as well as a series of specific learning objectives to give a purpose to the study of the LIFEPAC. The introduction and objectives are followed by a vocabulary section which may be found at the beginning of each section at the lower levels, at the beginning of the LIFEPAC in the middle grades, or in the glossary at the high school level. Vocabulary words are used to develop word recognition and should not be confused with the spelling words introduced later in the LIFEPAC. The student should learn all vocabulary words before working the LIFEPAC sections to improve comprehension, retention, and reading skills.

Each activity or written assignment has a number for easy identification, such as 1.1. The first number corresponds to the LIFEPAC section and the number to the right of the decimal is the number of the activity.

Teacher checkpoints, which are essential to maintain quality learning, are found at various locations throughout the LIFEPAC. The teacher should check 1) neatness of work and penmanship, 2) quality of understanding (tested with a short oral quiz), 3) thoroughness of answers (complete sentences and paragraphs, correct spelling, etc.), 4) completion of activities (no blank spaces), and 5) accuracy of answers as compared to the answer key (all answers correct).

The self test questions are also number coded for easy reference. For example, 2.015 means that this is the 15th question in the self test of Section II. The first number corresponds to the LIFEPAC section, the zero indicates that it is a self test question, and the number to the right of the zero the question number.

The LIFEPAC test is packaged at the centerfold of each LIFEPAC. It should be removed and put aside before giving the booklet to the student for study.

Answer and test keys have the same numbering system as the LIFEPACs and appear at the back of this handbook. The student may be given access to the answer keys (not the test keys) under teacher supervision so that he can score his own work.

A thorough study of the Curriculum Overview by the teacher before instruction begins is essential to the success of the student. The teacher should become familiar with expected skill mastery and understand how these grade level skills fit into the overall skill development of the curriculum. The teacher should also preview the objectives that appear at the beginning of each LIFEPAC for additional preparation and planning.

TEST SCORING and GRADING

Answer keys and test keys give examples of correct answers. They convey the idea, but the student may use many ways to express a correct answer. The teacher should check for the essence of the answer, not for the exact wording. Many questions are high level and require thinking and creativity on the part of the student. Each answer should be scored based on whether or not the main idea written by the student matches the model example. "Any Order" or "Either Order" in a key indicates that no particular order is necessary to be correct.

Most self tests and LIFEPAC tests at the lower elementary levels are scored at 1 point per answer; however, the upper levels may have a point system awarding 2 to 5 points for various answers or questions. Further, the total test points will vary; they may not always equal 100 points. They may be 78, 85, 100, 105, etc.

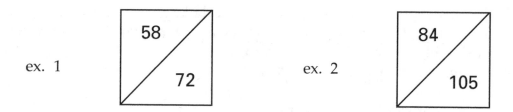

A score box similar to ex.1 above is located at the end of each self test and on the front of the LIFEPAC test. The bottom score, 72, represents the total number of points possible on the test. The upper score, 58, represents the number of points your student will need to receive an 80% or passing grade. If you wish to establish the exact percentage that your student has achieved, find the total points of his correct answers and divide it by the bottom number (in this case 72.) For example, if your student has a point total of 65, divide 65 by 72 for a grade of 90%. Referring to ex. 2, on a test with a total of 105 possible points, the student would have to receive a minimum of 84 correct points for an 80% or passing grade. If your student has received 93 points, simply divide the 93 by 105 for a percentage grade of 89%. Students who receive a score below 80% should review the LIFEPAC and retest using the appropriate Alternate Test found in the Teacher's Guide.

The following is a guideline to assign letter grades for completed LIFEPACs based on a maximum total score of 100 points.

LIFEPAC Test   =   60% of the Total Score (or percent grade)
Self Test   =   25% of the Total Score (average percent of self tests)
Reports   =   10% or 10* points per LIFEPAC
Oral Work   =   5% or 5* points per LIFEPAC
*Determined by the teacher's subjective evaluation of the student's daily work.

Example:

LIFEPAC Test Score	=	92%	92	x	.60		=	55 points
Self Test Average	=	90%	90	x	.25		=	23 points
Reports							=	8 points
Oral Work							=	4 points

TOTAL POINTS	=	90 points

Grade Scale based on point system:

100	–	94	=	A
93	–	86	=	B
85	–	77	=	C
76	–	70	=	D
Below		70	=	F

TEACHER HINTS and STUDYING TECHNIQUES

LIFEPAC Activities are written to check the level of understanding of the preceding text. The student may look back to the text as necessary to complete these activities; however, a student should never attempt to do the activities without reading (studying) the text first. Self tests and LIFEPAC tests are never open book tests.

Language arts activities (skill integration) often appear within other subject curriculum. The purpose is to give the student an opportunity to test his skill mastery outside of the context in which it was presented.

Writing complete answers (paragraphs) to some questions is an integral part of the LIFEPAC Curriculum in all subjects. This builds communication and organization skills, increases understanding and retention of ideas, and helps enforce good penmanship. Complete sentences should be encouraged for this type of activity. Obviously, single words or phrases do not meet the intent of the activity, since multiple lines are given for the response.

Review is essential to student success. Time invested in review where review is suggested will be time saved in correcting errors later. Self tests, unlike the section activities, are closed book. This procedure helps to identify weaknesses before they become too great to overcome. Certain objectives from self tests are cumulative and test previous sections; therefore, good preparation for a self test must include all material studied up to that testing point.

The following procedure checklist has been found to be successful in developing good study habits in the LIFEPAC curriculum.

1. Read the introduction and Table of Contents.
2. Read the objectives.
3. Recite and study the entire vocabulary (glossary) list.
4. Study each section as follows:
    a. Read the introduction and study the section objectives.
    b. Read all the text for the entire section, but answer none of the activities.
    c. Return to the beginning of the section and memorize each vocabulary word and definition.
    d. Reread the section, complete the activities, check the answers with the answer key, correct all errors, and have the teacher check.
    e. Read the self test but do not answer the questions.
    f. Go to the beginning of the first section and reread the text and answers to the activities up to the self test you have not yet done.
    g. Answer the questions to the self test without looking back.
    h. Have the self test checked by the teacher.
    i. Correct the self test and have the teacher check the corrections.
    j. Repeat steps a–i for each section.

5. Use the SQ3R* method to prepare for the LIFEPAC test.
6. Take the LIFEPAC test as a closed book test.
7. LIFEPAC tests are administered and scored under direct teacher supervision. Students who receive scores below 80% should review the LIFEPAC using the SQ3R* study method and take the Alternate Test located in the Teacher Handbook. The final test grade may be the grade on the Alternate Test or an average of the grades from the original LIFEPAC test and the Alternate Test.

    *SQ3R: Scan the whole LIFEPAC.
        Question yourself on the objectives.
        Read the whole LIFEPAC again.
        Recite through an oral examination.
        Review weak areas.

GOAL SETTING and SCHEDULES

Each school must develop its own schedule, because no single set of procedures will fit every situation. The following is an example of a daily schedule that includes the five LIFEPAC subjects as well as time slotted for special activities.

Possible Daily Schedule

8:15	–	8:25	Pledges, prayer, songs, devotions, etc.
8:25	–	9:10	Bible
9:10	–	9:55	Language Arts
9:55	–	10:15	Recess (juice break)
10:15	–	11:00	Mathematics
11:00	–	11:45	Social Studies
11:45	–	12:30	Lunch, recess, quiet time
12:30	–	1:15	Science
1:15	–		Drill, remedial work, enrichment*

*Enrichment: Computer time, physical education, field trips, fun reading, games and puzzles, family business, hobbies, resource persons, guests, crafts, creative work, electives, music appreciation, projects.

Basically, two factors need to be considered when assigning work to a student in the LIFEPAC curriculum.

The first is time. An average of 45 minutes should be devoted to each subject, each day. Remember, this is only an average. Because of extenuating circumstances a student may spend only 15 minutes on a subject one day and the next day spend 90 minutes on the same subject.

The second factor is the number of pages to be worked in each subject. A single LIFEPAC is designed to take 3 to 4 weeks to complete. Allowing about 3-4 days for LIFEPAC introduction, review, and tests, the student has approximately 15 days to complete the LIFEPAC pages. Simply take the number of pages in the LIFEPAC, divide it by 15 and you will have the number of pages that must be completed on a daily basis to keep the student on schedule. For example, a LIFEPAC containing 45 pages will require 3 completed pages per day. Again, this is only an average. While working a 45 page LIFEPAC, the student may complete only 1 page the first day if the text has a lot of activities or reports, but go on to complete 5 pages the next day.

Long range planning requires some organization. Because the traditional school year originates in the early fall of one year and continues to late spring of the following year, a calendar should be devised that covers this period of time. Approximate beginning and completion dates can be noted on the calendar as well as special occasions such as holidays, vacations and birthdays. Since each LIFEPAC takes 3-4 weeks or eighteen days to complete, it should take about 180 school days to finish a set of ten LIFEPACs. Starting at the beginning school date, mark off eighteen school days on the calendar and that will become the targeted completion date for the first LIFEPAC. Continue marking the calendar until you have established dates for the remaining nine LIFEPACs making adjustments for previously noted holidays and vacations. If all five subjects are being used, the ten established target dates should be the same for the LIFEPACs in each subject.

FORMS

The sample weekly lesson plan and student grading sheet forms are included in this section as teacher support materials and may be duplicated at the convenience of the teacher.

The student grading sheet is provided for those who desire to follow the suggested guidelines for assignment of letter grades found on page 3 of this section. The student's self test scores should be posted as percentage grades. When the LIFEPAC is completed the teacher should average the self test grades, multiply the average by .25 and post the points in the box marked self test points. The LIFEPAC percentage grade should be multiplied by .60 and posted. Next, the teacher should award and post points for written reports and oral work. A report may be any type of written work assigned to the student whether it is a LIFEPAC or additional learning activity. Oral work includes the student's ability to respond orally to questions which may or may not be related to LIFEPAC activities or any type of oral report assigned by the teacher. The points may then be totaled and a final grade entered along with the date that the LIFEPAC was completed.

The Student Record Book which was specifically designed for use with the Alpha Omega curriculum provides space to record weekly progress for one student over a nine week period as well as a place to post self test and LIFEPAC scores. The Student Record Books are available through the current Alpha Omega catalog; however, unlike the enclosed forms these books are not for duplication and should be purchased in sets of four to cover a full academic year.

WEEKLY LESSON PLANNER

Week of:

	Subject	Subject	Subject	Subject
Monday				
	Subject	Subject	Subject	Subject
Tuesday				
	Subject	Subject	Subject	Subject
Wednesday				
	Subject	Subject	Subject	Subject
Thursday				
	Subject	Subject	Subject	Subject
Friday				

WEEKLY LESSON PLANNER

Week of:

	Subject	Subject	Subject	Subject
Monday				
	Subject	Subject	Subject	Subject
Tuesday				
	Subject	Subject	Subject	Subject
Wednesday				
	Subject	Subject	Subject	Subject
Thursday				
	Subject	Subject	Subject	Subject
Friday				

Student Name _____   Year _____

Bible

LP #	Self Test Scores by Sections 1	2	3	4	5	Self Test Points	LIFEPAC Test	Oral Points	Report Points	Final Grade	Date
01											
02											
03											
04											
05											
06											
07											
08											
09											
10											

History & Geography

LP #	Self Test Scores by Sections 1	2	3	4	5	Self Test Points	LIFEPAC Test	Oral Points	Report Points	Final Grade	Date
01											
02											
03											
04											
05											
06											
07											
08											
09											
10											

Language Arts

LP #	Self Test Scores by Sections 1	2	3	4	5	Self Test Points	LIFEPAC Test	Oral Points	Report Points	Final Grade	Date
01											
02											
03											
04											
05											
06											
07											
08											
09											
10											

Student Name _____   Year _____

Mathematics

LP #	Self Test Scores by Sections 1	2	3	4	5	Self Test Points	LIFEPAC Test	Oral Points	Report Points	Final Grade	Date
01											
02											
03											
04											
05											
06											
07											
08											
09											
10											

Science

LP #	Self Test Scores by Sections 1	2	3	4	5	Self Test Points	LIFEPAC Test	Oral Points	Report Points	Final Grade	Date
01											
02											
03											
04											
05											
06											
07											
08											
09											
10											

Spelling/Electives

LP #	Self Test Scores by Sections 1	2	3	4	5	Self Test Points	LIFEPAC Test	Oral Points	Report Points	Final Grade	Date
01											
02											
03											
04											
05											
06											
07											
08											
09											
10											

NOTES

INSTRUCTIONS FOR TWELFTH GRADE MATHEMATICS

The LIFEPAC curriculum from grades two through twelve is structured so that the daily instructional material is written directly into the LIFEPACs. The student is encouraged to read and follow this instructional material in order to develop independent study habits. The teacher should introduce the LIFEPAC to the student, set a required completion schedule, complete teacher checks, be available for questions regarding both content and procedures, administer and grade tests, and develop additional learning activities as desired. Teachers working with several students may schedule their time so that students are assigned to a quiet work activity when it is necessary to spend instructional time with one particular student.

Mathematics is a subject that requires skill mastery. But skill mastery needs to be applied toward active student involvement. Measurements require measuring cups, rulers, empty containers. Boxes and other similar items help the study of solid shapes. Construction paper, beads, buttons, beans are readily available and can be used for counting, base ten, fractions, sets, grouping, and sequencing. Students should be presented with problem situations and be given the opportunity to find their solutions.

Any workbook assignment that can be supported by a real world experience will enhance the student's ability for problem solving. There is an infinite challenge for the teacher to provide a meaningful environment for the study of mathematics. It is a subject that requires constant assessment of student progress. Do not leave the study of mathematics in the classroom.

The Teacher Notes section of the Teacher's Guide lists the required or suggested materials for the LIFEPACs and provides additional learning activities for the students. Additional learning activities provide opportunities for problem solving, encourage the student's interest in learning and may be used as a reward for good study habits.

Materials Needed for LIFEPAC
    Required: Suggested:
                                      reference materials i.e. precalculus textbook

Additional Learning Activities
  Section I Ordered-Pair Numbers
1. Discuss symmetry with respect to the axes, with respect to a point, and with respect to the origin.
2. Have students plot the following sets of ordered pairs, one set to each graph. Then ask them to name the corresponding geometric figures.
   - a. (2, 5), (5, -2), (-1, -2)
   - b. (6, 4), (3, -1), (-5, -1), (-2, 4)
   - c. (0, 3), (3, -1), (6, -4), (3, 2)
   - d. (1, 4), (-2, 0), (0, -4), (5, -3), (6, 2)

  Section II The Algebra of Functions
1. The distance from a person to a strike of lightning is a function of the time between the flash and the thunder according to the following table:

Time	1	2	3	4	5
Distance (ft.)	1,100	2,200	3,300	4,400	5,500

   - a. Have the students draw a graph of the preceding relationship.
   - b. Have the students write a formula for this function.
   - c. How far away would a person be if the time between the flash and the thunder to the person were 11 seconds?

Additional Activity
The following activity may be reproduced as a student worksheet.

PLOTTING SYMMETRIC POINTS

Model: Plot (2, 3) and the point symmetric to it with respect to the *x*-axis. List its coordinates.

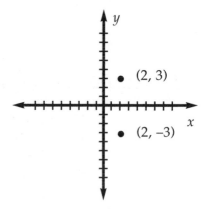

The point symmetric to (2, 3) with respect to the *x*-axis is (2, -3).

Plot the required points.

1. Plot (3, -7) and the point symmetric to it with respect to the *x*-axis. List its coordinates.

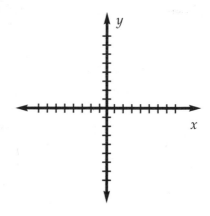

2. Plot (-4, 3) and the point symmetric to it with respect to the *y*-axis. List its coordinates.

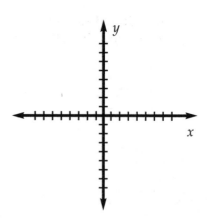

3. Plot (-3, -6) and the point symmetric to it with respect to the origin. List its coordinates.

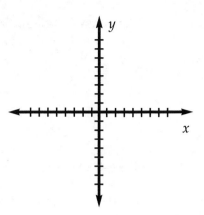

4. Plot (2, 5) and the point symmetric to it with respect to the *y*-axis. List its coordinates.

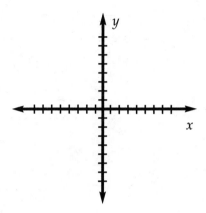

5. Plot (-5, 1) and the point symmetric to it with respect to the *x*-axis. List its coordinates.

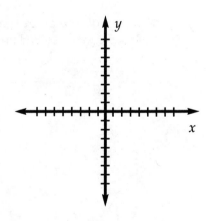

6. Plot (1, 7) and the point symmetric to it with respect to the origin. List its coordinates.

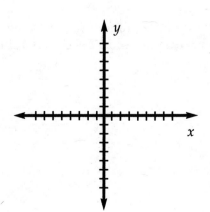

7. Plot (-2, -5) and the point symmetric to it with respect to the *x*-axis. List its coordinates.

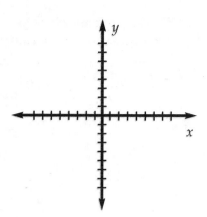

8. Plot (4, -2) and the point symmetric to it with respect to the origin. List its coordinates.

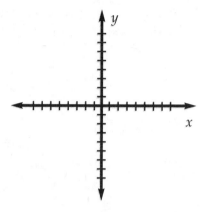

9. Plot (-1, -1) and the point symmetric to it with respect to the *y*-axis. List its coordinates.

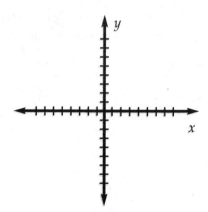

10. Plot (3, 6) and the point symmetric to it with respect to the *x*-axis. List its coordinates.

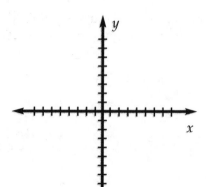

Additional Activity, Solution Key

1.

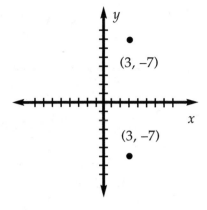

Point (3, 7) is symmetric to (3, -7) with respect to the *x*-axis.

4.

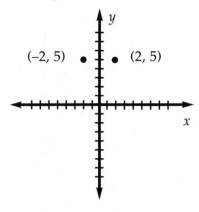

Point (-2, 5) is symmetric to (2, 5) with respect to the *y*-axis.

2.

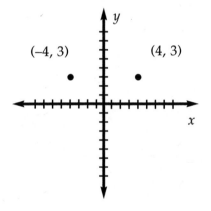

Point (4, 3) is symmetric to (-4, 3) with respect to the *y*-axis.

5.

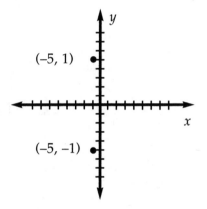

Point (-5, -1) is symmetric to (-5, 1) with respect to the *x*-axis.

3.

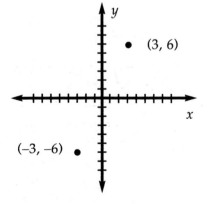

Point (3, 6) is symmetric to (-3, -6) with respect to the origin.

6.

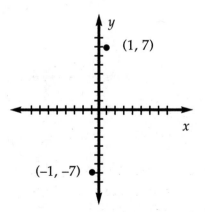

Point (-1, -7) is symmetric to (1, 7) with respect to the origin.

7.

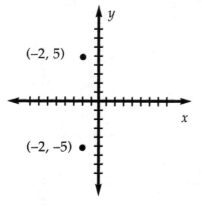

Point (2, 5) is symmetric to (-2, -5) with respect to the *x*-axis.

10.

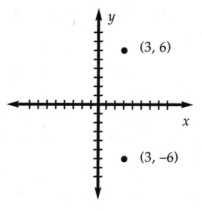

Point (3, -6) is symmetric to (3, 6) with respect to the *x*-axis.

8.

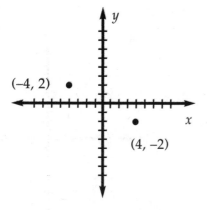

Point (-4, 2) is symmetric to (4, -2) with respect to the origin.

9.

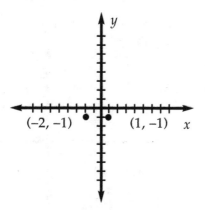

Point (1, -1) is symmetric to (-1, -1) with respect to the *y*-axis.

Materials Needed for LIFEPAC:
　　Required:　　　　　　　　　　Suggested:
　　　　　　　　　　　　　　　　reference materials i.e. precalculus textbook
　　　　　　　　　　　　　　　　straightedges
　　　　　　　　　　　　　　　　graph paper

Additional Learning Activities
　Section I Linear Functions
　　1.　Have students find the slope of the line through each of the following sets of points. After the students have found each slope, have them write the equation of the corresponding line in standard form. Answers are given for the teacher's information.

　　　　a.　(2, -3) and (4, -1)　　　　　　h.　(12, 9) and (9, 12)
　　　　　　$(m = 1; x - y = 5)$　　　　　　$(m = -1; x + y = 21)$

　　　　b.　(1, 2) and (3, 5)　　　　　　i.　(0, 0) and (4, 8)
　　　　　　$(m = \frac{3}{2}; 3x - 2y = -1)$　　　　$(m = 2; 2x - y = 0)$

　　　　c.　(-1, 3) and (2, 6)　　　　　　j.　(9, 8) and (0, 2)
　　　　　　$(m = 1; x - y = -4)$　　　　　　$(m = \frac{2}{3}; 2x - 3y = -6)$

　　　　d.　(5, -7) and (-6, 9)
　　　　　　$(m = -\frac{16}{11} \ 16x + 11y = 3)$

　　　　e.　(0, 4) and (4, 0)
　　　　　　$(m = -1; x + y = 4)$

　　　　　　(8, 2) and (-6, 3)
　　　　　　$(m = -\frac{1}{14}x + 14y = 36)$

　　　　g.　(1, -5) and (7, -6)
　　　　　　$(m = -\frac{1}{6}; x + 6y = 29)$

　Section II Second-Degree Functions
　　1.　Have students use the discriminant to determine the number of points each of the following parabolas has on the *x*-axis. Then have the students determine whether the graph of each parabola opens up or down based on the value of a_0 (the coefficient of x^2). The answers are given for the teacher's information.

　　　　a.　$y = x^2 + 4$ (no points; opens up)
　　　　b.　$y = 2x^2 + x$ (two points; opens up)
　　　　c.　$y = 3x^2 - 5$ (two points; opens up)
　　　　d.　$y = -x^2 + 1$ (two points; opens down)
　　　　e.　$y = x^2$ (one point; opens up)
　　　　f.　$y = -3x^2 - 3$ (no points; opens down)

g. $y = -x^2 + 8$ (two points; opens down)

h. $y = x^2 - x + \frac{1}{4}$ (one point; opens up)

i. $y = 4x^2 + x + \frac{1}{16}$ (one point; opens up)

j. $y = 6x^2 + 2$ (no points; opens up)

Section III Special Functions

1. Discuss transformation with respect to the graph of one relation and its alteration to obtain another relation.
2. In this experiment, students will draw a graph that can be used to multiply numbers by drawing lines between points on a parabola. Instruct students to draw a pair of axes on a sheet of graph paper, which is ruled 10 units per inch. Number the x-axis so that 1 inch represents 10 units, and the y-axis so that 1 inch represents 100 units. Have a table prepared of the function $y = x^2$, with points from 0 to 30, corresponding to x-values, and 0 to 900, corresponding to y-values. After all such points are plotted, they should be joined with a smooth curve. The resulting parabola is now ready for multiplying numbers. For example, to multiply 5 and 8, find these numbers on the x-axis, one to the left and the other to the right of the origin. (Note: do not use negative values for the second quadrant for values of x, but merely mirror the points marked off in the first quadrant). Locate the two points on the curve directly above 5 and 8 and use a straightedge to join them with a line. The point where this line crosses the y-axis shows that the answer is 40. Following this same procedure, have the class find the approximate values for the following operations.

    a. 10 x 9
    b. 12 x 18
    c. 19 x 20
    d. 21 x 25
    e. 26 x 26
    f. 31 x 12
    g. 28.5 x 27.5

Additional Activities

The following activities may be reproduced as student worksheets.

Graphing Functions

Graph the following functions.

1. $P(x) = x^3 - 3x^2 - 2x - 6$

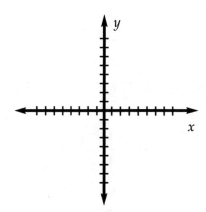

2. $P(x) = x^3 + 4x^2 - 3x - 12$

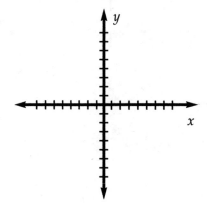

3. $P(x) = x^4 + x^3 = 7x^2 - x + 6$

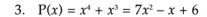

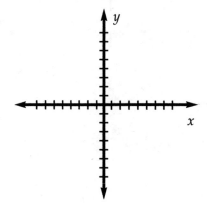

4. $P(x) = x^4 + 5x^3 + 5x^2 - 5x - 6$

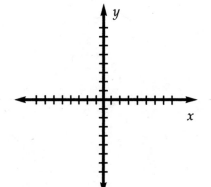

Translations

1. Sketch the graph of $y = 1 + x^2$. Show that by replacing y by $y - 1$ in this equation, you obtain a vertical translation in the graph.

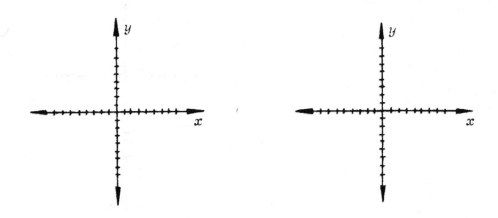

2. Sketch the graph $y = |x|$. Show that the graph of $y = |x + 2|$ results in a horizontal translation in the relation.

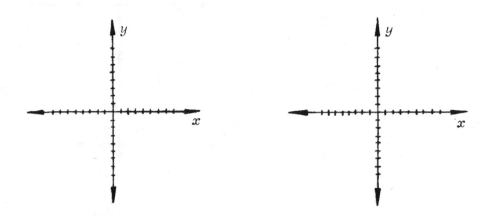

ADDITIONAL ACTIVITIES, Solution Key

Graphing Functions

1. Use synthetic division to locate points on the graph.

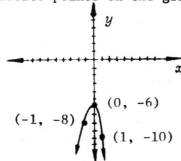

```
-1 | 1  -3  -2  -6
   |    -1   4  -2
   ---------------
     1  -4   2  -8
```

One point is (-1, -8).

```
0 | 1  -3  -2  -6
  |     0   0   0
  ---------------
    1  -3  -2  -6
```

Another point is (0, -6).

```
1 | 1  -3  -2  -6
  |     1  -2  -4
  ----------------
    1  -2  -4 -10
```

A third point is (1, -10).

2. Use synthetic division to locate points on the graph.

```
-2 | 1   4  -3  -12
   |    -2  -4   14
   ----------------
     1   2  -7    2
```

One point is (-2, 2).

```
-1 | 1   4  -3  -12
   |    -1  -3    6
   ----------------
     1   3  -6   -6
```

A second point is (-1, -6).

2. cont.

```
0 | 1   4  -3  -12
  |     0   0    0
  ----------------
    1   4  -3  -12
```

A third point is (0, -12).

```
1 | 1   4  -3  -12
  |     1   5    2
  ----------------
    1   5   2  -10
```

A fourth point is (1, -10).

```
2 | 1   4  - 3  -12
  |     2   12   18
  -----------------
    1   6    9    6
```

A fifth point is (2, 6).

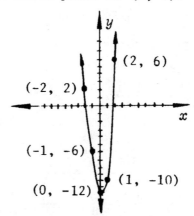

3. Use synthetic division to locate points on the graph.

```
3 | 1   1  -7  -1   6
  |    -3   6   3  -6
  --------------------
    1  -2  -1   2   0
```

One point is (-3, 0).

```
-2 | 1   1  -7  -1    6
   |    -2   2  10  -18
   -------------------
     1  -1  -5   9  -12
```

A second point is (-2, -12).

39

3. cont.

```
-1 │ 1   1   -7   -1    6
   │    -1    0    7   -6
   └─────────────────────
     1   0   -7    6    0
```

A third point is (-1, 0).

```
0 │ 1   1   -7   -1    6
  │     0    0    0    0
  └─────────────────────
    1   1   -7   -1    6
```

A fourth point is (0, 6).

```
1 │ 1   1   -7   -1    6
  │     1    2   -5   -6
  └─────────────────────
    1   2   -5   -6    0
```

A fifth point is (1, 0).

```
2 │ 1   1   -7   -1    6
  │     2    6   -2   -6
  └─────────────────────
    1   3   -1   -3    0
```

A sixth point is (2, 0).

Try a point between (1, 0) and (2, 0), such as $1\frac{1}{2}$ or $\frac{3}{2}$.

```
 3/2 │ 1    1     -7     -1      6
     │      3/2   15/4  -39/8  -141/16
     └──────────────────────────────
       1    5/2  -13/4  -47/8  -45/16
                               or -2 13/16
```

A seventh point is $(\frac{3}{2}, -\frac{45}{16})$.

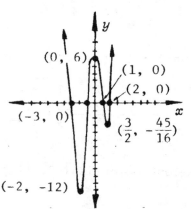

4. Use synthetic division to locate points on the graph.

```
-3 │ 1   5   5   -5   -6
   │    -3  -6    3    6
   └──────────────────────
     1   2  -1   -2    0
```

One point is (-3, 0).

```
-2 │ 1   5   5   -5   -6
   │    -2  -6    2    6
   └──────────────────────
     1   3  -1   -3    0
```

A second point is (-2, 0).

```
-1 │ 1   5   5   -5   -6
   │    -1  -4   -1    6
   └──────────────────────
     1   4   1   -6    0
```

A third point is (-1, 0).

```
0 │ 1   5   5   -5   -6
  │     0   0    0    0
  └──────────────────────
    1   5   5   -5   -6
```

A fourth point is (0, -6).

```
1 │ 1   5   5   -5   -6
  │     1   6   11    6
  └──────────────────────
    1   6  11    6    0
```

A fifth point is (1, 0).

Try a point between (-3, 0) and (-2, 0), such as $-2\frac{5}{8}$ or $-\frac{21}{8}$.

```
 -21/8 │ 1    5       5      -5        -6
       │     -21/8  -399/64  1,659/512  18,921/4,096
       └──────────────────────────────────────────
         1   19/8  -79/64  -901/512   -5,655/4,096
```

$-\frac{5,655}{4,096} \doteq -1.38$

Another point is $(-\frac{21}{8}, -1.38)$.

Try a point between (-2, 0) and (-1, 0), such as $-1\frac{1}{2}$ or $-\frac{3}{2}$.

4. cont.

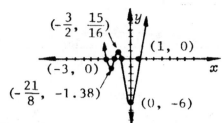

$$-\frac{3}{2} \quad \begin{array}{ccccc} 1 & 5 & 5 & -5 & -6 \end{array}$$

$$\begin{array}{ccccc} & -\frac{3}{2} & -\frac{21}{4} & \frac{3}{8} & \frac{111}{16} \end{array}$$

$$\begin{array}{ccccc} 1 & \frac{7}{2} & -\frac{1}{4} & -\frac{37}{8} & \frac{15}{16} \end{array}$$

Graph with points: $\left(-\frac{3}{2}, \frac{15}{16}\right)$, $(1, 0)$, $(-3, 0)$, $\left(-\frac{21}{8}, -1.38\right)$, $(0, -6)$

Translations

1. $y = 1 + x^2$

x	y
-2	5
-1	2
0	1
1	2
2	5

Graph labeled $y = 1 + x^2$

$$y - 1 = 1 + x^2$$
$$y - 1 + 1 = 1 + 1 + x^2$$
$$y = 2 + x^2$$

x	y
-2	6
-1	3
0	2
1	3
2	6

1. cont.

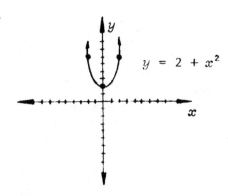

$y = 2 + x^2$

This graph is a vertical translation of the preceding graph (it is raised).

2. $y = |x|$

x	y
-2	2
-1	1
0	0
1	1
2	2

Graph labeled $y = |x|$

$y = |x + 2|$

x	y
-4	2
-3	1
-2	0
-1	1
0	2

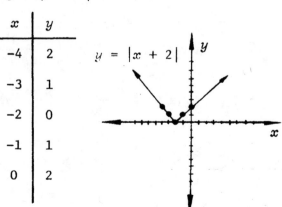

$y = |x + 2|$

This graph is a horizontal translation of the preceding graph (it is "moved" horizontally).

Materials Needed for LIFEPAC
Required: Suggested:
                                                 graph paper
                                                 reference materials i.e. precalculus textbook

Additional Learning Activities
  Section I Definition of the Trigonometric Functions
  1. To help your students understand why the functions have different signs depending on which quadrant they are located in, direct your students in this activity.

  Have your students draw an angle *AOB* in Quadrant I as shown.

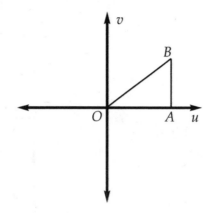

$\overline{0A}$ = side adjacent to the angle, $\overline{AB}$ = side opposite the angle, and $\overline{OB}$ = hypotenuse. Then have students write the sin, cos, tan, csc, see, and cot of $\angle AOB$:

$$\sin \angle AOB = \frac{\text{side opposite the angle}}{\text{hypotenuse}}$$

$$\cos \angle AOB = \frac{\text{side adjacent to the angle}}{\text{hypotenuse}}$$

$$\tan \angle AOB = \frac{\text{side opposite the angle}}{\text{side adjacent to the angle}}$$

$$\csc \angle AOB = \frac{\text{hypotenuse}}{\text{side opposite the angle}}$$

$$\sec \angle AOB = \frac{\text{hypotenuse}}{\text{side adjacent to the angle}}$$

$$\cot \angle AOB = \frac{\text{side adjacent to the angle}}{\text{side opposite the angle}}$$

See that students understand that csc $\angle AOB$ is the reciprocal of sin $\angle AOB$, sec $\angle AOB$ is the reciprocal of cos $\angle AOB$, and cot $\angle AOB$ is the reciprocal of tan $\angle AOB$.

Now have students label $\overline{OA}$ as u, $\overline{AB}$ as v, and $\overline{OB}$ as r for convenience and write the sin, cos, tan, csc, sec, and cot of $\angle AOB$ based on the previous information.

$$\sin \angle AOB = \frac{v}{r} \qquad\qquad\qquad \csc \angle AOB = \frac{r}{v}$$

$$\cos \angle AOB = \frac{u}{r} \qquad\qquad\qquad \sec \angle AOB = \frac{r}{u}$$

$$\tan \angle AOB = \frac{v}{u} \qquad\qquad\qquad \cot \angle AOB = \frac{u}{v}$$

Students should note that all the functions are positive in Quadrant I.

For Quadrant II, have students draw another angle AOB and label it as shown.

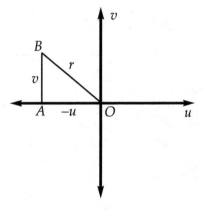

Then have students write the sin, cos, tan, csc, sec, and cot of $\angle AOB$. Students should note that only the sin and csc of the angle are positive in Quadrant II; all other functions are negative.

For Quadrant III have students draw a third angle AOB and label it as shown.

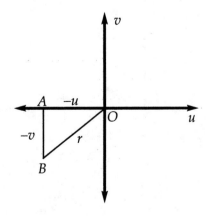

Then have students write the sin, cos, tan, csc, see, and cot of $\angle AOB$. Students should note than only the tan and cot of the angle are positive in Quadrant III; all other functions are negative.

For Quadrant IV, have students draw a fourth angle *AOB* and label it as shown.

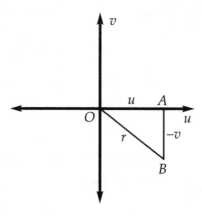

Then have students write the sin, cos, tan, csc, see, and cot of $\angle AOB$. Students should note that only the cos and sec of the angle are positive in Quadrant IV; all other functions are negative.

2. Discuss these questions with your class.
    a. In three-space are three mutually perpendicular axes called *u*, *v*, and *w*? If A is a point in space with coordinates (*u*, *v*, *w*), where *u*, *v*, and *w* are all positive numbers, what is the length of $\overline{OA}$, where *O* is the origin? What would the result be if one, two, or all three coordinates were negative?
    b. What is an algebraic expression for all angles that have the same terminal side?

Section II Evaluation of Functions
1. Using the given diagram, describe interpolation and the accuracy of its use.

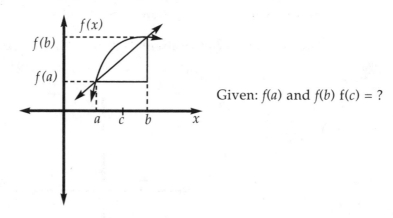

Given: $f(a)$ and $f(b)$ $f(c) = ?$

Section III Angle Location (No Activities)

Section IV Trigonometric Tables

1. Have students find sin 0° in the table at the end of the LIFEPAC and follow the values of sin ø to sin 90° to see that the sin function is an increasing function. Repeat the procedure for cos ø to show that it is a decreasing function. Repeat the procedure for each of the other functions.
2. Have the students find the answer to the following problem.
   a. If the sides of an isoceles triangle are 12 inches in length and the measure of the angle between them is 36°, what is the area of the triangle to the nearest square inch?

Section V Use of Tables and Interpolation

1. Have students interpolate to find each of the following function values. Answers are given for the teacher's information.
   a. sin 25° 12' (0.4258)
   b. cos 14° 33' (0.9679)
   c. tan 43° 58' (0.9646)
   d. cot 36° 36' (1.347)
   e. sin 9° 23' (0.1630)
   f. csc 54° 8' (1.234)
   g. sec 75° 48' (4.077)
   h. cos 89° 59' (0.0003)
   i. csc 10° 10' (5.665)
   j. tan 62° 44' (1.940)
2. Have students find the measure of each angle given the following functions. Answers are given for the teacher's information.
   a. cos Ø = 0.9636 (Ø = 15° 13')
   b. tan Ø = 0.6269 (Ø = 32° 5')
   c. csc Ø = 1.029 (Ø = 76° 16')
   d. sec Ø = 1.140 (Ø = 28° 39') .
   e. sin Ø = 0.8133 (Ø = 54° 35')
   f. cot Ø = 0.9506 (Ø = 46° 27')
   g. tan Ø = 1.984 (Ø = 63° 15')
   h. sin Ø = 0.9975 (Ø = 85° 55')
   i. sec Ø = 1.223 (Ø = 35° 8')
   j. cot Ø = 1.093 (Ø = 42° 28')

Section VI Reduction Formulas

1. Based on what the students know about the signs of the functions in the quadrants and by using the reduction formulas, have students find three angles equal to the given angle.

   Example: sin 30° = 0.5

   Three other angles equal to sin 30° are sin 150°, cos 60°, and cos 300°.
   a. sin 60°
   b. cos 45°
   c. cos 120°
   d. sin 40°
   e. csc 80°
   f. csc 50°
   g. sec 20°
   h. sec 150°
   i. sin 49° 10'
   j. cos 133° 40'

Section VII Quadrantal Angles (No Activities)

Section VIII Special Angles

1. Explain to your students that on page 31 in the LIFEPAC, Figure 4, the value of $\overline{AB}$ was found by using the Pythagorean Theorem.
2. Have the students find the area of an equilateral triangle in terms of the length of one of its sides.

Section IX Radian Measure

1. Have students familiarize themselves with radian measure by finding the values of functions of radians in the trigonometric table at the end of the LIFEPAC.

    Example: Find the value of the sin of 0.5236 radians.

    0.5236 rad = 30° and sin 30° = 0.5.

    Therefore, sin 0.5236 rad = 0.5.

2. Radian measure can be interpolated in the same way as angle measure is interpolated. Have students interpolate to find each of the following radian measures. Answers are given for the teacher's information.

    Example: Find sin 0.3500 radians.

    sin 0.3500 rad lies between sin 0.3491 rad and sin 0.3520 rad.

$$0.0029 \left\{ 0.0009 \left\{ \begin{array}{l} \sin 0.3491 \text{ rad} = 0.3420 \\ \sin 0.3500 \text{ rad} = \\ \sin 0.3520 \text{ rad} = 0.3448 \end{array} \right\} x \right\} 0.0028$$

Since these numbers are proportional,

$$\frac{0.0009}{0.0029} = \frac{x}{0.0028}$$

$(0.0009)(0.0028) = 0.0029x$

$0.0000025 = 0.0029x$

$$x = \frac{0.0000025x}{0.0029}$$

$x = 0.0009$ (rounding to the fourth decimal place)

Since sin is an increasing function, sin 0.3500 red = 0.3420 + 0.0009 = 0.3429. Therefore, sin 0.3500 rad = 0.3429.

a. sin 0.4198 rad (0.4076)
b. cos 0.6175 rad (0.8153)
c. tan 1.5090 rad (16.16)
d. cot 0.2189 rad (4.495)
e. cos 1.0000 rad (0.5403)
f. csc 0.8672 rad (1.311)
g. sec 0.6686 rad (1.274)
h. sin 1.4993 rad (0.9974)
i. tan 1.2459 rad (2.969)
j. sec 0.3215 rad (1.054)

3. Have the students answer the following questions.

    a. Through how many radians does the minute hand of a clock travel in one hour? one minute? one second? Have your students then convert these answers to degrees.

Additional Activity

This activity may be reproduced as a student worksheet.

ANGLE MEASURE CONVERSION

Other measures for angles are mils, where 3,200 mils equal π radians, and revolutions, where 1 revolution equals 360°. Using these definitions, convert the following measures as indicated.

1. 80 mils to radians

2. 0.8 radian to degrees

3. 108 degrees to mils

4. 10,000 degrees to mils

5. 10,000 mils to degrees

6. 108 degrees to revolutions

7. 80 degrees to revolutions

8. 0.8 revolution to mils

9. 800 mils to revolutions

10. 10,000 mils to revolutions

ADDITIONAL ACTIVITY, Answer Key

1. 3,200 mils = π radians
   80 mils = x radians

   $$\frac{3,200}{\pi} = \frac{80}{x}$$
   $$3,200x = 80\pi$$
   $$\frac{3,200x}{3,200} = \frac{80\pi}{3,200}$$
   $$x = \frac{\pi}{4} \text{ radians}$$

2. 0.8 radians = $0.8 \cdot \frac{180°}{\pi}$ =

   $$\frac{144°}{\pi} \text{ or } \frac{144}{3.14} \doteq 46°$$

3. Convert degrees to radians first.

   $$108° = 108° \cdot \frac{\pi}{180°} =$$

   $$\frac{\overset{3}{\cancel{108}}\pi}{\underset{5}{\cancel{180}}} = \frac{3\pi}{5} \text{ radians}$$

   Then convert radians to mils.
   3,200 mils = π radians
   x mils = $\frac{3\pi}{5}$ radians

   $$\frac{3,200}{\pi} = \frac{x}{\frac{3\pi}{5}}$$
   $$\pi x = (\frac{3\pi}{5})(3,200)$$
   $$\pi x = \frac{3\pi \cdot \overset{640}{\cancel{3,200}}}{\cancel{5}}$$
   $$\pi x = 1,920\pi$$
   $$\frac{\pi x}{\pi} = \frac{1,920\pi}{\pi}$$
   $$x = 1,920 \text{ mils}$$

4. Convert degrees to radians first.

   $$10,000° = 10,000° \cdot \frac{\pi}{180°}$$

   $$\frac{10,000\pi}{180} = \frac{500\pi}{9} \text{ radians}$$

   Then convert radians to mils.

4. cont.

   3,200 mils = π radians
   x mils = $\frac{500\pi}{9}$ radians

   $$\frac{3,200}{\pi} = \frac{x}{\frac{500\pi}{9}}$$
   $$\pi x = (\frac{500\pi}{9})(3,200)$$
   $$\pi x = \frac{1,600,000\pi}{9}$$
   $$\frac{\pi x}{\pi} = \frac{1,600,000\pi}{9\pi}$$
   $$x = \frac{1,600,000}{9} \text{ mils}$$

5. Convert mils to radians first.

   3,200 mils = π radians
   10,000 mils = x radians

   $$\frac{3,200}{\pi} = \frac{10,000}{x}$$
   $$3,200x = 10,000\pi$$
   $$\frac{3,200x}{3,200} = \frac{10,000\pi}{3,200}$$
   $$x = \frac{25\pi}{8} \text{ radians}$$

   Then convert radians to degrees.
   $$\frac{25\pi}{8} \text{ radians} = \frac{25\pi}{8} \cdot \frac{180°}{\pi} =$$

   $$\frac{25\pi}{\underset{2}{\cancel{8}}} \cdot \frac{\overset{45}{\cancel{180}}}{\cancel{\pi}} = \frac{1,125°}{2} = 562.5°$$

6. 360° = 1 revolution
   108° = x revolutions

   $$\frac{360}{1} = \frac{108}{x}$$
   $$360x = 108$$
   $$\frac{360x}{360} = \frac{108}{360}$$
   $$x = \frac{3}{10} \text{ revolution}$$

7. 360° = 1 revolution
    80° = x revolutions

    $$\frac{360}{1} = \frac{80}{x}$$
    $$360x = 80$$
    $$\frac{360x}{360} = \frac{80}{360}$$
    $$x = \frac{2}{9} \text{ revolution}$$

8. Convert revolutions to degrees first.
    1 revolution = 360°
    0.8 revolution = x°

    $$\frac{1}{360°} = \frac{0.8}{x}$$
    $$x = 360(0.8)$$
    $$x = 288°$$

    Second, convert degrees to radians.
    $$288° = 288° \cdot \frac{\pi}{180°} =$$
    $$\frac{\overset{8}{\cancel{288}}\pi}{\underset{5}{\cancel{180}}} = \frac{8\pi}{5} \text{ radians}$$

    Third, convert radians to mils.
    π radians = 3,200 mils
    $\frac{8\pi}{5}$ radians = x mils

    $$\frac{\pi}{3,200} = \frac{\frac{8\pi}{5}}{x}$$
    $$\pi x = (\frac{8\pi}{5})(\overset{640}{\cancel{3,200}})$$
    $$\pi x = 5,120\pi$$
    $$\frac{\pi x}{\pi} = \frac{5,120\pi}{\pi}$$
    $$x = 5,120 \text{ mils}$$

9. Convert mils to radians first.
    3,200 mils = π radians
    800 mils = x radians

9. cont.

    $$\frac{3,200}{\pi} = \frac{800}{x}$$
    $$3,200x = 800\pi$$
    $$\frac{3,200x}{3,200} = \frac{800\pi}{3,200}$$
    $$x = \frac{\pi}{4} \text{ radians}$$

    Second, convert radians to degrees.
    $$\frac{\pi}{4} \text{ radians} = \frac{\pi}{4} \cdot \frac{180°}{\pi} =$$
    $$\frac{\overset{45}{\cancel{180}}\cancel{\pi}}{\cancel{4}\cancel{\pi}} = 45°$$

    Third, convert degrees to revolutions.
    360° = 1 revolution
    45° = x revolutions

    $$\frac{360}{1} = \frac{45}{x}$$
    $$360x = 45$$
    $$\frac{360x}{360} = \frac{45}{360}$$
    $$x = \frac{1}{8} \text{ revolution}$$

10. Convert mils to radians first.
    3,200 mils = π radians
    10,000 mils = x radians

    $$\frac{3,200}{\pi} = \frac{10,000}{x}$$
    $$3,200x = 10,000\pi$$
    $$\frac{3,200x}{3,200} = \frac{10,000\pi}{3,200}$$
    $$x = \frac{25\pi}{8} \text{ radians}$$

    Second, convert radians to degrees.
    $$\frac{25\pi}{8} \text{ radians} = \frac{25\pi}{8} \cdot \frac{180°}{\pi} =$$
    $$\frac{25\cancel{\pi} \cdot \overset{45}{\cancel{180}}}{\underset{2}{\cancel{8}} \cdot \cancel{\pi}} = \frac{1,125°}{2}$$

10. cont.

Third, convert degrees to revolutions.

$$360° = 1 \text{ revolution}$$

$$\frac{1,125°}{2} = x \text{ revolutions}$$

$$\frac{360}{1} = \frac{\dfrac{1,125}{2}}{x}$$

$$360x = \frac{1,125}{2}$$

$$\frac{360x}{360} = \frac{\dfrac{1,125}{2}}{360}$$

$$x = \left(\frac{\overset{25}{\cancel{1,125}}}{2}\right)\left(\frac{1}{\underset{8}{\cancel{360}}}\right) =$$

$$\frac{25}{16} \text{ or } 1\frac{9}{16} \text{ revolutions}$$

Materials Needed for LIFEPAC

Required: Suggested:
                                            graph paper
                                            reference materials i.e. precalculus textbook

Additional Learning Activities

Section I The Circular Functions

1. Demonstrate how vector diagrams are used in the solution of many problems in mechanics. Diagram a car moving up an incline at a rate of 30 feet per second and making an angle of 35° with the horizontal. Have the class find the horizontal velocity OQ of the car; the vertical velocity OR of the car. The solution is given for the teacher's information.

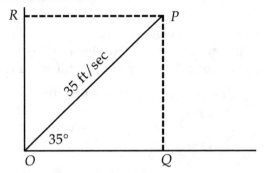

Horizontal velocity: $\dfrac{OQ}{OP}$ = cos 35°; OQ = OP cos 35°;

OQ = 30(0.8192); OQ = 24.58 ft./sec.

Vertical velocity: $\dfrac{OR}{OP}$ = sin 35°; OR = OP sin 35°;

OR = 30(0.5736); OR = 17.21 ft./sec.

2. Have the student copy and complete the following chart, giving the sign of each function in each of the four quadrants. The answer is given for the teacher's information.

Function / Quadrant	Sin	Cos	Tan	Csc	Sec	Cot
I	+	___	___	+	___	___
II	___	–	___	___	___	___
III	___	___	+	___	___	+
IV	___	___	___	___	+	___

Answer:

Function / Quadrant	Sin	Cos	Tan	Csc	Sec	Cot
I	+	+	+	+	+	+
II	+	−	−	+	−	−
III	−	−	+	−	−	+
IV	−	+	−	−	+	−

Section II Circular Functions of Special Angles

1. Have students subtract multiples of 360° where necessary and convert each degree measure to radian measure. Answers are given for the teacher's information.

   a. 720° (0° = 0)

   b. 540° (180° = π)

   c. 450° (90° = $\frac{\pi}{2}$)

   d. 36° ($\frac{\pi}{5}$)

   e. 20° ($\frac{\pi}{9}$)

   f. 630° (270° = $\frac{3\pi}{2}$)

   g. 22.5° ($\frac{\pi}{8}$)

   h. 855° (135° = $\frac{3\pi}{4}$)

   i. 1,395° (315° = $\frac{7\pi}{4}$

   j. 80° ($\frac{4\pi}{9}$)

Section III Graphs of Sin and Cos

1. Illustrate the relation between an angle and its sine.

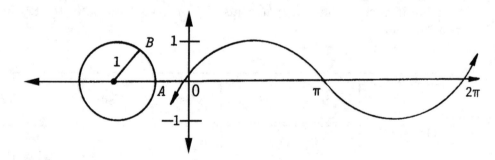

The radius of the circle is 1 and the circumference is 2π As the circle moves along the horizontal line, the distance of point B forms the sine wave. The distance from 0 to 2π equals the circumference of the circle. The wave continues indefinitely to the left and to the right.

Section IV Other Graphs (No Activities)

Section V Applications
1. Be sure students understand the difference between speed and velocity. Speed is the rate a body moves in any direction, whereas velocity is the rate a body moves in one fixed direction.

   The type of velocity the students work with in the LIFEPAC is uniform velocity (the velocity remains the same throughout the motion). Other types of velocity are variable velocity (the velocity changes during the motion) and accelerated velocity (which may be positive or negative).

Section VI Amplitude of Circular Functions
1. Inform students that the loudness of a sound depends upon the amplitude of its wave. Show the following sine curves and ask students to indicate which curve represents the loudest noise.

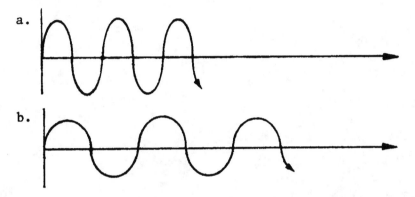

2. Research amplitude modulation (AM) and frequency modulation (FM), two kinds of radio broadcast waves.

Section VII Period of Circular Functions
1. Inform the class that the pitch or frequency of sound depends upon its period. A high frequency sound has a small period. Given the following diagram of three sound waves, have students indicate whether the waves have the same pitch or different pitch. Then have them tell which sound wave is the loudest based on the amplitude of each wave (from the group activity in Section VI Amplitude of Circular Functions).

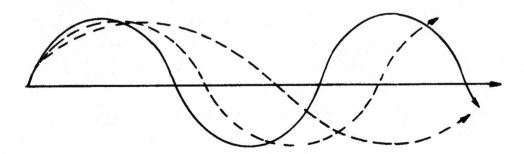

2. Research encyclopedias and other reference materials to learn about the periodic nature of the pendulum, vibrations, light, aspects of astronomy, and aspects of electricity.

Section VIII Phase Shift of Circular Functions

1. Have students graph $F(x) = \csc x$ and $G(x) = \sec x$ on the same axes to see that

   $\csc x = \sec (x - \frac{\pi}{2})$ (the graph of the cosecant function is the graph of the secant

   function moved $\frac{\pi}{2}$ radians to the right).

Materials Needed for Lifepac
Required: Suggested:
                                             reference materials i.e. precalculus textbook

Additional Learning Activities
   Section I Reciprocal Relations
     1. Have the class memorize the three reciprocal relations given at the top of page 14 in the LIFEPAC. Memorizing the relations will make simplifying trigonometric expressions easier for the students.
   Section II Pythagorean Relations
     1. Encourage the class to memorize the equations given in the definition box on the top of page 6 in the LIFEPAC.
     2. Have students verify that $\tan^2 \varnothing + 1 = \sec^2 \varnothing$ and that $\cot^2 \varnothing + 1 = \csc^2 \varnothing$ for various values of $\varnothing$
     3. Present the following situation to the class to solve. A boy jumped onto one end of a 13-foot log lying on the top of a hill. The log started rolling down the hill from the boy's impact. As it rolled, the boy managed to keep himself upright on the log and slowly walk across the log to the other end, which he reached just as the log came to rest at the bottom of the hill. The hill was 84 feet in length from where the log began to roll. The log was 2 feet in diameter. How far did the boy actually travel? How far would he have traveled has the log been 3 feet in diameter? (Note: The answer is the same, regardless of the diameter.)

     The solution is given for the teacher's information.
     Solution:

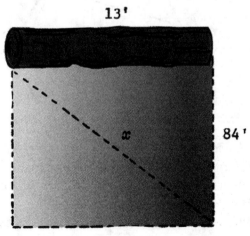

     Using the Pythagorean Theorem, let x be the distance the boy traveled.
     $x = \sqrt{13^2 + 84^2}$
     $x = \sqrt{169 + 7,056}$
     $x = \sqrt{7,225}$
     $x = 85'$; the distance the boy traveled.
   Section III Quotient Relations
     1. Encourage the class to memorize the quotient relations given in the definition box on the top of page 10 in the LIFEPAC.
     2. Have students verify that $\tan \theta = \frac{\sin\theta}{\cos\theta}$, $\theta \neq 0, \frac{\pi}{2}, \frac{3\pi}{2}$ ... and that $\cot \theta = \frac{\cos\theta}{\sin\theta}$, $\theta \neq 0, \pi$
   ... for various values of θ.

Section IV Trigonometric Identities

1. Have students prove the following identities.
   $$\sin^2\theta + \cos^2\theta = \sec^2\theta - \tan^2\theta$$
   $$\sin^2\theta + \cos^2\theta = \csc^2\theta - \cot^2\theta$$
   $$\sec^2\theta - \tan^2\theta = \csc^2\theta - \cot^2\theta$$
2. Have students derive the Pythagorean relations $\tan^2\theta + 1 = \sec^2\theta$ from $\sin^2\theta + \cos^2\theta = 1$; and derive $\cot^2\theta + 1 = \csc^2\theta$ from $\sin^2\theta + \cos^2\theta = 1$.
3. Discuss with the class whether every identity can be written as an expression of sin and cos only.
4. Have each student write several identities for the class to prove. Each student should keep the solutions to the identities he writes so answers may be checked.

Section V Cosine of the Sum of Two Angles

1. Encourage the class to memorize the formula for the cosine of the sum of two angles.
2. Have each student write several problems such as the ones on page 20 of the LIFEPAC for the class to solve. Each student should keep the solutions to the problems he writes so answers may be checked.

Section VI Additional Sum and Difference Formulas

1. Encourage the class to memorize the eight additional sum and difference formulas given on page 23 of the LIFEPAC.
2. Demonstrate to the class that Ptolemy's theorem implies the formula for $\sin(\alpha + \beta)$ Hint: Draw a quadrilateral such that $\overline{BD}$ is a diameter in a circle of diameter equal to 1 Then show that $\overline{AB} = \sin\alpha$; $\overline{AD} = \cos\alpha$; $\overline{BC} = \sin\beta$ $\overline{CD} = \cos\beta$; and $\overline{AC} = \sin(\alpha + \beta)$.

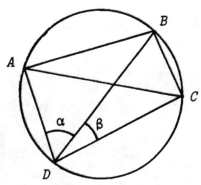

3. Have each student write several problems such as the ones on page 25 of the LIFEPAC for the class to solve. Each student should keep the solutions to the problems he writes so answers may be checked.

Section VII Double- and Half-Angle Formulas

1. Encourage the class to memorize the doubleand half angle formulas for sin, cos, and tan.
2. Discuss the fact that most binomial surds, of the form $a\sqrt{b} + c\sqrt{d}$ where a, b, c, and d are positive integers, do not have square roots that are also binomial surds. Give this example:

   a. If $\sin x = -\frac{3}{5}$ and x is in Quadrant III, what is $\sin 2x$? $\cos x = -\frac{4}{5}$ and, therefore,

   $$\sin 2x = 2(-\tfrac{3}{5})(-\tfrac{4}{5}) = \frac{24}{25}.$$

b. What is $\sin \frac{x}{2}$ if $\pi < x < \frac{3\pi}{2}$?

$$\sin \frac{x}{2} = +\sqrt{\frac{1 - (-\frac{4}{5})}{2}} = \frac{3}{\sqrt{10}} \text{, where the positive root}$$

is taken because $\frac{\pi}{2} < \frac{\pi}{2} < \frac{3\pi}{4} < \pi$.

3. Have each student write several problems such as the ones on page 29 of the LIFEPAC for the class to solve. Each student should keep the solutions to the problems he writes so answers may be checked.

Section VIII Identities
1. Have each student write several identities for the class to prove. Each student should keep the solutions to the identities he writes so answers may be checked.
2. Develop one or more of the formulas for sin 3x, cos 3x sin 4x, and cos 4x.

Section IX Trigonometric Equations
1. Have each student write several equations for the class to solve. Students should give the domain for their equations and keep the solutions to the equations they write so answers may be checked.

ADDITIONAL ACTIVITY
The following activity may be reproduced as a student worksheet.

APPLYING THE DOUBLE-ANGLE FORMULAS

Find $\sin 2x$, $\cos 2x$, and $\tan 2x$ given the following information.

1. $\cos x = -\dfrac{5}{13}$

2. $\tan x = \dfrac{1}{\sqrt{2}}$

3. $\sin x = a$, and x is in Quadrant III

Additional Activity, Solution Key

1.

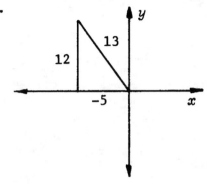

2.

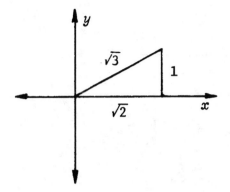

$\sin x = \dfrac{12}{13}$

$\cos x = \dfrac{-5}{13}$

$\sin 2x = 2 \sin x \cos x$

$\sin 2x = 2\left(\dfrac{12}{13}\right)\left(-\dfrac{5}{13}\right) = -\dfrac{120}{169}$

$\cos 2x = \cos^2 x - \sin^2 x$

$\cos 2x = \left(-\dfrac{5}{13}\right)^2 - \left(\dfrac{12}{13}\right)^2 =$

$\dfrac{25}{169} - \dfrac{144}{169} = -\dfrac{119}{169}$

$\tan 2x = \dfrac{2 \tan x}{1 - \tan^2 x}$

$\tan x = -\dfrac{12}{5}$

$\tan 2x = \dfrac{2\left(-\dfrac{12}{5}\right)}{1 - \left(-\dfrac{12}{5}\right)^2} =$

$\dfrac{-\dfrac{24}{5}}{1 - \dfrac{144}{25}} = \dfrac{-\dfrac{120}{25}}{\dfrac{25}{25} - \dfrac{144}{25}} =$

$\dfrac{-120}{25 - 144} = \dfrac{-120}{-119} = \dfrac{120}{119}$

$\sin x = \dfrac{1}{\sqrt{3}}$

$\cos x = \dfrac{\sqrt{2}}{\sqrt{3}}$

$\sin 2x = 2 \sin x \cos x$

$\sin 2x = 2\left(\dfrac{1}{\sqrt{3}}\right)\left(\dfrac{\sqrt{2}}{\sqrt{3}}\right) = \dfrac{2\sqrt{2}}{3}$

$\cos 2x = \cos^2 x - \sin^2 x$

$\cos 2x = \left(\dfrac{\sqrt{2}}{\sqrt{3}}\right)^2 - \left(\dfrac{1}{\sqrt{3}}\right)^2 =$

$\dfrac{2}{3} - \dfrac{1}{3} = \dfrac{1}{3}$

$\tan 2x = \dfrac{2 \tan x}{1 - \tan^2 x}$

$\tan 2x = \dfrac{2\left(\dfrac{1}{\sqrt{2}}\right)}{1 - \left(\dfrac{1}{\sqrt{2}}\right)^2} = \dfrac{\dfrac{2}{\sqrt{2}}}{1 - \dfrac{1}{2}} =$

$\dfrac{\dfrac{2}{\sqrt{2}}}{\dfrac{1}{2}} = \dfrac{2}{\sqrt{2}}(2) = \dfrac{4}{\sqrt{2}} =$

$\dfrac{4}{\sqrt{2}}\left(\dfrac{\sqrt{2}}{\sqrt{2}}\right) = \dfrac{4\sqrt{2}}{2} = 2\sqrt{2}$

3.

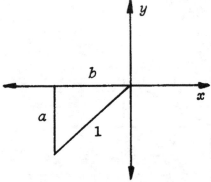

$\sin x = a$

$\cos x = b$

$\sin 2x = 2 \sin x \cos x$

$\sin 2x = 2(a)(b) = 2ab$

$\cos 2x = \cos^2 x - \sin^2 x$

$\cos 2x = (b)^2 - (a)^2 = b^2 - a^2$

$$\tan 2x = \frac{2 \tan x}{1 - \tan^2 x}$$

$$\tan x = \frac{a}{b}$$

$$\tan 2x = \frac{2\left(\frac{a}{b}\right)}{1 - \left(\frac{a}{b}\right)^2} =$$

$$\frac{\frac{2a}{b}}{1 - \frac{a^2}{b^2}} = \frac{\frac{2ab}{b^2}}{\frac{b^2}{b^2} - \frac{a^2}{b^2}} =$$

$$\frac{2ab}{b^2 - a^2}$$

Materials Needed for Lifepac
    Required: Suggested:
                                              reference materials i.e. precalculus textbook

Additional Learning Activities
  Section I Trigonometric Functions of Any Angle
    1. A circle is inscribed in a square and an equilateral triangle is inscribed in the circle. If the radius of the circle is r, have students find the ratio of the area of the square to the area of the triangle.

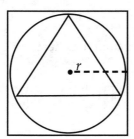

  Section II Applied Problems
    1. Discuss the method of finding the resultant of a vector polygon through the addition of each vector in succession.
    2. Using trigonometric functions and the following diagram (or the one given on page 11 of the LIFEPAC), show that $\overrightarrow{OA}$ (horizontal component) = $\overrightarrow{OB} \cos \theta$ and that $\overrightarrow{AB}$ (vertical component) = $OB \sin \theta$.

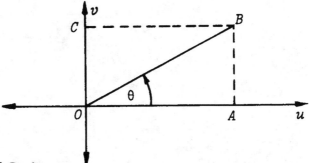

  Section III Law of Cosines
    1. Have the students solve this problem.

        A boat travels at 8 miles per hour in still water. At what angle with the shore must the boat be steered to reach a point directly opposite the shore if the velocity of the current is 4 miles per hour? (Hint: Have the students construct a parallelogram such that the scale representing 8 mi./hr. is drawn from O to R. Then solve for $\angle DOB$.)

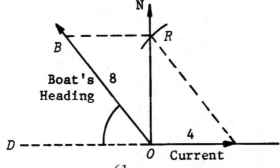

2. Research encyclopedias and other reference materials to learn how the Law of Cosines is used by surveyors to measure distances when no direct measurement can be made.

Section IV Law of Sines

1. Discuss Mollweide's equations

$$\left[\; \frac{a-b}{c} = \frac{\sin\frac{1}{2}(A-B)}{\cos\frac{1}{2}C} \right.$$

$$\left. \frac{a+b}{c} = \frac{\cos\frac{1}{2}(A-B)}{\sin\frac{1}{2}C} \;\right] \text{ as a convenient means for checking the accuracy of problems}$$

involving the Laws of Sines and Cosines. Have the students use the Mollweide equations to check several of the LIFEPAC test items where appropriate.

Section V More Applications (No Activities)
Section VI Additional Application Problems

1. Research encyclopedias and other reference materials to learn how trigonometry is used in navigation.

Materials Needed for LIFEPAC
    Required: Suggested:
                                                reference materials i.e. precalculus textbook

Additional Learning Activities
  Section I The Inverse Sin Function
    1. Explain to the class that $y = \arcsin x$ means "y is an angle with sin of x."
  Section II The Inverse Cos Function
    1. Explain to the class that to simplify problems such as $\cos\left(\arcsin \frac{1}{2}\right)$, first draw an angle with the given function value and then find the other function value.

        Example: Simplify $\cos\left(\arcsin \frac{1}{2}\right)$. $\arcsin \frac{1}{2}$ is an angle θ with sin of $\frac{1}{2}$. The cos of the angle is $\frac{\sqrt{3}}{2}$.

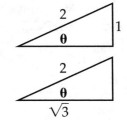

    2. Explain to the class that $\arccos(\cos x) = x$ and $\arcsin(\sin y) = y$. The same principle holds true for the other inverse functions in following sections.
    3. After students understand how to find the arccos and arcsin of various angles, have each student write several problems for the class to simplify. Each student should keep the solutions to the problems he writes so answers can be checked.
    4. Discuss these questions with your class.
        a.   Does arcsin 1 equal arccos 1? Why?
        b.   Does $\arcsin \frac{1}{2}$ equal $\arccos \frac{1}{2}$? Why?
        c.   Can arcsin x equal arccos y? If so, when?

  Section III The Inverse Tan Function
    1. Have each student write several problems for the class to simplify. Each student should keep the solutions to the problems he writes so answers can be checked.
  Section IV The Other Inverse Functions
    1. Find the range and domain sets for arccsc, arcsec, and arccot. Remember to consider any undefined elements within the domain and/or range sets.
  Section V Graphs of Inverse Functions
    1. Direct the students to graph arctan x, arccot x, arccsc x, and arcsec x and discover whether each graph is a relation or a function.
  Section VI Graphing Polar Coordinates
    1. Have students find equivalent coordinates to each of the points given in Problems 6.1 through 6.24 on page 22 of the LIFEPAC.
    2. Have students graph the sine curve on a polar graph. They should utilize every 10° angle in the total circle and plot all points corresponding to the sin values of 0° through 360° inclusive. Have students name the curve after it is finished.
    3. Have students graph the cosine curve on a polar graph, utilizing every 10° angle in the total circle and plotting all points corresponding to the cos values of 0° through 360° inclusive. Have students name the curve after it is finished.

4. Have students graph the tangent curve on a polar graph, utilizing every 10° angle from 0° through 80° inclusive. From 81° through 89° have students utilize each 1° angle if calculators with trigonometric functions are available. Otherwise, have students find tan 89° 10′, tan 89° 20′, tan 89° 30′, tan 89° 40′, and tan 89° 50′ from a trigonometric table. The large values need not be graphed. Have students notice what happens to the curve as they find the tangent of each progressively larger angle.

5. Have students graph the cosecant curve, secant curve, and cotangent curve in the same way as they graphed the sine curve, cosine curve, and tangent curve in the preceding activities.

6. Graph the sine curve, cosine curve, tangent curve, cosecant curve, secant curve, and cotangent curve as outlined in the preceding group activities.

Section VII Converting Coordinates (No Activities)

Section VIII Converting Cartesian Equations to Polar Equations

1. Have students write $-2 + 2\sqrt{3}i$ in polar form, i.e., show that

$$-2 + 2\sqrt{3}i = 4(\cos \frac{2\pi}{3} + i \sin \frac{2\pi}{3})$$

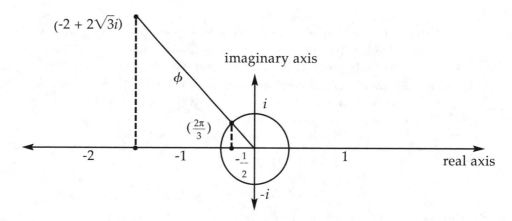

Section IX Converting Polar Equations to Cartesian Equations

1. Discuss the use of addition formulas to obtain a graphical interpretation of the product of two complex numbers. (Note: the addition of the complex numbers have a simple geometric representation in terms of the parallelogram law as shown.)

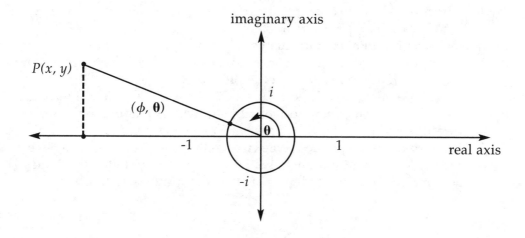

Because θ (for $r \neq 0$) is determined only to a multiple of 2π each point has infinitely many polar coordinates, $\theta + 2\pi K$ where K is an integer. For the complex number $x + iy$ we have

$x = r \cos \theta$ y $= r \sin \theta$ and
$x + iy = r(\cos \theta + i \sin \theta)$.

Based on the preceding notation, the polar form of the complex number is given by
$z = x + iy = r(\cos \theta + i \sin \theta)$.

The absolute value of a complex number, z = x + yi, is the number
$|x + iy| = \sqrt{x^2 + y^2}$

Section X Graphing Polar Equations

1. Have students tell how the graphs of Problems 10.5 through 10.12 on page 40 of the LIFEPAC are symmetric.

   Examples: The graph of $r = \sin \theta$ is symmetric about the line $\theta = 90°$.

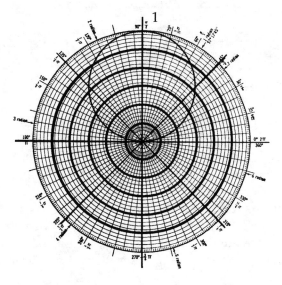

The graph of $r = \cos 2\theta$ is symmetric by pairs about each of the lines $\theta = 0°$ and $\theta = 90°$ (the coordinate axes).

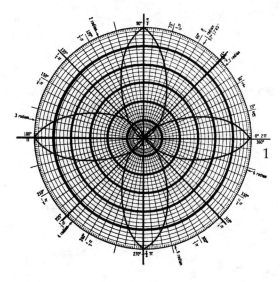

65

Materials Needed for LIFEPAC
Required: Suggested:
                                             reference materials i.e. precalculus textbook

Additional Learning Activities
Section I Conic Sections: Circle and Ellipse
1. For the system
    $$\begin{array}{ll} \text{a.} & (x-2)^2 + (y-1)^2 \leq 25 \\ \text{b.} & (x-2)^2 + (y-1)^2 \geq 16 \end{array}$$
    show that the solutions of Equation (a) are all points on or inside the circle with equation $(x-2)^2 + (y-1)^2 = 25$, and the solutions of Equation (b) are all points on or inside the circle with equation $(x-2)^2 + (y-1)^2 = 16$. Therefore, the solutions of the system are all points on the solid band as shown.

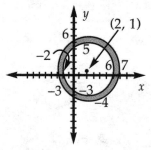

2. Have the student graph the following system.
    $$\begin{array}{l} (x-3)^2 + (y-1)^2 \geq 4 \\ (x-3)^2 + (y-1)^2 \leq 16 \end{array}$$
    Note: This activity may also be a group activity. Similar systems may also be graphed by changing the centers and/or the radii.

Section II Conic Sections: Parabola and Hyperbola
1. Have students sketch the graph of $y^2 = x(x-1)^2$. They should be able to determine that the graph is symmetric with respect to the x-axis; the reason is if x and y satisfy the equation, so do x and $-y$. Also, they should note that x must $= 0$; if $x \neq 0$, y cannot be a real number.
2. Have students draw a hyperbola with foci F_1 and F_2 as shown. Three points on this hyperbola are labeled A, B, and C. If the distance AF_1 is 1.8", AF_2 is 0.8", BF_1 is 0.6", and BF_2 is 1.6", have the students determine distances CF_1 and CF_2.

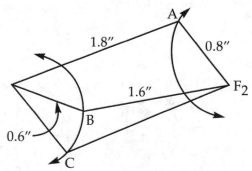

3. Research encyclopedias and other reference materials to learn about applications of parabolas, such as in television antennas, light reflectors, paths of objects sent into the atmosphere against gravity, and mirrors on reflecting telescopes.

Section III Transformations

1. Have students verify whether each of the following equations is an ellipse, a parabola, or a hyperbola by using the appropriate formula. Answers are given for the teacher's information.

If $B^2 - 4AC < 0$, the curve is an ellipse.
If $B^2 - 4AC = 0$, the curve is a parabola.
If $B^2 - 4AC > 0$, the curve is a hyperbola.

Example: $5x^2 + 7xy + 9y^2 - 80x + 54y + 221 = 0$
$A = 5, B = 7, C = 9$
$B^2 - 4AC = 7^2 - 4(5)(9) = 49 - 180 = -131$
$-131 < 0$, so the curve is an ellipse.

a. $x^2 + 3xy + 6y^2 + 8x - 12y + 3 = 0$ (ellipse)
b. $x^2 + 4xy + y^2 = 16$ (hyperbola)
c. $4x^2 - 12xy + 9y^2 + 12x - 6y + 9 = 0$ (parabola)
d. $25x^2 + 15xy + 9y^2 - 36y + 100x - 89 = 0$ (ellipse)
e. $x^2 - 2xy + y^2 + 2x - 4y + 3 = 0$ (parabola)
f. $2x^2 + 8xy + 4y^2 + x - 4y + 16 = 0$ (hyperbola)
g. $6x^2 + 12xy + y^2 - 3x - y + 8 = 0$ (hyperbola)
h. $8x^2 - 4xy + 5y^2 = 36$ (ellipse)
i. $3x^2 + 6xy + 3y^2 + 6x - 4y + 7 = 0$ (parabola)
j. $2x^2 + 8xy + 8y^2 + 18x + y - 8 = 0$ (parabola)

Additional Information

Since the LIFEPAC is long and somewhat difficult, each section can be shortened by eliminating some problems from each set. The section on transformations is rather difficult and can be used as optional work.

Materials Needed for LIFEPAC
    Required:

    Suggested:
    calculators
    reference materials i.e. precalculus textbook

Additional Learning Activities
    Section I Random Experiments and Probability
      1. Learn how probability is used in insurance.
      2. Learn how probability is used in predicting results of Presidential elections.
    Section II Permutations and Combinations
      3. The French mathematician Blaise Pascal discovered a method for computing combinations, called Pascal's triangle. The $(r + 1)$th place of the $(n + 1)$th row equals the number of combinations of n things taken r at a time, or $_nC_r$. For example, if $n = 5$ and $r = 3$, the number of combinations is $_5C_2 = \dfrac{5!}{2!3!} = 10$.

The number 10 is found in the 6th row and the 3rd place (circled). Ten is also found in the 4th place of the same row (dashed circle). Because the triangle is symmetrical, the element in the $(r + 1)$th place of the $(n + 1)$th row always equals the element n the $(n - r + 1)$th place of that row. Therefore, $_nC_r = _nC_{n-r}$. For example, $_5C_3 = \dfrac{5!}{3!2!} = 10$, which is the same number of combinations as $_5C_2$

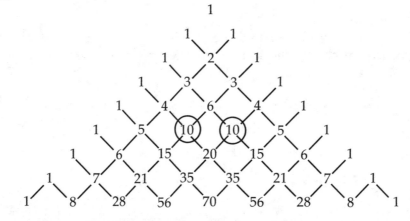

Have students find the second place in the fifth row, the third place in the seventh row, and the sixth place in the eighth row. By using combinations, students can find any place in any row.

      4. Many models and features of cars are available. For example, assume that the Ford Contour sedan comes in 7 colors with a choice of either vinyl or cloth upholstery. Have the students solve the following problems.
          a. How may different choices of standard models do you have?
          b. Assume that the available options on the Ford Contour are power brakes, power steering, remote keyless entry, dual aribags, air conditioner, and AM/FM radio/CD player. How many combinations are available for each car? (Note that in each option, you have two choices: you can decide to take it, or you can decide not to take it.)
          c. If a Ford dealer wants to have one car with each possible combination of options on his lot, how many cars will he need to have?

Section III Applications

1. You may wish to introduce your students to another form of the binomial theorem, which in general form is

$$(a + b)^n = a^n + \frac{n}{1^a}n - 1b + \frac{n(n-1)}{1 \cdot 2} a^{n-2}b^2 + \frac{n(n-1)(n-2)}{1 \cdot 2 \cdot 3} a^n - 3b^3 + \dots + b^n.$$

This formula gives the same results as the one given for binomial distribution on page 43 of the LIFEPAC. The coefficients of the terms of the binomial theorem are the same as the elements of Pascal's triangle.

In general, letting r represent any term of the expansion, to find the rth term, use the following formula.

$$\frac{n(n-1)(n-2)(n-r+2)\dots(n-r+2)}{1 \cdot 2 \cdot 3 \dots (r-1)} a^n - r + 1 \, b^r - 1$$

This formula gives the same results as the one previously mentioned that is in the LIFEPAC.

2. Have students solve the following hypothetical situation. An absent-minded professor wrote three letters and addressed three envelopes. Then he put each of the letters into an envelope without paying attention to which letter belonged in each envelope. Have the students find the following probabilities.

    a. The probability that exactly one letter is mailed to the correct person.

    b. The probability that exactly one letter is mailed to the wrong person.

    c. The probability that one or more letters is mailed to the correct person.

Before students solve the problem, show the following set-up.

Envelopes

	A	B	C
1	a	b	c
2	a	c	b
3	b	c	a
4	b	a	c
5	c	a	b
6	c	b	a

Possible Outcomes   Letters

Note that in the first outcome, each of the three letters is mailed to the correct person, whereas in each of the other cases, at least one letter is mailed to the wrong person.

Materials Needed for LIFEPAC
   Required: Suggested:
                                                 reference materials i.e. precalculus textbook

Additional Learning Activities
   Section I Mathematical Induction
   1. The summation used to find e, in natural logarithms, is

$$2 + \sum_{i=2}^{n} \frac{1}{i!}$$ Have students evaluate the summation to $n = 8$;

   they should find e equal to 2.7182...

   Section II Functions and Limits

   1. Have students evaluate each of the following geometric series using the formula

$$\lim_{x \to \infty} S_x = \frac{a}{1-r},$$ where S_x is the sum of the series, a is the first term of the series, and

   r is the common ratio (in the following series, r is $\frac{1}{2}, \frac{1}{3}, \frac{1}{4}$, and $\frac{1}{5}$ respectively).

   Example: Find $\lim (1 + \frac{1}{6} + \frac{1}{36} + \frac{1}{216} + ...)$

   $$S_x = 1 + \frac{1}{6} + \frac{1}{36} + \frac{1}{216} + ...$$

   $$a = 1$$

   $$r = \frac{1}{6} \qquad \lim_{x \to \infty} S_x = \frac{1}{1 - \frac{1}{6}} = \frac{1}{\frac{5}{6}} = \frac{6}{5} \text{ or } 1\frac{1}{5}$$

   a. $\lim_{x \to \infty} (1 + \frac{1}{2} + \frac{1}{4} + \frac{1}{8} + ...)$

   b. $\lim_{x \to \infty} (1 + \frac{1}{3} + \frac{1}{9} + \frac{1}{27} + ...)$

   c. $\lim_{x \to \infty} (1 + \frac{1}{4} + \frac{1}{16} + \frac{1}{64} + ...)$

   d. $\lim_{x \to \infty} (1 + \frac{1}{5} + \frac{1}{25} + \frac{1}{125} + ...)$

   2. Have students find functions that have a limit of 2; of 3; of 4.

   Section III Slopes of Functions
   1. Discuss these questions with your class.
         a. Does the slope of $f(x) = x^2 + 12$ equal the slope of the curve
             $g(x) = x^2 - 9$? Why?
         b. Does the slope of the curve $f(x) = 3x^2 - 7$ equal the slope of the curve
             $g(x) = 3x^2 + 2$? Why?
         c. Can the angle of intersection be found for two lines? two curves? A
             line and a curve?

2. Have students examine the following equations of curves and their respective slopes to determine a shortcut for finding the slope of a curve (with one variable such as such that x is not a radical).

  a. $f(x) = x^2 + 3$

  $m = 2x$

  b. $g(x) = x^4$

  $m = 4x^3$

  c. $h(x) = x^2 - 6x$

  $m = 2x - 6$

  d. $j(x) = x^3 + 4x^2$

  $m = 3x^2 + 8x$

  e. $k(x) = 6 - \dfrac{3x}{8}$

  $m = -\dfrac{3}{8}$

The method of the short cut is to multiply the exponent of each term by that term's coefficient and subtract 1 from the exponent. If a term has no variable (if the term is a constant), it drops out (becomes 0).

  Example: Find the slope of $f(x) = x^2 + 5$. Multiply the term x^2 by 2 to get $2x^2$ and subtract 1 from the exponent to get $2x^{2-1} = 2x^1$ = $2x$. The constant 5 drops out (becomes 0). Therefore, the slope of $f(x) = x^2 + 5$ is $2x$

The process of finding the slope by this method is actually done by using the derivative and is explained and studied in detail in calculus courses. This activity should be done after students are familiar with finding the slope by the limit process. After students find the short cut, they should be able to find the slope of a function (with one variable) by inspection.

Section IV Mathematics LIFEPACs 1201 through 1210 Review

1. Have students write review problems for the class to solve. Students should keep the solutions to the problems they write so answers can be checked.

Additional Information

All students should study mathematical induction prior to taking college mathematics courses. However, the study of limits and slopes is not critical since these topics are covered more thoroughly in the calculus. Some students, however, will find the work with limits and slopes very interesting and will benefit from the study as an introduction to the calculus.

TESTS

Reproducible Tests
for use with the Mathematics
1200 Teacher's Guide

Name _____

Write the required information (each answer, 3 points).

1. State the range of the relation $G = \{(4, \sqrt[3]{7}), (6, \sqrt[3]{9}, (8, \sqrt[3]{11})\}$.

    _____

2. Let $x = \{1, 2, 3, 4\}$ and $y = \{a, b, c\}$. Let H be the set of ordered pairs $\{(1, b), (2, a), (3, b), (1, a), (4, c)\}$. Is H a function?

    _____

3. Write the set of ordered pairs for the relation $\{(x, y): x = |4y + 1| \text{ and } y \in \{-2, -1, 0, 1, 2\}\}$.

    _____

4. The following figures are graphs of relations between real numbers. Which graphs are functions?

    _____

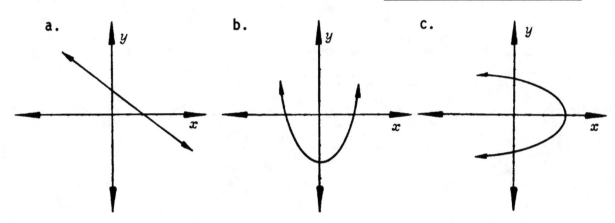

a.   b.   c.

5. State the domain of $\{(x, y): y = 3x^2 - 2\}$.

    _____

Write the required rules (each answer, 5 points).

6. $A = \{(x, f(x)): (4, 2), (9, 3), (16, 4), (25, 5)\}$.

    _____

7. $B = \{(x, g(x)): (0, -1), (-1, -4), (2, 5), (-2, -7)\}$.

    _____

Perform the required operations on the following functions (each answer, 5 points).

Given: $F(x) = 2x^2 - 2$, $G(x) = x + 1$, $H(x) = x$

8. $F(3)$ _____

9. $F(x) - G(x)$ _____

10. $F \circ G$ _____

11. $G^{-1}(x)$ _____

12. $F(1) + G(2) - 3H(-1)$ _____

13. $(F \cdot G)(x)$ _____

14. $\left(\frac{F}{G}\right)(x)$ _____

15. $G \circ H$ _____

16. $G^{-1} \circ H^{-1}$ _____

17. $(F + G)(x)$ _____

18. $(G + H)(x)$ _____

19. $(G \cdot H)(x)$ _____

20. Is $F^{-1}(x)$ a function? _____

$\boxed{\frac{72}{\ 90}}$

Date _____

Score _____

Name _____

Write the required information (each answer, 5 points).

1. Given $F(x) = x - 3$, find the missing values in the table of solutions.

x	0	0.1	$-\frac{1}{2}$	d. _____
$F(x)$	a. _____	b. _____	c. _____	3

2. Given a line containing the points $P_1(2, -5)$ and $P_2(6, 3)$, find the slope of the line.

   _____

3. Graph the linear inequality $2x - y + 4 > 0$.

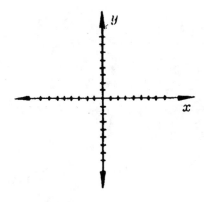

4. Find the remainder if $P(x) = x^3 - 2x^2 + 1$ is divided by $x - 2$.

   _____

5. Find the zero of the function $G(x) = \dfrac{4x^2 - 25}{2x + 5}$.

   _____

6. Determine if $x - 4$ is a factor of $f(x) = x^4 - x^3 - 14x^2 + 5x + 12$.

   _____

7. Write the inverse of $G(x) = \log_4 x$.

   _____

Sketch the required graphs (each graph, 5 points).

8. Graph $f(x) = 2^x + 2^{-x}$

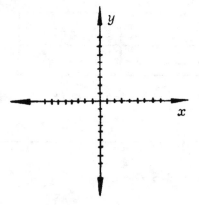

9. Graph $f(x) = x^3 - 1$.

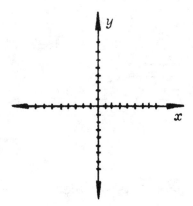

10. Graph $(f + g)x$, given $f(x) = x^2 - 2$ and $g(x) = -\frac{1}{2}x + 1$.

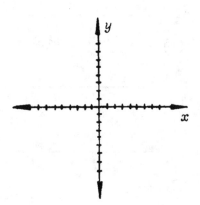

11. Graph $f(x) = \dfrac{x^2}{1 - x^2}$

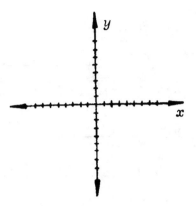

$$\begin{array}{|c|}\hline 56 \\ \diagup \\ 70 \\ \hline \end{array}$$

Date _____

Score _____

Name _____

Find the value of the following expressions; the tables may be used if necessary (each answer, 2 points).

1. sin 90° + cos 120° + tan 225° + cos 180° = _____ .

2. (sin 315°)(cos 150°) - (sin 60°)(cos 45°) = _____ .

3. (sin 330°)(tan 135°) - (sin 210°)(cos 300°)(tan 180°) = _____ .

4. $\dfrac{\cot 270° - \tan (-180°)}{(\sec 240°)[\sec (-180°)](\sin 90°)}$ = _____ .

Express each of the following angles as a function of a positive acute angle (each answer, 2 points).

5. sec 105° = _____

6. tan (-70°) = _____

7. sin 237° = _____

8. cos (-325°) = _____

9. cos 49° 10' = _____

Given that tan θ = -$\dfrac{4}{3}$, sketch the two possible angles (graph, 4 points) and determine the value of the other functions of both possibilities (each answer, 2 points).

10. a.

QUADRANT _____   QUADRANT _____

b. sin θ = _____   g. sin θ = _____

c. cos θ = _____   h. cos θ = _____

d. cot θ = _____   i. cot θ = _____

e. sec θ = _____   j. sec θ = _____

f. csc θ = _____   k. csc θ = _____

Given that ∠θ is in the third quadrant and cos θ = -$\dfrac{1}{2}$, find the value of each of the other five functions of θ (each answer, 2 points).

11. a. sin θ = _____   d. sec θ = _____

b. tan θ = _____   e. csc θ = _____

c. cot θ = _____

Evaluate by using the tables (each answer, 2 points).

12. csc 217° 40' = _____

13. sin 98° 23' = _____

14. cot (-12° 35') = _____

Find ∠θ (each answer, 2 points).

15. sin θ = 0.7396; ∠θ = _____

16. cot θ = 0.2905; ∠θ = _____

Simplify (each answer, 2 points).

17. (cos 180°)^6 = _____

18. (tan 180° - sec 0°)^3 + sin 270° = _____

19. (cos 0°·3 sin 90°)^4 = _____

20. csc 270°·sin (-90°) + 4 tan 225° - cot^2 90° = _____

Complete the following table (each answer, 2 points).

	Degrees	Radians	Quadrant
21.	75°	a. _____	b. _____
22.	a. _____	$\frac{7\pi}{4}$	b. _____
23.	225°	a. _____	b. _____
24.	150°	a. _____	b. _____
25.	a. _____	$\frac{\pi}{3}$	b. _____

Date _____

Score _____

Name _____

Sketch these graphs (each graph, 4 points).

1. Graph on the same axes $y = \cos x$, $-\pi < x < \pi$; and
    $y = \sec x$, $-\pi < x < \pi$.

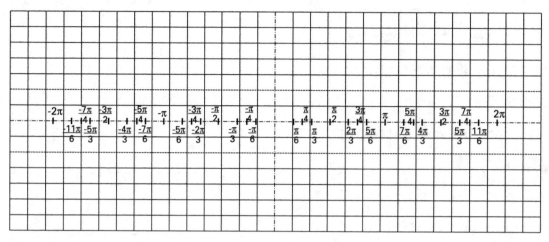

2. $y = \tan x$, $-\dfrac{\pi}{2} \le x \le \dfrac{3\pi}{2}$.

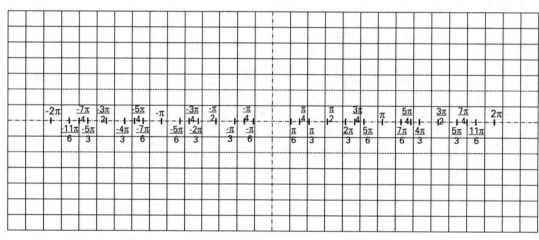

3. $y = 2 \sin x$, $-\dfrac{\pi}{6} \le x \le 2\pi$.

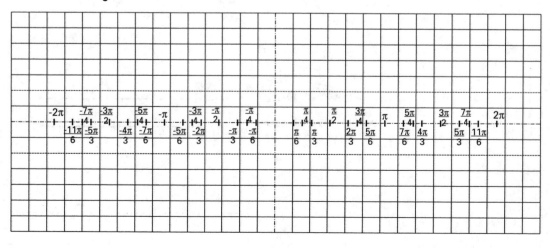

4. $y = \cot x$, $0 \leq x \leq 2\pi$.

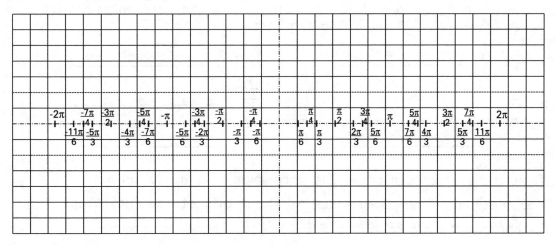

Solve these problems (each answer, 4 points).

5. A flywheel with a 4-ft. radius is revolving counterclockwise with a circumferential velocity of 75 feet per second. Find the angular velocity (to the nearest whole number).

_____

6. A wheel moves with an angular velocity of 12 radians per second. Find the diameter of the wheel if its speed is 180 inches per second.

_____

7. A record 10 inches in diameter is turning at the rate of 33 r.p.m. Find the speed, in radians per minute, of a point on the rim of the record.

_____

Complete these items (each answer, 3 points).

8. Evaluate $\cot \frac{\pi}{4} + \sin 2\pi = \cos \frac{3\pi}{2}$. _____

9. Evaluate $2 \cos \frac{5\pi}{2}$. _____

10. The period of $y = \sin \frac{x}{4}$ is _____ .

11. *T* is the point at a given distance from *P*(1, 0) on the unit circle with its center at (0, 0). Determine the quadrant in which *T* lies given each of the following distances.

a. $\frac{3}{4}\pi$ _____   d. $\frac{10}{6}\pi$ _____

b. $\frac{6}{5}\pi$ _____   e. $\frac{\pi}{5}$ _____

c. $\frac{2}{3}\pi$ _____   f. $\frac{11\pi}{6}$ _____

12. If on the unit circle *C* the distance from *P*(1, 0) to the point *T* is *x*, determine the coordinates of the points at the indicated distance on *C* from *P*. Given *T* $(\frac{\sqrt{2}}{4}, \frac{\sqrt{2}}{4})$.

a. $\pi + x$ _____   e. $2\pi - x$ _____

b. $\frac{\pi}{2} + x$ _____   f. 2π _____

                                      g. π _____

c. $-x$ _____

                                      h. $\frac{3\pi}{2}$ _____

d. $2\pi + x$ _____

13. Find the phase shift of each of the following functions.

a. $y = 3 \sin (2x + 4)$ _____

b. $y = \cos (4x - 8)$ _____

c. $y = 4 \sin (3x - 15)$ _____

14. Find the amplitude and period of each of the following functions.

a. $y = 2 \sin 3x$ _____

b. $y = 3 \cos \frac{1}{2}x$ _____

Write *true* or *false* (each answer, 2 points).

15. _____ The trigonometric equation for sin using *A* = 1, period = $\frac{2}{3}\pi$, and phase shift = $-\frac{\pi}{2}$, is $y = -\sin 3(x + \frac{\pi}{2})$.

16. _____ The maximum value of $y = \sin x$ for $-\frac{\pi}{2} \leq x \leq \frac{\pi}{2}$ is 0.5.

Date _____

Score _____

Name _____

Complete these activities (each answer, 5 points).

1. Verify that $\dfrac{1}{\cos \theta} - \cos \theta = \tan \theta \cdot \sin \theta$. _____

2. Verify that $(1 - \sin \theta)(1 + \sin \theta) = \dfrac{1}{1 + \tan^2 \theta}$. _____

Answer these questions (each answer, 5 points).

3. If $x = 90°$, does $\tan \dfrac{x}{2} = \dfrac{\sin x}{1 + \cos x}$? Justify your answer.

_____

4. If $\theta = \pi$, does $\cos \dfrac{\pi}{12} = \dfrac{\sqrt{2} + \sqrt{6}}{4}$? Justify your answer.

_____

Complete these activities (each answer, 5 points).

5. Derive a formula for $\sin 2\alpha$ from $\sin (\alpha + \beta)$. _____

6. Express $\tan (\theta - \dfrac{\pi}{4})$ in terms of $\sin \theta$ and $\cos \theta$. _____

7. Simplify $\dfrac{\csc^2 \theta - 1}{\csc^2 \theta}$. _____

8. Express $\dfrac{1 - \tan^2 x}{1 + \tan^2 x}$ in terms of $\sin x$ and $\cos x$. _____

9. If $\sin \alpha = \dfrac{2}{5}$ and $\cos \beta = \dfrac{10}{35}$, find $\cos (\alpha - \beta)$. _____

Given: $\sin \theta = \dfrac{12}{15}$ and $\cos \phi = -\dfrac{3}{5}$; evaluate the following expressions
(each answer, 5 points).

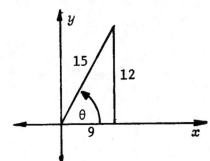
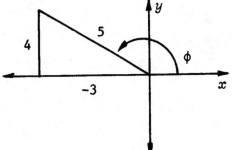

10. $\sin (\theta - \phi) =$ _____   12. $\cos (\theta - \phi) =$ _____

11. $\sin (\theta + \phi) =$ _____   13. $\cos (\theta + \phi) =$ _____

14. $\tan(\theta + \phi) =$ _____

15. $\sin \frac{1}{2}\theta =$ _____

16. $\cos 2\phi =$ _____

17. $\tan 2\theta =$ _____

18. $\cos 4\theta =$ _____

19. $\cos 3\phi =$ _____

Prove this identity (5 points).

20. $\tan\left(\frac{\pi}{2} - \theta\right) = \cot\theta.$

Date _____

Score _____

Name _____

Complete this activity (each answer, 3 points).

1. Given:

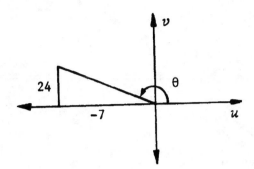

Find these items.

a. sin θ = _____   d. csc θ = _____

b. cos θ = _____   e. sec θ = _____

c. tan θ = _____   f. cot θ = _____

Solve these problems (each answer, 5 points).   (Work Space)

2. The resultant of two forces at right
   angles is 100 lbs. If one of the
   forces makes an angle of 30° with the
   resultant, compute that force.

   _____

3. A block of weight W = 450 lbs. rests
   on a smooth board inclined at 25°
   with the horizontal.

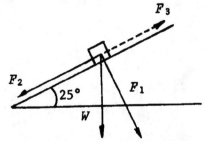

   a. Find the vertical and horizontal
      components of W.

   _____

   b. What force F_3 parallel to the
      plane is required to draw the
      block up the plane?

      F_3 = _____

4. Two airplanes leave an airport at the same time. One travels on a heading of 40° at 400 mph and the other on a heading of 135° at 450 mph. After two hours, how far apart are the airplanes (rounded to the nearest whole number)?

(Work Space)

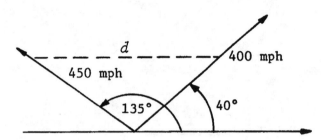

5. Two highways intersect at point *A* at an angle of 43° 30'. The distance from *A* to *B* along one highway is 10 miles; the distance from *A* to *C* along the other highway is 15 miles. A third highway connects *B* to *C*. How long will a car take averaging 45 mph to drive the complete circuit (from *A* to *B* to *C* and back to *A*)?

6. A ship sails east from a harbor for 20 nautical miles. It then sails in the direction of N 80° E for 12 nautical miles. How far is it then from the harbor, to the nearest nautical mile?

7. A telephone pole is supported by two guy wires, each running from the top of the pole to the ground. One wire is 75 feet long and makes an angle of 45° with the ground. If the second wire is 65 feet long, what angle does it make with the ground?

8. An airplane is headed in direction 62° with an air speed of 300 mph. The course is 78° with a ground speed of 270 mph. Find the wind speed.

(Work Space)

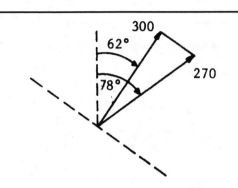

9. A missile is fired at an angle of 75° from the horizontal. At one point its speed was 900 mph. Find its horizontal velocity in miles per minute.

10. Given the triangle shown, find ∠C, ∠B, and b.

    a. ∠C = _____

    b. ∠B = _____

    c.   b = _____

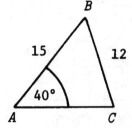

63 / 78

Date _____

Score _____

Complete these items (each answer, 5 points).

1. Compute $\sin^{-1}\left(\dfrac{-1}{\sqrt{2}}\right)$

   _____

2. Simplify $\arctan\left(\tan \dfrac{2\pi}{3}\right)$.

   _____

3. Simplify $\arccos\left[\sin\left(\dfrac{-5\pi}{6}\right)\right]$.

   _____

4. Compute $\arcsin \dfrac{\sqrt{3}}{2}$.

   _____

5. Compute $\arccos 0.8888$.

   _____

6. Graph $y = \arcsin x,\ -\dfrac{\pi}{2} \le x \le \dfrac{\pi}{2}$.

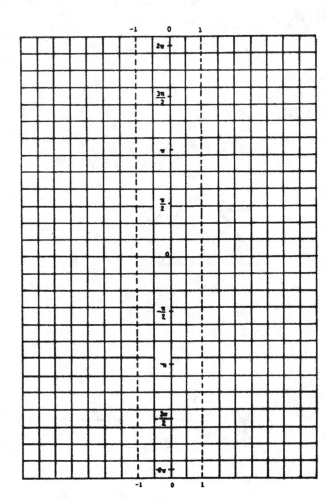

7. Graph $y = \arctan x$, $-\frac{\pi}{2} \leq \frac{\pi}{2}$. _____

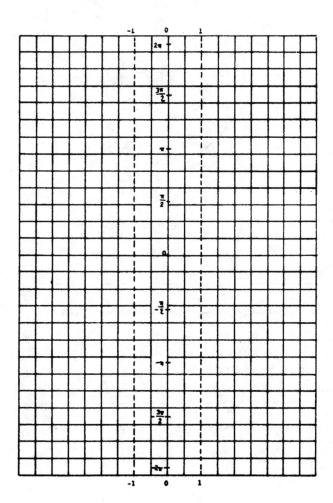

8. Find the inverse function of
   $F(x) = 3 \cos^{-1} x$.   _____

9. If F is a function and $F(x) = \arccos x$, identify the range and domain of F.   _____

10. For what real number x is $\arcsin (2x^2 - 2x) = -\frac{\pi}{6}$?   _____

Graph the following polar coordinates (each answer, 5 points).

11. $A(5, 135°)$

12. $B(-6, 45°)$

13. $C(4, \frac{7\pi}{4})$

14. $D(-3, \frac{3\pi}{4})$

15. $E(2, 280°$

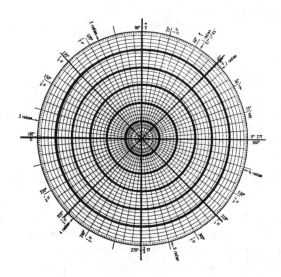

Convert the following polar coordinates to Cartesian coordinates (each answer, 5 points).

16. $(2, 315°)$ _____

17. $(5, 135°)$ _____

18. $(3, 90°)$ _____

19. $(6, 225°)$ _____

20. $(4, 120°)$ _____

Convert the following Cartesian coordinates to polar coordinates (each answer, 5 points).

21. $(2, -1)$ _____

22. $(-4, 4\sqrt{3})$ _____

23. $(-\frac{\sqrt{2}}{2}, -\frac{\sqrt{2}}{2})$ _____

24. $(0, 3)$ _____

25. $(-2, 2)$ _____

Express the following Cartesian equations in polar equation form (each answer, 5 points).

26. $x^2 + y^2 - 2x = 0$ _____

27. $x^2 + y^2 = 9y$ _____

Express the following polar equations in Cartesian equation form (each answer, 5 points).

28. $r^2 = 6 \cos 2x$ _____

29. $r^2 = 4 \tan 2\theta$ _____

Graph the following polar equations (each answer, 5 points).

30. $r = 1 + 2 \cos \theta$

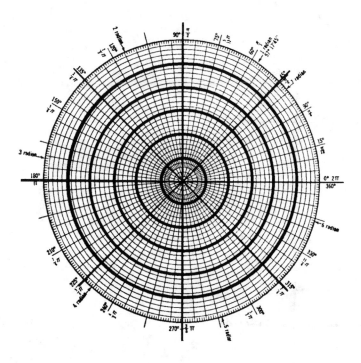

31. $r = \theta$

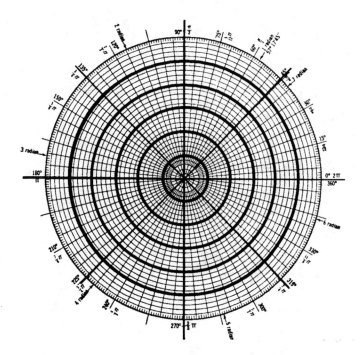

124	
	155

Date _____

Score _____

Name _____

Identify each of the following loci, define each conic's properties, and sketch each graph (properties, 5 points; each graph, 5 points).

1. $x^2 + y^2 - 6x + 4y - 87 = 0$

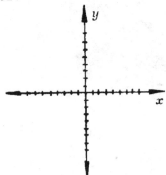

2. $9x^2 + 36y^2 = 324$

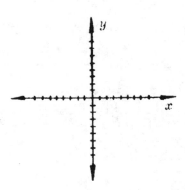

3. $x^2 - 10x - 20y - 15 = 0$

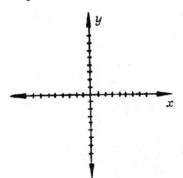

4. $4x^2 - 49y^2 = 196$

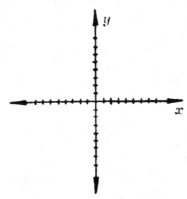

Translate or rotate the following equations as indicated and sketch each graph (each equation, 5 points; each graph, 5 points).

5. Translate the equation $2x^2 + 3y^2 - 8x + 6y - 7 = 0$ to the origin.

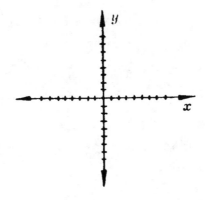

6. By rotating, find the equation in general form of $9x^2 - 3\sqrt{3}xy + 6y^2 = 94.5$.

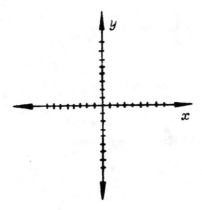

Find the necessary information for the following problems (each problem, 5 points).

7. Simplify the equation $x^2 + 4xy + y^2 = 16$.

8. Find the equation in general form of the circle that passes through the points $(4, 5)$, $(3, -2)$, and $(1, -4)$.

9. Find the center and radius of the circle $x^2 + y^2 + 8x - 10y + 1 = 0$.

10. Find the eccentricity of $3x^2 - 4y^2 + 12x + 8y - 4 = 0$.

Date _____

Score _____

Name _____

Compute the answers to the following problems (each answer, 4 points).

1. Evaluate the following permutations and combinations.

   a. 6^P4 _____

   b. 5!   _____

   c. $\begin{pmatrix} 8 \\ 4 \end{pmatrix}$ _____

   d. 7^C2 _____

2. In how many ways can Ann, Barbara, Andy, Rick, and Diane be seated around a round table?

   _____

3. A coin is flipped two times.

   a. What is the probability of obtaining exactly one head?

   _____

   b. What is the probability of obtaining at least one head?

   _____

   c. What is the probability of obtaining exactly two heads?

   _____

   d. What is the probability of obtaining no heads?

   _____

4. A spinner is divided into sectors by means of radii. The area of each of the sectors is red sector, 30%; yellow sector, 40%; blue sector, 20%; and white sector, 10%. Find the following probabilities.

   a. The probability that the spinner will stop on either red or blue.

   _____

   b. The probability that the spinner will stop on any color except yellow.

   _____

c. The probability that the spinner will stop on either red, white, or blue.

_____

5. In a multiple-choice test containing 10 questions, each question is to be answered by selecting one of five possible answers, of which only one answer is correct. Find the probability that a student who answers each questions by guessing will have

a. exactly 6 of his answers correct.

_____

b. at least 6 of his answers correct. Do set-up only.

_____

6. A floor in a building is divided into seven offices. You are free to choose any four offices for your staff. In how many ways can you choose the four offices?

_____

7. How many different three-digit numbers can be formed from the ten digits from 0 through 9?

_____

8. In a sample of 75 voters, 30 voters indicated that they favored Candidate A, 13 favored Candidate B, and the remaining voters favored Candidates C or D. If this sample is representative of the population, what is the probability that a voter will favor Candidate A or Candidate B?

_____

9. A number is chosen at random from the positive odd integers from 1 to 49. List the sample space and find the probability that the number chosen is a multiple of 3 and a multiple of 5.

_____

10. A study showed that ten hamsters out of a population of fifty hamsters did not like orange-flavored jelly beans. Considering that a success is a subject who does not like orange-flavored jelly beans, find the following probabilities of this binomial distribution.

   a. The probability of obtaining 4 successes in a sample of 10?

   _____

   b. The probability of obtaining 7 successes in a sample of 10?

   _____

   c. The probability of obtaining $\frac{1}{5}$ success in a sample of 5?

   _____

   d. The probability of obtaining $\frac{3}{5}$ success in a sample of 5?

   _____

$\begin{array}{|c|}\hline 70 \\ \diagdown \\ 88 \\ \hline\end{array}$

Date _____

Score _____

Name _____

1. Prove the following statement by mathematical induction (this proof, 5 points).

$$\sum_{i=1}^{n} i = \frac{n(n+1)}{2}$$

Evaluate the following summation (this item, 3 points).

2. $\displaystyle\sum_{i=1}^{3} i^i$

Given $f(x) = 2x^2 - 6x - 1$, evaluate the following function (this item, 3 points).

3. $f(-1)$

Evaluate the difference quotient $\dfrac{f(a+h) - f(a)}{h}$ for the following function (this item, 3 points).

4. $f(x) = 8x^2 + 7$

Evaluate each of the following limits (each answer, 3 points).

5. $\displaystyle\lim_{x \to 4} 3x^2$

6. $\lim\limits_{x \to \infty} \dfrac{x^2 + 2x}{3}$

Find the slope of the following function (this item, 3 points).

7. $f(x) = 4x - 6$

Find the angle of intersection between the following pair of equations in the first quadrant (this item, 4 points).

8. $f(x) = x^2$
   $g(x) = 4$

List the domain and the range of the function $f(x) = -\dfrac{x^2}{3}$ (each answer, 3 points).

9. domain _____

10. range _____

Given $f(x) = 3x^2 + 1$ and $g(x) = 5x - 3$, find the following function (this item, 5 points).

11. Find $f(x) + g(x)$. _____

Work the following exercises as indicated (each answer, 5 points).

12. Solve $8x^2 + 2x - 3 \leq 0$. _____

13. Find $P(4)$ by synthetic division if $P(x) = 2x^2 - 5x + 8$. _____

101

Answer the following **items** (each answer, 2 points).

14. Find sec 24° 20'. _____

15. Express 95° in radians. _____

Sketch this graph (this item, 4 points).

16. Graph $y > \sin 3x$, $0 < x < 2\pi$.

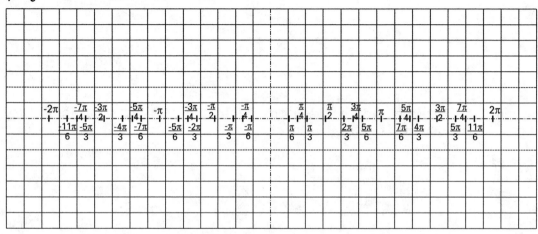

Solve this problem (this item, 4 points).

17. A wheel turns 60° per hour. Through how many radians does it turn in a 24-hour day?

_____

Solve this equation; domain 0° $\leq \theta \leq$ 360°; answer to the nearest whole degree (this item, 5 points).

18. $\sin 2\theta = 2 \sin \theta$ _____

Given: $\sin \theta = \frac{1}{2}$, $\cos \phi = -\frac{1}{2}$, θ is in the first quadrant, and ϕ is in the third quadrant, evaluate this expression (this item, 5 points).

19. $\cos (\theta + \phi)$ _____

Solve this problem (this item, 5 points).

20. A block of ice weighing 75 pounds rests on an incline that makes an angle of 15° with the horizontal. How much of the friction force is needed to prevent the block of ice from sliding down the incline?

_____

Complete this item (this item, 3 points).

21. Given triangle *DEF*, $\angle D = 15°$, $\angle F = 30°$, and $f = 10$, find d (round to the nearest whole number).

_____

Graph this polar coordinate (this item, 5 points).

22. $A\left(3, \dfrac{5\pi}{6}\right)$

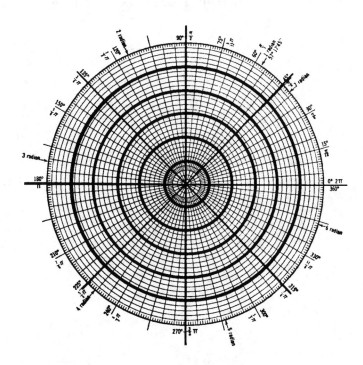

Express this Cartesian equation in polar equation form (this item, 5 points).

23. $x^2 + 3y^2 - 6 = 0$ _____

Write the standard equation for the given conic and then graph the curve (equation, 5 points; graph, 5 points).

24. Parabola in Position I with vertex at (0, 0) and focus at (2, 0).

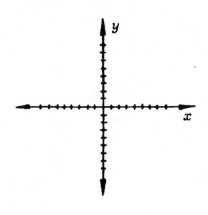

Compute the answers to the following problems (each answer, 4 points).

25. In how many ways can 6 marbles be chosen from 8 marbles?

   _____

26. The probability of rain is $\frac{1}{4}$ for each day during a particular week. What is the probability of rain for 3 days of the week?

   _____

85 / 106

Date _____

Score _____

A
N
S
W
E
R

K
E
Y
S

MATHEMATICS 1201
SOLUTION KEY

I. SECTION ONE

1.1   a. {5, 6, 7}
      b. {0, 1, 2}

1.2   a. {6, 7, 8, 9}
      b. {$\sqrt{2}$, $\sqrt{3}$, $\sqrt{4}$, $\sqrt{5}$}

1.3   a. {$\frac{1}{2}$}
      b. {$\frac{\pi}{6}$, $\frac{\pi}{4}$, $\frac{\pi}{3}$, $\frac{\pi}{2}$}

1.4   a. {6.2, 7.3, 8.4, 9.5}
      b. {0.3}

1.5   {(10, $2), (15, $3), (20, $4),
      (30, $6), (60, $8), (90, $10)}

1.6 F = {(1, 16), (2, 64),
          (3, 144), (4, 256),
          (5, 400)}

1.7   {x: $x \in R$, $x \geq 0$}

1.8   {r: $r \in R$, $r \neq 0$}

1.9   {a: $a \in R$, $a \neq 0$}

1.10 a. {x: x is an even integer}
      b. {y: y is an odd integer}

1.11 a. {x: $x \in R$}
      b. {y: $y \geq 0$}

1.12 a. yes
      b. ---

1.13 a. no
      b. 1 is not paired with a
         unique second element
         of the range.

1.14 a. yes
      b. ---

1.15 a. yes
      b. ---

1.16 a. no
      b. The empty set is not a set
         of ordered-pair numbers.

1.17 a. yes
      b. No two points lie on the
         same vertical line.

1.18 a. no
      b. Two or more points lie
         on the same vertical
         line.

1.19 a. yes
      b. No two points lie on
         the same vertical line.

1.20 a. no
      b. Two or more points lie
         on the same vertical
         line.

1.21 a. no
      b. Two or more pointe lie
         on the same vertical
         line.

1.22 Multiply x by 3 and subtract
      1; hence, $y = 3x - 1$.

1.23 Divide x by 2 and add 2;
      hence, $y = \frac{x}{2} + 2$.

1.24 Multiply x by 3 and subtract
      3; hence, $y = 3x - 3$.

1.25 y is the square of x; hence,
      $y = x^2$.

1.26 Multiply x by 5 and add 5;
      hence, $y = 5x + 5$.

1.27 Subtract 3 from n, multiply
      by n, and divide by 2;
      hence, $D = \frac{n(n-3)}{2}$.

1.28 D is 50 times t; hence,
      $D = 50t$.

1.29 S is 16 times the square
      of t; hence, $S = 16t^2$.

1.30 a. $S_1 = \frac{0}{2}(0 + 1) = 0$

b. $S_2 = \frac{1}{2}(1 + 1) = 1$

c. $S_3 = \frac{2}{2}(2 + 1) = 3$

d. $6 = \frac{n}{2}(n + 1)$

$12 = n(n + 1)$

$n = 3$ or $n = -4$

e. $S_5 = \frac{100}{2}(100 + 1)$

$= 5{,}050$

1.31 a.

$A = 2{,}000$ sq. ft.

$xl = 2{,}000$

$l = \frac{2{,}000}{x}$

$c(x) = 0.50x + 0.30x$

$\qquad + 2 \cdot (0.30) \cdot \frac{2{,}000}{x}$

$c(x) = 0.80x + 0.60(\frac{2{,}000}{x})$

$c(x) = 0.80x + \frac{1{,}200}{x}$

b. $x > 0$

II. SECTION TWO

2.1 $F(1) = 1^2 + 3(1) - 2$

$= 1 + 3 - 2$

$= 2$

2.2 $F(3) = 3^2 + 3(3) - 2$

$= 9 + 9 - 2$

$= 16$

2.3 $F(-1) = (-1)^2 + 3(-1) - 2$

$= 1 - 3 - 2$

$= -4$

2.4 $F(a) = a^2 + 3a - 2$

2.5 $F(x - 1) = (x - 1)^2 + 3(x - 1)$

$\qquad - 2$

$= x^2 - 2x + 1 + 3x$

$\qquad - 3 - 2$

$= x^2 + x - 4$

2.6 $G(6) = 3(6)^2 - 2(6) - 1$

$= 3(36) - 12 - 1$

$= 108 - 12 - 1$

$= 95$

2.7 $G(a + b) = 3(a + b)^2$

$\qquad - 2(a + b) - 1$

$= 3(a^2 + 2ab + b^2)$

$\qquad - 2a - 2b - 1$

$= 3a^2 + 6ab + 3b^2$

$\qquad - 2a - 2b - 1$

2.8 $F(x + h) = (x + h)^2 + 2$

$= x^2 + 2xh + h^2 + 2$

2.9 $F(x - h) = (x - h)^2 + 2$

$= x^2 - 2xh + h^2 + 2$

2.10 $F(x^2) = (x^2)^2 + 2 = x^4 + 2$

2.11 $\{2, 4, 6\}$

2.12 $(F + G)(x) = \{(2, 9), (4, 13),$

$(6, 17)\}$

2.13 $(F \cdot G)(x) = \{(2, 20), (4, 42),$

$(6, 72)\}$

2.14 $(\frac{F}{G})(x) = \{(2, \frac{4}{5}), (4, \frac{6}{7}),$

$(6, \frac{8}{9})\}$

2.15 $(F - G)(x) = \{(2, -1),$

$(4, -1),$

$(6, -1)\}$

2.16 $(f + g)(x) = (x + 2)$

$\qquad + (3x + 5)$

$= 4x + 7$

2.17 $(g \cdot f)(x) = (3x + 5)(x + 2)$

$= 3x^2 + 6x + 5x + 10$

$= 3x^2 + 11x + 10$

2.18 $(f - g)(x) = (x + 2)$

$\qquad - (3x + 5)$

$= x + 2 - 3x - 5$

$= -2x - 3$

2.19 $(\frac{f}{g})(x) = \frac{x + 2}{3x + 5}$; $3x + 5 \neq 0$;

$x \neq -\frac{5}{3}$

2.20 $[f(x)]^2 = (x + 2)^2 = x^2 + 4x + 4$

2.21 $2(x + 2) - \frac{1}{x - 1}$

$= 2x + 4 - \frac{1}{x - 1}$; $x \neq 1$

2.22 $\frac{\left[\frac{1}{x - 1}\right]^2}{x + 2} = \frac{1}{(x - 1)^2} \cdot \frac{1}{x + 2}$

$= \frac{1}{(x - 1)^2(x + 2)}$

2.23 $(x + h)^2 + 2(x + h) + 1$
$= x^2 + 2xh + h^2 + 2x + 2h + 1$

2.24 $\frac{2(x + h) + 3 - (2x + 3)}{h}$

$= \frac{2x + 2h + 3 - 2x - 3}{h}$

$= \frac{2h}{h} = 2$

2.25 $\frac{(x + h)^2 - x^2}{h}$

$= \frac{x^2 + 2xh + h^2 - x^2}{h}$

$= \frac{2xh + h^2}{h} = \frac{h(2x + h)}{h} = 2x + h$

2.26 $\frac{(x + h)^3 - x^3}{h}$

$= \frac{x^3 + 3x^2h + 3xh^2 + h^3 - x^3}{h}$

$= \frac{3x^2h + 3xh^2 + h^3}{h} = \frac{h(3x^2 + 3xh + h^2)}{h}$

$= 3x^2 + 3xh + h^2$

2.27 $\frac{\sqrt{x + h} - \sqrt{x}}{h} = \frac{\sqrt{x + h} - \sqrt{x}}{h}$

$\cdot \frac{\sqrt{x + h} + \sqrt{x}}{\sqrt{x + h} + \sqrt{x}} = \frac{x + h - x}{h(\sqrt{x + h} + \sqrt{x})}$

$= \frac{h}{h(\sqrt{x + h} + \sqrt{x})} = \frac{1}{\sqrt{x + h} + \sqrt{x}}$

2.27 cont.

$- \frac{1}{\sqrt{x + h} + \sqrt{x}} \cdot \frac{\sqrt{x + h} - \sqrt{x}}{\sqrt{x + h} - \sqrt{x}}$

$= \frac{\sqrt{x + h} - \sqrt{x}}{x + h - x} = \frac{\sqrt{x + h} - \sqrt{x}}{h}$

2.28 $\frac{[(x + h)^2 + 6(x + h) + 9]}{h}$

$- \frac{(x^2 + 6x + 9)}{h}$

$= \frac{x^2 + 2xh + h^2 + 6x + 6h}{h}$

$+ \frac{9 - x^2 - 6x - 9}{h}$

$= \frac{2xh + h^2 + 6h}{h} = \frac{h(2x + h + 6)}{h}$

$= 2x + h + 6$

2.29 a. $3(x + 5) + 2$
$= 3x + 15 + 2 = 3x + 17$
b. $(3x + 2) + 5 = 3x + 7$
c. all real numbers
d. all real numbers

2.30 a. $(2x - 1)^2 + 6$
$= 4x^2 - 4x + 1 + 6$
$= 4x^2 - 4x + 7$
b. $2(x^2 + 6) - 1$
$= 2x^2 + 12 - 1$
$= 2x^2 + 11$
c. all real numbers
d. all real numbers

2.31 a. $(x^2 + 1) + 7 = x^2 + 8$
b. $(x + 7)^2 + 1$
$= x^2 + 14x + 49 + 1$
$= x^2 + 14x + 50$
c. all real numbers
d. all real numbers

2.32 a. $\frac{1}{(3x - 4) + 2} = \frac{1}{3x - 2}$
b. $3\left(\frac{1}{x + 2}\right) - 4 = \frac{3}{x + 2} - 4$
c. $x \neq \frac{2}{3}$
d. $x \neq -2$

2.33 a. $\dfrac{1}{\left(\dfrac{1}{2x+4}\right)^2} = \dfrac{1}{\dfrac{1}{(2x+4)^2}}$

$= 1 \cdot \dfrac{(2x+4)^2}{1}$

$= 4x^2 + 16x + 16$

b. $\dfrac{1}{2\left(\dfrac{1}{x^2}\right) + 4} = \dfrac{1}{\dfrac{2}{x^2} + 4}$

$= \dfrac{1}{\dfrac{2 + 4x^2}{x^2}} = 1 \cdot \dfrac{x^2}{2 + 4x^2}$

$= \dfrac{x^2}{4x^2 + 2}$

c. all real numbers, $x \neq -2$
d. all real numbers, $x \neq 0$

2.34 $g[I(x)] = x^2 + 2$ and $I[g(x)]$
$= x^2 + 2$ and $g(x) = x^2 + 2$

2.35 $f\{g[h(x)]\} = f[g(7)]$
$= f(7 + 6) = f(13) = 13^2$
$= 169$

2.36 $g\{f[h(x)]\} = g[f(7)] = g(7^2)$
$= g(49) = 49 + 6 = 55$

2.37 $h\{g[f(x)]\} = h[g(x^2)]$
$= h(x^2 + 6) = 7$
$h(x)$ is constant at 7; hence,
h of any value x is 7.

2.38 Given that $f[g(x)] = I$ and $I = x$.
Then $f[g(x)] = x$ and $f(ax + b)$
$= x$.
Now let f be some function,
such as $f(x) = Px + c$.
Then $f(ax + b) = P(ax + b) + c$.
Therefore, $P(ax + b) + c = x$
and $Pax + Pb + c = x$.
Hence, $Pa = 1$ and $Pb + c = 0$;

$P = \dfrac{1}{a}$ and $c = -Pb$

$= -\dfrac{b}{a}$.

Then, $f(x) = \dfrac{1}{a}x - \dfrac{b}{a} = \dfrac{x - b}{a}$.

2.39 a. $\{(4, 1), (3, 2), (8, 5),$
$(7, 4)\}$
b. yes

2.40 a. $\{(3, 5), (3, 2),$
$(4, 6)\}$
b. No, the first element
3 has two values.

2.41 a. $\{(1, 0)\}$
b. yes

2.42 a. $\{(1, 2), (2, 3),$
$(1, 4), (3, 5)\}$
b. No, the first element 1
has two values.

2.43 a. Let $y = F(x)$. Then
$y = 3x + 6$. Interchange
the variables: $x = 3y + 6$
and $y = \dfrac{x - 6}{3}$.
$\therefore F^{-1}(x) = \dfrac{x - 6}{3}$.
b. yes

2.44 a. Let $y = F(x)$. Then
$y = x^2 + 5$. Interchange
the variables:
$x = y^2 + 5$ and $y^2 = x - 5$.
$y = \pm\sqrt{x - 5}$ or $F^{-1}(x)$
$= \pm\sqrt{x - 5}$
b. No, for each value of x
in the domain of F^{-1}, two
function values occur.

2.45 a. Let $y = G(x)$. Then
$y = \dfrac{1}{x - 1}$. Interchange
the variables: $x = \dfrac{1}{y - 1}$
and $y - 1 = \dfrac{1}{x}$. $y = \dfrac{1}{x} + 1$
and $F^{-1}(x) = \dfrac{1}{x} + 1$
b. yes

2.46 a. Let $y = H(x)$. Then
$y = \sqrt{x^2 - 1}$. Interchange
the variables:
$x = \sqrt{y^2 + 1}$. $x^2 = y^2 + 1$,
$y^2 = x^2 - 1$; $y = \pm\sqrt{x^2 - 1}$
and $F^{-1}(x) = \pm\sqrt{x^2 - 1}$
b. No, for each value of x
in the domain of F^{-1}, two
function values occur.

MATHEMATICS 1202
SOLUTION KEY

I. SECTION ONE

1.1

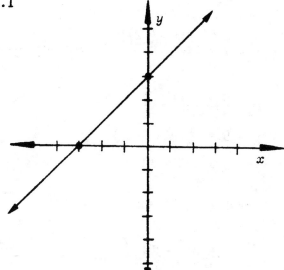

1.2

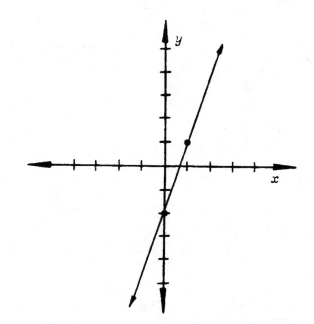

1.3

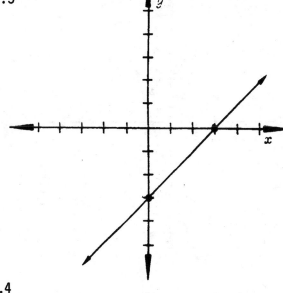

1.4

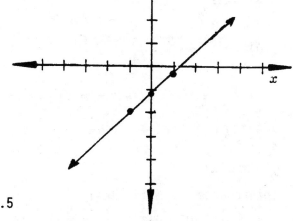

1.5

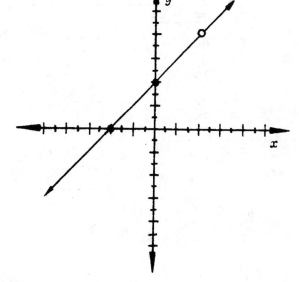

1.6

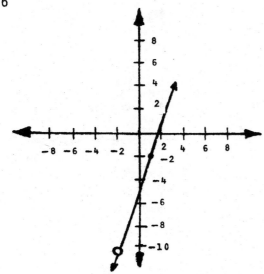

1.7
$$F(x) = x + 3$$
$$F^{-1}(x) = x - 3$$
$$0 = x - 3$$
$$x = 3$$

1.8
$$g(x) = \frac{3x - 5}{4}$$
for $x = 0$,
$$g(0) = \frac{3(0) - 5}{4} = -\frac{5}{4}$$

1.9
$$g(x) = \frac{3x - 5}{4}. \text{ Let } y = g(x);$$
$$y = \frac{3x - 5}{4}$$
$$4y = 3x - 5$$
$$x = \frac{4y + 5}{3}$$
Interchange the variables:
$$y = \frac{4x + 5}{3} \text{ or } g^{-1}(x) = \frac{4x + 5}{3}$$

1.10
$$0 = \frac{9x^2 - 25}{3x + 5}$$
$$9x^2 + 25 = 0(3x + 5)$$
$$9x^2 - 25 = 0$$
$$x^2 = \frac{25}{9}$$
$$x = \pm\frac{5}{3}$$
$$(x \neq -\frac{5}{3})$$

1.11
$$h(0) = \frac{0^2 - 16}{0 - 4} = \frac{-16}{-4} = 4$$

1.12
$$m = \frac{y_2 - y_1}{x_2 - x_1} = \frac{-3 - 3}{2 - (-4)} = \frac{-6}{6}$$
$$= -1$$

1.13
$$m = \frac{y_2 - y_1}{x_2 - x_1} = \frac{\frac{1}{2} - \frac{2}{3}}{\frac{1}{3} - (-\frac{5}{6})} = \frac{-\frac{1}{6}}{\frac{7}{6}}$$
$$= -\frac{1}{7}$$

1.14
$$y - 3 = -4[x - (-2)]$$
$$y - 3 = -4x - 8$$
$$y = -4x - 5$$

1.15
$$m = \frac{5 - (-1)}{-2 - 3} = \frac{6}{-5} = -\frac{6}{5}$$
$$y - 5 = -\frac{6}{5}[x - (-2)]$$
$$y = \frac{-6x}{5} + \frac{13}{5}$$

1.16 Given $(-1, 0)$ and $(0, 3)$
$$m = \frac{3 - 0}{0 - (-1)} = \frac{3}{1} = 3$$
$$y - 3 = 3(x - 0)$$
$$y = 3x + 3$$

1.17 Given $m = -1$ and $(3, 0)$
$$y - 0 = -1(x - 3)$$
$$y = -x + 3$$
$$x + y = 3$$

1.18
$$y = -4x - 5;$$
$$y + 5 = 4x$$
$$y + \frac{x}{\frac{1}{4}} = -5$$
$$-\frac{y}{5} - \frac{x}{\frac{5}{4}} = 1$$

1.19
$$y = -\frac{6}{5}x + \frac{13}{5}$$

1.20
$$ax + by + c = 0$$
a.
$$by = -ax - c$$
$$y = -\frac{a}{b}x - \frac{c}{b}$$
$$m = -\frac{a}{b}$$
b. Let $x = 0$. Then
$$by + c = 0.$$
$$by = -c$$
$$y = -\frac{c}{b}$$
c. Let $y = 0$. Then
$$ax + c = 0.$$
$$ax = -c$$
$$x = -\frac{c}{a}$$

1.21 $F(x) = -\frac{2}{3}x - 4$. Let

$y = F(x)$. Then $y = -\frac{2}{3}x - 4$.

a. $m = -\frac{2}{3}$

b. no

c. $0 = -\frac{2}{3}x - 4$

$\frac{2}{3}x = -4$

$x = -6$

1.22 $y > 3x - 1$

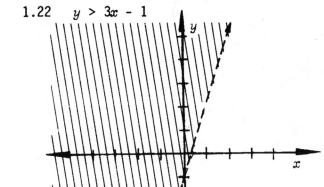

1.23 $9x + 3y - 7 \geq 0$

$3y \geq -9x + 7$

$y \geq -3x + \frac{7}{3}$

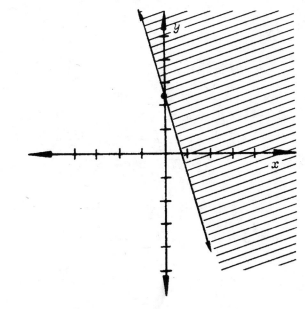

1.24 $3y - x - 8 > 0$

$3y > x + 8$

$y > \frac{1}{3}x + \frac{8}{3}$

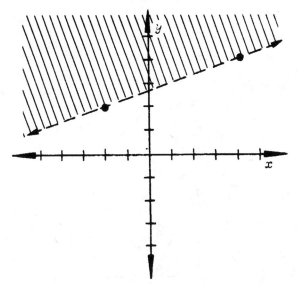

1.25 $3x - 5 \geq 0$

$3x \geq 5$

$x \geq \frac{5}{3}$

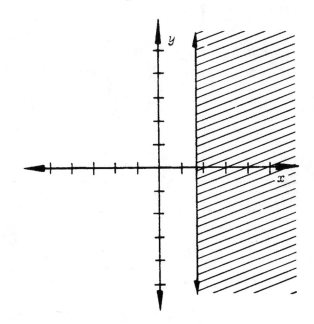

1.26 1.23 and 1.25 because of equals

1.27 no; two points lie on the same vertical line

1.28 $2x + y \geq 4$
$\qquad y \geq -2x + 4$

$\quad y - 2x \geq 4$
$\qquad y \geq 2x + 4$

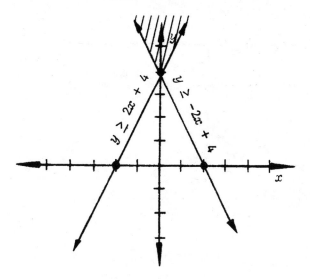

1.29 $x - 2y - 4 < 0$
$\qquad -2y \quad < -x + 4$
$\qquad\qquad y > \dfrac{x}{2} - 2$

$y > -6x + 11$

$4x + 5y < 29$
$\qquad 5y < -4x + 29$
$\qquad y < -\dfrac{4}{5}x + \dfrac{29}{5}$

1.29 cont.

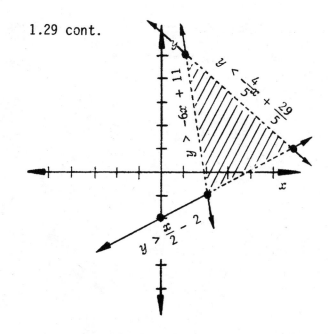

II. SECTION TWO

2.1 $\qquad 6x^2 - 5x = 50$
$\qquad 6x^2 - 5x - 50 = 0$
$\quad (3x - 10)(2x + 5) = 0$
$\quad 3x - 10 = 0 \quad 2x + 5 = 0$
$\qquad x = \dfrac{10}{3} \qquad x = -\dfrac{5}{2}$
$\{\dfrac{10}{3}, -\dfrac{5}{2}\}$

2.2 $\qquad 9x^2 - 16 = 0$
$\quad (3x - 4)(3x + 4) = 0$
$\quad 3x - 4 = 0 \quad 3x + 4 = 0$
$\qquad x = \dfrac{4}{3} \qquad x = -\dfrac{4}{3}$
$\{\pm\dfrac{4}{3}\}$

2.3 $\qquad 2x^2 - x = 2 - 4x$
$\quad 2x^2 + 3x - 2 = 0$
$\quad (2x - 1)(x + 2) = 0$
$\quad 2x - 1 = 0 \quad x + 2 = 0$
$\qquad x = \dfrac{1}{2} \qquad x = -2$
$\{\dfrac{1}{2}, -2\}$

2.4 $\quad 2x^2 - 5x - 12 = 0$
$\quad (2x + 3)(x - 4) = 0$
$\quad 2x + 3 = 0 \quad x - 4 = 0$
$\qquad x = -\dfrac{3}{2} \qquad x = 4$
$\{-\dfrac{3}{2}, 4\}$

2.5　$2x^2 + 5x - 12 = 0$
　　$a = 2,\ b = 5,\ c = -12$
　　$x = \dfrac{-5 \pm \sqrt{25 + 96}}{4}$
　　$x = \dfrac{-5 \pm \sqrt{121}}{4}$
　　$x = \dfrac{-5 \pm 11}{4}$
　　$x = \dfrac{-5 + 11}{4}$
　　　$= \dfrac{6}{4} = \dfrac{3}{2}$
　　$x = \dfrac{-5 - 11}{4}$
　　$x = \dfrac{-16}{4} = -4$
　　　　$\{\dfrac{3}{2},\ -4\}$

2.6　$x^2 + x - 1 = 0$
　　$a = 1,\ b = 1,\ c = -1$
　　$x = \dfrac{-1 \pm \sqrt{1 + 4}}{2}$
　　$x = \dfrac{-1 \pm \sqrt{5}}{2}$
　　$\{\dfrac{-1 \pm \sqrt{5}}{2}\}$

2.7　$4x^2 - 2x = 7$
　　$4x^2 - 2x - 7 = 0$
　　$a = 4,\ b = -2,\ c = -7$
　　$x = \dfrac{2 \pm \sqrt{4 + 112}}{8}$
　　$x = \dfrac{2 \pm 2\sqrt{29}}{8}$
　　$x = \dfrac{1 \pm \sqrt{29}}{4}$
　　$\{\dfrac{1 \pm \sqrt{29}}{4}\}$

2.8　$x^4 = (x^2)^2$ solve for x^2
　　$9(x^2)^2 + 5x^2 - 4 = 0$
　　$a = 9,\ b = 5,\ c = -4$
　　$x^2 = \dfrac{-5 \pm \sqrt{5^2 - 4\ (9)\ (-4)}}{2\ (9)}$
　　$x^2 = \dfrac{-5 \pm \sqrt{25 + 144}}{18}$
　　$x^2 = \dfrac{-5 \pm 13}{18}$
　　$x^2 = \dfrac{4}{9}$ or -1　　$x = \pm\dfrac{2}{3}$ or $\pm i$

2.9　Turning point is (0, 0), axis of symmetry is $x = 0$, a point is (1, 2).

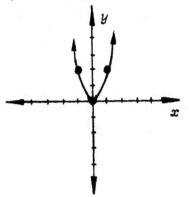

2.10　Turning point is (0, 0), axis of symmetry is $x = 0$, a point is $(1,\ \dfrac{1}{4})$.

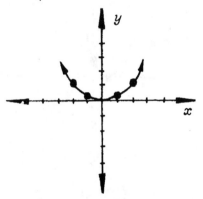

2.11　Graph by plotting solutions to the equation. Use table for square root numbers.

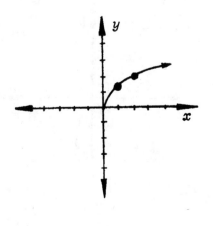

2.12 $F(x) = (x + 2)^2 - 4$
Turning point is (-2, -4),
axis of symmetry is $x = -2$,
a point is (-4, 0).

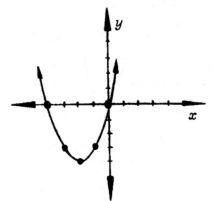

2.13 $F(x) = (x + 1)^2 + 0$
Turning point is (-1, 0),
axis of symmetry is $x = -1$,
a point is (-2, 1).

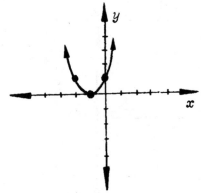

2.14 $G(x) = -3(x - 0)^2 + 0$
Turning point is (0, 0),
axis of symmetry is $x = 0$,
a point is (1, -3), concave
down.

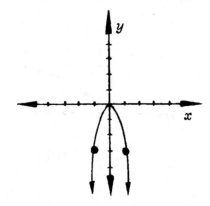

2.15 $G(x) = -(x + \frac{1}{2})^2 + \frac{1}{4}$

Turning point is $(-\frac{1}{2}, \frac{1}{4})$,

axis of symmetry is $x = -\frac{1}{2}$,

a point is (-1, 0),

concave down.

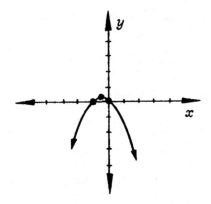

2.16 $H(x) = 3x^2 - 2x + 1$

$= 3(x^2 - \frac{2}{3}x) + 1$

$= 3(x^2 - \frac{2}{3}x + \frac{1}{9}) + 1 - \frac{1}{3}$

$= 3(x - \frac{1}{3})^2 + \frac{2}{3}$

Turning point is $(\frac{1}{3}, \frac{2}{3})$,
axis of symmetry is
$x = \frac{1}{3}$, concave up.

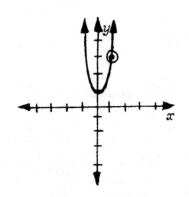

2.17 a. $F(x) = 2x^2$; let $y = F(x)$
$= 2x^2$. Solve for x:
$x = \pm\sqrt{\frac{y}{2}}$. Interchange the
variables: $y = \pm\sqrt{\frac{x}{2}}$.

b.

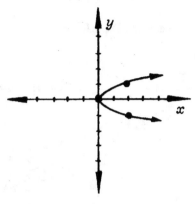

(not a function)

2.18 a. $F(x) = \sqrt{2x}$; let $y = F(x)$
$= \sqrt{2x}$. Solve for x:
$y^2 = 2x$, $x = \frac{y^2}{2}$.
Interchange the variables:
$y = \frac{x^2}{2}$, $x \geq 0$.

b.

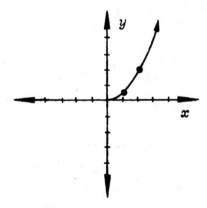

This inverse must have
the same domain as the
function.

2.19 $y > x^2$

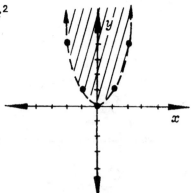

2.20 $y \geq x^2 + 3$

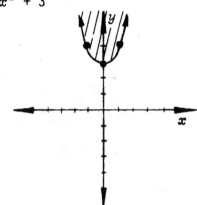

2.21 $y \leq 3x^2 + 2$

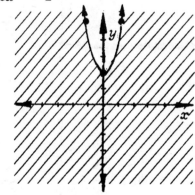

2.22 $y \geq 2x^2 - 5x + 1$

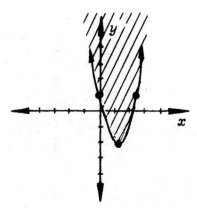

2.23 $16 \leq x^2 + y^2 \leq 25$

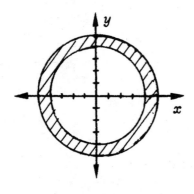

2.26
$$2x^2 - 5x + 2 < 0$$
$$(2x - 1)(x - 2) < 0$$
$$(2x - 1 < 0 \cap x - 2 > 0) \cup$$
$$(2x - 1 > 0 \cap x - 2 < 0)$$
$$(x < \frac{1}{2} \cap x > 2) \cup$$
$$(x > \frac{1}{2} \cap x < 2)$$
$$\phi \cup x > \frac{1}{2} \cap x < 2$$
$$\frac{1}{2} < x < 2$$

2.24 $x^2 - 3x \geq 0$
Graph $y = x^2 - 3x$.
$$x^2 \geq 3x$$
$$x \geq 3 \cup x \leq 0$$

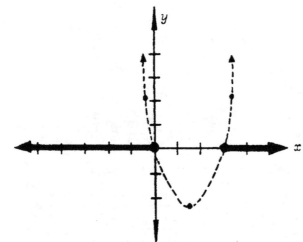

2.27
$$x^2 - 3x + 2 \geq 0$$
$$(x - 2)(x - 1) \geq 0$$
$$(x - 2 \geq 0 \cap x - 1 \geq 0) \cup$$
$$(x - 2 \leq 0 \cap x - 1 \leq 0)$$
$$(x \geq 2 \cap x \geq 1) \cup$$
$$(x \leq 2 \cap x \leq 1)$$
$$x \geq 2 \cup x \leq 1$$

2.28 $y \leq 1 - x^2$
$y \geq -1$

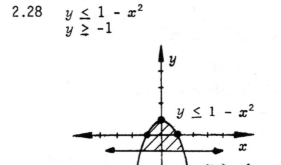

III. SECTION THREE

3.1
$$\begin{array}{r|rrr} 3 & 3 & - 2 & - 4 \\ & 0 & + 9 & + 21 \\ \hline & 3 & + 7 & + 17 \end{array}$$

remainder = 17

2.25 $x^2 - 3x + 2 \leq 0$
Graph $y = x^2 - 3x + 2$.
$$1 \leq x \leq 2$$

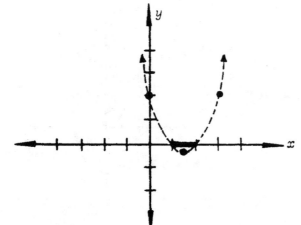

3.2
$$\begin{array}{r|rrrr} 3 & 1 & + 0 & + 4 & - 7 \\ & 0 & + 3 & + 9 & + 39 \\ \hline & 1 & + 3 & + 13 & + 32 \end{array}$$

remainder = 32

3.3

$$\begin{array}{r|rrrrr} 2 & 1 & -2 & -3 & -4 & -8 \\ & 0 & +2 & +0 & -6 & -20 \\ \hline & 1 & +0 & -3 & -10 & -28 \end{array}$$

remainder = -28

3.4

$$\begin{array}{r|rrrrr} 4 & 2 & -3 & -20 & +0 & -6 \\ & 0 & +8 & +20 & +0 & +0 \\ \hline & 2 & +5 & +0 & +0 & -6 \end{array}$$
remainder = -6

3.5 Let $f(x) = x^4 + 3x^3 - 5x^2 + 2x - 24.$

$$\begin{aligned} f(2) &= 2^4 + 3(2)^3 - 5(2)^2 \\ &\quad + 2(2) - 24 \\ &= 16 + 24 - 20 + 4 \\ &\quad - 24 \\ &= 20 - 20 \\ &= 0 \end{aligned}$$

yes, $x - 2$ is a factor;
remainder = 0

3.6 Let $f(x) = x^3 - 4x^2 - 18x + 9.$

$$\begin{aligned} f(-3) &= (-3)^3 - 4(-3)^2 \\ &\quad - 18(-3) + 9 \\ &= -27 - 36 + 54 + 9 \\ &= -63 + 63 \\ &= 0 \end{aligned}$$

yes, $x + 3$ is a factor;
remainder = 0

3.7 Let $f(x) = x^3 - 2x^2 - 25x - 50.$

$$\begin{aligned} f(5) &= 5^3 + 2(5)^2 - 25(5) \\ &\quad - 50 \\ &= 125 + 50 - 125 - 50 \\ &= 0 \end{aligned}$$

yes, $x - 5$ is a factor;
remainder = 0

3.8 Let $f(x) = 2x^4 + 5x^3 + 3x^2 + 8x + 12.$

$$\begin{aligned} f(-\tfrac{3}{2}) &= 2(-\tfrac{3}{2})^4 + 5(-\tfrac{3}{2})^3 \\ &\quad + 3(-\tfrac{3}{2})^2 + 8(-\tfrac{3}{2}) + 12 \\ &= 2(\tfrac{81}{16}) + 5(-\tfrac{27}{8}) + 3(\tfrac{9}{4}) \\ &\quad - 12 + 12 \\ &= \frac{81}{8} - \frac{135}{8} + \frac{27}{4} \\ &= -\frac{54}{8} + \frac{54}{8} \\ &= 0 \end{aligned}$$

yes, $2x + 3$ is a factor;
remainder = 0

3.9 Let $f(x) = 9x^3 + 6x^2 + 4x + 2.$

$$\begin{aligned} f(-\tfrac{1}{3}) &= 9(-\tfrac{1}{3})^3 + 6(-\tfrac{1}{3})^2 + \\ &\quad 4(-\tfrac{1}{3}) + 2 \\ &= 9(-\tfrac{1}{27}) + 6(\tfrac{1}{9}) - \\ &\quad \frac{4}{3} + 2 \\ &= -\frac{9}{27} + \frac{6}{9} + \frac{2}{3} \\ &= -\frac{1}{3} + \frac{2}{3} + \frac{2}{3} \\ &= 1 \end{aligned}$$

no, $3x + 1$ is not a factor;
remainder is not 0

3.10 Let $f(x) = x^4 - 5x^3 + 3x^2 + 15x - 2$

$$\begin{aligned} f(3) &= 3^4 - 5(3)^3 \\ &\quad + 3(3)^2 + 15(3) \\ &\quad - 2 \\ &= 81 - 135 + 27 \\ &\quad + 45 - 2 \\ &= 16 \end{aligned}$$

no, $x - 3$ is not a factor;
remainder is not 0

3.11 $f(x) = 4x^5 - 16x^4 + 17x^3 - 19x^2 + 13x - 3$

$$\begin{array}{r|rrrrrr} 3 & 4 & -16 & +17 & -19 & +13 & -3 \\ & 0 & +12 & -12 & +15 & -12 & +3 \\ \hline \tfrac{1}{2} & 4 & -4 & +5 & -4 & +1 & -0 \\ & 0 & +2 & -1 & +2 & -1 & \\ \hline \tfrac{1}{2} & 4 & -2 & +4 & -2 & +0 & \\ & 0 & +2 & +0 & +2 & & \\ \hline & 4 & +0 & +4 & +0 & & \end{array}$$

$$\begin{aligned} 4x^2 + 4 &= 0 \\ x^2 &= -1 \\ x &= \pm\sqrt{-1} = \pm i \end{aligned}$$

Roots = $\{3, \tfrac{1}{2}, \tfrac{1}{2}, \pm i\}$

3.12 $f(x) = x^3 - 3x^2 + 4$

$\underline{2|}$ $1 - 3 + 0 + 4$

   $\underline{0 + 2 - 2 - 4}$

   $1 - 1 - 2 + 0$

   $x^2 - x - 2 = 0$
   $(x - 2)(x + 1) = 0$
   $x = 2 \quad x = -1$

   Roots = {2, 2, -1}

3.13 $f(x) = (x^2 - 4x + 4)$
             $(x^2 + 3x - 10) = 0$
         $= (x - 2)(x - 2)$
             $(x + 5)(x - 2) = 0$
   $x = 2, x = 2, x = -5, x = 2$

   Roots = {2, -5}

3.14 $f(x) = (3x + 5)(x^2 - 6x + 9)^2 = 0$
         $= (3x + 5)(x - 3)(x - 3)$
             $(x - 3)(x - 3) = 0$

   $x = -\dfrac{5}{3}, x = 3$

   Roots = $\{-\dfrac{5}{3}, 3\}$

3.15 $f(x) = x^3 - 3x^2 - 2x + 15$
       Let $r = 1, 2, 3, \ldots$

   $\underline{1|}$ $1 - 3 - 2 + 15$

      $\underline{0 + 1 - 2 - 4}$

      $1 - 2 - 4 + 11$

   $\underline{2|}$ $1 - 3 - 2 + 15$

      $\underline{0 + 2 - 2 - 8}$

      $1 - 1 - 4 + 7$

   $\underline{3|}$ $1 - 3 - 2 + 15$

      $\underline{0 + 3 + 0 - 6}$

      $1 + 0 - 2 + 9$

   $\underline{4|}$ $1 - 3 - 2 + 15$

      $\underline{0 + 4 + 4 + 8}$

      $1 + 1 + 2 + 23$

   $r = 4$ is an upper limit
   since the signs in the third
   row are all positive.

3.15 cont.

   Let $r = -1, -2, -3, \ldots$

   $\underline{-1|}$ $1 - 3 - 2 + 15$

      $\underline{0 - 1 + 4 - 2}$

      $1 - 4 + 2 + 13$

   $\underline{-2|}$ $1 - 3 - 2 + 15$

      $\underline{0 - 2 + 10 - 16}$

      $1 - 5 + 8 - 1$

   $r = -2$ is a lower limit
   since the signs in the third
   row alternate.

3.16 $f(x) = x^5 - 3x^3 + 24$

   Let $r = 1, 2, 3, \ldots$

   $\underline{2|}$ $1 + 0 - 3 + 0 + 24$

      $\underline{0 + 2 + 4 + 2 + 4}$

      $1 + 2 + 1 + 2 + 28$

   $r = 2$ is an upper limit
   since the signs in the
   third row are all positive.

   Let $r = -1, -2, -3, \ldots$

   $\underline{-3|}$ $1 + 0 - 3 + 0 + 24$

      $\underline{0 - 3 + 9 - 18 + 54}$

      $1 - 3 + 6 - 18 + 78$

   $r = -3$ is a lower limit
   since the signs in the third
   row alternate.

3.17 $f(x) = x^4 - 4x^3 + x^2 + 6x + 2$

   Let $r = 1, 2, 3, \ldots$

   $\underline{4|}$ $1 - 4 + 1 + 6 + 2$

      $\underline{0 + 4 + 0 + 4 + 40}$

      $1 + 0 + 1 + 10 + 42$

   $r = 4$ is an upper limit
   since the signs in the third
   row are all positive.

3.17 cont.

Let $r = -1, -2, -3, \ldots$

$$
\begin{array}{r|rrrrr}
-2 & 1 & -4 & +1 & +6 & +2 \\
 & 0 & -2 & +12 & -26 & +40 \\
\hline
 & 1 & -6 & +13 & -20 & +42
\end{array}
$$

$r = -2$ is a lower limit since the signs in the third row alternate.

3.18 $f(x) = 2x^3 - 2x^2 + x + 8$

Let $r = 1, 2, 3, \ldots$

$$
\begin{array}{r|rrrr}
1 & 2 & -2 & +1 & +8 \\
 & 0 & +2 & +0 & +1 \\
\hline
 & 2 & +0 & +1 & +9
\end{array}
$$

$r = 1$ is an upper limit since the signs in the third row are all positive.

Let $r = -1, -2, -3, \ldots$

$$
\begin{array}{r|rrrr}
-2 & 2 & -2 & +1 & +8 \\
 & 0 & -4 & +12 & -26 \\
\hline
 & 2 & -6 & +13 & -18
\end{array}
$$

$r = -2$ is a lower limit since the signs in the third row alternate.

IV. SECTION FOUR

4.1

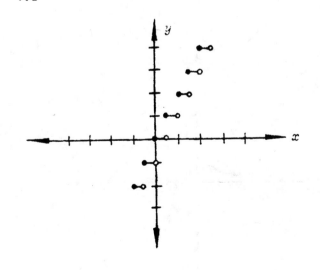

4.2

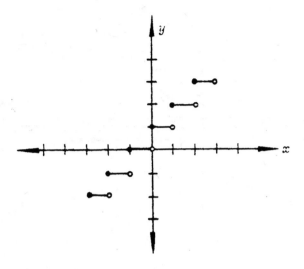

4.3

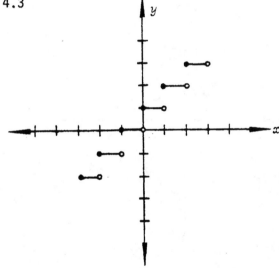

4.4

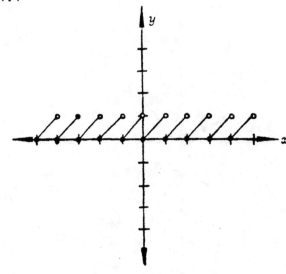

4.5

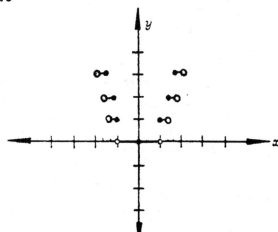

4.8

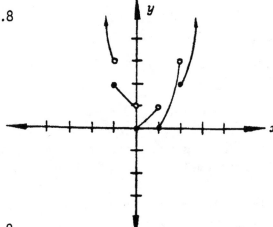

4.9

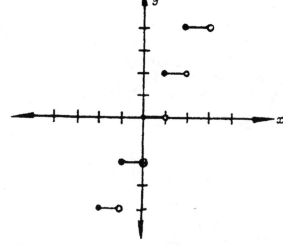

4.6

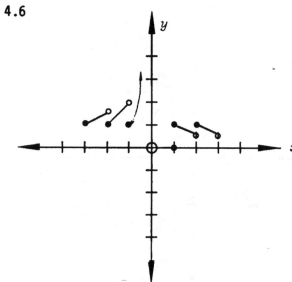

4.10   Let x = number of minutes.
For $0 < x < 3$, $C(x) = 0.75$.
For $3 \leq x < 6$, $C(x) = 1.50$.
For $6 \leq x < 9$, $C(x) = 2.25$.

$$\text{Then } C(x) = \begin{cases} 0.75, & 0 < x < 3 \\ 1.50, & 3 \leq x < 6 \\ 2.25, & 6 \leq x < 9 \end{cases}$$

$$y = 0.75\left(\frac{x}{3} + 1\right)$$

4.7

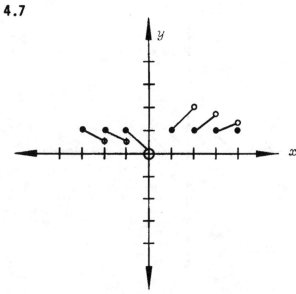

4.11

4.12

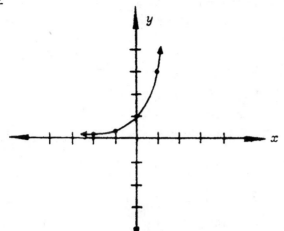

4.15

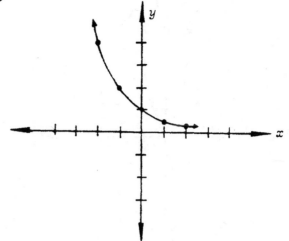

4.13

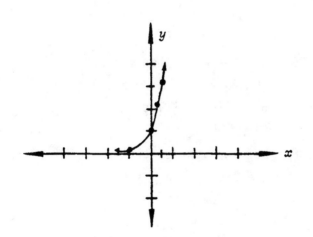

4.16

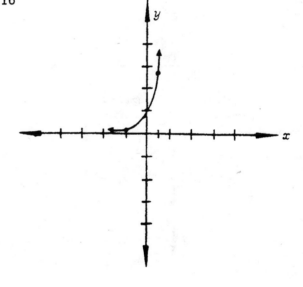

4.14

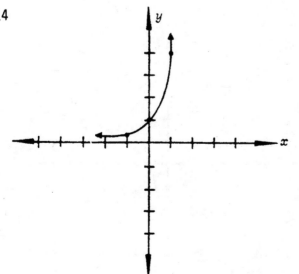

4.17

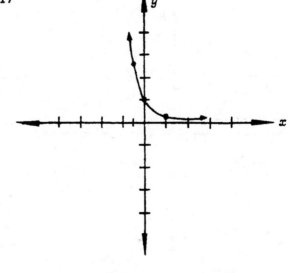

4.18

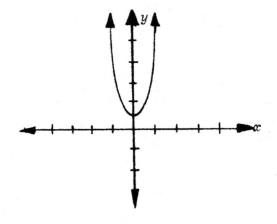

4.19

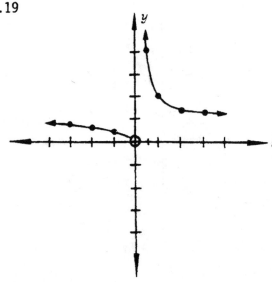

4.20

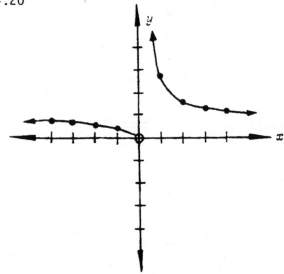

4.21 Let $y = 6^x$; then $x = 6^y$ and $y = \log_6 x$; $F^{-1}(x) = \log_6 x$.

4.22 Let $y = 6^{x+1}$; then $x = 6^{y+1}$ and $y + 1 = \log_6 x$; $y = \log_6 x - 1$ or $F^{-1}(x) = \log_6 x - 1$.

4.23 Let $y = 3^{x-1}$; then $x = 3^{y-1}$ and $y - 1 = \log_3 x$; $y = \log_3 x + 1$ or $F^{-1}(x) = \log_3 x + 1$.

4.24 Let $y = e^x$; then $x = e^y$ and $y = \log_e x$ or $G^{-1}(x) = \log_e x$.

4.25 Let $y = e^{2x}$; then $x = e^{2y}$ and $2y = \log_e x$; $y = \frac{1}{2} \log_e x$ or $H^{-1}(x) = \frac{1}{2} \log_e x$.

4.26 Let $y = \log_6 x$; then $x = \log_6 y$ and $y = 6^x$ or $G^{-1}(x) = 6^x$

4.27 Let $y = 2 \log_7 x$; then $x = 2 \log_7 y$ and $\frac{x}{2} = \log_7 y$; $y = 7^{\frac{x}{2}}$ or $H^{-1}(x) = 7^{\frac{x}{2}}$

4.28

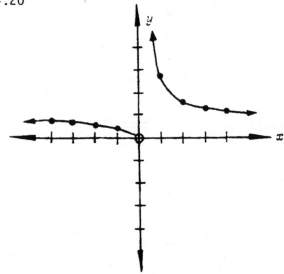

4.29

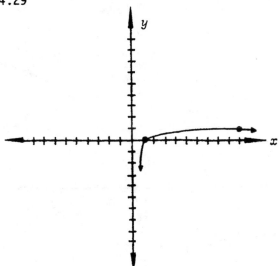

4.30

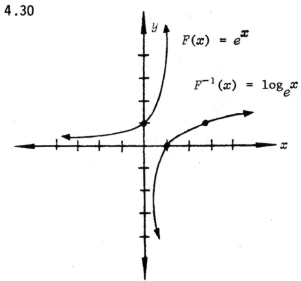

$F(x) = e^x$

$F^{-1}(x) = \log_e x$

4.31 $(F + G)(x) = 3x + 1$

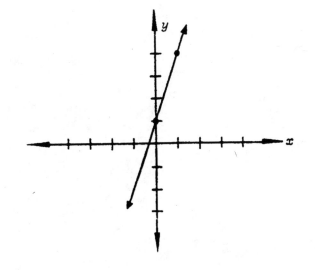

4.32 $H(x) = 3x + 1$. Let $y = 3x + 1$. Then $x = 3y + 1$ and $y = \dfrac{x - 1}{3}$ or $(F + G)^{-1}(x) = \dfrac{x - 1}{3}$.

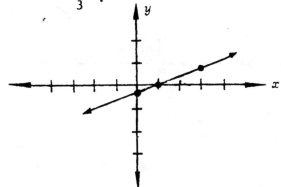

4.33 $(F - G)(x) = 2^x - x$

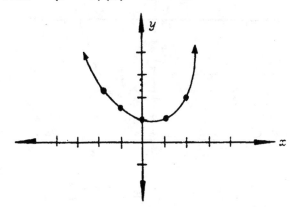

4.34 $(F + G)(x) = e^x + e^{-x}$

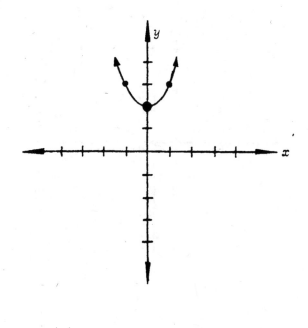

4.35 $\dfrac{F}{G}(x) = \dfrac{2}{x}$

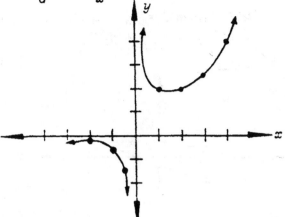

4.38 $(F \cdot G)(x) = x \log_{10} x, \ x > 0$

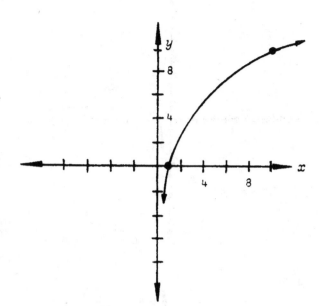

4.36 $(F - G)(x) = x^2 - 3x - 1$

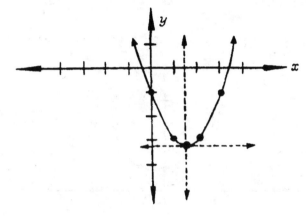

4.37 $\dfrac{F}{G}(x) = \dfrac{x}{x + 1}, \ x \neq -1$

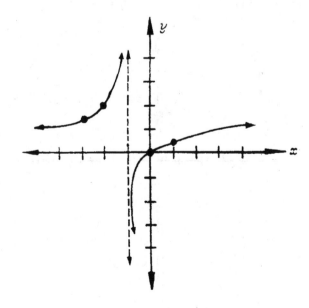

MATHEMATICS 1203
SOLUTION KEY

I. SECTION ONE

1.1   II   + - - + - -

1.2   IV   - + - - + -

1.3   II   + - - + - -

1.4   III   - - + - - +

1.5   IV   - + - - + -

1.6   III   - - + - - +

1.7   I   + + + + + +

1.8   II   + - - + - -

1.9   I   + + + + + +

1.10 II   + - - + - -

1.11 IV   - + - - + -

1.12 II   + - - + - -

1.13 IV   - + - - + -

1.14 I

1.15 I, IV

1.16 I, III

1.17 I

1.18 I, II

1.19 IV

1.20 I

1.21 III

1.22 IV

1.23 III

1.24 I

1.25 II

1.26 III

1.27 IV

1.28 IV

1.29 III

1.30 III

1.31 IV

1.32 II

II. SECTION TWO

2.1

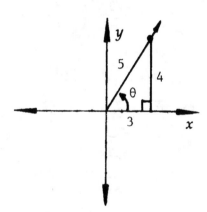

$x = 3$
$r = 5$
$y = \sqrt{5^2 - 3^2}$
$ = \sqrt{25 - 9}$
$ = \sqrt{16}$
$ = 4$ (first quadrant)

$\sin \theta = \dfrac{4}{5}$

$\cos \theta = \dfrac{3}{5}$

$\tan \theta = \dfrac{4}{3}$

$\csc \theta = \dfrac{5}{4}$

$\sec \theta = \dfrac{5}{3}$

$\cot \theta = \dfrac{3}{4}$

2.2   a.

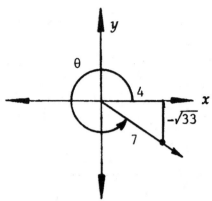

$x = 4$
$r = 7$
$y = \sqrt{7^2 - 4^2}$
$ = \sqrt{49 - 16}$
$ = \sqrt{33}$
$ = -\sqrt{33}$ (fourth quadrant)

$\sin \theta = \dfrac{-\sqrt{33}}{7} = -\dfrac{\sqrt{33}}{7}$

$\cos \theta = \dfrac{4}{7}$

$\tan \theta = \dfrac{-\sqrt{33}}{4} = -\dfrac{\sqrt{33}}{4}$

$\csc \theta = \dfrac{7}{-\sqrt{33}} = -\dfrac{7\sqrt{33}}{33}$

$\sec \theta = \dfrac{7}{4}$

$\cot \theta = \dfrac{4}{-\sqrt{33}} = -\dfrac{4\sqrt{33}}{33}$

b.

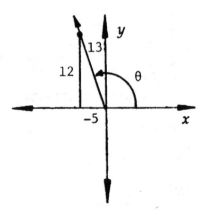

$r = 13$
$x = -5$
$y = \sqrt{13^2 - (-5)^2}$
$ = \sqrt{169 - 25}$
$ = \sqrt{144}$
$ = 12$ (second quadrant)

2.2 cont.

$\sin \theta = \dfrac{12}{13}$

$\cos \theta = \dfrac{-5}{13} = -\dfrac{5}{13}$

$\tan \theta = \dfrac{12}{-5} = -\dfrac{12}{5}$

$\csc \theta = \dfrac{13}{12}$

$\sec \theta = \dfrac{13}{-5} = -\dfrac{13}{5}$

$\cot \theta = \dfrac{-5}{12} = -\dfrac{5}{12}$

c.

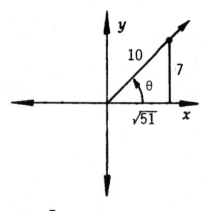

$y = 7$
$r = 10$
$x = \sqrt{10^2 - 7^2}$
$ = \sqrt{100 - 49}$
$ = \sqrt{51}$ (first quadrant)

$\sin \theta = \dfrac{7}{10}$

$\cos \theta = \dfrac{\sqrt{51}}{10}$

$\tan \theta = \dfrac{7}{\sqrt{51}} = \dfrac{7\sqrt{51}}{51}$

$\csc \theta = \dfrac{10}{7}$

$\sec \theta = \dfrac{10}{\sqrt{51}} = \dfrac{10\sqrt{51}}{51}$

$\cot \theta = \dfrac{\sqrt{51}}{7}$

2.2 cont.

d.

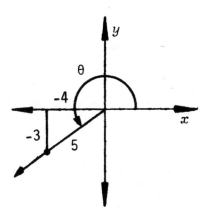

$y = -3$

$x = -4$

$r = \sqrt{(-3)^2 + (-4)^2}$

$= \sqrt{9 + 16}$

$= \sqrt{25}$

$= 5$ (third quadrant)

$\sin \theta = \dfrac{-3}{5} = -\dfrac{3}{5}$

$\cos \theta = \dfrac{-4}{5} = -\dfrac{4}{5}$

$\tan \theta = \dfrac{-3}{-4} = \dfrac{3}{4}$

$\csc \theta = \dfrac{5}{-3} = -\dfrac{5}{3}$

$\sec \theta = \dfrac{5}{-4} = -\dfrac{5}{4}$

$\cot \theta = \dfrac{-4}{-3} = \dfrac{4}{3}$

2.3   a.   Sin is positive in Quadrants I and II.

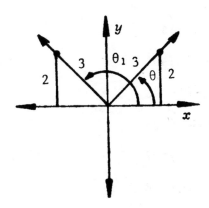

2.3 cont.

b.

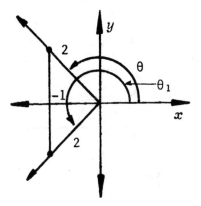

c.   Tan is negative in Quadrants II and IV.

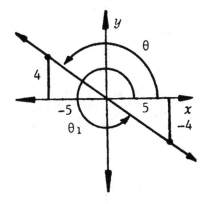

d.   Cot is positive in Quadrants I and III.

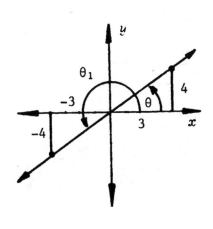

2.3 cont.

e. Sec is negative in Quadrants II and III.

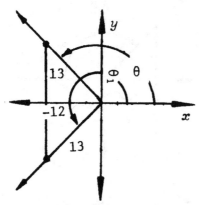

f. Csc is positive in Quadrants I and II.

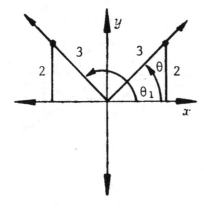

III. SECTION THREE

3.1 II

3.2 III

3.3 IV

3.4 II

3.5 II

3.6 I

3.7 II

3.8 III

3.9 III

3.10 II

3.11 III

3.12 II

3.13 I

3.14 IV

3.15 none--180° is a quadrantal angle

IV. SECTION FOUR

4.1 true

4.2 true

4.3 true

4.4 false

4.5 true

4.6 false

4.7 true

4.8 false

4.9 false

4.10 false

4.11 0.0349

4.12 0.9528

4.13 0.7627

4.14 0.8004

4.15 1.004

4.16 16° 00' or 16°

4.17   72° 30'

4.18   56° 00' or 56°

4.19   29° 50'

4.20   22° 10'

4.21   0.4746

4.22   0.3145

4.23   0.9601

4.24   1.000

4.25   0.9929

4.26   0.2004

4.27   0.8796

4.28   1.063

4.29   0.3393

4.30   1.844

4.31   1.039

4.32   3.647

4.33   0.5783

4.34   0.9492

4.35   0.2126

4.36   6°

4.37   16° 50'

4.38   31° 10'

4.39   38° 30'

4.40   39°

4.41   56° 40'

4.42   72° 20'

4.43   36° 30'

4.44   19°

4.45   65° 10'

4.46   84°

V.   SECTION FIVE

5.1 $\cos 18° 15' = \cos 18° 10' - \frac{1}{2}(\cos 18° 10' - \cos 18° 20')$
$= .9502 - \frac{1}{2}(.9502 - .9492)$
$= .9502 - \frac{1}{2}(.0010)$
$= .9502 - .0005$
$= .9497$

5.2 $\tan 40° 23' = \tan 40° 20' + \frac{3}{10}(\tan 40° 30' - \tan 40° 20')$
$= .8491 + \frac{3}{10}(.8541 - .8491)$
$= .8491 + \frac{3}{10}(.0050)$
$= .8491 + .0015$
$= .8506$

5.3 $\sin 37° 14' = \sin 37° 10' + \frac{4}{10}(\sin 37° 20' - \sin 37° 10')$
$= .6041 + \frac{4}{10}(.6065 - .6041)$
$= .6041 + \frac{4}{10}(.0024)$
$= .6041 + .0010$
$= .6051$

5.4 $\cot 43° 48' = \cot 43° 40' - \frac{8}{10}(\cot 43° 40' - \cot 43° 50')$
$= 1.048 - \frac{8}{10}(1.048 - 1.042)$
$= 1.048 - \frac{8}{10}(.005)$
$= 1.048 - .005$
$= 1.043$

5.5 $\cos 14° 36' = \cos 14° 30' -$
$\frac{6}{10}(\cos 14° 30' - \cos 14° 40)$
$= .9681 - \frac{6}{10}(.9681 - .9674$
$= .9681 - \frac{6}{10}(.0007)$
$= .9681 - .0004$
$= .9677$

5.6 $\sin 82° 47' = \sin 82° 40' +$
$\frac{7}{10}(\sin 82° 50' - \sin 82° 40')$
$= .9918 + \frac{7}{10}(.9922 - .9918)$
$= .9918 + .0004)$
$= .9918 + .0003$
$= .9921$

5.7 $\cos 64° 9' = \cos 64° 0' -$
$\frac{9}{10}(\cos 64° - \cos 64° 10')$
$= .4384 - \frac{9}{10}(.4384 - .4358)$
$= .4384 - \frac{9}{10}(.0026)$
$= .4384 - .0023$
$= .4361$

5.8 $\sec 30° 52' = \sec 30° 50' +$
$\frac{2}{10}(\sec 31° - \sec 30° 50')$
$= 1.165 + \frac{2}{10}(1.167 - 1.165)$
$= 1.165 + \frac{2}{10}(.002)$
$= 1.165 + .0004$
$= 1.1654 = 1.165$
(correct to three places)

5.9 $\sin 25° 25' = \sin 25° 20' +$
$\frac{1}{2}(\sin 25° 30' - \sin 25° 30')$
$= .4279 + \frac{1}{2}(.4305 - .4279)$
$= .4279 + \frac{1}{2}(.0026)$
$= .4279 + .0013$
$= .4292$

5.10 $\tan 72° 56' = \tan 72° 50' +$
$\frac{6}{10}(\tan 73 - \tan 72° 50')$
$= 3.237 + \frac{6}{10}(3.271 - 3.237)$
$= 3.237 + \frac{6}{10}(.034)$
$= 3.237 + .020$
$= 3.257$

5.11
$$10\left\{x\left\{\begin{matrix}\cos 62° 30' = .4617 \\ \cos \theta = .4600 \\ \cos 62° 40' = 45.92\end{matrix}\right\}.0017\right\}.0025$$

$\dfrac{x}{10} = \dfrac{.0017}{.0025}$
$.0025x = .017$
$x = 6.8 \doteq 7$
$\theta = 62° 30' + 7' = 62° 37'$

5.12
$$10\left\{x\left\{\begin{matrix}\sin 27° 30' = .4617 \\ \sin \theta = .4630 \\ \sin 27° 40' = .4643\end{matrix}\right\}.0013\right\}.0026$$

$\dfrac{x}{10} = \dfrac{.0013}{.0026}$
$.0026x = .013$
$x = 5$
$\theta = 27° 30' + 5' = 27° 35'$

5.13
$$10\left\{x\left\{\begin{matrix}\cot 70° 30' = .3541 \\ \cot \theta = .3510 \\ \cot 70° 30' = .3508\end{matrix}\right\}.0031\right\}.0033$$

$\dfrac{x}{10} = \dfrac{.0031}{.0033}$
$.0033x = .031$
$x = 9.4 \doteq 9$
$\theta = 70° 30' + 9' = 70° 39'$

5.14
$$10\left\{x\left\{\begin{matrix}\tan 47° 30' = 1.091 \\ \tan \theta = 1.0925 \\ \text{or} \\ \tan 47° 40' = 1.098\end{matrix}\right\}.002\right\}.007$$

5.14 cont.

$$\frac{x}{10} = \frac{.0015}{.007}$$

$$.007x = .015$$

$$x = 0.015 \div .007$$

$$\theta = 47° \ 30' + 2' = 47° \ 32'$$

5.15

$$10 \left\{ x \begin{cases} \sin 20° = .3420 \\ \sin \theta = .3432 \\ \sin \\ 20° \ 10' = .3448 \end{cases} .0012 \right\} .0028$$

$$\frac{x}{10} = \frac{.0012}{.0028}$$

$$.0028x = .012$$

$$x = 4.3 \doteq 4$$

$$\theta = 20° \ 0' + 4' = 20° \ 4'$$

5.16

$$10 \left\{ x \begin{cases} \cot 80° = .1763 \\ \cot \theta = .1748 \\ \cot \\ 80° \ 10' = .1783 \end{cases} .0015 \right\} .0030$$

$$\frac{x}{10} = \frac{.0015}{.0030}$$

$$.0030x = .015$$

$$x = 5$$

$$\theta = 80° \ 0' + 5' = 80° \ 5'$$

5.17

$$10 \left\{ x \begin{cases} \cos \\ 25° \ 30' = .9026 \\ \cos \theta = .9018 \\ \cos \\ 25° \ 40' = .9013 \end{cases} .008 \right\} .0013$$

$$\frac{x}{10} = \frac{.0008}{.0013}$$

$$.0013x = .008$$

$$x = 6.2 \doteq 6$$

$$\theta = 25° \ 30' + 6' = 25° \ 36'$$

5.18

$$10 \left\{ x \begin{cases} \sec \\ 42° \ 40' = 1.3600 \\ \sec \theta = 1.3619 \\ \sec \\ 42° \ 50' = 1.3640 \end{cases} .0019 \right\} .0046$$

5.18 cont.

$$\frac{x}{10} = \frac{.0019}{.0040}$$

$$.0040x = .019$$

$$x = 4.75 \doteq 5$$

$$\theta = 42° \ 40' + 5' = 42° \ 45'$$

5.19   33°

5.20

$$10 \left\{ x \begin{cases} \tan 54° = 1.3760 \\ \tan \theta = 1.3840 \\ \tan \\ 54° \ 10' = 1.3850 \end{cases} .0080 \right\} .0090$$

$$\frac{x}{10} = \frac{.0080}{.0090}$$

$$.0090x = .080$$

$$x = 8.9 \doteq 9$$

$$\theta = 54° \ 0' + 9' = 54° \ 9'$$

VI.   SECTION SIX

6.1 $\cos 125° = \cos(180° - 55°)$
$= -\cos 55°$

6.2 $\tan 370° = \tan(370° - 360°)$
$= \tan 10°$

6.3 $\cos 115° = \cos(180° - 65°)$
$= -\cos 65°$

6.4 $\tan 245° = \tan(180° + 65°)$
$= \tan 65°$

6.5 $\sec 100° = \sec(180° - 80°)$
$= -\sec 80°$

6.6 $\csc 190° = \csc(180° + 10°)$
$= -\csc 10°$

6.7 $\sin 312° = \sin(360° - 48°)$
$= -\sin 48°$

6.8 $\tan 105° = \tan(180° - 75°)$
$= -\tan 75°$

6.9   sin 200° = sin(180° + 20°)
              = -sin 20°

6.10   tan 205° = tan(180° + 25°)
              = tan 25° = .4663

6.11   sin 215° = sin(180° + 35°)
              = -sin 35° = -.5736

6.12   cos 75° = .2588

6.13   tan 115° 50' = tan(180° - 64° 10')
              = -tan 64° 10'
              = -2.066

6.14   cos 97° 31' = cos(180° - 82° 29')
              = -cos 82° 29'

$$10\left\{\begin{array}{l}9\left\{\begin{array}{l}\cos 82° \ 20' = .1334 \\ \cos 82° \ 29' = \end{array}\right\}x \\ \cos 82° \ 30' = .1305\end{array}\right\}.0029$$

$\dfrac{9}{10} = \dfrac{x}{.0029}$

$10x = .0261$

$x = .00261 \doteq .0026$

-cos 82° 29' = -(.1334 - .0026)
              = -.1308

6.15   sec 205° = sec(180° + 25°)
              = -sec 25° = -1.103

6.16   tan 332° = tan(360° - 28°)
              = -tan 28° = -.5317

6.17   cos 230° 40' = cos(180° + 50° 40')
              = -cos 50° 40'
              = -.6338

6.18   sin 311° 20' = sin(360° - 48° 40')
              = -sin 48° 40'
              = -.7509

VII.   SECTION SEVEN

7.1   0; 1; 0; und; 1; und

7.2   0; und; 1

7.3   0; -1; 0; und; -1; und

7.4   -1; 0; und; 0; und; -1

7.5   (2 cos 90°)·sin 180° +
              tan 180°·sec 180° =
              2(0)·0 + 0·(-1) =
                                0

7.6   (sin 180°)(cos 0°) -
              4(sin 90°) =
              0·1 - 4(1) =
              0 - 4 =
                -4

7.7   [csc 90°·cos 180°]³ =
              [1·(-1)]³ =
              (-1)³ =
                -1

7.8   cos 0° + sec 180° -
              5(sin 270°) =
              1 + (-1) - 5(-1) =
              0 + 5 =
                5

7.9   [csc 90° + cos 180° -
              csc 270°]⁵ =
              [1 - 1 - (-1)]⁵ =
              1⁵ =
                1

7.10   tan(-20°) =
              tan 340° =
        tan(360° - 20°) =
              -tan 20°

7.11   cos(-49°) =
              cos 311° =
        cos(360° - 49°) =
              cos 49°

7.12   sin(-150°) =
              sin 210° =
        sin(180° + 30°) =
              -sin 30°

7.13 $\sec(-121)° =$
$\sec 239° =$
$\sec(180° + 59°) =$
$-\sec 59°$

7.14 $\cos(-170°) =$
$\cos 190° =$
$\cos(180° + 10°) =$
$-\cos 10°$

7.15 $\tan(-163°) =$
$\tan 197° =$
$\tan(180° + 17°) =$
$\tan 17°$

7.16 $\csc(-112°) =$
$\csc 248° =$
$\csc(180° + 68°) =$
$-\csc 68°$

7.17 $\sin(-295°) = \sin 65°$

7.18 $\cos(-15°) =$
$\cos 345° =$
$\cos(360° - 15°) =$
$\cos 15°$

7.19 $\tan(-216°) =$
$\tan 144° =$
$\tan(180° - 36°) =$
$-\tan 36°$

7.20 $\cos(035.5°) =$
$\cos 324.5° =$
$\cos(360° - 35.5°) =$
$\cos 35.5°$

7.21 $\sin(-167.75°) =$
$\sin 192.25° =$
$-\sin(180° + 12.25°) =$
$-\sin 12.25°$

VIII.   SECTION EIGHT

8.1 $\tan 30° = \dfrac{\frac{a}{2}}{\frac{\sqrt{3}a}{2}} = \dfrac{a}{\sqrt{3}a} = \dfrac{1}{\sqrt{3}} = \dfrac{\sqrt{3}}{3}$

8.2 $\cot 30° = \dfrac{\frac{\sqrt{3}a}{2}}{\frac{a}{2}} = \dfrac{\sqrt{3}a}{a} = \sqrt{3}$

8.3 $\sec 30° = \dfrac{a}{\frac{\sqrt{3}a}{2}} = \dfrac{2}{\sqrt{3}} \quad \dfrac{2\sqrt{3}}{3}$

8.4 $\csc 30° = \dfrac{a}{\frac{a}{2}} = 2$

8.5 $\tan 45° = \dfrac{b}{b} = 1$

8.6 $\cot 45° = \dfrac{b}{b} = 1$

8.7 $\sec 45° = \dfrac{b\sqrt{2}}{b} = \sqrt{2}$

8.8 $\csc 45° = \dfrac{b\sqrt{2}}{b} = \sqrt{2}$

8.9

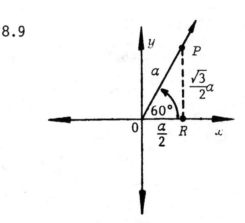

8.10 $\sin 60° = \dfrac{\frac{\sqrt{3}}{2}a}{a} = \dfrac{\sqrt{3}}{2}$

8.11 $\cos 60° = \dfrac{\frac{a}{2}}{a} = \dfrac{1}{2}$

8.12 $\tan 60° = \dfrac{\frac{\sqrt{3}}{2}a}{\frac{a}{2}} = \dfrac{\sqrt{3}a}{a} = \sqrt{3}$

8.13 $\cot 60° = \dfrac{\frac{a}{2}}{\frac{\sqrt{3}}{2}a} = \dfrac{a}{\sqrt{3}a} = \dfrac{1}{\sqrt{3}} = \dfrac{\sqrt{3}}{3}$

8.14 $\sec 60° = \dfrac{a}{\dfrac{a}{2}} = 2$

8.15 $\csc 60° = \dfrac{a}{\dfrac{\sqrt{3}}{2}a} \quad \dfrac{2}{\sqrt{3}} \quad \dfrac{2\sqrt{3}}{3}$

8.16

		30°	45°	60°	120°	135°	150°	210°	225°	240°	300°	315°	330°
a.	sin	$\frac{1}{2}$	$\frac{\sqrt{2}}{2}$	$\frac{\sqrt{3}}{2}$	$\frac{\sqrt{3}}{2}$	$\frac{\sqrt{2}}{2}$	$\frac{1}{2}$	$-\frac{1}{2}$	$-\frac{\sqrt{2}}{2}$	$-\frac{\sqrt{3}}{2}$	$-\frac{\sqrt{3}}{2}$	$-\frac{\sqrt{2}}{2}$	$-\frac{1}{2}$
b.	cos	$\frac{\sqrt{3}}{2}$	$\frac{\sqrt{2}}{2}$	$\frac{1}{2}$	$-\frac{1}{2}$	$-\frac{\sqrt{2}}{2}$	$-\frac{\sqrt{3}}{2}$	$-\frac{\sqrt{3}}{2}$	$-\frac{\sqrt{2}}{2}$	$-\frac{1}{2}$	$\frac{1}{2}$	$\frac{\sqrt{2}}{2}$	$\frac{\sqrt{3}}{2}$
c.	tan	$\frac{\sqrt{3}}{3}$	1	$\sqrt{3}$	$-\sqrt{3}$	-1	$-\frac{\sqrt{3}}{3}$	$\frac{\sqrt{3}}{3}$	1	$\sqrt{3}$	$-\sqrt{3}$	-1	$\frac{\sqrt{3}}{3}$
d.	cot	$\sqrt{3}$	1	$\frac{\sqrt{3}}{3}$	$-\frac{\sqrt{3}}{3}$	-1	$-\sqrt{3}$	$\sqrt{3}$	1	$\frac{\sqrt{3}}{3}$	$-\frac{\sqrt{3}}{3}$	-1	$-\sqrt{3}$
e.	sec	$\frac{2\sqrt{3}}{3}$	$\sqrt{2}$	2	-2	$-\sqrt{2}$	$-\frac{2\sqrt{3}}{3}$	$-\frac{2\sqrt{3}}{3}$	$-\sqrt{2}$	-2	2	$\sqrt{2}$	$\frac{2\sqrt{3}}{3}$
f.	csc	2	$\sqrt{2}$	$\frac{2\sqrt{3}}{3}$	$\frac{2\sqrt{3}}{3}$	$\sqrt{2}$	2	-2	$-\sqrt{2}$	$-\frac{2\sqrt{3}}{3}$	$-\frac{2\sqrt{3}}{3}$	$-\sqrt{2}$	-2

8.17 $\sec(-45°) \cdot \csc(-135°) =$
$-\sec 45°(-\csc 135°) =$
$\sec 45°(-\csc 45°) =$
$\sqrt{2}(-\sqrt{2}) =$
-2

8.18 $-[\tan 315° \cdot \cos(-240°)] =$
$-[-\tan 45°(-\cos 60°)] =$
$-[-1(-\frac{1}{2})] =$
$-\frac{1}{2}$

8.19 $\sin 120° + \cos 120° + \tan 45° =$
$\sin 60° - \cos 60° + \tan 45° =$
$\dfrac{\sqrt{3}}{2} - \dfrac{1}{2} + 1 =$
$\dfrac{\sqrt{3}}{2} + \dfrac{1}{2} =$
$\dfrac{\sqrt{3} + 1}{2} =$

8.20 $\sin 240° \cdot \sec 45° -$
$\tan 30° \cdot \tan 45° =$
$-\sin 60° \cdot \sec 45° -$
$\tan 30° \cdot \tan 45° =$
$-\dfrac{\sqrt{3}}{2} \cdot \sqrt{2} - \dfrac{\sqrt{3}}{3} \cdot 1 =$
$-\dfrac{\sqrt{6}}{2} - \dfrac{\sqrt{3}}{3} =$
$-\left(\dfrac{3\sqrt{6} + 2\sqrt{3}}{6}\right) =$

8.21 $[\tan 45° \cdot \cos 120°]^2 =$
$[\tan 45°(-\cos 60°)]^2 =$
$[1(-\frac{1}{2})]^2 =$
$(-\frac{1}{2})^2 =$
$\dfrac{1}{4}$

IX. SECTION NINE

9.1   a.   I

       b. $18° = 18° \cdot \dfrac{\pi}{180°} = \dfrac{\pi}{10}$

9.2   a.   II

       b. $120° = 120° \cdot \dfrac{\pi}{180°} = \dfrac{2\pi}{3}$

9.3   a.   III

       b. $-135° = -135° \dfrac{\pi}{180°} = -\dfrac{3\pi}{4}$

9.4   a. $720° - 720° = 0°$;
           none(quadrantal angle)

       b. $720° = 2 \cdot 360° = 2 \cdot 2\pi = 4\pi$

9.5   a.   IV

       b. $-22\frac{1}{2}° = -\dfrac{45°}{2} \cdot \dfrac{\pi}{180°} = -\dfrac{\pi}{8}$

9.6   a.   I

       b. $60° = 60° \cdot \dfrac{\pi}{180°} = \dfrac{\pi}{3}$

9.7   a.   none(quadrantal angle)

       b. $270° = 270° \cdot \dfrac{\pi}{180°} = \dfrac{3\pi}{2}$

9.8   a.   II

       b. $150° = 150° \cdot \dfrac{\pi}{180°} = \dfrac{5\pi}{6}$

9.9   a.   III

       b. $200° = 200° \cdot \dfrac{\pi}{180°} = \dfrac{10\pi}{9}$

9.10   a.   IV

       b. $330° = 330° \cdot \dfrac{\pi}{180°} = \dfrac{11\pi}{6}$

9.11 $\pi = 180°$

9.12 $\dfrac{\pi}{2} = \dfrac{\pi}{2} \cdot \dfrac{180°}{\pi} = 90°$

9.13 $\dfrac{\pi}{4} = \dfrac{\pi}{4} \dfrac{180°}{\pi} = 45°$

9.14 $\dfrac{3\pi}{2} = \dfrac{3\pi}{2} \cdot \dfrac{180°}{\pi} = 270°$

9.15 $\dfrac{\pi}{15} = \dfrac{\pi}{15} \cdot \dfrac{180°}{\pi} = 12°$

9.16 $\dfrac{5\pi}{4} = \dfrac{5\pi}{4} \cdot \dfrac{180°}{\pi} = 225°$

9.17 $\dfrac{\pi}{5} = \dfrac{\pi}{5} \cdot \dfrac{180°}{\pi} = 36°$

9.18 $\dfrac{\pi}{3} = \dfrac{\pi}{3} \cdot \dfrac{180°}{\pi} = 60°$

9.19 $\dfrac{2\pi}{3} = \dfrac{2\pi}{3} \cdot \dfrac{180°}{\pi} = 120°$

9.20 $\dfrac{15\pi}{2} = \dfrac{15\pi}{2} \cdot \dfrac{180°}{\pi} = 15 \cdot 90° = 1{,}350°$
                       $= 270°$

MATHEMATICS 1204
SOLUTION KEY

I.   SECTION ONE

1.1   I

1.2   II

1.3   II

1.4   II

1.5   IV

1.6   I

1.7   III

1.8   IV

1.9   III

1.10   III

1.11   a.

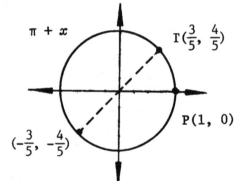

b.

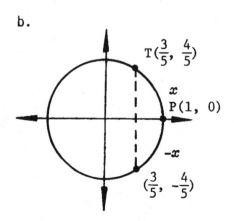

1.11 cont.

c.

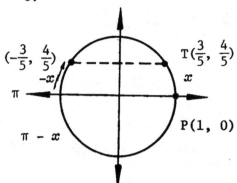

d.

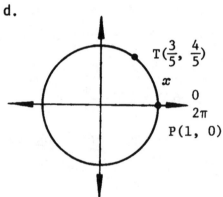

1.12   a.

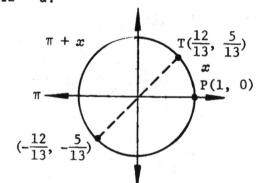

1.12 cont.

b.

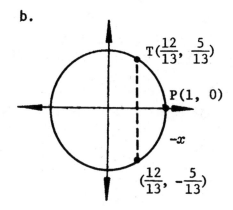

c.

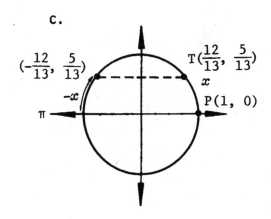

d.

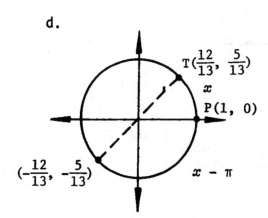

II. SECTION TWO

2.1 $30° \cdot \dfrac{\pi}{180°} = \dfrac{\pi}{6}$

2.2 $45° \cdot \dfrac{\pi}{180°} = \dfrac{\pi}{4}$

2.3 $60° \cdot \dfrac{\pi}{180°} = \dfrac{\pi}{3}$

2.4 $120° \cdot \dfrac{\pi}{180°} = \dfrac{2\pi}{3}$

2.5 $136° \cdot \dfrac{\pi}{180°} = \dfrac{3\pi}{4}$

2.6 $150° \cdot \dfrac{\pi}{180°} = \dfrac{5\pi}{6}$

2.7 $210° \cdot \dfrac{\pi}{180°} = \dfrac{7\pi}{6}$

2.8 $225° \cdot \dfrac{\pi}{180°} = \dfrac{5\pi}{4}$

2.9 $240° \cdot \dfrac{\pi}{180°} = \dfrac{4\pi}{3}$

2.10 $300° \cdot \dfrac{\pi}{180°} = \dfrac{5\pi}{3}$

2.11 $315° \cdot \dfrac{\pi}{180°} = \dfrac{7\pi}{4}$

2.12 $330° \cdot \dfrac{\pi}{180°} = \dfrac{11\pi}{6}$

2.13 $90° \cdot \dfrac{\pi}{180°} = \dfrac{\pi}{2}$

2.14 $180° \cdot \dfrac{\pi}{180°} = \pi$

2.15 $270° \cdot \dfrac{\pi}{180°} = \dfrac{3\pi}{2}$

2.16 $\frac{1}{2}\cdot\frac{\sqrt{3}}{2} = \frac{1}{2}\cdot\frac{\sqrt{3}}{2}$; true

2.17 $\frac{1}{2} = (\frac{\sqrt{3}}{2})^2 + (\frac{1}{2})^2 = \frac{3}{4} + \frac{1}{4} = 1$; false

2.18 $\frac{1}{2} + \frac{\sqrt{3}}{2} = -\sqrt{3}$; false

2.19 $0\cdot\frac{\sqrt{2}}{2} + 1\cdot\frac{\sqrt{2}}{2} = \frac{\sqrt{2}}{2}$

$0 + \frac{\sqrt{2}}{2} = \frac{\sqrt{2}}{2}$

$\frac{\sqrt{2}}{2} = \frac{\sqrt{2}}{2}$; true

2.20 $0 + 1 = -1$; false

2.21 $(\frac{\sqrt{3}}{2})^2 = \frac{3}{4}$

2.22 $[1 - (-1) + 0 + 1]^2 = 3^2 = 9$

2.23 $(-2)^3 = -8$

2.24 $\frac{\sqrt{2}}{2} + \frac{\sqrt{2}}{2} = \frac{2\sqrt{2}}{2} = \sqrt{2}$

III. SECTION THREE

3.1 **true**

3.2 **true**

3.3 **true**

3.4 **true**

3.5 **true**

3.6

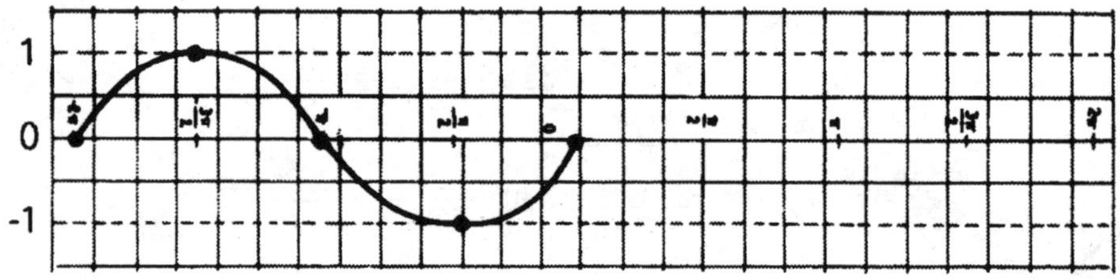

3.7

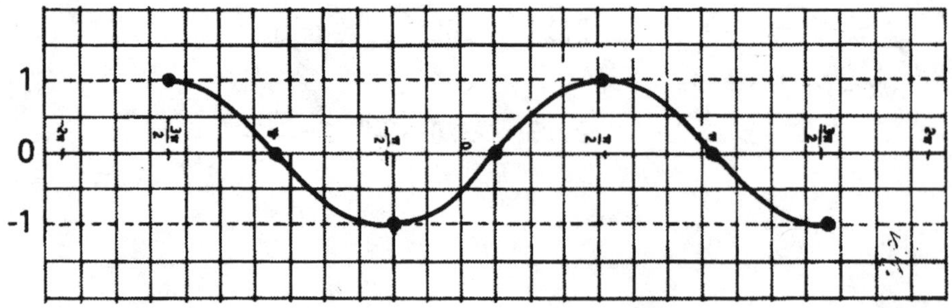

140

3.8

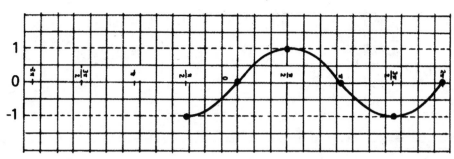

3.9

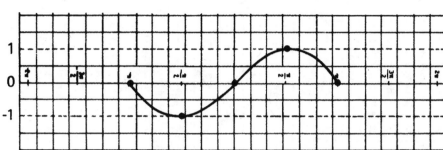

3.10

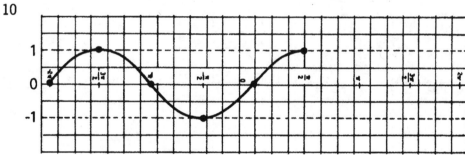

3.11   false

3.12   true

3.13   true

3.14   true

3.15   true

3.16

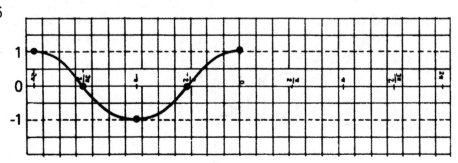

3.17

3.18

3.19

3.20

3.21

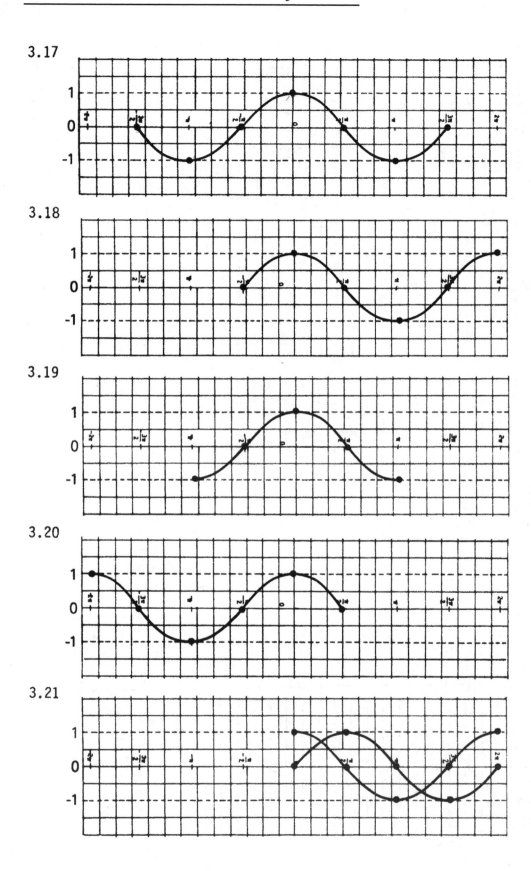

IV. SECTION FOUR

4.1 π

4.2 $\{.\ .\ .,\ -\frac{\pi}{2},\ \frac{\pi}{2},\ \frac{3\pi}{2},\ \frac{5\pi}{2}\}$ or

$(2n - 1)\frac{\pi}{2}$, n = {integers}

4.3   all real numbers;
$-\infty < \tan x < \infty$

4.4

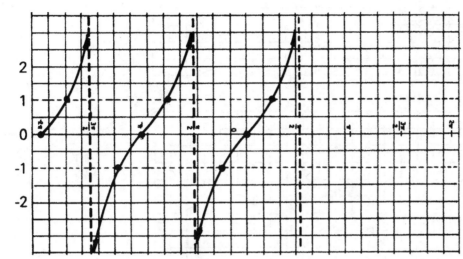

4.5

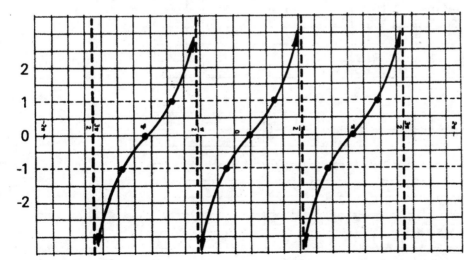

4.6

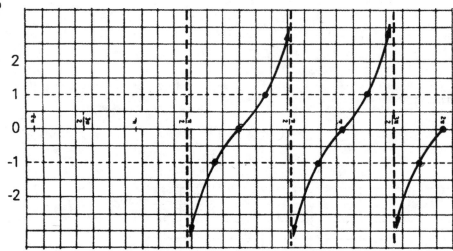

4.7

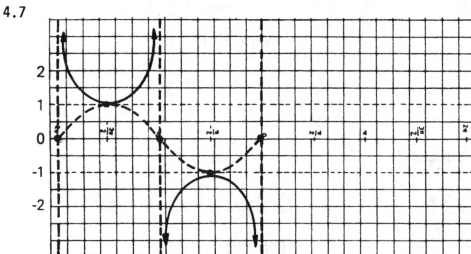

4.8

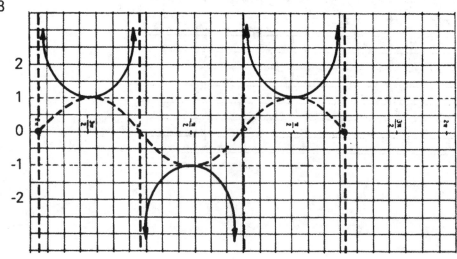

4.9

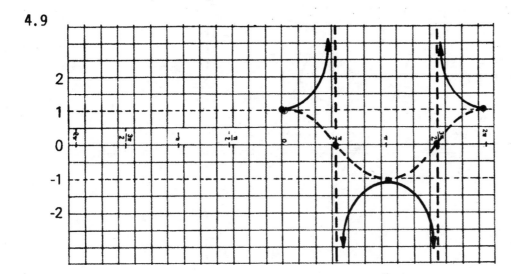

4.10

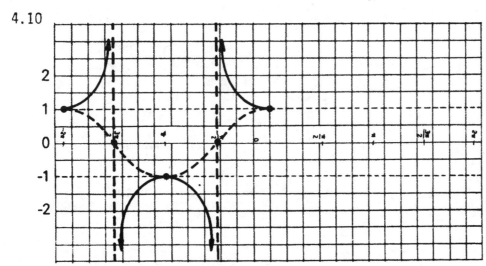

4.11

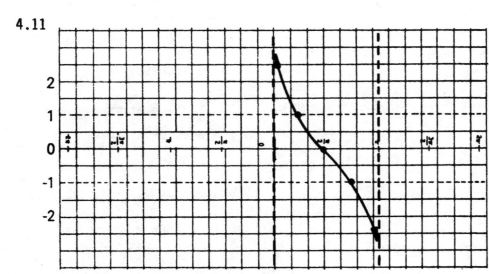

4.12

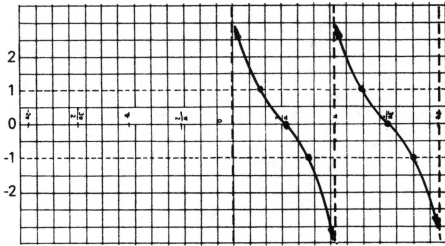

V. SECTION FIVE

5.1 $s = r \cdot \theta = 24 \cdot \frac{\pi}{2} = 12\pi$

5.2 $s = r \cdot \theta = 18.4 \cdot \frac{3\pi}{4} = 13.8\pi$

5.3 $r = \frac{s}{\theta} = \frac{26.4}{\frac{3\pi}{2}} = \frac{2(26.4)}{3\pi} = \frac{17.6}{\pi}$

5.4 $r = \frac{s}{\theta} = \frac{27.6}{\pi}$

5.5 $\theta = \frac{s}{r} = \frac{27}{10} = 2.7 \doteq 3$ **radians**

5.6 $\theta = \frac{s}{r} = \frac{81}{16.3} \doteq 5$ **radians**

5.7 $20 \cdot 2\pi = 40\pi$ radians per minute

5.8 $\frac{200}{60} = \frac{\text{rev.}}{\text{sec.}}$;

$\frac{200}{60} \cdot 2\pi = \frac{400\pi}{60}$

$= \frac{20\pi}{3}$ radians per second

5.9 $60° = \frac{\pi}{3}$ radians per hour

$\frac{\pi}{3} \cdot 24 = 8\pi$ radians per 24-
hour day

5.10 $v = r\omega = (4.5)(50)$
$= 225$ feet per second

5.11 $v = r\omega = 224$ inches per second

5.12 240 rpm $= 240(2\pi)$ radians
per minute
$= 480\pi$ radians per
minute

5.13 $r = \frac{s}{\theta} = \frac{23.5}{52° \left(\frac{\pi}{180°}\right)} = \frac{180° \cdot 23.5}{52° \cdot \pi}$

$= \frac{4,230}{163.362} = 25.893$

$\doteq 26$ inches

5.14 $\omega = \frac{v}{r} = \frac{12}{14} = \frac{6}{7} =$ approximately
0.86 radians per second

5.15 30 revolutions per 10 seconds =
3 rps
$\therefore 3 \cdot 2\pi = 6\pi$ radians per second

5.16 a. $90 \cdot 2\pi = 180\pi$ radians per
minute

b. $v = r\omega = \frac{9(180\pi)}{12}$ ft. per min.

$= \frac{9(180\pi)}{12(60)}$ ft. per sec.

$= 2.25\pi$ ft. per sec.

VI. SECTION SIX

6.1   Amplitude = 3. Multiply each value of $y = \sin x$ by 3.

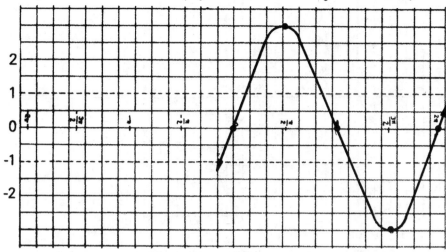

6.2   Amplitude = $\frac{1}{2}$. Multiply each value of $y = \sin x$ by $\frac{1}{2}$.

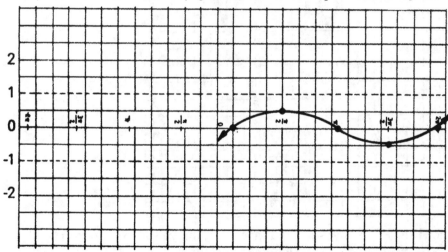

6.3   Amplitude = $\frac{1}{3}$. Multiply each value of $y = \cos x$ by $\frac{1}{3}$.

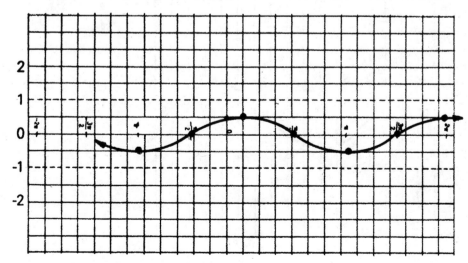

6.4   Amplitude = 2. Multiply each function value by 2.

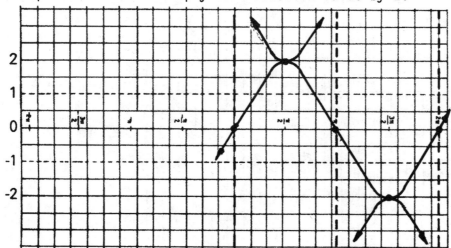

6.5   Amplitude = 2. Multiply each function value by 2.

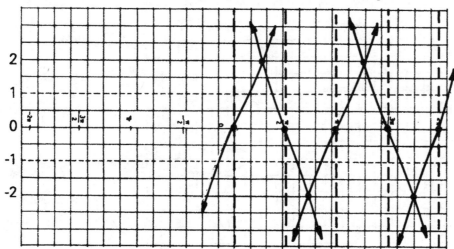

6.6   Multiply each function value by -1. Each function value is opposite
       in sign from $y = \sin x$; hence, the inverted graph.

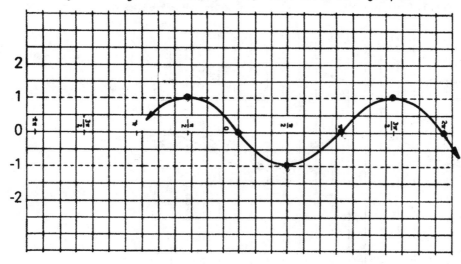

6.7 Multiplying each function value by (-2) inverts the graph.

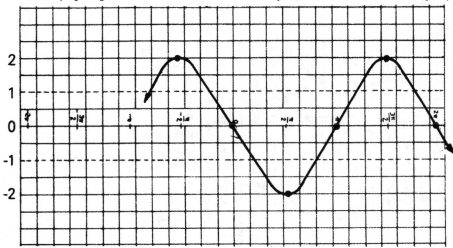

6.8 $A = |\frac{2}{3}| = \frac{2}{3}$

6.9 $A = |-3| = 3$

6.10 $-5 \leq F(x) \leq 5$

7.3 $P = \frac{2\pi}{B}$, $B = \frac{1}{3}$; $P = \frac{2\pi}{\frac{1}{3}} = 6\pi$

7.4 $P = \frac{\pi}{B}$, $B = 2$; $P = \frac{\pi}{2}$

7.5 $P = \frac{2\pi}{B}$, $B = 2$; $P = \frac{2\pi}{2} = \pi$

VII. SECTION SEVEN

7.1 $P = \frac{2\pi}{B}$, $B = 4$; $P = \frac{2\pi}{4} = \frac{\pi}{2}$

7.2 $P = \frac{2\pi}{B}$, $B = \frac{1}{4}$; $P = \frac{2\pi}{\frac{1}{4}} = 8\pi$

7.6 Amplitude = 1, period = $\frac{\pi}{2}$; graph a complete cycle or wave in each quadrant.

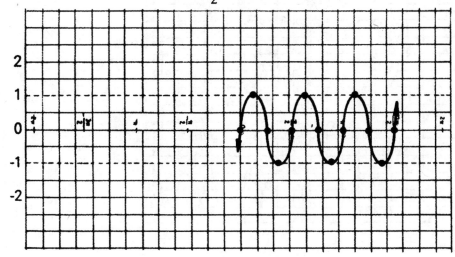

7.7 Period = $\frac{2\pi}{\frac{1}{2}}$ = 4 . Each branch of the curve requires π units instead of $\frac{\pi}{2}$

for a normal period.

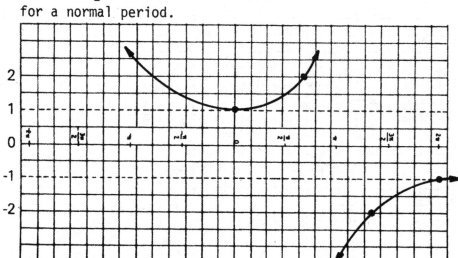

7.8 Amplitude = 2; period = $\frac{2\pi}{2}$ = π.

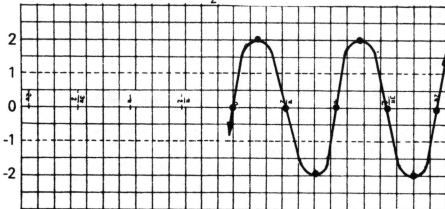

7.9 Amplitude = 2, period = π.

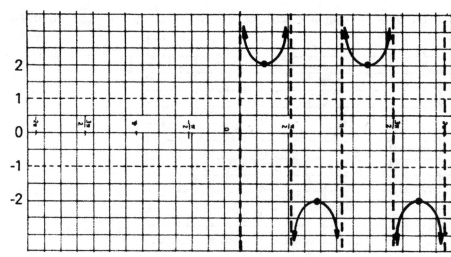

7.10   Amplitude = $|-2| = 2$, period = $\frac{2\pi}{3}$; graph is inverted because of negative function.

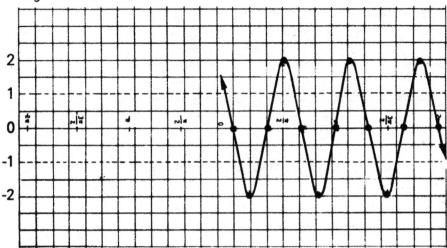

VIII. SECTION EIGHT

8.1 $p = \frac{\pi}{2}$; shift $\frac{\pi}{2}$ units to the right

8.2 $p = -\frac{\pi}{4}$; shift $\frac{\pi}{4}$ units to the left

8.3 $p = 3$; shift 3 units to the right

8.4 $p = -5\pi$; shift 5π units to the left

8.5 $h(x) = \tan(2x + \pi) = \tan 2(x + \frac{\pi}{2})$

      $p = -\frac{\pi}{2}$; shift $\frac{\pi}{2}$ units to the left

8.6 $G(x) = \csc(3x - 3\pi) = \csc 3(x - \pi)$
$p = \pi$; shift π units to the right

8.7 $y = 3 \sin(2x - 1)$

      $= 3 \sin 2(x - \frac{1}{2})$

      $p = \frac{1}{2}$; shift $\frac{1}{2}$ unit to the right

8.8 $y = 5 \cos(2x + \frac{\pi}{2})$

      $= 5 \cos 2(x + \frac{\pi}{4})$

      $p = -\frac{\pi}{4}$; shift $\frac{\pi}{4}$ units to the left

8.9   Amplitude = 1, $P = \frac{2\pi}{2} = \pi$,

      $p = -\frac{\pi}{2}$. Construct the sin curve for a period of π and move the entire graph $\frac{\pi}{2}$ units to the left.

8.9 cont.

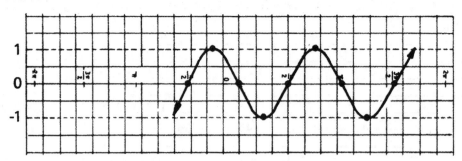

8.10 Construct the sec graph and move $\frac{\pi}{2}$ units to the right. This graph is the same as the csc graph.

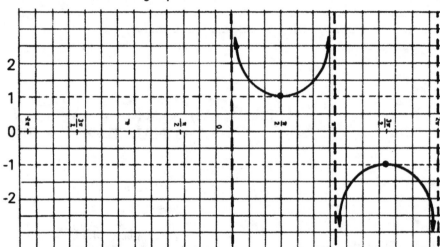

MATHEMATICS 1205
SOLUTION KEY

1.3 cont.

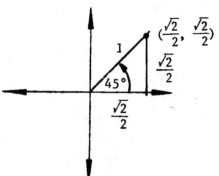

I. SECTION ONE

1.1 $\sin \theta = \frac{4}{5}$; $\csc \theta = \frac{5}{4}$;

$\frac{4}{5} \cdot \frac{5}{4} = 1$

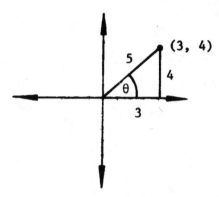

1.2 $\tan \theta = \frac{-4}{-3} = \frac{4}{3}$;

$\cot \theta = \frac{-3}{-4} = \frac{3}{4}$;

$\frac{4}{3} \cdot \frac{3}{4} = 1$

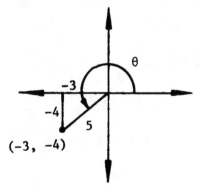

1.3 $\cos \frac{\pi}{4} \cdot \sec \frac{\pi}{4}$

$= \frac{\sqrt{2}}{2} \cdot \sqrt{2}$

$= \frac{2}{2}$

$= 1$

1.4 $\sin \frac{\pi}{3} \cdot \csc \frac{\pi}{3}$

$= \frac{\sqrt{3}}{2} \cdot \frac{2\sqrt{3}}{3}$

$= \frac{2(3)}{6}$

$= \frac{6}{6}$

$= 1$

1.5 $\tan \theta \, \sin \theta \, \cot \theta$

$= \tan \theta \, \cot \theta \, \sin \theta$

$= 1 \cdot \sin \theta$

$= \sin \theta$

1.6 $\dfrac{1}{\cos \theta \, \sec \theta} \cdot \cot \theta$

$= \frac{1}{1} \cdot \cot \theta$

$= \cot \theta$

1.7 $1 + \tan \theta \, \cot \theta - \dfrac{\sin \theta \, \csc \theta}{2}$

$= 1 + 1 - \frac{1}{2}$

$= 2 - \frac{1}{2}$

$= 1\frac{1}{2}$

1.8 $\dfrac{\sin \theta}{\csc \theta} = \dfrac{\sin \theta}{\frac{1}{\sin \theta}} = \sin^2 \theta$

1.9 $\dfrac{\tan \theta}{\cot \theta} = \dfrac{\tan \theta}{\frac{1}{\tan \theta}} = \tan^2 \theta$

1.10 $\dfrac{\sec \theta}{\cos \theta} = \dfrac{\sec \theta}{\dfrac{1}{\sec \theta}} = \sec^2 \theta$

II. SECTION TWO

2.1 $\tan \theta = \dfrac{y}{x}$, $\sec \theta = \dfrac{r}{\omega}$

$\tan^2 \theta + 1 = \sec^2 \theta$

$\left(\dfrac{y}{x}\right)^2 + 1 = \left(\dfrac{r}{x}\right)^2$

$\dfrac{y^2}{x^2} + \dfrac{x^2}{x^2} = \dfrac{r^2}{x^2}$

$\dfrac{x^2 + y^2}{x^2} = \dfrac{r^2}{x^2}$

$\dfrac{r^2}{x^2} = \dfrac{r^2}{x^2}$

2.2 $\cot \theta = \dfrac{x}{y}$, $\csc \theta = \dfrac{r}{y}$

$\cot^2 \theta + 1 = \csc^2 \theta$

$\left(\dfrac{x}{y}\right)^2 + 1 = \left(\dfrac{r}{y}\right)^2$

$\dfrac{x^2}{y^2} + \dfrac{y^2}{y^2} = \dfrac{r^2}{y^2}$

$\dfrac{x^2 + y^2}{y^2} = \dfrac{r^2}{y^2}$

$\dfrac{r^2}{y^2} = \dfrac{r^2}{y^2}$

2.3 $\cot^2 \theta + 1 = \csc^2 \theta$

$\cot^2 \dfrac{\pi}{4} + 1 = \csc^2 \dfrac{\pi}{4}$

$1^2 + 1 = (\sqrt{2})^2$

$2 = 2$

2.4 Tan and cot are reciprocal functions.

$\tan \theta = \dfrac{1}{\cot \theta}$, $\theta \neq 0, \dfrac{\pi}{2}, \pi, \dfrac{3\pi}{2}$

2.5 $\tan^2 \theta + 1 = \sec^2 \theta$

$\sqrt{\sec^2 \theta} = \pm\sqrt{\tan^2 \theta + 1}$

$\sec \theta = \pm\sqrt{\tan^2 \theta + 1}$;

$\theta \neq \dfrac{\pi}{2}, \dfrac{3\pi}{2}$

2.6 $\sin^2 x + \sin x + \cos^2 x - 1$

$= \sin^2 x + \cos^2 x + \sin x - 1$

$= \cancel{1} + \sin x - \cancel{1}$

$= \sin x$

2.7 $\sqrt{\dfrac{\tan^2 x + 1}{\cot^2 x + 1}} = \sqrt{\dfrac{\sec^2 x}{\csc^2 x}} = \dfrac{\sec x}{\csc x} =$

$\dfrac{\dfrac{1}{\cos x}}{\dfrac{1}{\sin x}} = \dfrac{\sin x}{\cos x} = \tan x$

2.8 $\dfrac{1}{2}(-\sin^2 x - \cos^2 x)$

$= -\dfrac{1}{2}(\sin^2 x + \cos^2 x)$

$= -\dfrac{1}{2}(1)$

$= -\dfrac{1}{2}$

2.9 $\sin^2 \theta + \cos^2 \theta = 1$

$\cos^2 \theta = 1 - \sin^2 \theta$

$\sqrt{\cos^2 \theta} = \pm\sqrt{1 - \sin^2 \theta}$

$\cos \theta = \pm\sqrt{1 - \sin^2 \theta}$

2.10 $\cot^2 x + 1 = \csc^2 x$; therefore,

$\sqrt{\cot^2 x + 1} = \sqrt{\csc^2 x} = \csc x$

III. SECTION THREE

3.1 $\dfrac{\sin^2 \theta}{\cos \theta} = \dfrac{\sin \theta \cdot \sin \theta}{\cos \theta} = \dfrac{\sin \theta}{\cos \theta} \cdot$

$\sin \theta = \tan \theta \sin \theta$ or $\dfrac{\sin^2 \theta}{\cos \theta} =$

$\dfrac{1 - \cos^2 \theta}{\cos \theta}$

3.2 $\dfrac{\cos^2 \theta}{\sin \theta} = \dfrac{\cos \theta \cdot \cos \theta}{\sin \theta} =$

$\dfrac{\cos \theta}{\sin \theta} \cdot \cos \theta = \cot \theta \cos \theta$

3.3 $\dfrac{\sin^3 \theta \cos \theta}{\cos^4 \theta} = \dfrac{\sin^3 \theta \cos \theta}{\cos^3 \theta \cos \theta} =$

$\dfrac{\sin^3 \theta}{\cos^3 \theta} \cdot 1 = \tan^3 \theta$

3.4 $\dfrac{\cos\theta\,\tan\theta}{\sin\theta} = \dfrac{\cos\theta}{\sin\theta}\cdot\tan\theta =$
$\cot\theta\cdot\tan\theta = 1$

3.5 $\dfrac{\sin\theta}{\cos\theta\,\tan\theta} = \dfrac{\sin\theta}{\cos\theta}\cdot\dfrac{1}{\tan\theta} =$
$\tan\theta\cdot\dfrac{1}{\tan\theta} = 1$

3.6 $\sin\theta\,\cos\theta\,\tan\theta =$
$\sin\theta\,\cos\theta\,\dfrac{\sin\theta}{\cos\theta} = \sin^2\theta$

3.7 $\dfrac{\cot\theta\,\sin\theta}{\cos\theta} = \cot\theta\cdot\dfrac{\sin\theta}{\cos\theta} =$
$\cot\theta\,\tan\theta = 1$

3.8 $\dfrac{\sin\theta}{\cos\theta} + \dfrac{\sin\theta}{\cos\theta} = \tan\theta + \tan\theta =$
$2\tan\theta$

3.9 $\dfrac{\sin\theta}{\cos\theta} + \tan\theta = \tan\theta + \tan\theta =$
$2\tan\theta$

3.10 $\cot\theta + \dfrac{1}{\tan\theta} + \dfrac{\cos\theta}{\sin\theta} =$
$\cot\theta + \cot\theta + \cot\theta = 3\cot\theta$

IV. SECTION FOUR

4.1 $\cos x\,\tan x = \cos x\,\dfrac{\sin x}{\cos x} = \sin x$

4.2 $\tan A - \sec A = \dfrac{\sin A}{\cos A} - \dfrac{1}{\cos A} =$
$\dfrac{\sin A - 1}{\cos A}$

4.3 $\cos B\,\cot B - \tan B = \cos B\cdot$
$\dfrac{\cos B}{\sin B} - \dfrac{\sin B}{\cos B} = \dfrac{\cos^2 B}{\sin B} - \dfrac{\sin B}{\cos B} =$
$\dfrac{\cos^3 B - \sin^2 B}{\sin B\,\cos B}$

4.4 $\sec\theta\,\cot\theta = \dfrac{1}{\cos\theta}\cdot\dfrac{\cos\theta}{\sin\theta} =$

$\dfrac{1}{\sin\theta}$

4.5 $\csc A - \sin A = \dfrac{1}{\sin A} - \sin A =$
$\dfrac{1}{\sin A} - \dfrac{\sin^2 A}{\sin A} = \dfrac{1 - \sin^2 A}{\sin A} =$
$\dfrac{\cos^2 A}{\sin A}$

4.6 $\sin\theta\,\sec\theta = \tan\theta$
$\sin\theta\,\dfrac{1}{\cos\theta} =$
$\dfrac{\sin\theta}{\cos\theta} =$
$\tan\theta = \tan\theta$

4.7 $\sin B\,\sec B\,\cot B = 1$
$\sin B\cdot\dfrac{1}{\cos B}\cdot\cot B =$
$\dfrac{\sin B}{\cos B}\cdot\cot B =$
$\tan B\cdot\cot B =$
$\qquad 1 = 1$

4.8 $\cos^2 A - \sin^2 A = 1 - 2\sin^2 A$
$(1 - \sin^2 A) - \sin^2 A =$
$1 - 2\sin^2 A = 1 - 2\sin^2 A$

4.9 $\cot B\,\sec B = \csc B$
$\dfrac{\cos B}{\sin B}\cdot\dfrac{1}{\cos B} =$
$\dfrac{1}{\sin B} =$
$\csc B = \csc B$

4.10 $\cos^2 x + \cos^2 x\,\tan^2 x = 1$
$\cos^2 x(1 + \tan^2 x) =$
$\cos^2 x(\sec^2 x) =$
$\cos^2 x\left(\dfrac{1}{\cos^2 x}\right) =$
$\qquad 1 = 1$

4.11 $\dfrac{\sin x}{\csc x} + \dfrac{\cos x}{\sec x} = 1$
$\sin x\cdot\dfrac{1}{\csc x} +$
$\cos x\cdot\dfrac{1}{\sec x} =$
$\sin x\cdot\sin x +$
$\cos x\cdot\cos x =$
$\sin^2 x + \cos^2 x =$
$\qquad 1 = 1$

4.12
$$1 - \frac{\cos^2 x}{1 + \sin x} = \sin x$$

$$\frac{1 + \sin x}{1 + \sin x} - \frac{\cos^2 x}{1 + \sin x} =$$

$$\frac{1 + \sin x - \cos^2 x}{1 + \sin x} =$$

$$\frac{1 - \cos^2 x + \sin x}{1 + \sin x} =$$

$$\frac{\sin^2 x + \sin x}{1 + \sin x} =$$

$$\frac{\sin x (\cancel{\sin x + 1})}{\cancel{1 + \sin x}} =$$

$$\sin x = \sin x$$

4.13
$$\cot x + \frac{\sin x}{1 + \cos x} = \csc x$$

$$\frac{\cos x}{\sin x} + \frac{\sin x}{1 + \cos x} =$$

$$\frac{\cos x (1 + \cos x) + \sin x \sin x}{\sin x (1 + \cos x)} =$$

$$\frac{\cos x + \cos^2 x + \sin^2 x}{\sin x (1 + \cos x)} =$$

$$\frac{\cancel{\cos x + 1}}{\sin x \cancel{(1 + \cos x)}} =$$

$$\frac{1}{\sin x} =$$

$$\csc x = \csc x$$

4.14
$$\frac{1}{1 - \sin A} + \frac{1}{1 + \sin A} = 2 \sec^2 A$$

$$\frac{1 + \sin A + 1 - \sin A}{(1 - \sin A)(1 + \sin A)} =$$

$$\frac{2}{1 - \sin^2 A} =$$

$$\frac{2}{\cos^2 A} =$$

$$2 \sec^2 A = 2 \sec^2 A$$

4.15
$$\sec^2 x \csc^2 x = \sec^2 x + \csc^2 x$$

$$\frac{1}{\cos^2 x} \cdot \frac{1}{\sin^2 x} = \frac{1}{\cos^2 x} + \frac{1}{\sin^2 x}$$

$$\frac{1}{\cos^2 x \sin^2 x} = \frac{\sin^2 x + \cos^2 x}{\cos^2 x \sin^2 x}$$

$$\frac{1}{\cos^2 x \sin^2 x} = \frac{1}{\cos^2 x \sin^2 x}$$

4.16

$$\frac{\sin x}{1 + \cos x} + \frac{1 + \cos x}{\sin x} = 2 \csc x$$

$$\frac{\sin^2 x}{\sin x(1 + \cos x)} + \frac{(1 + \cos x)^2}{\sin x(1 + \cos x)} =$$

$$\frac{\sin^2 x + 1 + 2 \cos x + \cos^2 x}{\sin x(1 + \cos x)} =$$

$$\frac{\sin^2 x + \cos^2 x + 1 + 2 \cos x}{\sin x(1 + \cos x)} =$$

$$\frac{1 + 1 + 2 \cos x}{\sin x(1 + \cos x)} =$$

$$\frac{2 + 2 \cos x}{\sin x(1 + \cos x)} =$$

$$\frac{2(1 + \cos x)}{\sin x(1 + \cos x)} =$$

$$\frac{2}{\sin x} =$$

$$2 \csc x = 2 \csc x$$

4.17 $\tan t + \cot t = \sec t \csc t$

$$\frac{\sin t}{\cos t} + \frac{\cos t}{\sin t} =$$

$$\frac{\sin^2 t + \cos^2 t}{\cos t \sin t} =$$

$$\frac{1}{\cos t \sin t} =$$

$$\sec t \csc t = \sec t \csc t$$

4.18 $1 - 2 \cos^2 r = 2 \sin^2 r - 1$

$1 - 2(1 - \sin^2 r) =$

$1 - 2 + 2 \sin^2 r =$

$-1 + 2 \sin^2 r =$

$2 \sin^2 r - 1 = 2 \sin^2 r - 1$

4.19 $\tan x \sin x = \sec x - \cos x$

$$\frac{\sin x}{\cos x} \cdot \sin x =$$

$$\frac{\sin^2 x}{\cos x} =$$

$$\frac{1 - \cos^2 x}{\cos x} =$$

$$\frac{1}{\cos x} - \frac{\cos^2 x}{\cos x} =$$

$$\sec x - \cos x = \sec x - \cos x$$

4.20 $\dfrac{1 + \tan^2 x}{\tan^2 x} = \csc^2 x$

$$\frac{1}{\tan^2 x} + \frac{\tan^2 x}{\tan^2 x} =$$

$$\cot^2 x + 1 =$$

$$\csc^2 x = \csc^2 x$$

V.   SECTION FIVE

5.1 $\cos(\frac{\pi}{2} - x) = \cos \frac{\pi}{2} \cos x +$

$\sin \frac{\pi}{2} \sin x = 0 \cdot \cos x + 1 \cdot \sin x =$

$\sin x$

5.2 $\cos(180° + \theta) = \cos 180° \cos \theta -$

$\sin 180° \sin \theta = -1 \cdot \cos \theta -$

$0 \cdot \sin \theta = -\cos \theta$

5.3 $\cos(\frac{3\pi}{2} + x) = \cos \frac{3\pi}{2} \cos x -$

$\sin \frac{3\pi}{2} \sin x = 0 \cdot \cos x -$

$(-1)\sin x = \sin x$

5.4 $\cos(270° - \theta) = \cos 270° \cos \theta + \sin 270° \sin \theta = 0 \cdot \cos \theta + (-1)\sin \theta = -\sin \theta$

5.5 $\cos(\pi - x) = \cos \pi \cos x + \sin \pi \sin x = -1 \cdot \cos x + 0 \cdot \sin x = -\cos x$

5.6 $\sin \alpha = \dfrac{4}{5}$

$x = 3$

$\cos \alpha = \dfrac{3}{5}$

$\cos \beta = \dfrac{5}{13}$

$y = 12$

$\sin \beta = \dfrac{12}{13}$

a. $\cos(\alpha + \beta) = \cos \alpha \cos \beta - \sin \alpha \sin \beta$

$= \dfrac{3}{5} \cdot \dfrac{5}{13} - \dfrac{4}{5} \cdot \dfrac{12}{13}$

$= \dfrac{15}{65} - \dfrac{48}{65}$

$= -\dfrac{33}{65}$

b. $\cos(\alpha - \beta) = \cos \alpha \cos \beta + \sin \alpha \sin \beta$

$= \dfrac{3}{5} \cdot \dfrac{5}{13} + \dfrac{4}{5} \cdot \dfrac{12}{13}$

$= \dfrac{15}{65} + \dfrac{48}{65}$

$= \dfrac{63}{65}$

5.7 $\cos \alpha = \dfrac{15}{17}$

$y = 8$

$\sin \alpha = \dfrac{8}{17}$

$\sin \beta = \dfrac{3}{5}$

$x = 4$

$\cos \beta = \dfrac{4}{5}$

5.7 cont.

a. $\cos(\alpha + \beta) = \cos \alpha \cos \beta - \sin \alpha \sin \beta$

$= \dfrac{15}{17} \cdot \dfrac{4}{5} - \dfrac{8}{17} \cdot \dfrac{3}{5}$

$= \dfrac{60}{85} - \dfrac{24}{85}$

$= \dfrac{36}{85}$

b. $\cos(\alpha - \beta) = \cos \alpha \cos \beta + \sin \alpha \sin \beta$

$= \dfrac{15}{17} \cdot \dfrac{4}{5} + \dfrac{8}{17} \cdot \dfrac{3}{5}$

$= \dfrac{60}{85} + \dfrac{24}{85}$

$= \dfrac{84}{85}$

5.8 $\sin \alpha = \dfrac{1}{2}$

$x = \sqrt{3}$

$\cos \alpha = \dfrac{\sqrt{3}}{2}$

$\cos \beta = \dfrac{2}{3}$

$y = \sqrt{5}$

$\sin \beta = \dfrac{\sqrt{5}}{3}$

a. $\cos(\alpha + \beta) = \cos \alpha \cos \beta - \sin \alpha \sin \beta$

$= \dfrac{\sqrt{3}}{2} \cdot \dfrac{2}{3} - \dfrac{1}{2} \cdot \dfrac{\sqrt{5}}{3}$

$= \dfrac{\sqrt{3}}{3} - \dfrac{\sqrt{5}}{6}$

$= \dfrac{2\sqrt{3} - \sqrt{5}}{6}$

b. $\cos(\alpha - \beta) = \cos \alpha \cos \beta + \sin \alpha \sin \beta$

$= \dfrac{\sqrt{3}}{2} \cdot \dfrac{2}{3} + \dfrac{1}{2} \cdot \dfrac{\sqrt{5}}{3}$

$= \dfrac{2\sqrt{3}}{6} + \dfrac{\sqrt{5}}{6}$

$= \dfrac{2\sqrt{3} + \sqrt{5}}{6}$

5.9 $\sin \alpha = \dfrac{3}{5}$

$x = 4$

$\cos \alpha = \dfrac{4}{5}$

5.9 cont.

$\cos \beta = \dfrac{12}{37}$

$y = 35$

$\sin \beta = \dfrac{35}{37}$

a. $\cos(\alpha + \beta) = \cos \alpha \cos \beta - \sin \alpha \sin \beta$

$= \dfrac{4}{5} \cdot \dfrac{12}{37} - \dfrac{3}{5} \cdot \dfrac{35}{37}$

$= \dfrac{48}{185} - \dfrac{105}{185}$

$= -\dfrac{57}{185}$

b. $\cos(\alpha - \beta) = \cos \alpha \cos \beta + \sin \alpha \sin \beta$

$= \dfrac{4}{5} \cdot \dfrac{12}{37} + \dfrac{3}{5} \cdot \dfrac{35}{37}$

$= \dfrac{48}{185} + \dfrac{105}{185}$

$= \dfrac{153}{185}$

5.10 $\cos \alpha = \dfrac{8}{17}$

$y = 15$

$\sin \alpha = \dfrac{15}{17}$

$\sin \beta = \dfrac{12}{13}$

$x = 5$

$\cos \beta = \dfrac{5}{13}$

a. $\cos(\alpha + \beta) = \cos \alpha \cos \beta - \sin \alpha \sin \beta$

$= \dfrac{8}{17} \cdot \dfrac{5}{13} - \dfrac{15}{17} \cdot \dfrac{12}{13}$

$= \dfrac{40}{221} - \dfrac{180}{221}$

$= -\dfrac{140}{221}$

b. $\cos(\alpha - \beta) = \cos \alpha \cos \beta + \sin \alpha \sin \beta$

$= \dfrac{8}{17} \cdot \dfrac{5}{13} + \dfrac{15}{17} \cdot \dfrac{12}{13}$

$= \dfrac{40}{221} + \dfrac{180}{221}$

$= \dfrac{220}{221}$

VI. SECTION SIX

6.1 through 6.5

$\sin \alpha = \dfrac{5}{13}$

$x = 12$

$\cos \alpha = \dfrac{12}{13}$

$\tan \alpha = \dfrac{5}{12}$

$\cos \beta = \dfrac{3}{5}$

$y = 4$

$\sin \beta = \dfrac{4}{5}$

$\tan \beta = \dfrac{4}{3}$

6.1 $\sin(\alpha - \beta) = \sin \alpha \cos \beta - \cos \alpha \sin \beta$

$= \dfrac{5}{13} \cdot \dfrac{3}{5} - \dfrac{12}{13} \cdot \dfrac{4}{5}$

$= \dfrac{15}{65} - \dfrac{48}{65}$

$= -\dfrac{33}{65}$

6.2 $\cos(\alpha + \beta) = \cos \alpha \cos \beta - \sin \alpha \sin \beta$

$= \dfrac{12}{13} \cdot \dfrac{3}{5} - \dfrac{5}{13} \cdot \dfrac{4}{5}$

$= \dfrac{36}{65} - \dfrac{20}{65}$

$= \dfrac{16}{65}$

6.3 $\sin(\alpha + \beta) = \sin \alpha \cos \beta + \cos \alpha \sin \beta$

$= \dfrac{5}{13} \cdot \dfrac{3}{5} + \dfrac{12}{13} \cdot \dfrac{4}{5}$

$= \dfrac{15}{65} + \dfrac{48}{65}$

$= \dfrac{63}{65}$

6.4 $\cos(\alpha - \beta) = \cos \alpha \cos \beta +$
$\sin \alpha \sin \beta$

$$= \frac{12}{13} \cdot \frac{3}{5} + \frac{5}{13} \cdot \frac{4}{5}$$

$$= \frac{36}{65} + \frac{20}{65}$$

$$= \frac{56}{65}$$

6.5 $\tan(\alpha - \beta) = \dfrac{\tan \alpha - \tan \beta}{1 + \tan \alpha \tan \beta}$

$$= \frac{\dfrac{5}{12} - \dfrac{4}{3}}{1 + \dfrac{5}{12} \cdot \dfrac{4}{3}}$$

Multiply numerator and denominator by 36.

$$= \frac{15 - 48}{36 + 20}$$

$$= -\frac{33}{56}$$

6.6 $\sin(\pi - x) = \sin \pi \cos x -$
$\cos \pi \sin x$
$= 0 \cdot \cos x - (-1)\sin x$
$= 0 + \sin x$
$= \sin x$

6.7 $\sin(180° + \theta) = \sin 180° \cos \theta +$
$\cos 180° \sin \theta$
$= 0 \cdot \cos \theta + (-1)\sin \theta$
$= 0 + (-\sin \theta)$
$= -\sin \theta$

6.8 through 6.10

$$\sin \theta = -\frac{5}{13}$$
$$x = -12$$
$$\cos \theta = -\frac{12}{13}, \ \tan \theta = \frac{5}{12}$$

$$\tan \phi = -\frac{8}{15}$$
$$r = \sqrt{8^2 + (-15)^2}$$
$$= \sqrt{64 + 225}$$
$$= \sqrt{289}$$
$$= 17$$

$$\sin \phi = \frac{8}{17}, \ \cos \phi = -\frac{15}{17}$$

6.8 $\sin(\theta + \phi) = \sin \theta \cos \phi +$
$\sin \phi \cos \theta$

$$= -\frac{5}{13} \cdot \left(-\frac{15}{17}\right) + \frac{8}{17} \cdot \left(-\frac{12}{13}\right)$$

$$= \frac{75}{221} - \frac{96}{221}$$

$$= -\frac{21}{221}$$

6.9 $\cos(\theta - \phi) = \cos \theta \cos \phi +$
$\sin \theta \sin \phi$

$$= -\frac{12}{13} \cdot \left(-\frac{15}{17}\right) + \left(-\frac{5}{13}\right) \cdot \frac{8}{17}$$

$$= \frac{180}{221} - \frac{40}{221}$$

$$= \frac{140}{221}$$

6.10 $\tan(\pi + \theta) = \dfrac{\tan \pi + \tan \theta}{1 - \tan \pi \tan \theta}$

$$= \frac{0 + \dfrac{5}{12}}{1 - 0 \cdot \dfrac{5}{12}}$$

$$= \frac{5}{12}$$

6.11 $\sin\left(\dfrac{\pi}{6} + \beta\right) = \sin \dfrac{\pi}{6} \cos \beta +$
$\cos \dfrac{\pi}{6} \sin \beta$

$$= \frac{1}{2} \cos \beta + \frac{\sqrt{3}}{2} \sin \beta$$

$$= \frac{\cos \beta + \sqrt{3} \sin \beta}{2}$$

6.12 $\cos(45° + \alpha) = \cos 45° \cos \alpha -$
$\sin 45° \sin \alpha$

$$= \frac{\sqrt{2}}{2} \cos \alpha - \frac{\sqrt{2}}{2} \sin \alpha$$

$$= \frac{\sqrt{2}}{2}(\cos \alpha - \sin \alpha)$$

6.13 $\tan(60° + \alpha) = \dfrac{\tan 60° + \tan \alpha}{1 - \tan 60° \tan \alpha}$

$$= \frac{\sqrt{3} + \tan \alpha}{1 - \sqrt{3} \tan \alpha}$$

6.14 $\tan(\frac{\pi}{6} - \beta) = \dfrac{\tan \frac{\pi}{6} - \tan \beta}{1 + \tan \frac{\pi}{6} \tan \beta}$

$\qquad\qquad = \dfrac{\frac{\sqrt{3}}{3} - \tan \beta}{1 + \frac{\sqrt{3}}{3} \tan \beta}$

$\qquad\qquad = \dfrac{\sqrt{3} - 3 \tan \beta}{3 + \sqrt{3} \tan \beta}$

6.15 Given that $\sin(\frac{\pi}{2} - \alpha) = \cos \alpha$ and $\cos(\frac{\pi}{2} - \alpha) = \sin \alpha$:

$\sin(\alpha - \beta) = \cos(\frac{\pi}{2} - (\alpha - \beta))$

$\qquad\qquad = \cos((\frac{\pi}{2} - \alpha) + \beta)$

$\qquad\qquad = \cos(\frac{\pi}{2} - \alpha) \cos \beta -$

$\qquad\qquad\quad \sin(\frac{\pi}{2} - \alpha) \sin \beta$

$\qquad\qquad = \sin \alpha \cos \beta -$
$\qquad\qquad\quad \cos \alpha \sin \beta$

VIII. SECTION SEVEN

7.1 Let $\tan 2x = \tan(x + x)$;
then using the formula for
$\tan(\alpha + \beta) = \dfrac{\tan \alpha + \tan \beta}{1 - \tan \alpha \tan \beta}$,
$\alpha = x$ and $\beta = x$.

$\tan 2x = \tan(x + x)$

$\qquad = \dfrac{\tan x + \tan x}{1 - \tan x \tan x}$

$\qquad = \dfrac{2 \tan x}{1 - \tan^2 x}$

7.2 Let $\tan \frac{x}{2} = \dfrac{\sin \frac{x}{2}}{\cos \frac{x}{2}}$

$\qquad\qquad = \dfrac{\pm\sqrt{\dfrac{1 - \cos x}{2}}}{\pm\sqrt{\dfrac{1 + \cos x}{2}}}$

7.2 cont.

$\qquad = \pm\sqrt{\dfrac{\dfrac{1 - \cos x}{2}}{\dfrac{1 + \cos x}{2}}}$

$\qquad = \pm\sqrt{\dfrac{1 - \cos x}{1 + \cos x}}.$

Therefore, $\left|\tan \frac{x}{2}\right| = \sqrt{\dfrac{1 - \cos x}{1 + \cos x}}.$

7.3 through 7.8

$P(u, v) = (3, 4)$; therefore,
$r = \sqrt{3^2 + 4^2} = \sqrt{9 + 16} = \sqrt{25} = 5$
$\cos \theta = \frac{3}{5}$, $\sin \theta = \frac{4}{5}$, $\tan \theta = \frac{4}{3}$

7.3 $\cos 2\theta = 2 \cos^2 \theta - 1$

$\qquad\qquad = 2(\frac{3}{5})^2 - 1$

$\qquad\qquad = 2(\frac{9}{25}) - 1$

$\qquad\qquad = \frac{18}{25} - 1$

$\qquad\qquad = -\frac{7}{25}$

7.4 $\sin \frac{1}{2}\theta = \sqrt{\dfrac{1 - \cos \theta}{2}}$

$\qquad\qquad = \sqrt{\dfrac{1 - \frac{3}{5}}{2}}$

$\qquad\qquad = \sqrt{\dfrac{\frac{2}{5}}{2}}$

$\qquad\qquad = \sqrt{\dfrac{1}{5}}$

$\qquad\qquad = \dfrac{\sqrt{5}}{5}$

7.5 $\tan 2\theta = \dfrac{2 \tan \theta}{1 - \tan^2 \theta}$

$\qquad\qquad = \dfrac{2(\frac{4}{3})}{1 - (\frac{4}{3})^2}$

$\qquad\qquad = \dfrac{\frac{8}{3}}{1 - \frac{16}{9}}$

7.5 cont.

$$= \frac{\frac{8}{3}}{-\frac{7}{9}}$$

$$= -\frac{72}{21}$$

$$= -\frac{24}{7}$$

7.6 $\quad \tan \frac{1}{2}\theta = \sqrt{\frac{1 - \cos \theta}{1 + \cos \theta}}$

$$= \sqrt{\frac{1 - \frac{3}{5}}{1 + \frac{3}{5}}}$$

$$= \sqrt{\frac{\frac{2}{5}}{\frac{8}{5}}}$$

$$= \sqrt{\frac{1}{4}}$$

$$= \frac{1}{2}$$

7.7 $\quad \sin 2\theta = 2 \sin \theta \cos \theta$

$$= 2\left(\frac{4}{5}\right)\left(\frac{3}{5}\right)$$

$$= \frac{24}{25}$$

7.8 $\quad \cos \frac{1}{2}\theta = \sqrt{\frac{1 + \cos \theta}{2}}$

$$= \sqrt{\frac{1 + \frac{3}{5}}{2}}$$

$$= \sqrt{\frac{\frac{8}{5}}{2}}$$

$$= \sqrt{\frac{8}{10}}$$

$$= \sqrt{\frac{4}{5}}$$

$$= \frac{2}{\sqrt{5}}$$

$$= \frac{2\sqrt{5}}{5}$$

7.9 through 7.16

$$\cos x = \frac{\sqrt{2}}{2}$$

$$u = \sqrt{2}, \ r = 2$$

$$v = -\sqrt{2^2 - (\sqrt{2})^2}$$

$$= -\sqrt{4 - 2}$$

$$= -\sqrt{2}$$

7.9 $\quad \sin x = \frac{v}{r} = -\frac{\sqrt{2}}{2}$

7.10 $\quad \tan x = \frac{r}{u} = -\frac{\sqrt{2}}{\sqrt{2}} = -1$

7.11 $\quad \sin 2x = 2 \sin x \cos x$

$$= 2\left(-\frac{\sqrt{2}}{2}\right)\left(\frac{\sqrt{2}}{2}\right)$$

$$= 2\left(-\frac{1}{2}\right)$$

$$= -1$$

7.12 $\quad \cos 2x = 2 \cos^2 x - 1$

$$= 2\left(\frac{\sqrt{2}}{2}\right)^2 - 1$$

$$= 2\left(\frac{1}{2}\right) - 1$$

$$= 0$$

7.13 $\quad \tan 2x = \frac{2 \tan x}{1 - \tan^2 x}$

$$= \frac{2(-1)}{1 - (-1)^2}$$

$$= -\frac{2}{0}$$

Tan $2x$ is undefined because $x = 45°$ and $2x = 90°$; tan $90°$ is undefined.

7.14 $\quad \sin \frac{1}{2} x = \sqrt{\frac{1 - \cos x}{2}}$

$$= \sqrt{\frac{1 - \frac{\sqrt{2}}{2}}{2}}$$

$$= \sqrt{\frac{2 - \sqrt{2}}{4}}$$

$$= \frac{\sqrt{2 - \sqrt{2}}}{2}$$

7.15 $\cos \frac{1}{2} x = \sqrt{\dfrac{1 + \cos x}{2}}$

$= \sqrt{\dfrac{1 + \frac{\sqrt{2}}{2}}{2}}$

$= \sqrt{\dfrac{2 + \sqrt{2}}{4}}$

$= \dfrac{\sqrt{2 + \sqrt{2}}}{2}$

7.16 $\tan \frac{1}{2} x = \sqrt{\dfrac{1 - \cos x}{1 + \cos x}}$

$= \sqrt{\dfrac{1 - \frac{\sqrt{2}}{2}}{1 + \frac{\sqrt{2}}{2}}}$

$= \sqrt{\dfrac{2 - \sqrt{2}}{2 + \sqrt{2}}}$

$= \sqrt{\dfrac{(2 - \sqrt{2})(2 - \sqrt{2})}{(2 + \sqrt{2})(2 - \sqrt{2})}}$

$= \sqrt{\dfrac{4 - 4\sqrt{2} + 2}{4 - 2}}$

$= \sqrt{\dfrac{6 - 4\sqrt{2}}{2}}$

$= \sqrt{3 - 2\sqrt{2}}$

7.17 $\dfrac{1 - \tan^2 \theta}{1 + \tan^2 \theta} = \dfrac{1 - \frac{\sin^2 \theta}{\cos^2 \theta}}{1 + \frac{\sin^2 \theta}{\cos^2 \theta}}$

$= \dfrac{\frac{\cos^2 \theta - \sin^2 \theta}{\cos^2 \theta}}{\frac{\cos^2 \theta + \sin^2 \theta}{\cos^2 \theta}}$

$= \dfrac{\cos^2 \theta - \sin^2 \theta}{\cos^2 \theta + \sin^2 \theta}$

$= \dfrac{\cos^2 \theta - \sin^2 \theta}{1}$

$= \cos^2 \theta - \sin^2 \theta$

$= \cos 2\theta$

7.17 cont.

Therefore, $\cos 2\theta = \dfrac{1 - \tan^2 \theta}{1 + \tan^2 \theta}$.

7.18 $\tan \frac{1}{2}\theta = \sqrt{\dfrac{1 - \cos \theta}{1 + \cos \theta}}$; therefore, multiply numerator and denominator of the right side of the equation by $\sqrt{1 + \cos \theta}$.

$\sqrt{\dfrac{1 - \cos \theta}{1 + \cos \theta}} \cdot \dfrac{\sqrt{1 + \cos \theta}}{\sqrt{1 + \cos \theta}} =$

$\sqrt{\dfrac{(1 - \cos \theta)(1 + \cos \theta)}{(1 + \cos \theta)^2}} =$

$\dfrac{\sqrt{1 - \cos^2 \theta}}{1 + \cos \theta} = \dfrac{\sqrt{\sin^2 \theta}}{1 + \cos \theta} =$

$\dfrac{\sin \theta}{1 + \cos \theta}$

Therefore, $\tan \frac{1}{2}\theta = \dfrac{\sin \theta}{1 + \cos \theta}$.

7.19 Simplify the right member of the equation:

$\dfrac{1 + \cos 2\theta}{2} = \dfrac{1 + (2 \cos^2 \theta - 1)}{2} =$

$\dfrac{2 \cos^2 \theta}{2} = \cos^2 \theta$

Therefore, $\cos^2 \theta = \dfrac{1 + \cos 2\theta}{2}$.

7.20 Simplify the right member of the equation:

$\dfrac{1 - \cos 2x}{2} = \dfrac{1 - (1 - 2 \sin^2 x)}{2} =$

$\dfrac{2 \sin^2 x}{2} = \sin^2 x$

Therefore, $\sin^2 x = \dfrac{1 - \cos 2x}{2}$.

7.21 Simplify the right member by $\tan x = \dfrac{\sin x}{\cos x}$:

$\dfrac{2 \tan x}{1 + \tan^2 x} = \dfrac{2\frac{\sin x}{\cos x}}{1 + \frac{\sin^2 x}{\cos^2 x}}$

7.21 cont.

Now multiply numerator and denominator by $\cos^2 x$;

$$\frac{2\sin x \cos x}{\cos^2 x + \sin^2 x} = 2\sin x \cos x$$

$$= \sin 2x$$

Therefore, $\sin 2x = \dfrac{2\tan x}{1 + \tan^2 x}$.

VIII. SECTION EIGHT

8.1 $\tan x \tan \dfrac{x}{2}$

$\dfrac{\sin x}{\cos x} \cdot \sqrt{\dfrac{1 - \cos x}{1 + \cos x}}$

$\dfrac{\sin x}{\cos x} \cdot \sqrt{\dfrac{1 - \cos x}{1 + \cos x} \cdot \dfrac{1 + \cos x}{1 + \cos x}}$

$\dfrac{\sin x}{\cos x} \cdot \dfrac{\sqrt{1 - \cos^2 x}}{1 + \cos x}$

$\dfrac{\sin x}{\cos x} \cdot \dfrac{\sin x}{1 + \cos x}$

$\dfrac{\sin^2 x}{\cos x (1 + \cos x)}$

$\dfrac{1 - \cos^2 x}{\cos x (1 + \cos x)}$

$\dfrac{(1 - \cos x)\cancel{(1 + \cos x)}}{\cos x \cancel{(1 + \cos x)}}$

$\dfrac{1 - \cos x}{\cos x}$

|

$\sec x - 1$

$\dfrac{1}{\cos x} - 1$

$\dfrac{1}{\cos x} - \dfrac{\cos x}{\cos x}$

$\dfrac{1 - \cos x}{\cos x}$

$\dfrac{1 - \cos x}{\cos x}$

8.2 $\dfrac{2\tan x}{1 + \tan^2 x}$

$\dfrac{2\dfrac{\sin x}{\cos x}}{1 + \dfrac{\sin^2 x}{\cos^2 x}}$

$\dfrac{2\dfrac{\sin x}{\cos x}}{1 + \dfrac{\sin^2 x}{\cos^2 x}} \cdot \dfrac{\cos^2 x}{\cos^2 x}$

$\dfrac{2\sin x \cos x}{\cos^2 x + \sin^2 x}$

$\dfrac{2\sin x \cos x}{1}$

$\sin 2x$

|

$\sin 2x$

$\sin 2x$

8.3 $(\sin \alpha - \cos \alpha)^2$ $1 - \sin 2\alpha$

$\sin^2 \alpha - 2 \sin \alpha \cos \alpha + \cos^2 \alpha$

$\sin^2 \alpha + \cos^2 \alpha - 2 \sin \alpha \cos \alpha$

$1 - 2 \sin \alpha \cos \alpha$

$1 - \sin 2\alpha$ $1 - \sin 2\alpha$

8.4 $\dfrac{\sin 2x}{1 + \cos 2x}$ $\tan x$

$\dfrac{2 \sin x \cos x}{1 + (2 \cos^2 x - 1)}$

$\dfrac{2 \sin x \cos x}{2 \cos^2 x}$

$\dfrac{\sin x}{\cos x}$

$\tan x$ $\tan x$

8.5 $\tan (\theta + 45°)$ $\dfrac{1 + \tan \theta}{1 - \tan \theta}$

$\dfrac{\tan \theta + \tan 45°}{1 - \tan \theta \tan 45°}$

$\dfrac{\tan \theta + 1}{1 - \tan \theta (1)}$

$\dfrac{1 + \tan \theta}{1 - \tan \theta}$ $\dfrac{1 + \tan \theta}{1 - \tan \theta}$

8.6 $\cos^4 \alpha - \sin^4 \alpha$ $\cos 2\alpha$

$(\cos^2 \alpha + \sin^2 \alpha)(\cos^2 \alpha - \sin^2 \alpha)$

$1 \cdot (\cos^2 \alpha - \sin^2 \alpha)$

$\cos 2\alpha$ $\cos 2\alpha$

8.7 $(1 - \cos^2 x)(\cos^2 x)$ $\dfrac{1}{4} \sin^2 2x$

$\sin^2 x \cos^2 x$

$\dfrac{4}{4} \sin^2 x \cos^2 x$

$\dfrac{1}{4}(2 \sin x \cos x)^2$

$\dfrac{1}{4}(\sin 2x)^2$

$\dfrac{1}{4} \sin^2 2x$ $\dfrac{1}{4} \sin^2 2x$

8.8 $\dfrac{\sin 2\theta}{\sin \theta} + \dfrac{1 + \cos 2\theta}{\cos \theta}$ $\qquad\qquad 4 \cos \theta$

$\dfrac{2 \sin \theta \cos \theta}{\sin \theta} + \dfrac{1 + 2\cos^2 \theta - 1}{\cos \theta}$

$2 \cos \theta + 2 \cos \theta$

$4 \cos \theta \qquad\qquad\qquad\qquad 4 \cos \theta$

8.9 $\dfrac{1 - \tan^2 \frac{x}{2}}{1 + \tan^2 \frac{x}{2}}$ $\qquad\qquad\qquad \cos x$

$\dfrac{1 - \left(\sqrt{\dfrac{1 - \cos x}{1 + \cos x}}\right)^2}{1 + \left(\sqrt{\dfrac{1 - \cos x}{1 + \cos x}}\right)^2}$

$\dfrac{1 - \dfrac{1 - \cos x}{1 + \cos x}}{1 + \dfrac{1 - \cos x}{1 + \cos x}}$

$\dfrac{(1 + \cos x) - (1 - \cos x)}{(1 + \cos x) + (1 - \cos x)}$

$\dfrac{1 + \cos x - 1 + \cos x}{1 + \cos x + 1 - \cos x}$

$\dfrac{2 \cos x}{2}$

$\cos x \qquad\qquad\qquad\qquad \cos x$

8.10 $\sin \left(\frac{\pi}{6} + x\right)$ $\qquad\qquad \cos \left(\frac{\pi}{3} - x\right)$

$\sin \frac{\pi}{6} \cos x + \cos \frac{\pi}{6} \sin x \qquad \cos \frac{\pi}{3} \cos x + \sin \frac{\pi}{3} \sin x$

$\frac{1}{2} \cos x + \frac{\sqrt{3}}{2} \sin x \qquad\qquad \frac{1}{2} \cos x + \frac{\sqrt{3}}{2} \sin x$

8.11 $\sin \left(\frac{\pi}{4} + x\right) - \sin \left(\frac{\pi}{4} - x\right)$ $\qquad\qquad \sqrt{2} \sin x$

$\left(\sin \frac{\pi}{4} \cos x + \cos \frac{\pi}{4} \sin x\right) - \left(\sin \frac{\pi}{4} \cos x - \cos \frac{\pi}{4} \sin x\right)$

$\sin \frac{\pi}{4} \cos x + \cos \frac{\pi}{4} \sin x - \sin \frac{\pi}{4} \cos x + \cos \frac{\pi}{4} \sin x$

$2 \cos \frac{\pi}{4} \sin x$

$2 \cdot \frac{\sqrt{2}}{2} \sin x$

$\sqrt{2} \sin x \qquad\qquad\qquad\qquad \sqrt{2} \sin x$

8.12 $2 \cos \alpha \cos \beta$ | $\cos(\alpha + \beta) + \cos(\alpha - \beta)$
| $\cos \alpha \cos \beta - \text{sin } \alpha \text{ sin } \beta + \cos \alpha \cos \beta + \text{sin } \alpha \text{ sin } \beta$
$2 \cos \alpha \cos \beta$ | $2 \cos \alpha \cos \beta$

8.13 $2 \sin \alpha \sin \beta$ | $\cos(\alpha - \beta) - \cos(\alpha + \beta)$
| $\cos \alpha \cos \beta + \sin \alpha \sin \beta - (\cos \alpha \cos \beta - \sin \alpha \sin \beta)$
| $\text{cos } \alpha \text{ cos } \beta + \sin \alpha \sin \beta - \text{cos } \alpha \text{ cos } \beta + \sin \alpha \sin \beta$
$2 \sin \alpha \sin \beta$ | $2 \sin \alpha \sin \beta$

IX. SECTION NINE

9.1 $2 \cos \theta + 1 = 0$
$$2 \cos \theta = -1$$
$$\cos \theta = -\frac{1}{2}$$
$$\theta = \{120°, \ 240°\}$$

9.2 $4 \sin^2 \theta = 1$
$$\sin^2 \theta = \frac{1}{4}$$
$$\sqrt{\sin^2 \theta} = \pm\sqrt{\frac{1}{4}}$$
$$\sin \theta = \pm\frac{1}{2}$$
$$\theta = \{30°, \ 150°, \ 210°, \ 330°\}$$

9.3 $\cot^2 \phi - 3 = 0$
$$\cot^2 \phi = 3$$
$$\sqrt{\cot^2 \phi} = \pm\sqrt{3}$$
$$\cot \phi = \pm\sqrt{3}$$
$$\phi = \{30°, \ 150°, \ 210°, \ 330°\}$$

9.4 $3 \tan^2 x = 1$
$$\tan^2 x = \frac{1}{3}$$
$$\sqrt{\tan^2 x} = \pm\sqrt{\frac{1}{3}}$$
$$\tan x = \pm\sqrt{\frac{1}{3}} = \pm\frac{\sqrt{3}}{3}$$
$$x = \{30°, \ 150°, \ 210°, \ 330°\}$$

9.5 $2 \sin^2 x - \cos^2 x = 2$
$$2 \sin^2 x - (1 - \sin^2 x) = 2$$
$$2 \sin^2 x - 1 + \sin^2 x = 2$$
$$3 \sin^2 x - 1 = 2$$
$$3 \sin^2 x = 3$$
$$\sin^2 x = 1$$
$$\sqrt{\sin^2 x} = \pm\sqrt{1}$$
$$\sin x = \pm 1$$
$$x = \{90°, \ 270°\}$$

9.6 $\sqrt{3} \tan \alpha = 1$
$$\tan \alpha = \frac{1}{\sqrt{3}} = \frac{\sqrt{3}}{3}$$
$$\alpha = \{30°, \ 210°\}$$

9.7 $\tan \theta - \cot \theta = 0$
$$\tan \theta - \frac{1}{\tan \theta} = 0$$
$$\frac{\tan^2 \theta}{\tan \theta} - \frac{1}{\tan \theta} = 0$$
$$\tan^2 \theta - 1 = 0$$
$$\tan^2 \theta = 1$$
$$\sqrt{\tan^2 \theta} = \pm\sqrt{1}$$
$$\tan \theta = \pm 1$$
$$\theta = \{45°, \ 135°, \ 225°, \ 315°\}$$

9.8 $3 \cot x + \sqrt{3} = 0$
$$3 \cot x = -\sqrt{3}$$
$$\cot x = -\frac{\sqrt{3}}{3}$$
$$x = \{120°, \ 300°\}$$

9.9
$$\sin^2 x - 7 \sin x = 0$$
$$\sin x(\sin x - 7) = 0$$

$$\sin x = 0 \qquad \text{or} \sin x = 7$$
$$x = \{0°, 180°, \quad \text{or} \quad x = \phi$$
$$360°\}$$

9.10
$$\tan^2 \beta = 4$$
$$\sqrt{\tan^2 \beta} = \pm\sqrt{4}$$
$$\tan \beta = \pm 2$$
$$\beta = \{63°, 117°, 243°,$$
$$297°\}$$

9.11
$$\cos 2\theta - \sin \theta = 0$$
$$1 - 2 \sin^2 \theta - \sin \theta = 0$$
$$2 \sin^2 \theta + \sin \theta - 1 = 0$$
$$(2 \sin \theta - 1)(\sin \theta + 1) = 0$$

$$2 \sin \theta - 1 = 0$$
$$2 \sin \theta = 1$$
$$\sin \theta = \frac{1}{2}$$
$$\theta = 30°$$
$$\theta = \{30°\}$$
or
$$\sin \theta + 1 = 0$$
$$\sin \theta = -1$$
$$\theta = 270°$$

9.12
$$\sin 2\theta + \sin \theta = 0$$
$$2 \sin \theta \cos \theta + \sin \theta = 0$$
$$\sin \theta(2 \cos \theta + 1) = 0$$

$$\sin \theta = 0 \qquad \text{or } 2 \cos \theta + 1 = 0$$
$$\theta = 0° \qquad\qquad 2 \cos \theta = -1$$
$$\theta = \{0°\} \text{ or} \qquad \cos \theta = -\frac{1}{2}$$
$$\theta = 120°$$

9.13
$$\sin 2\theta = \cos 2\theta$$
$$\frac{\sin 2\theta}{\cos 2\theta} = 1$$
$$\tan 2\theta = 1$$
$$2\theta = 45°$$
$$\theta = \{22\tfrac{1}{2}°\}$$

9.14
$$\tan \frac{\theta}{2} - \cos \theta = -1$$
$$\tan \frac{\theta}{2} = \cos \theta - 1$$
$$\sqrt{\frac{1 - \cos \theta}{1 + \cos \theta}} = \cos \theta - 1$$
$$\left(\sqrt{\frac{1 - \cos \theta}{1 + \cos \theta}}\right)^2 = (\cos \theta - 1)^2$$
$$\frac{1 - \cos \theta}{1 + \cos \theta} = \cos^2 \theta - 2 \cos \theta + 1$$
$$\frac{1 - \cos \theta}{1 + \cos \theta}(1 + \cos \theta) = (\cos^2 \theta - 2 \cos \theta + 1)(1 + \cos \theta)$$
$$1 - \cos \theta = \cos^2 \theta - 2 \cos \theta + 1 + \cos^3 \theta - 2 \cos^2 \theta + \cos \theta$$
$$\cancel{1} - \cancel{\cos \theta} = \cos^3 \theta - \cos^2 \theta - \cancel{\cos \theta} + \cancel{1}$$
$$0 = \cos^3 \theta - \cos^2 \theta$$
$$\cos^2 \theta(\cos \theta - 1) = 0$$

$$\cos^2 \theta = 0 \qquad \text{or } \cos \theta - 1 = 0$$
$$\sqrt{\cos^2 \theta} = \pm\sqrt{0} \qquad\qquad \cos \theta = 1$$
$$\cos \theta = 0 \qquad\qquad\qquad \theta = 0°$$
$$\theta = 90° \qquad \text{or}$$
$$\theta = \{0°, 90°\}$$

9.15

$$\csc^2 \theta = 4$$
$$\sqrt{\csc^2 \theta} = \pm\sqrt{4}$$
$$\csc \theta = \pm 2$$
$$\theta = \{30°\}$$

9.16

$$\cos 2x + \cos x = 0$$
$$2\cos^2 x - 1 + \cos x = 0$$
$$2\cos^2 x + \cos x - 1 = 0$$
$$(2\cos x - 1)(\cos x + 1) = 0$$

$$2\cos x - 1 = 0 \quad \text{or} \quad \cos x + 1 = 0$$
$$2\cos x = 1 \qquad\qquad \cos x = -1$$
$$\cos x = \frac{1}{2} \qquad\qquad x = \pi$$
$$x = \frac{\pi}{3}, \frac{5\pi}{3}$$
$$x = \{\frac{\pi}{3}, \pi, \frac{5\pi}{3}\}$$

9.17

$$\sin 2x - \cos x = 0$$
$$2\sin x \cos x - \cos x = 0$$
$$\cos x(2\sin x - 1) = 0$$

$$\cos x = 0 \quad \text{or} \quad 2\sin x - 1 = 0$$
$$x = \frac{\pi}{2}, \frac{3\pi}{2} \qquad 2\sin x = 1$$
$$x = \{\frac{\pi}{6}, \frac{\pi}{2} \qquad\qquad \sin x = \frac{1}{2}$$
$$\frac{5\pi}{6}, \frac{3\pi}{2}\} \qquad\qquad x = \frac{\pi}{6}, \frac{5\pi}{6}$$

9.18

$$\sin \frac{x}{2} = \tan \frac{x}{2}$$
$$\sin \frac{x}{2} = \frac{\sin \frac{x}{2}}{\cos \frac{x}{2}}$$
$$\sin \frac{x}{2} \cos \frac{x}{2} = \sin \frac{x}{2}$$
$$\sin \frac{x}{2} \cos \frac{x}{2} - \sin \frac{x}{2} = 0$$
$$\sin \frac{x}{2}(\cos \frac{x}{2} - 1) = 0$$

$$\sin \frac{x}{2} = 0 \qquad \text{or} \quad \cos \frac{x}{2} = 1$$
$$\frac{x}{2} = 0, \pi \qquad\qquad \frac{x}{2} = 0$$
$$x = 0, 2\pi \qquad\qquad x = 0$$
$$x = \{0, 2\pi\}$$

9.19

$$\cos x = \sin \frac{x}{2}$$
$$1 - 2\sin^2 \frac{x}{2} = \sin \frac{x}{2}$$
$$2\sin^2 \frac{x}{2} + \sin \frac{x}{2} - 1 = 0$$
$$(2\sin \frac{x}{2} - 1)(\sin \frac{x}{2} + 1) = 0$$

$$2\sin \frac{x}{2} - 1 = 0$$
$$2\sin \frac{x}{2} = 1$$
$$\sin \frac{x}{2} = \frac{1}{2}$$
$$\frac{x}{2} = \frac{\pi}{6}, \frac{5\pi}{6}$$
$$x = \frac{\pi}{3}, \frac{5\pi}{3}$$
$$x = \{\frac{\pi}{3}, \frac{5\pi}{3}\}$$
$$\text{or}$$
$$\sin \frac{x}{2} + 1 = 0$$
$$\sin \frac{x}{2} = -1$$
$$\frac{x}{2} = \frac{3\pi}{2}$$
$$x = 3\pi$$

9.20

$$\cos 2x = \cos^2 x - 1$$
$$2\cos^2 x - 1 = \cos^2 x - 1$$
$$\cos^2 x = 0$$
$$\cos x = 0$$
$$x = \{\frac{\pi}{2}, \frac{3\pi}{2}\}$$

MATHEMATICS 1206
SOLUTION KEY

I. SECTION ONE

1.1 $x = 4$
$y = 5$
$r = \sqrt{4^2 + 5^2}$
$\quad = \sqrt{16 + 25}$
$\quad = \sqrt{41}$

a. $\sin \theta = \dfrac{y}{r} = \dfrac{5}{\sqrt{41}} = \dfrac{5\sqrt{41}}{41}$

b. $\cos \theta = \dfrac{x}{r} = \dfrac{4}{\sqrt{41}} = \dfrac{4\sqrt{41}}{41}$

c. $\tan \theta = \dfrac{y}{x} = \dfrac{5}{4} = \dfrac{5}{4}$

1.2 $x = -5$
$y = -3$
$r = \sqrt{(-5)^2 + (-3)^2}$
$\quad = \sqrt{25 + 9}$
$\quad = \sqrt{34}$

a. $\sin \theta = \dfrac{y}{r} = \dfrac{-3}{\sqrt{34}} = -\dfrac{3\sqrt{34}}{34}$

b. $\cos \theta = \dfrac{x}{r} = \dfrac{-5}{\sqrt{34}} = -\dfrac{5\sqrt{34}}{34}$

c. $\tan \theta = \dfrac{y}{x} = \dfrac{-3}{-5} = \dfrac{3}{5}$

1.3 $x = 5$
$y = 5$
$r = \sqrt{5^2 + 5^2}$
$\quad = \sqrt{50}$
$\quad = 5\sqrt{2}$

a. $\sin \theta = \dfrac{y}{r} = \dfrac{5}{5\sqrt{2}} = \dfrac{1}{\sqrt{2}} = \dfrac{\sqrt{2}}{2}$

b. $\cos \theta = \dfrac{x}{r} = \dfrac{5}{5\sqrt{2}} = \dfrac{1}{\sqrt{2}} = \dfrac{\sqrt{2}}{2}$

c. $\tan \theta = \dfrac{y}{x} = \dfrac{5}{5} = 1$

1.4 $x = -4$
$y = 3$
$r = \sqrt{(-4)^2 + 3^2}$
$\quad = \sqrt{16 + 9}$
$\quad = \sqrt{25}$
$\quad = 5$

a. $\sin \theta = \dfrac{y}{r} = \dfrac{3}{5}$

b. $\cos \theta = \dfrac{x}{r} = \dfrac{-4}{5} = \dfrac{4}{5}$

c. $\tan \theta = \dfrac{y}{x} = \dfrac{3}{-4} = -\dfrac{3}{4}$

1.5 $x = 6$
$y = -5$
$r = \sqrt{6^2 + (-5)^2}$
$\quad = \sqrt{36 + 25}$
$\quad = \sqrt{61}$

a. $\sin \theta = \dfrac{y}{r} = \dfrac{-5}{\sqrt{61}} = -\dfrac{5\sqrt{61}}{61}$

b. $\cos \theta = \dfrac{x}{r} = \dfrac{6}{\sqrt{61}} = \dfrac{6\sqrt{61}}{61}$

c. $\tan \theta = \dfrac{y}{x} = \dfrac{-5}{5} = -\dfrac{5}{6}$

1.6 a.

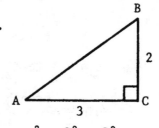

$c^2 = 3^2 + 2^2$
$c^2 = 9 + 4$
$c^2 = 13$
$\sqrt{c^2} = \sqrt{13}$
$\quad c = \sqrt{13} =$ approximately
$\qquad\qquad\qquad$ 3.6 or 4 (rounded)

$\tan \angle A = \dfrac{2}{3}$ or 0.6
$\quad \angle A = 34°$

$\angle B + \angle A = 90°$
$\quad \angle B = 90° - \angle A$
$\quad \angle B = 90° - 34°$
$\quad \angle B = 56°$

1.6 cont.

b.

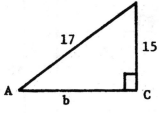

$$b^2 = 17^2 - 15^2$$
$$b^2 = 289 - 225$$
$$b^2 = 64$$
$$\sqrt{b^2} = \sqrt{64}$$
$$b = 8$$

$$\sin \angle A = \frac{15}{17} \text{ or } 0.882$$
$$\angle A = 62°$$

$$\angle B + \angle A = 90°$$
$$\angle B = 90° - \angle A$$
$$\angle B = 90° - 62°$$
$$\angle B = 28°$$

c.

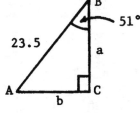

$$\angle A + 51° = 90°$$
$$\angle A = 90° - 51°$$
$$\angle A = 39°$$

$$\cos 51° = \frac{a}{23.5}$$
$$a = 23.5(\cos 51°)$$
$$a = 23.5(.629)$$
$$a = 15$$

$$\sin 51° = \frac{b}{23.5}$$
$$b = 23.5(\sin 51°)$$
$$b = 23.5(0.777)$$
$$b = 18$$

1.7

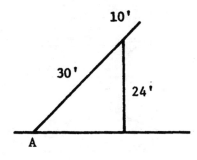

1.7 cont.

$$\sin \angle A = \frac{24}{30}$$
$$\sin \angle A = .8$$
$$\angle A = 53°$$

1.8

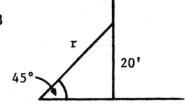

$$\sin 45° = \frac{20}{r}$$
$$r = \frac{20}{\sin 45°}$$
$$r = \frac{20}{\frac{\sqrt{2}}{2}}$$
$$r = \frac{40}{\sqrt{2}}$$
$$r = 28$$
$$r + 2 = 30 \text{ ft.}$$

1.9

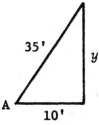

a.
$$y^2 = 35^2 - 10^2$$
$$y^2 = 1,225 - 100$$
$$y^2 = 1,125$$
$$\sqrt{y^2} = \sqrt{1,125}$$
$$y = 33.5 \text{ or } 34 \text{ ft.}$$
$$\text{(rounded)}$$

b.
$$\cos \angle A = \frac{10}{35}$$
$$\cos \angle A = .2857$$
$$\angle A = 73°$$

1.10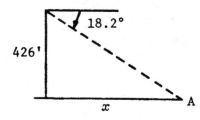

$$A = 18.2°$$
$$\cot A = \frac{x}{426}$$
$$x = 426 \cot 18.2°$$
$$x = 426(3.04)$$
$$x = 1{,}296 \text{ ft.}$$

1.11

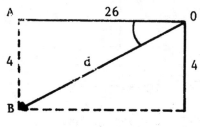

$$\tan \angle A = \frac{31.5}{618}$$
$$\tan \angle A = .0510$$
$$\angle A = 3°$$

1.12

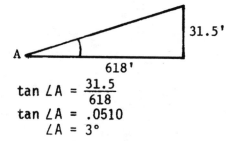

$$\tan \angle AOB = \frac{4}{26}$$
$$\tan \angle AOB = .1538$$
$$\angle AOB = 9°$$

a. direction is 9° south of 270° or 261° from north

b.
$$d^2 = 4^2 + 26^2$$
$$d^2 = 16 + 676$$
$$d^2 = 692$$
$$\sqrt{d^2} = \sqrt{692}$$
$$d = 26 \text{ mph}$$

1.13

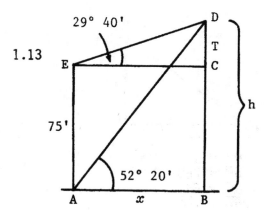

In △ECD:
$$\tan 29° 40' = \frac{T}{x}$$
$$x = \frac{T}{\tan 29° 40'}$$

In △ABD:
$$\tan 52° 20' = \frac{h}{x}$$
$$x = \frac{h}{\tan 52° 20'}$$

$$\therefore \frac{h}{\tan 52° 20'} = \frac{T}{\tan 29° 40'}$$

Also, T = h - 75;
$$\therefore \frac{h}{\tan 52° 20'} = \frac{h - 75}{\tan 29° 40'}$$

$$h \tan 29° 40' = (h - 75) \cdot (\tan 52° 20')$$
$$h \tan 29° 40' = h \tan 52° 20' - 75 \tan 52° 20'$$
$$h \tan 29° 40' - h \tan 52° 20' = -75 \tan 52° 20'$$
$$(\tan 29° 40' - \tan 52° 20')h = -75 \tan 52° 20'$$
$$h = \frac{-75 \tan 52° 20'}{\tan 29° 40' - \tan 52° 20'}$$
$$h = \frac{-75(1.295)}{.5696 - 1.295}$$
$$h = \frac{-75(1.295)}{-.7254}$$
$$h = \frac{-97.125}{-.7254}$$
$$h = 133.9 = 134 \text{ ft.}$$

1.14

1.14 cont.

$$\sin 12° \, 30' = \frac{y}{70}$$
$$y = 70(\sin 12° \, 30')$$
$$y = 70(.2164)$$
$$y = 15 \text{ ft.}$$

1.15

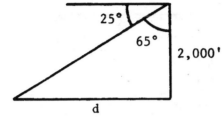

$$\tan 65° = \frac{d}{2,000}$$
$$d = 2,000(\tan 65°)$$
$$d = 2,000(2.145)$$
$$d = 4,289 \text{ ft.}$$

1.16

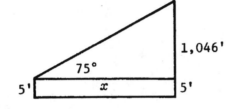

$$\cot 75° = \frac{x}{1,046}$$
$$x = 1,046 \cot 75°$$
$$x = 1,046(.268)$$
$$x = 280 \text{ ft.}$$

II. SECTION TWO

2.1

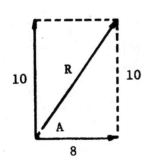

2.1 cont.

a. $R = \sqrt{8^2 + 10^2}$
   $R = \sqrt{64 + 100}$
   $R = \sqrt{164}$
   $R = 12.8$
   $R = 13$ lbs. (rounded)

b. $\tan \angle A = \frac{10}{8}$
   $\tan \angle A = 1.25$
   $\angle A = 51°$

   $\angle B = 90° - \angle A$
   $\angle B = 90° - 51°$
   $\angle B = 39°$

2.2

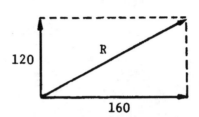

$R = \sqrt{120^2 + 160^2}$
$R = \sqrt{14,400 + 25,600}$
$R = \sqrt{40,000}$
$R = 200$ lbs.

2.3   a. $F_1^2 + F_2^2 = (5\sqrt{2})^2$ and
            $F_1 = F_2$

            $\therefore \; 2F_1^2 = 50$
            $F_1^2 = 25$
            $\sqrt{F_1^2} = \sqrt{25}$
            $F_1 = 5$

          b. $F_2 = F_1 = 5$

          c. $\sin \theta = \frac{5}{5\sqrt{2}} \quad \frac{1}{\sqrt{2}} \quad \frac{\sqrt{2}}{2}$
            $\theta = 45°$

          d. $\phi = 90° - \theta$
            $\phi = 90° - 45°$
            $\phi = 45°$

2.4

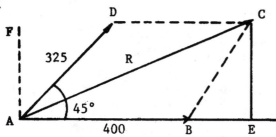

Draw $\overline{CE} \perp \overline{AE}$, then in
rt. $\triangle BEC$, $\angle CBE = 45°$
and $\overline{BE} = \overline{CE}$ and $\overline{BC} = 325$ lbs.

a. $(BE)^2 + (\overline{EC})^2 = 325^2$
$\qquad 2(\overline{EC})^2 = 325^2$
$\qquad\quad (\overline{EC})^2 = \dfrac{325^2}{2}$
$\qquad\quad (EC)^2 = \dfrac{105,625}{2}$
$\qquad\quad (EC)^2 = 52,812.5$
$\qquad \sqrt{(EC)^2} = \sqrt{52,812.5}$
$\qquad\qquad \overline{EC} = 230$ (rounded)

$R^2 = (\overrightarrow{AB} + \overline{BE})^2 + (\overline{CE})^2$
$R^2 = (400 + 230)^2 + 230^2$
$R^2 = 630^2 + 230^2$
$R^2 = 396,900 + 52,900$
$R^2 = 449,800$
$\sqrt{R^2} = \sqrt{449,800}$
$\quad R = 670.6 = 671$ lbs.
$\qquad\qquad$ (rounded)

b. Find $\angle EAC$ and $\angle FAC$.
$\tan \angle EAC = \dfrac{CE}{AE} = \dfrac{230}{630}$
$\tan \angle EAC = 0.365$
$\qquad \angle EAC = 20°$

$\angle DAC = 45° - 20°$
$\angle DAC = 25°$

2.5

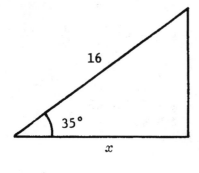

2.5 cont.

$\cos 35° = \dfrac{x}{16}$
$\qquad x = 16 \cos 35°$
$\qquad x = 16(.8192)$
$\qquad x = 13$ lbs.

2.6

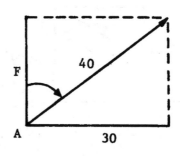

a. $F = \sqrt{40^2 - 30^2}$
$F = \sqrt{1,600 - 900}$
$F = \sqrt{700}$
$F = 26$ lbs. (rounded)

b. $\cos \angle A = \dfrac{F}{40}$

$\cos \angle A = \dfrac{26}{40}$

$\cos \angle A = .6500$
$\qquad \angle A = 49°$

2.7 a. $\angle DAB = 30°$
$\cos 30° = \dfrac{\overrightarrow{AD}}{10}$
$\overrightarrow{AD} = 10 \cos 30°$
$\overrightarrow{AD} = 10(.866)$
$F_1 = \overrightarrow{AD}$
$F_1 = 8.7 = 9$ lbs.
$\qquad\qquad$ (rounded)

b. $\angle ABC = 30°$
$\sin 30° = \dfrac{F_2}{10}$
$F_2 = 10 \sin 30°$
$F_2 = 10(\tfrac{1}{2})$
$F_2 = 5$ lbs.

174

2.8 a. $\sin 30° = \dfrac{\sqrt{3}}{R}$

$R = \dfrac{\sqrt{3}}{\sin 30°} = \dfrac{\sqrt{3}}{\frac{1}{2}} = 2\sqrt{3}$

$r = 3 \text{ (rounded)}$

b. $\cot 30° = \dfrac{\overrightarrow{AB}}{\sqrt{3}}$

$\overrightarrow{AB} = \sqrt{3}\,\cot 30°$
$\overrightarrow{AB} = \sqrt{3} \cdot \sqrt{3}$
$\overrightarrow{AB} = 3$

c. $\angle\phi = 90° - \angle CAB$
$\angle\phi = 90° - 30°$
$\angle\phi = 60°$

2.9

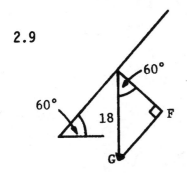

$\sin 60° = \dfrac{\overrightarrow{GF}}{18}$
$\overrightarrow{GF} = 18 \sin 60°$
$\overrightarrow{GF} = 18(.866)$
$\overrightarrow{GF} = 16 \text{ lbs.}$

2.10

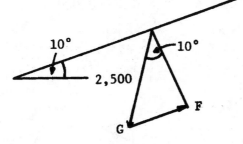

$\sin 10° = \dfrac{\overrightarrow{GF}}{2,500}$
$\overrightarrow{GF} = 2,500 \sin 10°$
$\overrightarrow{GF} = 2,500(.1736)$
$\overrightarrow{GF} = 434 \text{ lbs.}$

III. SECTION THREE

3.1

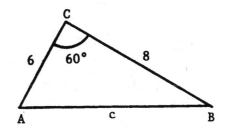

a. $c^2 = a^2 + b^2 - 2ab \cos C$
$c^2 = 8^2 + 6^2 - 2(8)(6)\cdot$
$\qquad \cos 60°$
$c^2 = 64 + 36 - 96(\tfrac{1}{2})$
$c^2 = 100 - 48 = 52$
$\sqrt{c^2} = \sqrt{52} = 2\sqrt{13}$
$c = 7.2$

b. $a^2 = b^2 + c^2 - 2bc \cos A$
$8^2 = 6^2 + (\sqrt{52})^2 -$
$\qquad 2(6)(\sqrt{52}) \cos A$
$64 = 36 + 52 - 12\sqrt{52} \cos A$
$64 = 88 - 12\sqrt{52} \cos A$
$-24 = -12\sqrt{52} \cos A$
$\cos A = \dfrac{24}{12\sqrt{52}}$
$\cos A = .2773$
$\angle A = 74°$

c. $\angle B = 180° - \angle A - \angle C$
$\angle B = 180° - 74° - 60°$
$\angle B = 180° - 134°$
$\angle B = 46°$

3.2

3.2 cont.

a. $b^2 = a^2 + c^2 - 2ac \cos B$
$b^2 = 9^2 + 5^2 - 2(9) \cdot$
   $(5) \cos 120°$
$b^2 = 81 + 25 - 90(-\frac{1}{2})$
$b^2 = 81 + 25 + 45$
$b^2 = 151$
$b = \sqrt{151}$
$b = 12.3$

b. $a^2 = b^2 + c^2 - 2bc \cos A$
$9^2 = 151 + 5^2 - 2(5) \cdot$
   $(\sqrt{151}) \cos A$
$81 = 25 + 151 - 10\sqrt{151} \cos A$
$-95 = -10\sqrt{151} \cos A$
$\cos A = \dfrac{95}{10\sqrt{151}}$
$\cos A = .7730$
$\angle A = 39°$

c. $\angle C = 180° - \angle A - \angle B$
$\angle C = 180° - \angle A - 120°$
$\angle C = 180° - 39° - 120°$
$\angle C = 60° - 39°$
$\angle C = 21°$

3.3

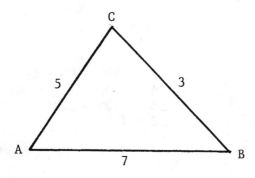

a. $a^2 = b^2 + c^2 - 2bc \cos A$
$3^2 = 5^2 + 7^2 - 2(5)(7) \cos A$
$9 = 25 + 49 - 70 \cos A$
$-65 = -70 \cos A$
$\cos A = \dfrac{65}{70}$
$\cos A = .9286$
$\angle A = 22°$

3.3 cont.

b. $b^2 = a^2 + c^2 - 2ac \cos B$
$5^2 = 3^2 + 7^2 - 2(3) \cdot$
   $(7) \cos B$
$25 = 9 + 49 - 42 \cos B$
$25 = 58 - 42 \cos B$
$-33 = -42 \cos B$
$\cos B = \dfrac{33}{42}$
$\cos B = .7857$
$\angle B = 38°$

c. $\angle C = 180° - \angle A - \angle B$
$\angle C = 180° - 22° - 38°$
$\angle C = 180° - 60°$
$\angle C = 120°$

3.4

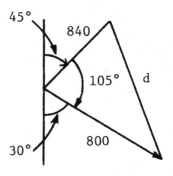

$d^2 = 840^2 + 800^2 - 2(840) \cdot$
   $(800)\cos 105°$
$d^2 = 705,600 + 640,000 -$
   $1,344,000(-.2588)$
$d^2 = 705,600 + 640,000 +$
   $347,827.2$
$d^2 = 1,693,427.2$
$\sqrt{d^2} = \sqrt{1,693,427.2}$
$d = 1,301.3$ mi. (rounded)

3.5

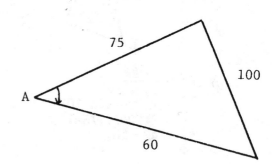

3.5 cont.

$$100^2 = 75^2 + 60^2 - 2(75) \cdot (60)\cos A$$
$$10,000 = 5,625 + 3,600 - 9,000 \cos A$$
$$9,000 \cos A = -775$$
$$\cos A = \frac{-775}{9,000}$$
$$\cos A = -.0861$$
$$\angle A = 180° - 85°$$
$$\angle A = 95°$$

IV. SECTION FOUR

4.1

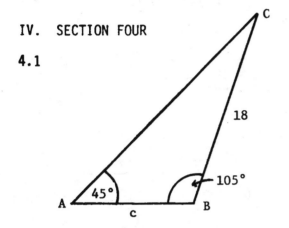

$$\angle C = 180° - 105° - 45°$$
$$\angle C = 180° - 150°$$
$$\angle C = 30°$$

$$\frac{c}{\sin 30°} = \frac{18}{\sin 45°}$$
$$c = \frac{18 \sin 30°}{\sin 45°}$$
$$c = \frac{18 \cdot \tfrac{1}{2}}{\frac{\sqrt{2}}{2}}$$
$$c = \frac{18}{\sqrt{2}}$$
$$c = \frac{18\sqrt{2}}{2}$$
$$c = 9\sqrt{2}$$

4.2

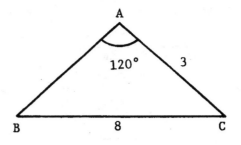

$$\frac{3}{\sin B} = \frac{8}{\sin 120°}$$
$$8 \sin B = 3 \sin 120°$$
$$\sin B = \frac{3 \sin 60°}{8}$$
$$\sin B = \frac{3(\frac{\sqrt{3}}{2})}{8}$$
$$\sin B = \frac{3\sqrt{3}}{16}$$
$$\sin B = .3248$$
$$\angle B = 19°$$

4.3

a. $\angle A = 180° - 48° - 62°$
   $\angle A = 180° - 110°$
   $\angle A = 70°$

b. $\dfrac{b}{\sin 62°} = \dfrac{18.2}{\sin 70°}$
   $b = \dfrac{18.2 \sin 62°}{\sin 70°}$
   $b = \dfrac{18.2(.8829)}{.9397}$
   $b = 17.1$ or 17 (rounded)

4.3 cont.

c. $\dfrac{c}{\sin 48°} = \dfrac{18.2}{\sin 70°}$

$c = \dfrac{18.2 \sin 48°}{\sin 70°}$

$c = \dfrac{18.2(.7431)}{.9397}$

$c = 14.39$ or 14 rounded

4.4

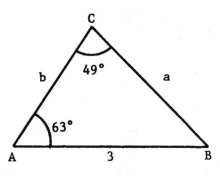

a. $\angle B = 180° - 49° - 63°$
$\angle B = 180° - 112°$
$\angle B = 68°$

b. $\dfrac{a}{\sin 63°} = \dfrac{3}{\sin 49°}$

$a = \dfrac{3 \sin 63°}{\sin 49°}$

$a = \dfrac{3(.8910)}{.7547}$

$a = 3.5$ or 4 (rounded)

c. $\dfrac{b}{\sin 68°} = \dfrac{3}{\sin 49°}$

$b = \dfrac{3 \sin 68°}{\sin 49°}$

$b = \dfrac{3(.9272)}{.7547}$

$b = 3.68$ or 4 (rounded)

4.5

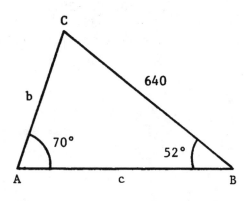

4.5 cont.

a. $\dfrac{b}{\sin 52°} = \dfrac{640}{\sin 70°}$

$b = \dfrac{640 \sin 52°}{\sin 70°}$

$b = \dfrac{640(.7880)}{.9397}$

$b = 537$

b. $\dfrac{c}{\sin 58°} = \dfrac{640}{\sin 70°}$

$c = \dfrac{640 \sin 58°}{\sin 70°}$

$c = \dfrac{640(8480)}{.9397}$

$c = 578$

c. $\angle C = 180° - 70° - 52°$
$\angle C = 180° - 122°$
$\angle C = 58°$

4.6

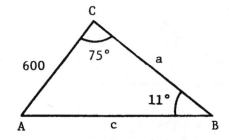

a. $\angle A = 180° - 75° - 11°$
$\angle A = 180° - 86°$
$\angle A = 94°$

b. $\dfrac{a}{\sin 94°} = \dfrac{600}{\sin 11°}$

$a = \dfrac{600 \sin 94°}{\sin 11°}$

$a = \dfrac{600 \sin 86°}{\sin 11°}$

$a = \dfrac{600(.9976)}{.1908}$

$a = 3,137$ or $3,140$
(rounded)

c. $\dfrac{c}{\sin 75°} = \dfrac{600}{\sin 11°}$

$c = \dfrac{600 \sin 75°}{\sin 11°}$

$c = \dfrac{600(.9659)}{.1908}$

$c = 3,037$ or $3,040$
(rounded)

4.7

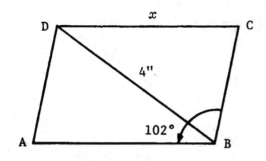

Note: $\overline{DB}$ bisects $\angle ADC$ and $\angle ABC$; therefore, $\angle DBC = \angle BDC = 51°$ and $\overline{DC} = \overline{BC}$; also, $\angle C = 180° - 102° = 78°$.

$$\frac{4}{\sin 78°} = \frac{x}{\sin 51°}$$
$$x = \frac{4 \sin 51°}{\sin 78°}$$
$$x = \frac{4(.7771)}{.9781}$$
$$x = 3.178 \text{ or } 3 \text{ in.}$$
$$\text{(rounded)}$$

4.8

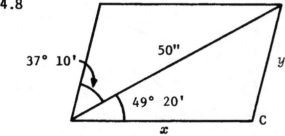

$\angle C = 180° - 37° 10' - 49° 20'$
$\angle C = 180° - 86° 30'$
$\angle C = 93° 30'$

a. $\frac{50}{\sin C} = \frac{x}{\sin 37° 10'}$

$x = \frac{50 \sin 37° 10'}{\sin C}$

$x = \frac{50 \sin 37° 10'}{\sin 93° 30'}$

$x = \frac{50(.6040)}{.9981}$

$x = 30 \text{ in. (rounded)}$

4.8 cont.

b. $\frac{50}{\sin C} = \frac{y}{\sin 49° 20'}$

$y = \frac{50 \sin 49° 20'}{\sin C}$

$y = \frac{50 \sin 49° 20'}{\sin 93° 30'}$

$y = \frac{50(.7585)}{.9981}$

$y = 38 \text{ in. (rounded)}$

V. SECTION FIVE

5.1

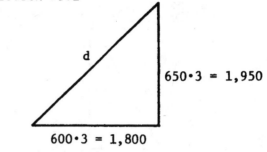

$d^2 = 1{,}800^2 + 1{,}950^2$
$d^2 = 3{,}240{,}000 + 3{,}802{,}500$
$d^2 = 7{,}042{,}500$
$\sqrt{d^2} = \sqrt{7{,}042{,}500}$
$d = 2{,}654 \text{ nautical miles}$

5.2

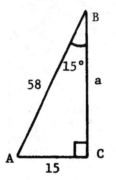

a. $\cos 15° = \frac{a}{58}$
$a = 58 \cos 15°$
$a = 58(.9659)$
$a = 56$

b. $\angle A = 180° - 90° - 15°$
$\angle A = 180° - 105°$
$\angle A = 75°$

5.3

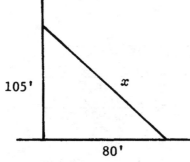

$$x^2 = 80^2 + 105^2$$
$$x^2 = 6,400 + 11,025$$
$$x^2 = 17,425$$
$$\sqrt{x^2} = \sqrt{17,425}$$
$$x = 132 \text{ ft.}$$

5.4

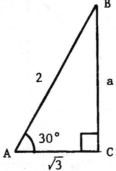

$$\sin 30° = \frac{a}{2}$$
$$a = 2 \sin 30°$$
$$a = 2(\tfrac{1}{2})$$
$$a = 1$$

5.5

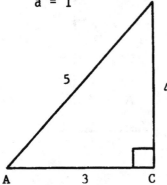

$$\tan \angle A = \frac{4}{3}$$
$$\tan \angle A = 1.333$$
$$\angle A = 53°$$

$$\angle B = 90° - \angle A$$
$$\angle B = 90° - 53°$$
$$\angle B = 37°$$

$\angle C = 90°$ because $3^2 + 4^2 = 5^2$

5.6

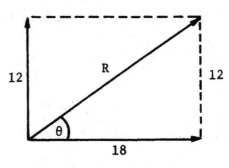

a. $\tan \theta = \frac{12}{18} = \frac{2}{3}$

   $\tan \theta = .666$

   $\theta = 34°$

b. $R^2 = 12^2 + 18^2$

   $R^2 = 144 + 324$

   $R^2 = 468$

   $\sqrt{R^2} = \sqrt{468}$

   $R = 22$ ft. per sec.

   (rounded)

5.7

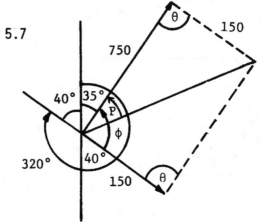

$$\angle \phi = 180° - 35° - 40°$$
$$\angle \phi = 180° - 75°$$
$$\angle \phi = 105°$$

$$\angle \theta = 180° - \angle \phi$$
$$\angle \theta = 180° - 105°$$
$$\angle \theta = 75°$$

Note: Compute R first (b).

a. $\dfrac{150}{\sin \angle P} = \dfrac{R}{\sin 75°}$

   $\dfrac{150}{\sin \angle P} = \dfrac{726}{\sin 75°}$

   $\sin \angle P = \dfrac{150 \sin 75°}{726}$

   $\sin \angle P = \dfrac{150(.9659)}{726}$

   $\sin \angle P = .1996$

   $\angle P = 11° \ 30'$

5.7 cont.

Direction of R = 35° + 11° 30'
= 46° 30' or 47°
(rounded)

b. $R^2 = 150^2 + 750^2 - 2(150) \cdot$
$(750) \cos 75°$
$R^2 = 22,500 + 562,500 -$
$225,000(.2588)$
$R^2 = 22,500 + 562,500 -$
$58,230$
$R^2 = 526,770$
$\sqrt{R^2} = \sqrt{526,770}$
$R = 726$ lbs.

5.8

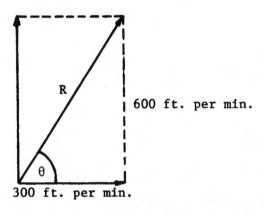

600 ft. per min.

300 ft. per min.

a. $\tan \theta = \dfrac{600}{300}$
$\tan \theta = 2$
$\theta = 63° 25'$ or $63°$
(rounded)

b. $R^2 = 600^2 + 300^2$
$R^2 = 360,000 + 90,000$
$R^2 = 450,000$
$\sqrt{R^2} = \sqrt{450,000}$
$R = 671$ ft. (rounded)

5.9

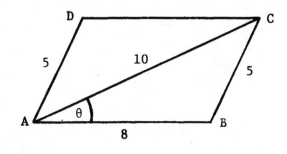

5.9 cont.

a. $\angle DAB = 180° - \angle ABC$
$10^2 = 8^2 + 5^2 - 2(8) \cdot$
$(5) \cos \angle ABC$
$100 = 64 + 25 - 80 \cos \angle ABC$
$100 = 89 - 80 \cos \angle ABC$
$11 = -80 \cos \angle ABC$

$\cos \angle ABC = -\dfrac{11}{80}$
$\cos \angle ABC = -.1375$
$\angle ABC = 98°$

$\angle DAB = 180° - 98°$
$\angle DAB = 82°$

b. $\angle CAB = \theta$
$\dfrac{5}{\sin \theta} = \dfrac{10}{\sin \angle ABC}$
$\sin \theta = \dfrac{5(.9902)}{10}$
$\sin \theta = .4951$
$\theta = 29° 36'$ or $30°$
(rounded)

5.10

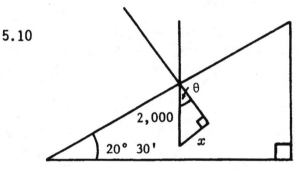

$\theta = 20° 30'$

$\sin \theta = \dfrac{x}{2,000}$
$x = 2,000 \sin 20° 30'$
$x = 2,000(.3502)$
$x = 700.4$ or 700 lbs.
(rounded)

5.11

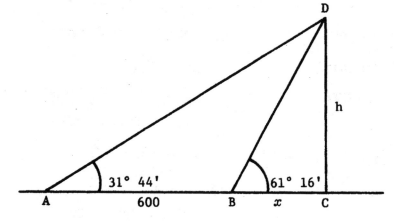

Let $x = \overline{BC}$.

$\cos 61° \ 16' = \dfrac{x}{h}$

$\qquad x = h \cot 61° \ 16'$

Also, $\cot 31° \ 44' = \dfrac{600 + x}{h}$

$\quad h \cot 31° \ 44' = 600 + x$

$\qquad\qquad x = h \cot 31° \ 44'$
$\qquad\qquad\qquad - 600$

Therefore,

$\qquad\qquad h \cot 61° \ 16' = h \cot 31° \ 44' - 600$

$h \cot 31° \ 44' - h \cot 61° \ 16' = 600$
$(\cot 31° \ 44' - \cot 61° \ 16')h = 600$

$\qquad\qquad h = \dfrac{600}{\cot 31° \ 44' - \cot 61° \ 16'}$

$\qquad\qquad h = \dfrac{600}{1.62 - .55}$

$\qquad\qquad h = \dfrac{600}{1.07}$

$\qquad\qquad h = 561$ ft. (rounded)

5.12

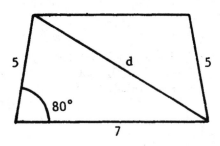

$d^2 = 5^2 + 7^2 - 2(5)(7)\cos 80°$
$d^2 = 25 + 49 - 70 \cos 80°$
$d^2 = 74 - 70(.1736)$
$d^2 = 74 - 12.16$
$d^2 = 61.84$
$\sqrt{d^2} = \sqrt{61.84}$
$\quad d = 7.86$ or 8 (rounded)

5.13

a. $\tan \theta = \dfrac{6}{5} = 1.2$

$\qquad\quad \theta = 50° \ 12'$

b. $\theta = 50°$

182

5.13 cont.

c. $d^2 = 5^2 + 6^2$
   $d^2 = 25 + 36$
   $d^2 = 61$
   $\sqrt{d^2} = \sqrt{61}$
   $d = \sqrt{61}$ mph
   $d = 7.8$ mph

d. $d = 8$ mph

5.14

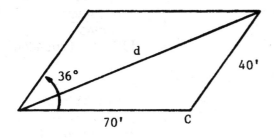

$\angle C = 180° - 36°$
$\angle C = 144°$

$d^2 = 70^2 + 40^2 - 2(70) \cdot$
    $(40)\cos 144°$
$d^2 = 4,900 + 1,600 -$
    $5,600(-.809)$
$d^2 = 4,900 + 1,600 + 4,530$
$d^2 = 11,030$
$\sqrt{d^2} = \sqrt{11,030}$
$d = 105$ ft. (rounded)

5.15

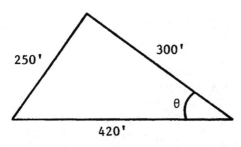

The smallest angle of a triangle lies opposite the smallest side.

$250^2 = 420^2 + 300^2 - 2(420) \cdot$
    $(300)\cos \theta$
$62,500 = 90,000 + 176,400 -$
    $252,000 \cos \theta$
$62,500 = 266,400 - 252,000 \cos \theta$
$-203,900 = -252,000 \cos \theta$
$\cos \theta = \dfrac{203,900}{252,000}$
$\cos \theta = .8091$
$\theta = 36°$

5.16

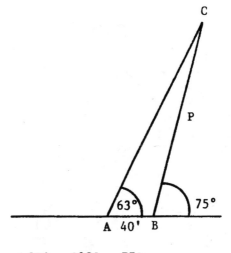

$\angle ABC = 180° - 75°$
$\angle ABC = 105°$

$\angle C = 180° - 63° - 105°$
$\angle C = 180° - 168°$
$\angle C = 12°$

$\dfrac{40}{\sin 12°} = \dfrac{P}{\sin 63°}$

$P = \dfrac{40 \sin 63°}{\sin 12°}$

$P = \dfrac{40(.8910)}{.2079}$

$P = 171$ ft. (rounded)

5.17

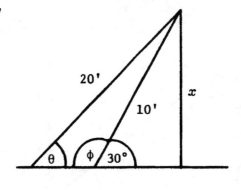

$\angle \phi = 180° - 30°$
$\angle \phi = 150°$

$\dfrac{20}{\sin 150°} = \dfrac{10}{\sin \theta}$

$\sin \theta = \dfrac{10 \sin 150°}{20}$

$\sin \theta = \dfrac{1}{2} \sin 30°$

$\sin \theta = \dfrac{1}{2}(\dfrac{1}{2})$

$\sin \theta = \dfrac{1}{4} = .25$

$\theta = 14°$

5.18

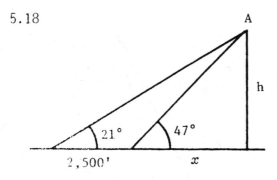

$$\cot 21° = \frac{2{,}500 + x}{h}$$

$$2{,}500 + x = h \cot 21°$$

$$x = h \cot 21° - 2{,}500$$

Also, $\cot 47° = \frac{x}{h}$ or

$$x = h \cot 47°$$

Therefore,

$h \cot 21° -$
$\quad 2{,}500 = h \cot 47°$

$h \cot 21° -$
$\quad h \cot 47° = 2{,}500$

$(\cot 21° -$
$\quad \cot 47°)h = 2{,}500$

$$h = \frac{2{,}500}{\cot 21° - \cot 47°}$$

$$h = \frac{2{,}500}{2.6 - .9}$$

$$h = \frac{2{,}500}{1.7}$$

$$h = 1{,}470 \text{ ft. (rounded)}$$

5.19

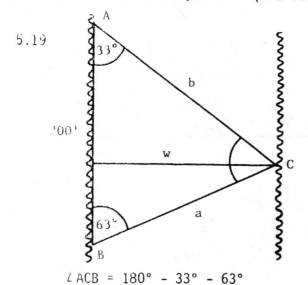

$\angle ACB = 180° - 33° - 63°$
$\angle ACB = 180° - 96°$
$\angle ACB = 84°$

5.19 cont.

a. $\dfrac{200}{\sin 84°} = \dfrac{b}{\sin 63°}$

$\quad b = \dfrac{200 \sin 63°}{\sin 84°}$

$\quad b = \dfrac{200(.8910)}{.9945}$

$\quad b = 179 \text{ ft. (rounded)}$

b. $\dfrac{200}{\sin 84°} = \dfrac{a}{\sin 33°}$

$\quad a = \dfrac{200 \sin 33°}{\sin 84°}$

$\quad a = \dfrac{200(.5446)}{.9945}$

$\quad a = 110 \text{ ft. (rounded)}$

c. $\sin 33° = \dfrac{w}{b}$

$\quad w = b \sin 33°$

$\quad w = (179)(.5446)$

$\quad w = 97.4 \text{ or } 97 \text{ ft.}$
$\quad\quad\quad \text{(rounded)}$

5.20

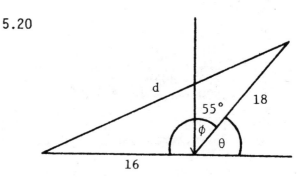

$\angle \theta = 90° - 55°$
$\angle \theta = 35°$

$\angle \phi = 180° - 35°$
$\angle \phi = 145°$

$d^2 = 16^2 + 18^2 - 2(16) \cdot$
$\quad\quad (18)\cos 145°$

$d^2 = 256 + 324 - 576(-.8192)$
$d^2 = 580 + 472$
$d^2 = 1052$
$d = 32.7 \text{ or } 33 \text{ na. mi. (rounded)}$
$\sqrt{d^2} = \sqrt{1052}$
$d = 32.4 \text{ or } 33 \text{ na. mi. (rounded)}$

VI. SECTION SIX

6.1

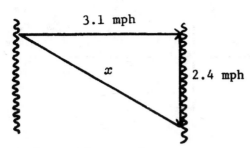

$x^2 = 3.1^2 + 2.4^2$
$x^2 = 9.61 + 5.76$
$x^2 = 15.37$
$\sqrt{x^2} = \sqrt{15.37}$
$x \doteq 3.92$ mph

6.2

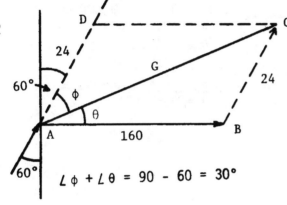

$\angle \phi + \angle \theta = 90 - 60 = 30°$

a. $\angle B = 150°$

$G^2 = 24^2 + 160^2 - 2(24) \cdot$
$\qquad (160)\cos 150°$
$G^2 = 576 + 25,600 -$
$\qquad 7,680(-.866)$
$G^2 = 576 + 25,600 + 6,651$
$G^2 = 32,827$
$\sqrt{G^2} = \sqrt{32,827}$
$G \doteq 181.18$ knots

b. $\dfrac{181}{\sin 150°} = \dfrac{24}{\sin \theta}$

$\sin \theta = \dfrac{24 \sin 150°}{181}$

$\sin \theta = \dfrac{24(.5)}{181}$

$\theta = 3.8°$
$\phi = 90° - 60° - 3.8°$
$\phi = 90° - 63.8°$
$\phi = 26.2°$
Direction of G $= 60° + 26.2°$
$\qquad\qquad\quad = 86.2°$ or $86°$

6.3

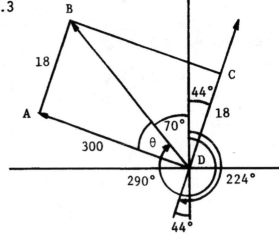

$\angle BDC = 70° + 44° = 114°$
$\angle ABD = \quad BDC = 114°$

$\dfrac{300}{\sin 114°} = \dfrac{18}{\sin \theta}$

$\sin \theta = \dfrac{18 \sin 114°}{300}$

$\sin \theta = \dfrac{18(.9135)}{300}$

$\sin \theta = .0548$
$\theta = 3.14°$ or $3° 8'$

6.4

$\angle C = 180° - 47° - 90°$
$\angle C = 180° - 137°$
$\angle C = 43°$

$\angle A = 90°$

$\angle B = 47°$

$\triangle ABC$ is rt. $\triangle$

185

6.4 cont.

a. $\cot 43° = \dfrac{b}{1}$

$b = 1.07$
$b = 1.1$ na. mi.
(rounded)

b. $\csc 43° = \dfrac{a}{1}$

$a = 1.46$
$a = 1.5$ na. mi.
(rounded)

6.5

$\angle AOB = 180° - 45° - 30°$
$\angle AOB = 180° - 75°$
$\angle AOB = 105°$

$d^2 = 840^2 + 800^2 - 2(840) \cdot$
$\quad\quad (800)\cos 105°$
$d^2 = 705,600 + 640,000 +$
$\quad\quad 1,344,000(.2588)$
$d^2 = 1,345,600 + 347,827.2$
$d^2 = 1,693,427.2$
$\sqrt{d^2} = \sqrt{1,693,427.2}$
$d = 1,301.3$ or $1,301$ mi.
$\quad\quad\quad$ (rounded)

6.6

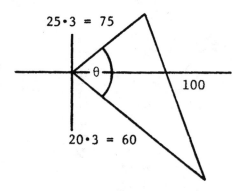

$100^2 = 75^2 + 60^2 - 2(75) \cdot$
$\quad\quad (60)\cos \theta$
$10,000 = 5,625 + 3,600 -$
$\quad\quad 9,000 \cos \theta$
$10,000 = 9,225 - 9,000 \cos \theta$
$775 = -9,000 \cos \theta$
$\cos \theta = -\dfrac{775}{9,000}$
$\cos \theta = -.0861$
$\theta = 180° - 85°$
$\theta = 95°$

MATHEMATICS 1207
SOLUTION KEY

I. SECTION ONE

1.1 $y = \arcsin 1$, $\sin y = 1$,
$y = \frac{\pi}{2} \pm 2\pi K$

1.2 $y = \arcsin \frac{1}{2}$, $\sin y = \frac{1}{2}$,
$y = \frac{\pi}{6} \pm 2\pi K$ or $\frac{5\pi}{6} \pm 2\pi K$

1.3 $y = \arcsin 0$, $\sin y = 0$,
$y = \pm \pi K$

1.4 $y = \arcsin(0.6428)$, $\sin y = 0.6428$,
$y = 40° \pm 360°K$ or $140° \pm 360°K$

1.5 $y = \arcsin(0.9659)$, $\sin y = 0.9659$, $y = 75° \pm 360°K$ or $105° \pm 360°K$

1.6 $y = \arcsin 1.2$, $\sin y = 1.2$,
$y = \phi$ (no solution)

1.7 $y = \arcsin \frac{1}{2}$, $\sin y = \frac{1}{2}$, $y = \frac{\pi}{6}$

1.8 $y = \arcsin \frac{\sqrt{3}}{2}$, $\sin y = \frac{\sqrt{3}}{2}$,
$y = \frac{\pi}{3}$

1.9 $y = \arcsin(0.6947)$, $\sin y = 0.6947$, $y = 44°$

1.10 $y = \arcsin(0.7071)$, $\sin y = 0.7071$, $y = \frac{\pi}{4}$ or $45°$

1.11 Let $y = \arcsin x$ where $x = \sin 40°$.
Then $x = \sin y$ and $\sin 40° = \sin y$.
$\therefore y = 40°$

1.12 Let $y = \arcsin x$ where $x = \sin 60°$.
Then $x = \sin y$ and $\sin 60° = \sin y$.
$\therefore y = 60°$

1.13 Let $y = \arcsin x$ where $x = \sin \frac{\pi}{2}$.
Then $x = \sin y$ and $\sin \frac{\pi}{2} = \sin y$.
$\therefore y = \frac{\pi}{2}$ or $90°$

1.14 Let $y = \arcsin x$ where $x = \sin 6\pi$.
Then $x = \sin y$ and $\sin 6\pi = \sin y$.
$\therefore y = 6\pi = 0°$

1.15 Let $y = \arcsin x$ where $x = \sin \left(-\frac{3\pi}{2}\right)$.
Then $x = \sin y$ and $\sin \left(-\frac{3\pi}{2}\right) = \sin y$.
$\therefore y = -\frac{3\pi}{2}$

II. SECTION TWO

2.1 $y = \cos^{-1}(1)$, $\cos y = 1$,
$y = \pm 2\pi K$

2.2 $y = \arccos \left(\frac{\sqrt{3}}{2}\right)$, $\cos y = \frac{\sqrt{3}}{2}$, $y = \pm \frac{\pi}{6} \pm 2\pi K$

2.3 $y = \arccos \left(\frac{1}{2}\right)$, $\cos y = \frac{1}{2}$,
$y = \pm \frac{\pi}{3} \pm 2\pi K$

2.4 $y = \cos^{-1}(0.8480)$, $\cos y = 0.8480$, $y = \pm 32° \pm 2\pi K$

2.5 $\cos(F(x)) = 0.5299$,
$F(x) = \pm 58° \pm 2\pi K$

2.6 $\cos y = \frac{1}{2}$,

   $y = 60°$ or $\frac{\pi}{3}$

2.7 $\cos y = \frac{\sqrt{3}}{2}$,

   $y = 30°$ or $\frac{\pi}{6}$

2.8 $y = \cos^{-1}(-1)$, $\cos y = -1$,
   $y = \pi$

2.9 $y = \cos^{-1}(-\frac{\sqrt{2}}{2})$, $\cos y = -\frac{\sqrt{2}}{2}$

   $y = \frac{3\pi}{4}$

2.10 $y = \cos^{-1}(0.3420)$, $\cos y = 0.3420$, $y = 70°$

2.11   Let $x = \arccos(\cos 50°)$.
   Then $\cos x = \cos 50°$ and $x = 50°$.

2.12   Let $x = \arccos(\cos \frac{\pi}{4})$.

   Then $\cos x = \cos \frac{\pi}{4}$ and $x = \frac{\pi}{4}$.

2.13   Let $x = \arcsin(-\frac{\sqrt{2}}{2})$.

   Then $\sin x = -\frac{\sqrt{2}}{2}$ and $x = \frac{5\pi}{4}$ or

   $\frac{7\pi}{4}$. Then $\cos \frac{5\pi}{4} = -\frac{\sqrt{2}}{2}$ and

   $\cos \frac{7\pi}{4} = \frac{\sqrt{2}}{2}$.

2.14   Let $x = \arcsin \frac{3}{5}$; find $\cos 2x$.

   $\sin x = \frac{3}{5}$.
   $\cos 2x = 2\cos^2 x - 1$
   $= 2 \cdot (\frac{4}{5})^2 - 1$

   $= 2 \cdot \frac{16}{25} - 1$

   $= \frac{32}{25} - \frac{25}{25}$

   $= \frac{7}{25}$

2.14 cont.

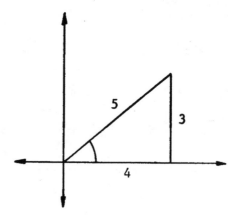

2.15   Let $\theta = \arcsin \frac{3}{5}$, $\phi =$

   $\arcsin \frac{15}{17}$, and $\alpha = \arcsin \frac{84}{85}$.

   If $\arcsin \frac{3}{5} + \arcsin \frac{15}{17} =$

   $\arccos(-\frac{13}{85})$, then $\sin(\arcsin \frac{3}{5} +$

   $\arcsin \frac{15}{17}) = \sin(\arccos(-\frac{13}{85}))$

   and $\sin(\theta + \phi) = \sin \alpha$.

   $\sin(\theta + \phi) = \sin(\arcsin \frac{3}{5}) \cdot$

   $\cos(\arcsin \frac{15}{17}) + \cos(\arcsin \frac{3}{5}) \cdot$

   $\sin(\arcsin \frac{15}{17})$

   $= \frac{3}{5} \cdot \frac{8}{17} + \frac{4}{5} \cdot \frac{15}{17}$

   $= \frac{24}{85} + \frac{60}{85}$

   $= \frac{84}{85}$

III.   SECTION THREE

3.1   Let $y = \arctan(-1)$.
   Then $\tan y = -1$, $y = \frac{3\pi}{4} \pm$

   $2\pi K$ or $\frac{7\pi}{4} \pm 2\pi K$.

3.2　Let $y = \arctan(\sqrt{3})$.

Then $\tan y = \sqrt{3}$, $y = \frac{\pi}{3} \pm 2\pi K$ or $\frac{4\pi}{3} \pm 2\pi K$.

3.3　Let $y = \arctan(0.7002)$.
Then $\tan y = 0.7002$, $y = 35° \pm 360°K$ or $215° \pm 360°K$.

3.4　Let $y = \arctan 5$; then $\tan y = 5$.

3.5　Let $y = \arctan \frac{1}{3}$; then $\tan y = \frac{1}{3}$.

3.6　Let $y = \arctan \frac{1}{3}$; find $\tan 2y$.

$\tan y = \frac{1}{3}$

$\tan 2y = \dfrac{2 \tan y}{1 - \tan^2 y} = \dfrac{2 \cdot \frac{1}{3}}{1 - (\frac{1}{3})^2} = \dfrac{\frac{2}{3}}{1 - \frac{1}{9}} = \dfrac{6}{8} = \dfrac{3}{4}$

3.7　Let $x = \arctan(1)$; find $\tan \frac{1}{2}x$.

$\tan x = 1$

$\tan \frac{1}{2}x = \sqrt{\dfrac{1 - \cos x}{1 + \cos x}}$

$= \sqrt{\dfrac{1 - \frac{\sqrt{2}}{2}}{1 + \frac{\sqrt{2}}{2}}}$

$= \sqrt{\dfrac{2 - \sqrt{2}}{2 + \sqrt{2}}}$

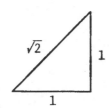

3.8　Let $x = \arctan \frac{1}{3}$ and $y = \arctan \frac{2}{3}$.
Then $\tan x = \frac{1}{3}$ and $\tan y = \frac{2}{3}$.

$x = 18°\ 26'$　　$y = 33°\ 41'$
　(approx.)　　approx.)

3.8 cont.

$x + y = 18°\ 26' + 33°\ 41'$
　　　$= 52°\ 7'$

3.9　Let $x = \arctan 5$ and $y = \arctan 6$.
Then $\tan x = 5$ and $\tan y = 6$.
　　　$x = 78°\ 40'$　$y = 80°\ 33'$

$x + y = 78°\ 40' + 80°\ 33'$
　　　$= 159°\ 13'$

3.10　Let $x = \arctan \frac{4}{7}$ and $y = \arctan \frac{7}{4}$.

Then $\tan x = \frac{4}{7}$ and $\tan y = \frac{7}{4}$.

Since $\frac{4}{7}$ and $\frac{7}{4}$ are reciprocals

of each other, $x + y = 90°$ or $\frac{\pi}{2}$

(see diagram).

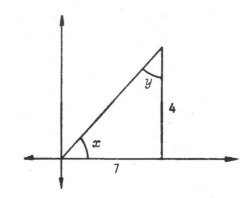

IV.　SECTION FOUR

4.1　$y = \text{arccsc } 2$; then $\csc y = 2$
and $y = \frac{\pi}{6} \pm 2\pi K$ or $\frac{5\pi}{6} \pm 2\pi K$

4.2　$y = \text{arcsec } 1$; then $\sec y = 1$
and $y = \pm 2\pi K$

4.3　$y = \text{arccot } 1$; then $\cot y = 1$
and $y = \frac{\pi}{4} \pm 2\pi K$ or $\frac{5\pi}{4} \pm 2\pi K$

4.4 $y = \text{arcsec}\ (-1)$; then $\sec y = -1$ and $y = \pi \pm 2\pi K$

4.5 $y = \sec^{-1}(\frac{1}{2})$; then $\sec y = \frac{1}{2}$; no solution since $\sec y > 1$ or $\sec y < -1$

4.6 Domain: $x \geq 1$ or $x \leq -1$
Range: $y \neq \frac{\pi}{2} \pm \pi K$

4.7 Domain: $x \geq 1$ or $x \leq -1$
Range: $y \neq \pi + \pi K$

4.8 Domain: all Real x
Range: $y \neq \pi + \pi K$

4.9 $\tan \frac{2\pi}{3} = -\sqrt{3}$.
Let $y = \text{arccot}\ (-\sqrt{3})$.
Then $\cot y = -\sqrt{3}$ and $y = \frac{5\pi}{6}$.

4.10 Let $x = \text{arccsc}\ 2$.
$\csc x = 2$
Therefore, $\sec\ (\text{arccsc}) = \sec x = \frac{2}{\sqrt{3}} = \frac{2}{3}\sqrt{3}$.

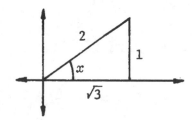

4.11 Let $x = \arctan 5$.
Then $\tan x = 5$; $\cot x = \frac{1}{\tan x}$.
Therefore, $\cot\ (\arctan 5) = \cot x = \frac{1}{5}$.

4.12 $\sin \frac{\pi}{6} = \frac{1}{2}$,
Let $x = \text{arccsc}\ (\frac{\pi}{6}) = \text{arccsc}\ \frac{1}{2}$.
$\csc x = \frac{1}{2}$
$x = \phi$ since $|\csc x| \geq 1$; no solution.

4.13 Let $x = \text{arcsec}\ \frac{1}{2}$. Then $\sec x = \frac{1}{2}$.
Therefore, $x = \phi$ since $|\sec x| \geq 1$; no solution.

4.14 Let $x = \arcsin \frac{1}{\sqrt{7}}$.
Then $\sin x = \frac{1}{\sqrt{7}}$.
$\cot(\arcsin \frac{1}{\sqrt{7}}) = \cot x = \frac{\sqrt{6}}{1} = \sqrt{6}$

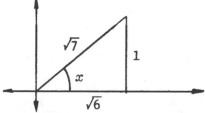

4.15 Let $x = \arcsin \frac{2}{3}$. Then $\sin x = \frac{2}{3}$ and $\sec x = \frac{3}{\sqrt{5}}$. Therefore,
$\sec\ (\arcsin \frac{2}{3}) = \frac{3}{\sqrt{5}} = \frac{3\sqrt{5}}{5}$.

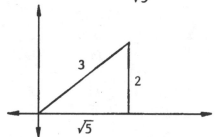

V. SECTION FIVE

5.1

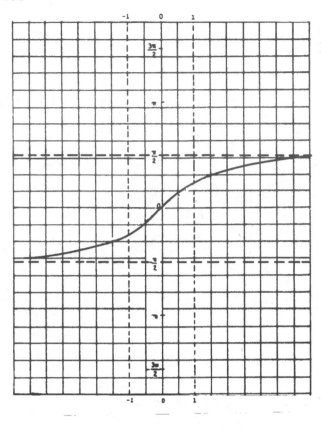

5.3

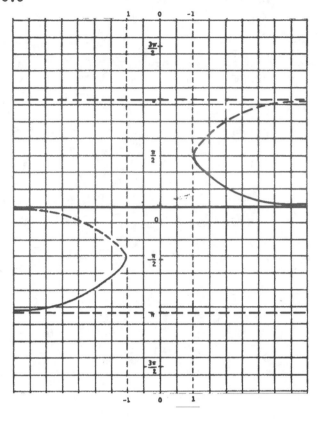

5.4

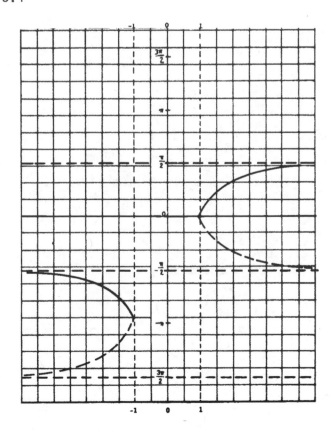

5.2

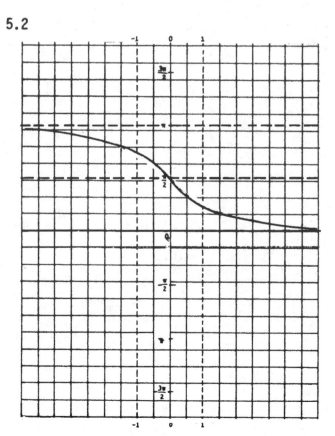

5.5   Domain: all Real x
Range: $-\frac{\pi}{2} < y < \frac{\pi}{2}$

5.6   Domain: all Real x
Range: $0 < y < \pi$

5.7   Domain: $x \geq 1$ or $x \leq -1$
Range: $-\pi \leq y < -\frac{\pi}{2}$
or $0 \leq y < \frac{\pi}{2}$

5.8   Domain: $x \geq 1$ or $x \leq -1$
Range: $-\pi < y \leq -\frac{\pi}{2}$
or $0 < y \leq \frac{\pi}{2}$

5.9   Let $y = \arcsin\frac{1}{2}$; $\sin y = \frac{1}{2}$,
$-\frac{\pi}{2} \leq y \leq \frac{\pi}{2}$.   Therefore, $y = \frac{\pi}{6}$
or 30°.

5.10   Let $y = \arccos\frac{\sqrt{2}}{2}$; $\cos y = \frac{\sqrt{2}}{2}$,
$0 \leq y \leq \pi$.   Therefore,
$y = \frac{\pi}{4}$ or 45°.

5.11   Let $y = \arctan\sqrt{3}$; $\tan y = \sqrt{3}$,
$-\frac{\pi}{2} \leq y \leq \frac{\pi}{2}$.   Therefore,
$y = \frac{\pi}{3}$ or 60°.

5.12   Let $y = \text{arcsec } 4$; $\sec y = 4$,
$0 \leq y \leq \frac{\pi}{2}$ or $0 \leq y \leq 90°$.
From the table of function
values, $y = 75°\ 30'$ (approx.).

5.13   Let $y = \text{arccsc } 3$; $\csc y = 3$,
$0 \leq y \leq 90°$.   From the table of
function values, $y = 19°\ 30'$
(approx.).

VI.   SECTION SIX

6.1 through 6.4

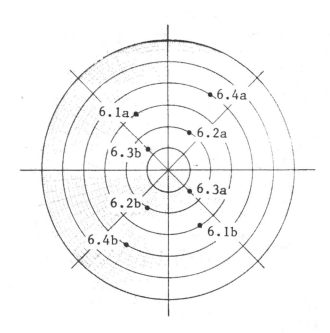

6.5 through 6.14

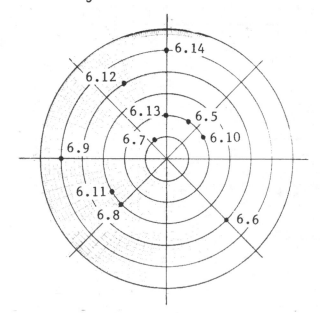

192

6.15 through 6.24

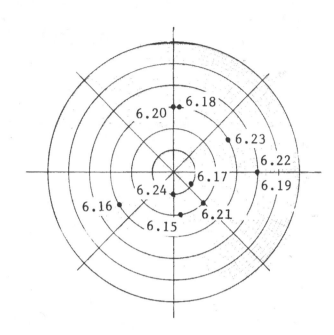

VII. SECTION SEVEN

7.1 $x = r \cos \theta$
$x = (-1)\cos 180°$
$x = (-1)(-1)$
$x = 1$

$y = r \sin \theta$
$y = (-1)\sin 180°$
$y = (-1)(0)$
$y = 0$

$(x, y) = (1, 0)$

7.2 $x = r \cos \theta$
$x = 3 \cos (-30°)$
$x = 3(\cos 30°)$
$x = 3(\frac{\sqrt{3}}{2})$
$x = \frac{3\sqrt{3}}{2}$

$y = r \sin \theta$
$y = 3 \sin(-30°)$
$y = -3(\sin 30°)$
$y = -3(\frac{1}{2})$
$y = -\frac{3}{2}$

$(x, y) = (\frac{3\sqrt{3}}{2}, -\frac{3}{2})$

7.3 $x = r \cos \theta$
$x = 2 \cos \frac{3\pi}{4}$
$x = 2(-\cos \frac{\pi}{4})$
$x = -2(\frac{\sqrt{2}}{2})$
$x = -\sqrt{2}$

$y = r \sin \theta$
$y = 2 \sin \frac{3\pi}{4}$
$y = 2(\sin \frac{\pi}{4})$
$y = 2(\frac{\sqrt{2}}{2})$
$y = \sqrt{2}$

$(x, y) = (-\sqrt{2}, \sqrt{2})$

7.4 $x = r \cos \theta$
$x = -4 \cos (-\frac{\pi}{2})$
$x = -4 \cos \frac{\pi}{2}$
$x = -4(0)$
$x = 0$

$y = r \sin \theta$
$y = -4 \sin (-\frac{\pi}{2})$
$y = 4 \sin \frac{\pi}{2}$
$y = 4(1)$
$y = 4$

$(x, y) = (0, 4)$

7.5 $x = r \cos \theta$
$x = -1 \cos 1.0472$
$x = -1(\frac{1}{2})$
$x = -\frac{1}{2}$

$y = r \sin \theta$
$y = -1 \sin 1.0472$
$y = -1(\frac{\sqrt{3}}{2})$
$y = -\frac{\sqrt{3}}{2}$

$(x, y) = (-\frac{1}{2}, -\frac{\sqrt{3}}{2})$

7.6 $x = r \cos \theta$
$x = -3 \cos 15°$
$x = -3(0.9659)$
$x = -2.897$

$y = r \sin \theta$
$y = -3 \sin 15°$
$y = -3(0.2588)$
$y = -0.7764$

$(x, y) = (-2.8977, -0.7764)$

$\cos 15° = \cos \frac{1}{2}(30°)$

$\cos 15° = \sqrt{\frac{1 + \cos 30°}{2}}$

$\cos 15° = \sqrt{\frac{1 + \frac{\sqrt{3}}{2}}{2}}$

$\cos 15° = \frac{\sqrt{\sqrt{2} + \sqrt{6}}}{2}$

$x = \frac{-3\sqrt{\frac{\sqrt{2} + \sqrt{6}}{2}}}{2}$

$\sin 15° = \sin \frac{1}{2}(30°)$

$\sin 15° = \sqrt{\frac{1 - \sin 30°}{2}}$

$\sin 15° = \sqrt{\frac{1 - \frac{1}{2}}{2}}$

$\sin 15° = \frac{\sqrt{\sqrt{2} - \frac{\sqrt{2}}{2}}}{2}$

$y = \frac{-3\sqrt{\sqrt{2} - \frac{\sqrt{2}}{2}}}{2}$

$(x, y) = \left(\frac{-3\sqrt{\frac{\sqrt{2} + \sqrt{6}}{2}}}{2}, \frac{-3\sqrt{\sqrt{2} - \frac{\sqrt{2}}{2}}}{2}\right)$

7.7 $x = r \cos \theta$

$x = 4 \cos \frac{\pi}{6}$

$x = 4\left(\frac{\sqrt{3}}{2}\right)$

$x = 2\sqrt{3}$

$y = r \sin \theta$

$y = 4 \sin \frac{\pi}{6}$

$y = 4\left(\frac{1}{2}\right)$

$y = 2$

$(x, y) = (2\sqrt{3}, 2)$

7.8 $x = r \cos \theta$

$x = 3 \cos \left(-\frac{3\pi}{4}\right)$

$x = 3 \cos \frac{3\pi}{4}$

$x = -3 \cos \frac{\pi}{4}$

$x = -\frac{3\sqrt{2}}{2}$

$y = r \sin \theta$

$y = 3 \sin \left(-\frac{3\pi}{4}\right)$

$y = -3 \sin \frac{3\pi}{4}$

$y = -3 \sin \frac{\pi}{4}$

$y = -\frac{3\sqrt{2}}{2}$

$(x, y) = \left(-\frac{3\sqrt{2}}{2}, -\frac{3\sqrt{2}}{2}\right)$

7.9 $x = r \cos \theta$

$x = -3 \cos \frac{5\pi}{6}$

$x = 3 \cos \frac{\pi}{6}$

$x = \frac{3\sqrt{3}}{2}$

$y = r \sin \theta$

$y = -3 \sin \frac{5\pi}{6}$

$y = -3 \sin \frac{\pi}{6}$

$y = -\frac{3}{2}$

$(x, y) = \left(\frac{3\sqrt{3}}{2}, -\frac{3}{2}\right)$

7.10 $x = r \cos \theta$
$x = 1 \cos 0°$
$x = 1(1)$
$x = 1$

$y = r \sin \theta$
$y = 1 \sin 0°$
$y = 1(0)$
$y = 0$

$(x, y) = (1, 0)$

7.11 $r = \sqrt{x^2 + y^2}$
$r = \sqrt{0 + 0}$
$r = 0$

$\theta = \tan^{-1}\left(\frac{x}{y}\right)$
$\theta = \tan^{-1}(0)$
$\theta = 0$

$(r, \theta) = (0, 0)$

7.12 $r = \sqrt{x^2 + y^2}$
$r = \sqrt{2^2 + 2^2}$
$r = \sqrt{4 + 4}$
$r = \sqrt{8}$
$r = 2\sqrt{2}$

$\theta = \tan^{-1}\left(\frac{x}{y}\right)$
$\theta = \tan^{-1}(1)$
$\theta = \frac{\pi}{4}$

$(r, \theta) = (2\sqrt{2}, 45°)$

7.13 $r = \sqrt{(-2)^2 + (2\sqrt{3})^2}$
$r = \sqrt{4 + 12}$
$r = \sqrt{16}$
$r = 4$

$\theta = \tan^{-1}\left(\frac{2\sqrt{3}}{-2}\right)$
$\theta = \tan^{-1}(-\sqrt{3})$
$\theta = 120°$

$(r, \theta) = (4, 120°)$

7.14 $r = \sqrt{(-\sqrt{3})^2 + (-1)^2}$
$r = \sqrt{3 + 1}$
$r = \sqrt{4}$
$r = 2$

$\theta = \tan^{-1}\left(\frac{-1}{-\sqrt{3}}\right)$
$\theta = \tan^{-1}\left(\frac{\sqrt{3}}{3}\right)$
$\theta = 210°$

$(r, \theta) = (2, 210°)$

7.15 $r = \sqrt{3^2 + (-4)^2}$
$r = \sqrt{9 + 16}$
$r = \sqrt{25}$
$r = 5$

$\theta = \tan^{-1}\left(-\frac{4}{3}\right)$
$\theta = 127°$

$(r, \theta) = (5, 127°)$

7.16 $r = \sqrt{(-3)^2 + \left(\frac{3}{2}\right)^2}$

$r = \sqrt{9 + \frac{9}{4}}$

$r = \sqrt{\frac{45}{4}}$

$r = \frac{3\sqrt{5}}{2}$

$\theta = \tan^{-1}\left(\frac{\frac{3}{2}}{-3}\right)$

$\theta = \tan^{-1}\left(-\frac{1}{2}\right)$

$\theta = 153°$

$(r, \theta) = \left(\frac{3\sqrt{5}}{2}, 153°\right)$

7.17 $r = \sqrt{4^2 + 0^2}$
$r = 4$

$\theta = \tan^{-1}\left(\frac{0}{4}\right)$
$\theta = \tan^{-1}(0)$
$\theta = 0°$

$(r, \theta) = (4, 0°)$

7.18 $r = \sqrt{\left(-\frac{\sqrt{3}}{2}\right)^2 + \left(\frac{1}{2}\right)^2}$

$r = \sqrt{\frac{3}{4} + \frac{1}{4}}$
$r = \sqrt{1}$
$r = 1$

7.18 cont.

$$\theta = \tan^{-1}\left(\frac{\frac{1}{2}}{-\frac{\sqrt{3}}{2}}\right)$$

$$\theta = \tan^{-1}\left(-\frac{\sqrt{3}}{3}\right)$$

$$\theta = \frac{5\pi}{6}$$

$$(r, \theta) = \left(1, \frac{5\pi}{6}\right)$$

7.19 $r = \sqrt{0^2 + 4^2}$
$r = 4$

$\theta = \tan^{-1}\left(\frac{4}{0}\right) = $ undefined

$\theta = 90°$
$(r, \theta) = (4, 90°)$

7.20 $r = \sqrt{0^2 + (-3)^2}$
$r = 3$

$\theta = \tan^{-1}\left(-\frac{3}{0}\right) = $ undefined

$\theta = \frac{3\pi}{2}$

$(r, \theta) = \left(3, \frac{3\pi}{2}\right)$

VIII. SECTION EIGHT

8.1 $x^2 + y^2 = r^2$,
$x^2 + y^2 = 16$,
$r = \sqrt{16} = 4$

8.2 $x^2 + y^2 + 2y = 0$,
$x^2 + y^2 = r^2$ and $y = r \sin \theta$
Then $r^2 + 2r \sin \theta = 0$ and
$r + 2 \sin \theta = 0$ or $r = -2 \sin \theta$.

8.3 $x^2 + y^2 = 0$ and $x^2 + y^2 = r^2$;
therefore, $r^2 = 0$ and $r = 0$

8.4 $y = 3$ and $y = r \sin \theta$; therefore,
$r \sin \theta = 3$ or $r = \dfrac{3}{\sin \theta}$ or
$r = 3 \csc \theta$

8.5 $x^2 + y^2 - 4x = 0$,
$x^2 + y^2 = r^2$ and
$x = r \cos \theta$; therefore,
$r^2 - 4r \cos \theta = 0$ and
$r - 4 \cos \theta = 0$ or $r = 4 \cos \theta$

8.6 $x^2 + y^2 = a^2$ and $x^2 + y^2 = r^2$;
therefore, $r^2 = a^2$ or $r = |a|$

8.7 $y^2 = 4(x + 1)$, $y = r \sin \theta$
and $x = r \cos \theta$; therefore,
$r^2 \sin^2 \theta = 4(r \cos \theta + 1)$ and
$r^2 \sin^2 \theta = 4r \cos \theta + 4$
$r^2 \sin^2 \theta - 4r \cos \theta - 4 = 0$
$r^2(1 - \cos^2 \theta) - 4r \cos \theta - 4 = 0$
$r^2 - r^2 \cos^2 \theta - 4r \cos \theta - 4 = 0$
$r^2 \cos^2 \theta + 4r \cos \theta + 4 - r^2 = 0$
$[r \cos \theta + (2 - r)] \cdot [r \cos \theta + (2 + r)] = 0$
$r \cos \theta + (2 - r) = 0$
$(\cos \theta - 1)r = -2$
$$r = \frac{2}{1 - \cos \theta}$$
or
$r(\cos \theta + 1) = -2$
$$r = \frac{-2}{\cos \theta + 1}$$

8.8 $(x^2 + y^2)^2 = 4(x^2 - y^2)$,
$x^2 + y^2 = r^2$,
$x = r \cos \theta$ and $y = r \sin \theta$
$(r^2)^2 = 4(r^2 \cos^2 \theta - r^2 \sin^2 \theta)$
$r^4 = 4r^2(\cos^2 \theta - \sin^2 \theta)$
$r^2 = 4(\cos^2 \theta - \sin^2 \theta)$
$r^2 = 4 \cos 2\theta$

8.9 $x^2 - y^2 = 16$,
$x = r \cos \theta$ and $y = r \sin \theta$
$r^2 \cos^2 \theta - r^2 \sin^2 \theta = 16$
$r^2(\cos^2 \theta - \sin^2 \theta) = 16$
$$r^2 = \frac{16}{\cos^2 \theta - \sin^2 \theta}$$
$$= \frac{16}{1 - 2 \sin^2 \theta}$$ or
$$r^2 = \frac{16}{\cos 2\theta}$$

8.10 $x^3 = 4y^2$

$x = r \cos \theta$ and $y = r \sin \theta$

$r^3 \cos^3 \theta = 4 r^2 \sin^2 \theta$

$r \cos^3 \theta = 4 \sin^2 \theta$

$r = \dfrac{4 \sin^2 \theta}{\cos^3 \theta}$

IX. SECTION NINE

9.1 $r^2 = 2 \sin 2\theta$,

$r^2 = 2(2 \sin \theta \cos \theta)$,

$r^2 = 4 \sin \theta \cos \theta$

$x^2 + y^2 = 4\left(\dfrac{y}{r}\right)\left(\dfrac{x}{r}\right)$

$x^2 + y^2 = \dfrac{4xy}{r^2}$

$x^2 + y^2 = \dfrac{4xy}{x^2 + y^2}$

$(x^2 + y^2)^2 = 4xy$

9.2 $\theta = 45°$

$\theta = \tan^{-1}\left(\dfrac{y}{x}\right)$ or $\tan \theta = \dfrac{y}{x}$

$\tan 45° = \dfrac{y}{x}$

$1 = \dfrac{y}{x}$, therefore, $y = x$

9.3 $r = \dfrac{6}{2 - 3 \sin \theta}$

$r = \sqrt{x^2 + y^2}$

$\sin \theta = \dfrac{y}{r}$

$r = \dfrac{6}{2 - 3\left(\dfrac{y}{r}\right)} = \dfrac{6r}{2r - 3y}$

$1 = \dfrac{6}{2r - 3y}$

$2r - 3y = 6$

$2r = 6 + 3y$

$2\sqrt{x^2 + y^2} = 6 + 3y$

$4(x^2 + y^2) = 36 + 36y + 9y^2$

$4x^2 + 4y^2 = 36 + 36y + 9y^2$

$4x^2 - 5y^2 - 36y - 36 = 0$

9.4 $r = 2$

$r = \sqrt{x^2 + y^2}$

$\sqrt{x^2 + y^2} = 2$ or $x^2 + y^2 = 4$

9.5 $\theta = -\dfrac{\pi}{6}$

$\theta = \tan^{-1}\left(\dfrac{y}{x}\right)$ or $\tan \theta = \dfrac{y}{x}$

$\dfrac{y}{x} = -\dfrac{\sqrt{3}}{3}$

$y = -\dfrac{\sqrt{3}}{3}x$

9.6 $r = 2 \sec \theta$

$\cos \theta = \dfrac{x}{r}$

$r = \sqrt{x^2 + y^2}$

$r = \dfrac{2}{\cos \theta}$

$r = \dfrac{2}{\dfrac{x}{r}}$

$r = \dfrac{2r}{x}$

$1 = \dfrac{2}{x}$

$x = 2$

9.7 $r = 2 \cos \theta$

$\cos \theta = \dfrac{x}{r}$

$r = \sqrt{x^2 + y^2}$

$r = 2\left(\dfrac{x}{r}\right)$

$r^2 = 2x$

$x^2 + y^2 = 2x$

9.8 $r^2 = \cos \theta$

$r^2 = \dfrac{x}{r}$

$r^3 = x$

$\left(x^2 + y^2\right)^{\frac{3}{2}} = x$ or

$\left(x^2 + y^2\right)^3 = x^2$

9.9 $r^2 = 4 \cos 2\theta$

$r^2 = 4(\cos^2 \theta - \sin^2 \theta)$

$r^2 = 4\left(\dfrac{x^2}{r^2} - \dfrac{y^2}{r^2}\right)$

$r^4 = 4x^2 - 4y^2$

$(x^2 + y^2)^2 = 4x^2 - 4y^2$

$(x^2 + y^2)^2 = 4(x^2 - y^2)$

X. SECTION TEN

10.1

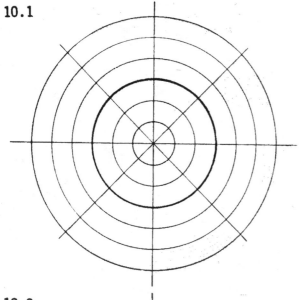

10.2

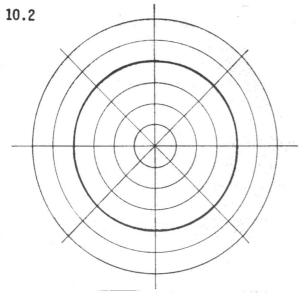

10.3

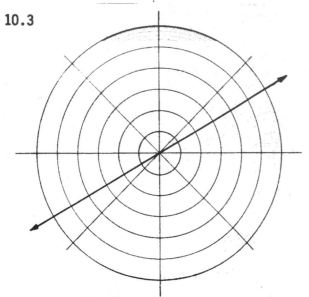

10.4

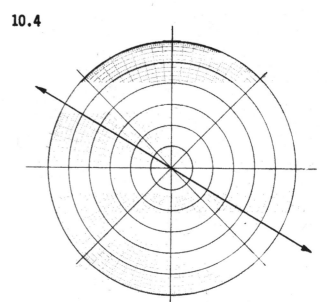

10.5

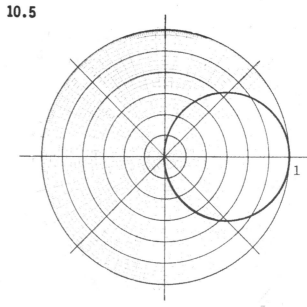

10.6

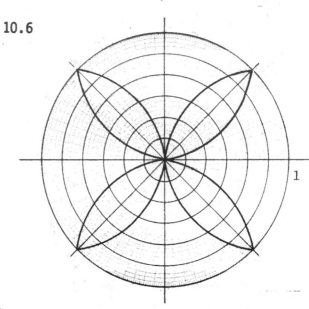

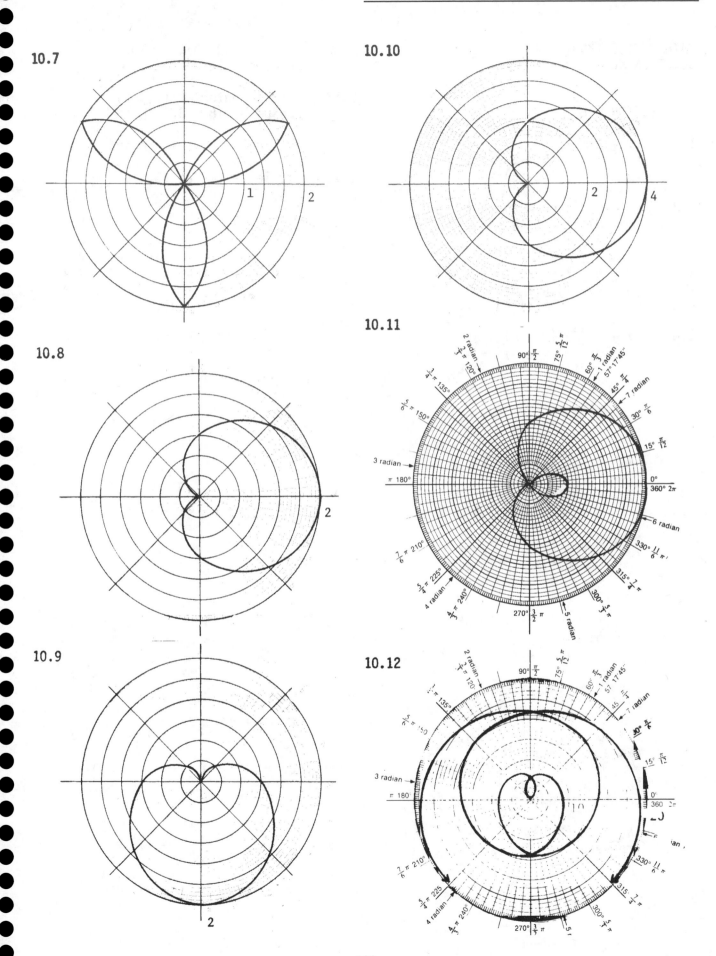

10.7

10.8

10.9

10.10

10.11

10.12

MATHEMATICS 1208
SOLUTION KEY

I. SECTION ONE

1.1
$$(x - h)^2 + (y - k)^2 = r^2$$
$$(x - 3)^2 + (y - 5)^2 = 5^2$$
$$(x - 3)^2 + (y - 5)^2 = 25$$

1.2
$$(x - h)^2 + (y - k)^2 = r^2$$
$$(x + 8)^2 + (y + 6)^2 = 10^2$$
$$(x + 8)^2 + (y + 6)^2 = 100$$

1.3
$$(x - h)^2 + (y - k)^2 = r^2$$
$$(x - 0)^2 + (y - 0)^2 = 4^2$$
$$x^2 + y^2 = 16$$

1.4
$$(x - h)^2 + (y - k)^2 = r^2$$
$$(x - 6)^2 + (y - 0)^2 = 6^2$$
$$(x - 6)^2 + y^2 = 36$$

1.5
$$(x - h)^2 + (y - k)^2 = r^2$$
$$r = \sqrt{(1 - 0)^2 + (-2 - 0)^2} =$$
$$\sqrt{1^2 + (-2)^2} =$$
$$\sqrt{1 + 4} = \sqrt{5}$$
$$(x - 1)^2 + (y + 2)^2 = (\sqrt{5})^2$$
$$(x - 1)^2 + (y + 2)^2 = 5$$

1.6 $(h, k) = (2, 0)$, $r = 2$

$$(x - h)^2 + (y - k)^2 = r^2$$
$$(x - 2)^2 + (y - 0)^2 = 2^2$$
$$(x - 2)^2 + y^2 = 4$$

1.7 $(h, k) = (0, -3)$, $r = 3$

$$(x - h)^2 + (y - k)^2 = r^2$$
$$(x - 0)^2 + (y + 3)^2 = 3^2$$
$$x^2 + (y + 3)^2 = 9$$

1.8 circle center at $(0, 0)$
radius $= \sqrt{36} = 6$

1.9 circle center at $(2, -3)$
radius $= \sqrt{49} = 7$

1.10 $(h, k) = (-3, 2)$, $r = 0$;
point circle

1.11 $(h, k) = (0, 0)$, $r = -4$;
impossible

1.12 $(h, k) = (0, 0)$, $r = 0$;
point circle

1.13 circle center at $(5, -4)$
radius $= \sqrt{18} = 3\sqrt{2}$

1.14 no circle-negative radius

1.15 circle center at $(3, -4)$
radius $= \sqrt{\dfrac{100}{10}} = \sqrt{10}$

1.16
$$x^2 + y^2 - 2x - 4y - 4 = 0$$
$$x^2 - 2x + y^2 - 4y = 4$$
$$x^2 - 2x + 1 + y^2 - 4y + 4 = 4 + 1 + 4$$
$$(x - 1)^2 + (y - 2)^2 = 9$$

$(h, k) = (1, 2)$
$r = \sqrt{9} = 3$

Domain: $-2 \le x \le 4$
Range: $-1 \le y \le 5$

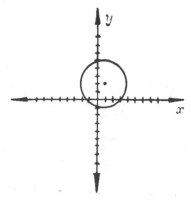

1.17
$$x^2 + y^2 + 6x - 8y + 24 = 0$$
$$x^2 + 6x + y^2 - 8y = -24$$
$$x^2 + 6x + 9 + y^2 - 8y + 16 = -24 + 9 + 16$$
$$(x + 3)^2 + (y - 4)^2 = 1$$

$(h, k) = (-3, 4)$
$r = \sqrt{1} = 1$
Domain: $-4 \le x \le -2$
Range: $3 \le y \le 5$

1.17 cont.

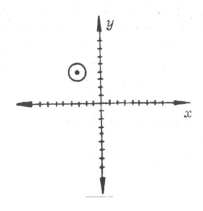

1.18
$$x^2 + y^2 + 2x = 0$$
$$x^2 + 2x + y^2 = 0$$
$$x^2 + 2x + 1 + y^2 = 1$$
$$(x + 1)^2 + y^2 = 1$$

$(h, k) = (-1, 0)$
$r = \sqrt{1} = 1$
Domain: $-2 \le x \le 0$
Range: $-1 \le y \le 1$

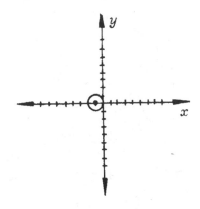

1.19
$$4x^2 + 4y^2 - 4x + 12y + 1 = 0$$
$$x^2 - x + y^2 + 3y = -\tfrac{1}{4}$$
$$x^2 - x + \tfrac{1}{4} + y^2 + 3y + \tfrac{9}{4} = -\tfrac{1}{4} + \tfrac{1}{4} + \tfrac{9}{4}$$
$$(x - \tfrac{1}{2})^2 + (y + \tfrac{3}{2})^2 = \tfrac{9}{4}$$

$(h, k) = (\tfrac{1}{2}, -\tfrac{3}{2})$

$r = \sqrt{\tfrac{9}{4}} = \tfrac{3}{2}$
Domain: $-1 \le x \le 2$
Range: $-3 \le y \le 0$

1.19 cont.

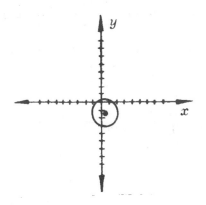

1.20
$$x^2 + y^2 + 2x - 8y + 18 = 0$$
$$x^2 + 2x + y^2 - 8y = -18$$
$$x^2 + 2x + 1 + y^2 - 8y + 16 = -18 + 1 + 16$$
$$(x + 1)^2 + (y - 4)^2 = -1$$

$r = \sqrt{-1}$
no graph; negative radius.
Domain: none
Range: none

1.21
$$x^2 + y^2 + 14x + 2y + 50 = 0$$
$$x^2 + 14x + y^2 + 2y = -50$$
$$x^2 + 14x + 49 + y^2 + 2y + 1 = -50 + 49 + 1$$
$$(x + 7)^2 + (y + 1)^2 = 0$$

$(h, k) = (-7, -1)$
$r = 0$
point circle-no radius
Domain: none
Range: none

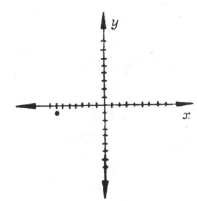

1.22
$$x^2 + y^2 - 2x - 4y + 5 = 0$$
$$x^2 - 2x + y^2 - 4y = -5$$
$$x^2 - 2x + 1 + y^2 - 4y + 4 = -5 + 1 + 4$$
$$(x - 1)^2 + (y - 2)^2 = 0$$

$(h, k) = (1, 2)$
$r = 0$
Domain: none
Range: none
point circle

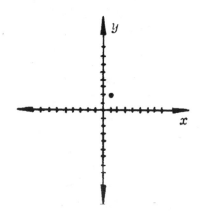

1.23
$$(x - 3)^2 + (y - 5)^2 = 25$$
$$x^2 - 6x + 9 + y^2 - 10y + 25 = 25$$
$$x^2 + y^2 - 6x - 10y + 9 = 0$$

1.24
$$(x + 8)^2 + (y + 6)^2 = 100$$
$$x^2 + 16x + 6y + y^2 + 12x + 36 = 100$$
$$x^2 + y^2 + 16x + 12y = 0$$

1.25 $x^2 + y^2 - 16 = 0$

1.26
$$(x - 6)^2 + y^2 = 36$$
$$x^2 - 12x + 36 + y^2 = 36$$
$$x^2 + y^2 - 12x = 0$$

1.27
$$(x - 1)^2 + (y + 2)^2 = 5$$
$$x^2 - 2x + 1 + y^2 + 4y + 4 = 5$$
$$x^2 + y^2 - 2x + 4y = 0$$

1.28
$$(x - 2)^2 + y^2 = 4$$
$$x^2 - 4x + 4 + y^2 = 4$$
$$x^2 + y^2 - 4x = 0$$

1.29 $x^2 + y^2 + dx + ey + f = 0$

$(1, 7)$: $1 + 49 + d + 7e + f = 0$
$(8, 6)$: $64 + 36 + 8d + 6e + f = 0$
$(7, -1)$: $49 + 1 + 7d - e + f = 0$

$$d + 7e + f = -50$$
$$8d + 6e + f = -100$$
$$7d - e + f = -50$$

Subtract:
$$\begin{array}{r} d + 7e + f = -50 \\ 8d + 6e + f = -100 \\ \hline -7d + e = 50 \end{array}$$
$$7d - e = -50$$
$$e = 7d + 50$$

Subtract:
$$\begin{array}{r} 8d + 6e + f = -100 \\ 7d - e + f = -50 \\ \hline d + 7e = -50 \end{array}$$

Substitute e:
$$d + 7(7d + 50) = -50$$
$$d + 49d + 350 = -50$$
$$50d + 350 = -50$$
$$50d = -400$$
$$d = -8$$

$e = 7d + 50$
$e = 7(-8) + 50$
$e = -56 + 50$
$e = -6$

$$d + 7e + f = -50$$
$$-8 + 7(-6) + f = -50$$
$$-8 - 42 + f = -50$$
$$-50 + f = -50$$
$$f = 0$$

$x^2 + y^2 - 8x - 6y = 0$

1.30 $x^2 + y^2 + dx + ey + f = 0$

$(-1, 2)$: $1 + 4 - d + 2e + f = 0$
$(4, 2)$: $16 + 4 + 4d + 2e + f = 0$
$(-3, 4)$: $9 + 16 - 3d + 4e + f = 0$

$$-d + 2e + f = -5$$
$$4d + 2e + f = -20$$
$$-3d + 4e + f = -25$$

Subtract:
$$\begin{array}{r} -d + 2e + f = -5 \\ 4d + 2e + f = -20 \\ \hline -5d = 15 \end{array}$$
$$d = -3$$

1.30 cont.

Subtract:
$$4d + 2e + f = -20$$
$$-3d + 4e + f = -25$$
$$\overline{7d - 2e = 5}$$
$$7(-3) - 2e = 5$$
$$-21 - 2e = 5$$
$$-2e = 26$$
$$e = -13$$

$$-d + 2e + f = -5$$
$$-(-3) + 2(-13) + f = -5$$
$$3 - 26 + f = -5$$
$$-23 + f = -5$$
$$f = 18$$

$$x^2 + y^2 - 3x - 13y + 18 = 0$$

1.31 $\quad x^2 + y^2 + dx + ey + f = 0$

$(0, 0): \quad 0 + 0 + 0 + 0 + f = 0$
$(6, 0): \quad 36 + 0 + 6d + 0 + f = 0$
$(0, -8): \quad 0 + 64 + 0 - 8e + f = 0$

$$f = 0$$
$$6d + f = -36$$
$$-8e + f = -64$$

Subtract:
$$f = 0$$
$$6d + f = -36$$
$$\overline{-6d = 36}$$
$$d = -6$$

Subtract:
$$f = 0$$
$$-8e + f = -64$$
$$\overline{8e = 64}$$
$$e = 8$$

$$x^2 + y^2 + (-6)x + 8y + 0 = 0$$
$$x^2 + y^2 - 6x + 8y = 0$$

1.32 $\quad x^2 + y^2 + dx + ey + f = 0$

$(1, 1): \quad 1 + 1 + d + e + f = 0$
$(1, 3): \quad 1 + 9 + d + 3e + f = 0$
$(9, 2): \quad 81 + 4 + 9d + 2e + f = 0$

$$d + e + f = -2$$
$$d + 3e + f = -10$$
$$9d + 2e + f = -85$$

1.32 cont.

Subtract:
$$d + e + f = -2$$
$$d + 3e + f = -10$$
$$\overline{ - 2e = 8}$$
$$e = -4$$

Subtract:
$$d + e + f = -2$$
$$9d + 2e + f = -85$$
$$\overline{-8d - e = 83}$$
$$-8d - (-4) = 83$$
$$-8d + 4 = 83$$
$$-8d = 79$$
$$d = -\frac{79}{8}$$

$$d + e + f = -2$$
$$-\frac{79}{8} + (-4) + f = -2$$
$$-\frac{79}{8} - 4 + f = -2$$
$$f = -2 + \frac{79}{8} + 4$$
$$f = \frac{95}{8}$$

$$x^2 + y^2 - \frac{79}{8}x - 4y + \frac{95}{8} = 0$$
$$8x^2 + 8y^2 - 79x - 32y + 95 = 0$$

1.33 $\quad x^2 + y^2 + dx + ey + f = 0$

$(-5, 0): \quad 25 + 0 - 5d + 0 + f = 0$
$(0, 4): \quad 0 + 16 + 0 + 4e + f = 0$
$(2, 4): \quad 4 + 16 + 2d + 4e + f = 0$

$$-5d + f = -25$$
$$4e + f = -16$$
$$2d + 4e + f = -20$$

Subtract:
$$-5d + f = -25$$
$$4e + f = -16$$
$$\overline{-5d - 4e = -9}$$

Subtract:
$$4e + f = -16$$
$$2d + 4e + f = -20$$
$$\overline{-2d = 4}$$
$$d = -2$$

$$-5d + f = -25$$
$$-5(-2) + f = -25$$
$$10 + f = -25$$
$$f = -35$$

$$4e + f = -16$$
$$4e + (-35) = -16$$
$$4e - 35 = -16$$
$$4e = 19$$
$$e = \frac{19}{4}$$

1.33 cont.

$$x^2 + y^2 - 2x + \tfrac{19}{4}y - 35 = 0$$
$$4x^2 + 4y^2 - 8x + 19y - 140 = 0$$

1.34 $d = \dfrac{|ax_1 + by_1 + c|}{\sqrt{a^2 + b^2}}$

$d = \dfrac{|5(-1) + (-4)(3) - 10|}{\sqrt{5^2 + 4^2}}$

$d = \dfrac{|-5 - 12 - 10|}{\sqrt{41}} = \dfrac{|-27|}{\sqrt{41}}$

$\quad = \dfrac{27\sqrt{41}}{41}$

1.35 $\bar{x} = \dfrac{6 + 20}{2} = \dfrac{26}{2} = 13$

$\bar{y} = \dfrac{-10 + 15}{2} = \dfrac{5}{2}$

$(13, \tfrac{5}{2})$

1.36 diameter $= \sqrt{(2 - 4)^2 + (0 - 8)^2}$
$\qquad\qquad = \sqrt{4 + 64}$
$\qquad\qquad = \sqrt{68}$
$\qquad\qquad = 2\sqrt{17}$

radius $= \dfrac{2\sqrt{17}}{2} = \sqrt{17}$

$(h, k) = (\dfrac{2 + 4}{2}, \dfrac{0 + 8}{2}) = (3, 4)$

$(x - 3)^2 + (y - 4)^2 = (\sqrt{17})^2$
$x^2 - 6x + 9 + y^2 - 8y + 16 = 17$
$\qquad x^2 + y^2 - 6x - 8y + 8 = 0$

1.37 diameter $= \sqrt{(5 + 3)^2 + (-2 - 6)^2}$
$\qquad\qquad = \sqrt{64 + 64}$
$\qquad\qquad = 8\sqrt{2}$

radius $= \dfrac{8\sqrt{2}}{2} = 4\sqrt{2}$

$(h, k) = (\dfrac{-3 + 5}{2}, \dfrac{6 - 2}{2})$
$\qquad = (1, 2)$

$(x - 1)^2 + (y - 2)^2 = 32$
$x^2 - 2x + 1 + y^2 - 4y + 4 = 32$
$\qquad x^2 + y^2 - 2x - 4y - 27 = 0$

1.38 $r = \dfrac{|ax_1 + by_1 + c|}{\sqrt{a^2 + b^2}}$

$r = \dfrac{|0 \cdot 1 + 0 \cdot 2 - 8|}{\sqrt{1 + 1}} = \dfrac{8}{\sqrt{2}}$

$\quad = \dfrac{8\sqrt{2}}{2} = 4\sqrt{2}$

$x^2 + y^2 = 32$

1.39 $r = \dfrac{|ax_1 + by_1 + c|}{\sqrt{a^2 + b^2}}$

$r = \dfrac{|-2(20) + 3(-21) - 42|}{\sqrt{20^2 + 21^2}}$

$r = \dfrac{|-40 - 63 - 42|}{\sqrt{841}}$

$r = \dfrac{145}{\sqrt{841}} = \dfrac{145}{29} = 5$

$(x + 2)^2 + (y - 3)^2 = 5^2$
$x^2 + 4x + 4 + y^2 - 6y + 9 = 25$
$\qquad x^2 + y^2 + 4x - 6y - 12 = 0$

1.40 Find three points on the circle.

$x - y = -2$
$2x + 3y = 1$
$4x + y = 17$

$3x - 3y = -6$
$\underline{2x + 3y = 1}$
$5x \qquad\;\; = -5$
$\qquad x = -1$
$\qquad y = 1$

$4x + 6y = 2$
$\underline{4x + \;\; y = 17}$
$\qquad 5y = -15$
$\qquad y = -3$
$\qquad x = 5$

$x - y = -2$
$\underline{4x + y = 17}$
$5x \qquad = 15$
$\qquad x = 3$
$\qquad y = 5$

The circle must pass through
$(-1, 1)$, $(5, -3)$, $(3, 5)$.

1.40 cont.

$$x^2 + y^2 + dx + ey + f = 0$$

$(-1, 1)$: $1 + 1 - d + e + f = 0$
$(5, -3)$: $25 + 9 + 5d - 3e + f = 0$
$(3, 5)$: $9 + 25 + 3d + 5e + f = 0$

$-d + e + f = -2$
$5d - 3e + f = -34$
$3d + 5e + f = -34$

Subtract:
$-d + e + f = -2$
$5d - 3e + f = -34$
$-6d + 4e \quad = 32$

Subtract:
$5d - 3e + f = -34$
$3d + 5e + f = -34$
$2d - 8e \quad = 0$

Add:
$-12d + 8e = 64$
$2d - 8e = 0$
$-10d \quad = 64$
$\quad d = -\frac{64}{10} = -\frac{32}{5}$

$-6d + 4e = 32$
$\quad 4e = 32 + 6d$
$\quad 4e = 32 + 6(-\frac{32}{5})$
$\quad 4e = 32 - \frac{192}{5}$
$\quad 4e = -\frac{32}{5}$
$\quad e = -\frac{32}{20} = -\frac{8}{5}$

$-d + e + f = -2$
$\quad f = -2 - e + d$
$\quad f = -2 + \frac{8}{5} - \frac{32}{5}$
$\quad f = -\frac{34}{5}$

$x^2 + y^2 - \frac{32}{5}x - \frac{8}{5}y - \frac{34}{5} = 0$
$5x^2 + 5y^2 - 32x - 8y - 34 = 0$

1.41 Use distance from point to line.

$4x - 3y - 65 = 0$
$7x - 24y + 55 = 0$
$3x + 4y - 5 = 0$

Let (h, k) = center of circle.

1.41 cont.

$$r_1 = \frac{4h - 3k - 65}{\sqrt{4^2 + 3^2}} = \frac{4h - 3k - 65}{5}$$

$$r_2 = \frac{7h - 24k + 55}{\sqrt{7^2 + 24^2}} = \frac{7h - 24k + 55}{25}$$

$$r_3 = \frac{3h + 4k - 5}{\sqrt{3^2 + 4^2}} = \frac{3h + 4k - 5}{5}$$

$r_1 = r_3$
$$\frac{4h - 3k - 65}{5} = \frac{3h + 4k - 5}{5}$$

$4h - 3k - 65 = 3h + 4k - 5$
$h - 3k - 65 = 4k - 5$
$h - 7k - 65 = -5$
$h - 7k = 60$

$r_1 = r_2$
$$\frac{4h - 3k - 65}{5} = \frac{7h - 24k + 55}{25}$$

$20h - 15k - 325 = 7h - 24k + 55$
$13h - 15k - 325 = -24k + 55$
$13h + 9k - 325 = 55$
$13h + 9k = 380$

$13h + 9k = 380$
$h - 7k = 60$

$13h + 9k = 380$
$13h - 91k = 780$
$\quad 100k = -400$
$\quad\quad k = -4$

$h = 60 + 7k$
$h = 60 - 28 = 32$

$(h, k) = (32, -4)$
$$r = \frac{4(32) - 3(-4) - 65}{5}$$
$$= \frac{128 + 12 - 65}{5} = \frac{75}{5} = 15$$

$(x - 32)^2 + (y + 4)^2 = 15^2$
$x^2 - 64x +$
$1{,}024 + y^2 + 8y + 16 = 225$
$x^2 + y^2 - 64x + 8y + 815 = 0$

1.42

$$(h - 7)^2 + (k - 2)^2 = 10^2$$
[distance from (h, k) **to** $(7, 2)$]

$$h^2 - 14h + 49 + k^2 - 4k + 4 = 100$$

Also, $\pm 10 = \dfrac{|3h - 4k - 13|}{5}$

(distance from point to line)

$$3h - 4k - 13 = 50$$
$$3h - 4k = 63$$
$$3h = 63 + 4k$$
$$h = \frac{63 + 4k}{3}$$

or

$$3h - 4k - 13 = -50$$
$$3h - 4k = -37$$
$$3h = -37 + 4k$$
$$h = \frac{-37 + 4k}{3}$$

$$\left(\frac{63 + 4k}{3}\right)^2 - 14\left(\frac{63 + 4k}{3}\right) + k^2 - 4k = 47$$

$$\frac{3,969 + 504k + 16k^2}{9} - \frac{882 - 56k}{3} + k^2 - 4k = 47$$

$$3,969 + 504k + 16k^2 - 2,646 - 168k + 9k^2 - 36k = 423$$
$$25k^2 + 300k + 1,323 = 423$$
$$25k^2 + 300k + 900 = 0$$
$$(25k + 150)(k + 6) = 0$$
$$25k + 150 = 0$$
$$25k = -150$$
$$k = -6$$

or

$$k + 6 = 0$$
$$k = -6$$

$$h = \frac{63 - 24}{3} = 13$$

$$(h, k) = (13, -6)$$

$$(x - 13)^2 + (y + 6)^2 = 100$$
$$x^2 - 26x + 169 + y^2 + 12y + 36 = 100$$
$$x^2 + y^2 - 26x + 12y + 105 = 0;$$
one solution

1.42 cont.

$$\left(\frac{-37 + 4k}{3}\right)^2 - 14\left(\frac{-37 + 4k}{3}\right) + k^2 - 4k = 47$$

$$\frac{1,369 - 296k + 16k^2}{9} + \frac{518 - 56k}{3} + k^2 - 4k = 47$$

$$1,369 - 296k + 16k^2 + 1,554 - 168k + 9k^2 - 36k = 423$$
$$25k^2 - 500k + 2,923 = 423$$
$$25k^2 - 500k + 2,500 = 0$$
$$k^2 - 20k + 100 = 0$$
$$(k - 10)^2 = 0$$
$$k - 10 = 0$$
$$k = 10$$

$$h = \frac{-37 + 40}{3} = \frac{3}{3} = 1$$

$$(h, k) = (1, 10)$$

$$(x - 1)^2 + (y - 10)^2 = 10^2$$
$$(x - 1)^2 + (y - 10)^2 = 100$$
$$x^2 - 2x + 1 + y^2 - 20y + 100 = 100$$
$$x^2 + y^2 - 2x - 20y + 1 = 0;$$
second solution

1.43

$$h^2 + k^2 = 100; \quad k^2 = 100 - h^2$$
$$(h - 3)^2 + (k - 4)^2 = 25$$

$$h^2 - 6h + 9 + k^2 - 8k + 16 = 25$$
$$h^2 - 6h + 9 + (100 - h^2) - 8\sqrt{100 - h^2} + 16 = 25$$

$$-6h + 100 = 8\sqrt{100 - h^2}$$
$$(-6h + 100)^2 = (8 \cdot \sqrt{100 - h^2})^2$$
$$36h^2 - 1,200h + 10,000 = 64(100 - h^2)$$
$$36h^2 - 1,200h + 10,000 = 6,400 - 64h^2$$
$$100h^2 - 1,200h + 10,000 = 6,400$$
$$100h^2 - 1,200h + 3,600 = 0$$
$$h^2 - 12h + 36 = 0$$
$$(h - 6)^2 = 0$$
$$h - 6 = 0$$
$$h = 6$$

$$k = \sqrt{100 - 6^2} = \sqrt{100 - 36} = \sqrt{64} = 8$$

$$(h, k) = (6, 8)$$

1.43 cont.

$$(x - 6)^2 + (y - 8)^2 = 5^2$$
$$x^2 - 12x + 36 +$$
$$y^2 - 16y + 64 = 25$$
$$x^2 - 12x + y^2 - 16y + 100 = 25$$
$$x^2 + y^2 - 12x - 16y + 75 = 0$$

1.44

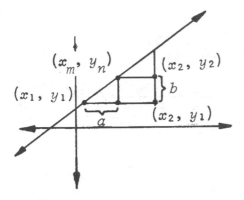

$$x_m = x_1 + a$$
$$a = \tfrac{1}{2}(x_2 - x_1)$$
$$x_m = x_1 + \tfrac{1}{2}(x_2 - x_1)$$
$$= \frac{2x_1 + x_2 - x_1}{2}$$
$$= \frac{x_1 + x_2}{2}$$

$$y_m = y_1 + b$$
$$b = \tfrac{1}{2}(y_2 - y_1)$$
$$y_m = y_1 + \tfrac{1}{2}(y_2 - y_1)$$
$$= \frac{2y_1 + y_2 - y_1}{2}$$
$$y_m = \frac{y_1 + y_2}{2}$$

$$(x_m, y_m) = (\frac{x_1 + x_2}{2}, \frac{y_1 + y_2}{2})$$

1.45

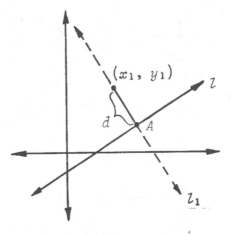

Given point (x, y) and line
$ax + by + c = 0$.

To find d, find the coordinates
of point A and use the
distance formula.

$l \perp l_1$

Slope of $l_1 = \dfrac{-a}{b}$

Slope of $l = \dfrac{b}{a}$

Equation of l is :

$$y - y_1 = \frac{b}{a}(x - x_1)$$
$$y = \frac{b}{a}(x - x_1) + y_1$$

Then
$$ax + b\left(\frac{b}{a}(x - x_1) + y_1\right) + c = 0$$
$$ax + \frac{b^2}{a}(x - x_1) + by_1 + c = 0$$
$$a^2x + b^2(x - x_1) + aby_1 + ac = 0$$
$$a^2x + b^2x - b^2x_1 + aby_1 + ac = 0$$
$$(a^2 + b^2)x - b^2x_1 + aby_1 + ac = 0$$
$$(a^2 + b^2)x = b^2x_1 - aby_1 - ac$$
$$x = \frac{b^2x_1 - aby_1 - ac}{a^2 + b^2}$$

1.45 cont.

$$y = \frac{b}{a}\left[\frac{b^2x_1 - aby_1 - ac}{a^2 + b^2} - x_1\right] + y_1$$

$$y = \frac{b}{a}\left[\frac{b^2x_1 - aby_1 - ac - x_1a^2 - x_1b^2}{a^2 + b^2}\right] + y_1$$

$$= \frac{b^2y_1 - bc - abx_1 + a^2y_1 + b^2y_1}{a^2 + b^2}$$

$$= \frac{a^2y_1 - abx_1 - bc}{a^2 + b^2}$$

$$d^2 = \left[\frac{b^2x_1 - aby_1 - ac}{a^2 + b^2} - x_1\right]^2 + \left[\frac{a^2y_1 - abx_1 - bc}{a^2 + b^2} - y_1\right]^2$$

$$= \left[\frac{b^2x_1 - aby_1 - ac - a^2x_1 - b^2x_1}{a^2 + b^2}\right]^2 + \left[\frac{a^2y_1 - abx_1 - bc - a^2y_1 - b^2y_1}{a^2 + b^2}\right]^2$$

$$= \frac{a^2[-by_1 - c - ax_1]^2 + b^2[-ax_1 - c - by_1]^2}{(a^2 + b^2)^2}$$

$$= \frac{(a^2 + b^2)[-by_1 - c - ax_1]^2}{(a^2 + b^2)^2}$$

$$= \frac{(ax_1 + by_1 + c)^2}{a^2 + b^2}$$

$$\sqrt{d^2} = \sqrt{\frac{(ax_1 + by_1 + c)^2}{a^2 + b^2}}$$

$$d = \frac{|ax_1 + by_1 + c|}{\sqrt{a^2 + b^2}}$$

optional activity-sample answer page 16

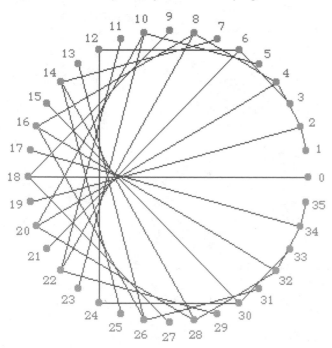

1.46   Position: I
$a = \sqrt{25} = 5$
$b = \sqrt{16} = 4$
$c = \sqrt{5^2 - 4^2} = \sqrt{25 - 16} = \sqrt{9} = 3$
Major axis = $2(5) = 10$
Minor axis = $2(4) = 8$

L.R. $= \frac{2(4)^2}{5} = \frac{2(16)}{5} = \frac{32}{5}$

$e = \frac{3}{5}$

Domain: $-5 \le x \le 5$
Range: $-4 \le y \le 4$

1.47   Position: I
$a = \sqrt{4} = 2$
$b = \sqrt{2}$
$c = \sqrt{2^2 - (\sqrt{2})^2} = \sqrt{4 - 2} = \sqrt{2}$
Major axis = $2(2) = 4$
Minor axis = $2\sqrt{2}$
L.R. $= \dfrac{2(\sqrt{2})^2}{2} = (\sqrt{2})^2 = 2$
$e = \dfrac{\sqrt{2}}{2}$
Domain: $-2 \le x \le 2$
Range: $\sqrt{2} \le y \le \sqrt{2}$

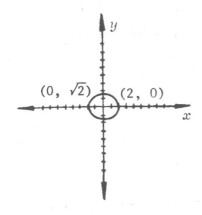

$(0, \sqrt{2})$ $(2, 0)$

1.48   Position: I
$a = \sqrt{169} = 13$
$b = \sqrt{144} = 12$
$c = \sqrt{13^2 - 12^2} = \sqrt{169 - 144}$
   $= \sqrt{25} = 5$
Major axis = $2(13) = 26$
Minor axis = $2(12) = 24$
L.R. $= \dfrac{2(12)^2}{13} = \dfrac{2(144)}{13} = \dfrac{288}{13}$
$e = \dfrac{5}{13}$
Domain: $-13 < x < 13$
Range: $-12 \le y \le 12$

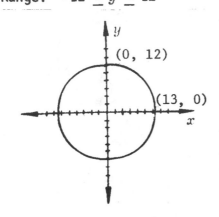

$(0, 12)$

$(13, 0)$

1.49 $36x^2 + 4y^2 = 9$
$\dfrac{36}{9}x^2 + \dfrac{4}{9}y^2 = \dfrac{9}{9}$
$4x^2 + \dfrac{4}{9}y^2 = 1$
$\dfrac{x^2}{\frac{1}{4}} + \dfrac{y^2}{\frac{9}{4}} = 1$
Position: II
$a = \sqrt{\frac{9}{4}} = \frac{3}{2}$
$b = \sqrt{\frac{1}{4}} = \frac{1}{2}$
$c = \sqrt{(\frac{3}{2})^2 - (\frac{1}{2})^2} = \sqrt{\frac{9}{4} - \frac{1}{4}}$
   $= \sqrt{\frac{8}{4}} = \sqrt{2}$
Major axis = $2(\frac{3}{2}) = 3$
Minor axis = $2(\frac{1}{2}) = 1$
L.R. $= \dfrac{2(\frac{1}{2})^2}{\frac{3}{2}} = \dfrac{2(\frac{1}{4})}{\frac{3}{2}} = \dfrac{\frac{1}{2}}{\frac{3}{2}} = \frac{1}{3}$
$e = \dfrac{\sqrt{2}}{\frac{3}{2}} = 2\dfrac{\sqrt{2}}{3}$
Domain: $-\frac{1}{2} \le x \le \frac{1}{2}$
Range: $-\frac{3}{2} \le y \le \frac{3}{2}$

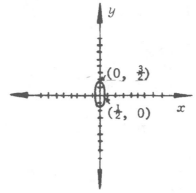

$(0, \frac{3}{2})$

$(\frac{1}{2}, 0)$

1.50 $9x^2 + 16y^2 = 144$
$\dfrac{9x^2}{144} + \dfrac{16y^2}{144} = \dfrac{144}{144}$
$\dfrac{x^2}{16} + \dfrac{y^2}{9} = 1$
Position: I
$a = \sqrt{16} = 4$
$b = \sqrt{9} = 3$
$c = \sqrt{4^2 - 3^2} = \sqrt{16 - 9} = \sqrt{7}$
Major axis = $2(4) = 8$
Minor axis = $2(3) = 6$
L.R. $= \dfrac{2(3)^2}{4} = \dfrac{2(9)}{4} = \dfrac{9}{2}$
$e = \dfrac{\sqrt{7}}{4}$
Domain: $-4 \le x \le 4$
Range: $-3 \le y \le 3$

1.50 cont.

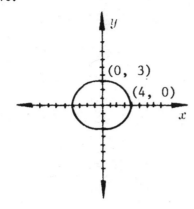

(0, 3)
(4, 0)

1.51   Position: I
Center = (2, 3)
$a = \sqrt{4} = 2$
$b = \sqrt{1} = 1$
$c = \sqrt{2^2 - 1^2} = \sqrt{4 - 1} = \sqrt{3}$
Major axis = 2(2) = 4
Minor axis = 2(1) = 2
L.R. $= \dfrac{2(1)^2}{2} = \dfrac{2(1)}{2} = 1$
$e = \dfrac{\sqrt{3}}{2}$
Domain: $0 \le x \le 4$
Range: $2 \le y \le 4$

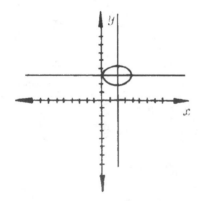

1.52   Position: I
Center = (-6, 4)
$a = \sqrt{20} = 2\sqrt{5}$
$b = \sqrt{16} = 4$
$c = \sqrt{(2\sqrt{5})^2 - 4^2} = \sqrt{20 - 16}$
    $= \sqrt{4} = 2$
Major axis = 2(2√5) = 4√5
Minor axis = 2(4) = 8

1.52 cont.

L.R. $= \dfrac{2(4)^2}{2\sqrt{5}} = \dfrac{4^2}{\sqrt{5}} = \dfrac{16}{\sqrt{5}} = \dfrac{16\sqrt{5}}{5}$

$e = \dfrac{2}{2\sqrt{5}} = \dfrac{1}{\sqrt{5}} = \dfrac{\sqrt{5}}{5}$

Domain: $-6 - 2\sqrt{5} \le x$
        $\le -6 + 2\sqrt{5}$
Range: $0 \le y \le 8$

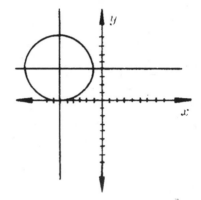

1.53 $\dfrac{12(x - 1)^2}{48} + \dfrac{4(y - 5)^2}{48} = \dfrac{48}{48}$

$\dfrac{(x - 1)^2}{4} + \dfrac{(y - 5)^2}{12} = 1$

Position: II
Center = (1, 5)
$a = \sqrt{12} = 2\sqrt{3}$
$b = \sqrt{4} = 2$
$c = \sqrt{(2\sqrt{3})^2 - 2^2} = \sqrt{12 - 4}$
    $= \sqrt{8} = 2\sqrt{2}$
Major axis = 2(2√3) = 4√3
Minor axis = 2(2) = 4
L.R. $= \dfrac{2(2)^2}{2\sqrt{3}} = \dfrac{2^2}{\sqrt{3}} = \dfrac{4}{\sqrt{3}} = \dfrac{4\sqrt{3}}{3}$

$e = \dfrac{2\sqrt{2}}{2\sqrt{3}} = \dfrac{\sqrt{2}}{\sqrt{3}} = \dfrac{\sqrt{6}}{3}$

Domain: $-1 \le x \le 3$
Range: $5 - 2\sqrt{3} \le y \le 5 + 2\sqrt{3}$

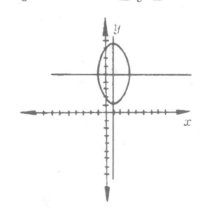

1.54

$$x^2 - 6x + 9y^2 - 18y = -9$$
$$(x^2 - 6x + 9) +$$
$$9(y^2 - 2y + 1) = -9 + 9 + 9$$
$$(x - 3)^2 + 9(y - 1)^2 = 9$$
$$\frac{(x - 3)^2}{9} + \frac{(y - 1)^2}{1} = 1$$

Position: I
Center = (3, 1)
$a = \sqrt{9} = 3$
$b = \sqrt{1} = 1$
$c = \sqrt{3^2 - 1^2} = \sqrt{9 - 1} = \sqrt{8} = 2\sqrt{2}$
Major axis = 2(3) = 6
Minor axis = 2(1) = 2

L.R. $= \frac{2(1)^2}{3} = \frac{2}{3}$

$e = \frac{2\sqrt{2}}{3}$

Domain: $0 < x < 6$
Range: $0 \le y \le 2$

1.56

$$16x^2 - 32x + 25y^2 - 100y = 284$$
$$16(x^2 - 2x + 1) +$$
$$25(y^2 - 4y + 4) = 284 +$$
$$16 +$$
$$100$$
$$16(x - 1)^2 + 25(y - 2)^2 = 400$$
$$\frac{(x - 1)^2}{25} + \frac{(y - 2)^2}{16} = 1$$

Position: I
Center = (1, 2)
$a = \sqrt{25} = 5$
$b = \sqrt{16} = 4$
$c = \sqrt{5^2 - 4^2} = \sqrt{25 - 16} = \sqrt{9} = 3$
Major axis = 2(5) = 10
Minor axis = 2(4) = 8

L.R. $= \frac{2(4)^2}{5} = \frac{2(16)}{5} = \frac{32}{5}$

$e = \frac{3}{5}$

Domain: $-4 < x < 6$
Range: $-2 \le y \le 6$

1.55

$$25x^2 + 100x + 9y^2 - 36y = 89$$
$$25(x^2 + 4x + 4) +$$
$$9(y^2 - 4y + 4) = 89 +$$
$$100 +$$
$$36$$
$$25(x + 2)^2 + 9(y - 2)^2 = 225$$
$$\frac{(x + 2)^2}{9} + \frac{(y - 2)^2}{25} = 1$$

Position: II
Center = (-2, 2)
$a = \sqrt{25} = 5$
$b = \sqrt{9} = 3$
$c = \sqrt{5^2 - 3^2} = \sqrt{25 - 9} = \sqrt{16} = 4$
Major axis = 2(5) = 10
Minor axis = 2(3) = 6

L.R. $= \frac{2(3)^2}{5} = \frac{2(9)}{5} = \frac{18}{5}$

$e = \frac{4}{5}$

Domain: $-5 < x < 1$
Range: $-3 < y < 7$

1.57

$$4x^2 + 3y^2 - 32x + 12y = -64$$
$$4(x^2 - 8x + 16) +$$
$$3(y^2 + 4y + 4) = -64 +$$
$$64 + 12$$
$$4(x - 4)^2 + 3(y + 2)^2 = 12$$
$$\frac{(x - 4)^2}{3} + \frac{(y + 2)^2}{4} = 1$$

Position: II
Center = (4, -2)
$a = \sqrt{4} = 2$
$b = \sqrt{3}$
$c = \sqrt{2^2 - (\sqrt{3})^2} = \sqrt{4 - 3} = \sqrt{1} = 1$
Major axis = 2(2) = 4
Minor axis = $2\sqrt{3}$

L.R. $= \frac{2(\sqrt{3})^2}{2} = (\sqrt{3})^2 = 3$

$e = \frac{1}{2}$

Domain: $4 - \sqrt{3} < x \le 4 + \sqrt{3}$
Range: $-4 \le y \le 0$

1.58

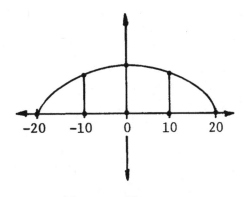

$a = 20, \; b = 15$

$\dfrac{x^2}{20^2} + \dfrac{y^2}{15^2} = 1$

$\dfrac{x^2}{400} + \dfrac{y^2}{225} = 1$

$225x^2 + 400y^2 = 90{,}000$

$400y^2 = 90{,}000 - 225x^2$

$y^2 = \dfrac{90{,}000 - 225x^2}{400}$

$\sqrt{y^2} = \sqrt{\dfrac{90{,}000 - 225x^2}{400}}$

$y = \dfrac{\sqrt{225(400 - x^2)}}{20}$

$y = \dfrac{15}{20}\sqrt{400 - x^2}$

$y = \dfrac{3}{4}\sqrt{400 - x^2}$

When $x = -20, \; y = \dfrac{3}{4}\sqrt{400 - 400} = 0$

$x = -10, \; y = \dfrac{3}{4}\sqrt{400 - 100}$

$= \dfrac{3}{4}\sqrt{300} = \dfrac{3}{4}(10)(\sqrt{3})$

$= \dfrac{15}{2}\sqrt{3} \doteq 13$

$x = 0, \quad y = \dfrac{3}{4}\sqrt{400} = \dfrac{3}{4}(20) =$

$= 15$

$x = 10, \quad y = \dfrac{3}{4}\sqrt{400 - 100}$

$= \dfrac{3}{4}\sqrt{300} = \dfrac{3}{4}(10)(\sqrt{3})$

$= \dfrac{15}{2}\sqrt{3} \doteq 13$

$x = 20, \quad y = \dfrac{3}{4}\sqrt{400 - 400} = 0$

1.59

$\dfrac{x^2}{a^2} + \dfrac{y^2}{b^2} = 1$

$c = 4, \; a = 5$

$a^2 - c^2 = b^2$

$5^2 - 4^2 = b^2$

$25 - 16 = b^2$

$9 = b^2$

$\sqrt{9} = \sqrt{b^2}$

$3 = b$

$\dfrac{x^2}{25} + \dfrac{y^2}{9} = 1$

1.60

$\dfrac{x^2}{a^2} + \dfrac{y^2}{b^2} = 1$

$c = 5,$

$e = \dfrac{c}{a} = \dfrac{5}{8}; \; \therefore \; a = 8$

$b^2 = a^2 - c^2$

$b^2 = 8^2 - 5^2$

$b^2 = 64 - 25 = 39$

$\dfrac{x^2}{64} + \dfrac{y^2}{39} = 1$

1.61

$(h, k) = (4, -1)$

$(x, y) = (8, 0)$

$\dfrac{(x - h)^2}{a^2} + \dfrac{(y - k)^2}{b^2} = 1$

$\dfrac{4^2}{a^2} + \dfrac{1}{b^2} = 1$

Also, $c = 3, \; a^2 - 9 = b^2$

$\dfrac{16}{a^2} + \dfrac{1}{a^2 - 9} = 1$

$16(a^2 - 9) + a^2(1) = 1(a^2)(a^2 - 9)$

$16a^2 - 144 + a^2 = a^4 - 9a^2$

$a^4 - 26a^2 + 144 = 0$

$(a^2 - 8)(a^2 - 18) = 0$

$a^2 - 8 = 0$

$\underline{a^2 = 8}$

or

$a^2 - 18 = 0$

$a^2 = 18$

$b^2 = 8 - 9$

$b^2 = -1; \; \text{reject}$

or

$b^2 = 18 - 9$

$b^2 = 9$

1.61 cont.

$$\frac{(x-4)^2}{18} + \frac{(y+1)^2}{9} = 1$$
$$(x-4)^2 + 2(y+1)^2 = 18$$
$$x^2 - 8x + 16 + 2y^2 + 4y + 2 = 18$$
$$x^2 + 2y^2 - 8x + 4y = 0$$

1.62 $a = 40,\ b = 30$

$$\frac{x^2}{40^2} + \frac{y^2}{30^2} = 1$$

Find y when $x = 15$:

$$\frac{15^2}{40^2} + \frac{y^2}{30^2} = 1$$
$$y^2 = \frac{40^2 \cdot 30^2 - 30^2 \cdot 15^2}{40^2}$$
$$y^2 = \frac{(1,600)(900) - (900)(225)}{1,600}$$
$$y^2 = \frac{1,440,000 - 202,500}{1,600}$$
$$y^2 = \frac{1,237,500}{1,600}$$
$$y^2 = \frac{12,375}{16}$$
$$\sqrt{y^2} = \sqrt{\frac{12,375}{16}}$$
$$y = \frac{15\sqrt{55}}{4}$$

1.63 $\sqrt{(x-2)^2 + (y+3)^2} + \sqrt{(x-2)^2 + (y-7)^2} = 12$

$$\sqrt{(x-2)^2 + (y+3)^2} = 12 - \sqrt{(x-2)^2 + (y-7)^2}$$
$$\left(\sqrt{(x-2)^2 + (y+3)^2}\right)^2 = \left(12 - \sqrt{(x-2)^2 + (y-7)^2}\right)^2$$
$$(x-2)^2 + (y+3)^2 = 144 - 24\sqrt{(x-2)^2 + (y-7)^2} + (x-2)^2 + (y-7)^2$$
$$24\sqrt{(x-2)^2 + (y-7)^2} + (y+3)^2 = 144 + (y-7)^2$$
$$24\sqrt{(x-2)^2 + (y-7)^2} + y^2 + 6y + 9 = 144 + y^2 - 14y + 49$$
$$24\sqrt{(x-2)^2 + (y-7)^2} = 144 - 20y + 40$$
$$24\sqrt{(x-2)^2 + (y-7)^2} = 184 - 20y$$
$$6\sqrt{(x-2)^2 + (y-7)^2} = 46 - 5y$$
$$\left(6\sqrt{(x-2)^2 + (y-7)^2}\right)^2 = (46 - 5y)^2$$
$$36[(x-2)^2 + (y-7)^2] = (46 - 5y)^2$$
$$36(x^2 - 4x + 4 + y^2 - 14y + 49) = 2,116 - 460y + 25y^2$$
$$36x^2 - 144x + 144 + 36y^2 - 504y + 1,764 = 2,116 - 460y + 25y^2$$
$$36x^2 + 36y^2 - 144x - 504y + 1,908 = 25y^2 - 460y + 2,116$$
$$36x^2 + 11y^2 - 144x - 44y - 208 = 0$$

1.64 $\frac{x^2}{36} + \frac{y^2}{4} = 1$

$a = \sqrt{36} = 6$

$b = \sqrt{4} = 2$

Area $= \pi ab = \pi(6)(2) = 12\pi$

1.65 $\frac{x^2}{16} + \frac{y^2}{9} = 1$

$x = r \cos \theta$

$y = r \sin \theta$

$$\frac{r^2 \cos^2 \theta}{16} + \frac{r^2 \sin^2 \theta}{9} = 1$$

$9r^2 \cos^2 \theta + 16r^2 \sin^2 \theta = 144$

$r^2(9\cos^2 \theta + 16\sin^2 \theta) = 144$

$r^2 = \dfrac{144}{9\cos^2 \theta + 16\sin^2 \theta}$

II. SECTION TWO

2.1 $y^2 = 4(1)x$

$p = 1$

Position: I
Vertex $= (0, 0)$
Focus $= (1, 0)$
L.R. $= 4(1) = 4$
Directrix: $x = -1$
Domain: $x \geq 0$
Range: all real numbers

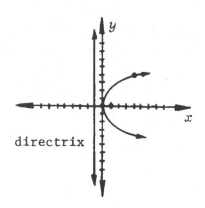

2.2 $x^2 = 4(\frac{3}{2})y$

$p = \frac{3}{2}$

Position: II
Vertex $= (0, 0)$
Focus $= (0, \frac{3}{2})$
L.R. $= 4(\frac{3}{2}) = 6$

2.2 cont.

Directrix: $y = -\frac{3}{2}$
Domain: all real numbers
Range: $y \geq 0$

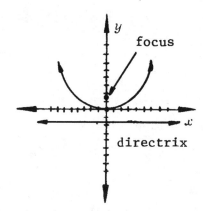

2.3 $x^2 = -10y$

$x^2 = -4(\frac{5}{2})y$

$p = \frac{5}{2}$

Position: II
Vertex $= (0, 0)$
Focus $= (0, -\frac{5}{2})$
L.R. $= 4(\frac{5}{2}) = 10$
Directrix: $y = \frac{5}{2}$
Domain: all real numbers
Range: $y \leq 0$

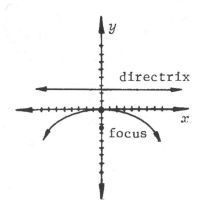

2.4 $y^2 = \frac{1}{2}x$

$y^2 = 4(\frac{1}{8})x$

$p = \frac{1}{8}$

Position: I
Vertex $= (0, 0)$
Focus $= (\frac{1}{8}, 0)$
L.R. $= 4(\frac{1}{8}) = \frac{1}{2}$
Directrix: $x = -\frac{1}{8}$
Domain: $x \geq 0$
Range: all real numbers

2.4 cont.

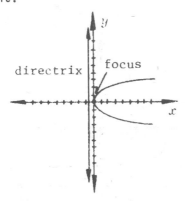

2.5 $x^2 = 4(\tfrac{3}{4})y$
$p = \tfrac{3}{4}$

Position: II
Vertex = (0, 0)
Focus = $(0, \tfrac{3}{4})$
L.R. = $4(\tfrac{3}{4})$ = 3
Directrix: $y = -\tfrac{3}{4}$
Domain: all real x
Range: $y \geq 0$

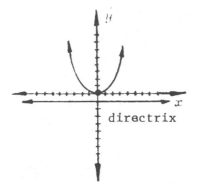

2.6 $x^2 = \tfrac{y}{2}$
$x^2 = \tfrac{1}{2}y$
$x^2 = 4(\tfrac{1}{8})y$

$x^2 = 2y$
$x^2 = 4(\tfrac{1}{2})y$

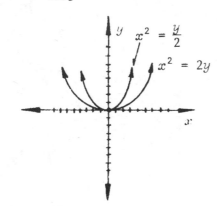

2.7 $x^2 = y$
$x^2 = 4(\tfrac{1}{4})y$

$x^2 = 4y$
$x^2 = 4(1)y$

$x^2 = \tfrac{y}{4}$

$x^2 = 4(\tfrac{1}{16})y$

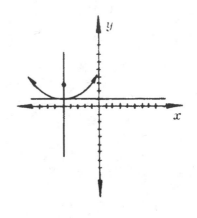

2.8   The smaller the focus value, the more closed the curve is. The larger the focus value, the more open the curve is.

2.9   No. Each x in the domain has 2 values of y.

2.10   Position: II
Vertex = (-5, 1)
Focus = $4p = 4$, $p = 1$, (-5, 2)
L.R. = 4
Directrix: $y = 0$
Domain: all real x
Range: $y \geq 1$

2.11   Position: I
        Vertex = (-2, -4)
        Focus = $4p$ = 12, p = 3, (-5, -4)
        L.R. = 12
        Directrix: x = 1
        Domain: $x \leq -2$
        Range: all real y

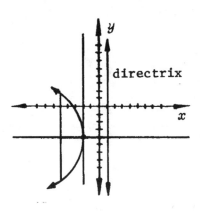

2.12   Position: II
        Vertex = (1, 1)
        Focus = $4p$ = 1, $p = \frac{1}{4}$, (1, $1\frac{1}{4}$)
        L.R. = 1
        Directrix: $y = \frac{3}{4}$
        Domain: all real x
        Range: $y \geq 1$

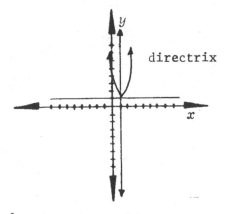

2.13 x^2 + 8x - 10y - 34 = 0
                x^2 + 8x = 10y + 34
        x^2 + 8x + 16 = 10y + 50
                $(x + 4)^2$ = 10(y + 5)

        Position: II
        Vertex = (-4, -5)
        Focus = $4p$ = 10, $p = \frac{5}{2}$, (-4, $-2\frac{1}{2}$)
        L.R. = 10
        Directrix: $y = -7\frac{1}{2}$
        Domain: all real numbers
        Range: $y \geq -5$

2.13 cont.

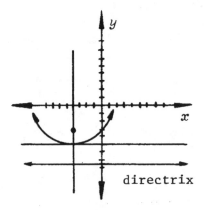

2.14 $2y^2$ - 15x - 4y - 28 = 0
                $2y^2$ - 4y = 15x + 28
        2(y^2 - 24 + 1) = 15x + 30
              2(y - 1)^2 = 15(x + 2)
               $(y - 1)^2$ = $\frac{15}{2}$(x + 2)

        Position: I
        Vertex = (-2, 1)
        Focus = $4p = \frac{15}{2}$, $p = \frac{15}{8}$, $(-\frac{1}{8}$, 1)
        L.R. = $\frac{15}{2}$
        Directrix: $x = -3\frac{7}{8}$
        Domain: $x \geq -2$
        Range: all real y

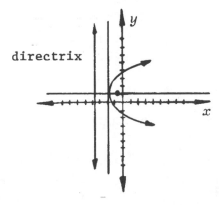

2.15 $4x^2$ - 20x + 24y + 61 = 0
                $4x^2$ - 20x = -24y - 61
        4(x^2 - 5x + $\frac{25}{4}$) = -24y - 61 + 25
              4(x - $\frac{5}{2}$)^2 = -24y - 36
               $(x - \frac{5}{2})^2$ = -6(y + $\frac{3}{2}$)

2.15 cont.

Position: II
Vertex = $(\frac{5}{2}, -\frac{3}{2})$
Focus = $4p = 6$, $p = \frac{3}{2}$, $(\frac{5}{2}, -3)$
L.R. = 6
Directrix: $y = 0$
Domain: all real x
Range: $y \leq -\frac{3}{2}$

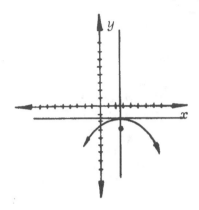

2.16 $4y^2 + 32x - 28y - 15 = 0$
$$4y^2 - 28y = -32x + 15$$
$$4\left(y^2 - 7y + \frac{49}{4}\right) = -32x + 64$$
$$\left(y - \frac{7}{2}\right)^2 = -8(x - 2)$$

Position: I
Vertex = $(2, \frac{7}{2})$
Focus = $4p = 8$, $p = 2$, $(0, \frac{7}{2})$
L.R. = 8
Directrix: $y = 4$
Domain: $x \leq -2$
Range: all real y

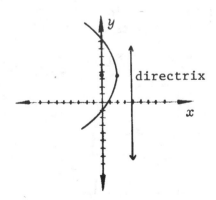

2.17 $3x^2 + 10x + 4y + 11 = 0$
$$3x^2 + 10x = -4y - 11$$
$$3\left(x^2 + \frac{10}{3}x + \frac{25}{9}\right) = -4y - 11 + \frac{25}{3}$$
$$3\left(x + \frac{5}{3}\right)^2 = -4y - \frac{8}{3}$$
$$3\left(x + \frac{5}{3}\right)^2 = -4\left(y + \frac{2}{3}\right)$$
$$\left(x + \frac{5}{3}\right)^2 = -\frac{4}{3}\left(y + \frac{2}{3}\right)$$

Position: II
Vertex = $(-\frac{5}{3}, -\frac{2}{3})$
Focus = $4p = \frac{4}{3}$, $p = \frac{1}{3}$, $(-\frac{5}{3}, -1)$
L.R. = $\frac{4}{3}$
Directrix: $y = -\frac{1}{3}$
Domain: all real x
Range: $y \leq -\frac{2}{3}$

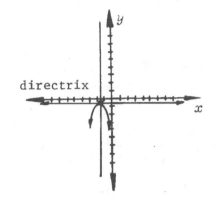

2.18 $$(x - 3)^2 = 8(y + 1)$$
$$x^2 - 6x + 9 = 8y + 8$$
$$x^2 - 6x - 8y + 1 = 0$$

2.19 $$5(y + 2)^2 - 6(x + 1) = 0$$
$$5y^2 + 20y + 20 - 6x - 6 = 0$$
$$5y^2 - 6x + 20y + 14 = 0$$

2.20 no, has x^2 and y^2 terms

2.21 yes

2.22 yes

2.23 no, has x^2 and y^2 terms

2.24 yes

2.25 $(h, k) = (-3, 3)$
Position: II
$p = 3$
$(x - h)^2 = 4p(y - k)$
$(x + 3)^2 = 4(3)(y - 3)$
$(x + 3)^2 = 12(y - 3)$

2.26

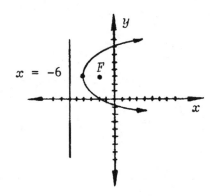

$x = -6$

Focus at (-2, 3)
Directrix: $x = -6$
Position: I
Vertex = (h, k) = (-4, 3)
$p = 2$

$(y - k)^2 = 4p(x - h)$
$(y - 3)^2 = 4(2)(x + 4)$
$(y - 3)^2 = 8(x + 4)$

$y^2 - 6y + 9 = 8x + 32$
$y^2 - 6y - 8x + 9 = 32$
$y^2 - 6y - 8x - 23 = 0$

2.27

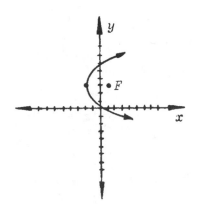

$(h, k) = (-2, 3)$
Focus at (1, 3)
Position: I
$p = 3$

$(y - k)^2 = 4p(x - h)$
$(y - k)^2 = 4(3)(x - h)$
$(y - 3)^2 = 12(x + 2)$

2.27 cont.

$y^2 - 6y + 9 = 12x + 24$
$y^2 - 6y - 12x + 9 = 24$
$y^2 - 6y - 12x - 15 = 0$

2.28 $x^2 = 4py$
(5, 4):
$5^2 = 4p(4)$
$25 = 16p$
$p = \frac{25}{16}$
$x^2 = 4 \cdot \frac{25}{16}y$
$x^2 = \frac{25}{4}y$
$4x^2 = 25y$

2.29
$y = a(x - h)^2 + k$
$y - k = a(x - h)^2$
$\frac{1}{a}(y - k) = (x - h)^2$

$(x - h)^2 = \frac{1}{a}(y - k)$

2.30 II

2.31
$y = a(x - h)^2 + k$
$y - k = a(x - h)^2$
$a(x - h)^2 = y - k$
$(x - h)^2 = \frac{(y - k)}{a}$

$4p = \frac{1}{a}$

$p = \frac{1}{4}a$

2.32 reverses-opens down or left

2.33 maximum or minimum height
(y coordinate of vertex)

2.34 If $a > 0$, k is minimum y.
If $a < 0$, k is maximum y.

2.35

$s = -\frac{1}{2}gt^2 + V_0 t + s_0$
When $t = 0$, $s_0 = 0$

$V_0 = 64$

2.35 cont.

$$s = -16t^2 + 64t$$
$$16(t^2 - 4t) = -s$$
$$16(t^2 - 4t + 4) = -s + 64$$
$$16(t - 2)^2 = -s + 64$$
$$(t - 2)^2 = -\frac{1}{16}(s - 64)$$

$(h, k) = (2, 64)$
Maximum height = 64 ft.
Time = 2 sec.

2.36 The ball starts falling when released due to gravity.

$$s = \frac{1}{2}gt^2$$
$$555 = 16t^2$$
$$t = \sqrt{\frac{555}{16}} = \frac{\sqrt{555}}{4} \doteq 5.9 \text{ sec to fall}$$
distance = $r \cdot t \doteq 40(5.9) \doteq 236$ ft.

2.37 $s = -\frac{1}{2}gt^2 + V_o t + s_o$

$$s = -\frac{1}{2}(4.9)t^2 + 49t$$
$$s = -2.45t^2 + 49t$$
$$s = -2.45(t^2 - 20t)$$
$$s = -2.45(t^2 - 20t + 100) + 245$$
$$s = -2.45(t - 10)^2 + 245$$

$h = 10, k = 245$
Maximum height = 245 m
Time for maximum height = 10 sec.
Total time = 2(10) = 20 sec.

2.38 $A = lw$ and
$$1,000 = 2l + w$$
$$1,000 - 2l = w$$

$$A = l(1,000 - 2l)$$
$$A = -2l^2 + 1,000l$$
$$A = -2(l^2 - 500l + 250^2) + 2(250)^2$$
$$A = -2(l - 250)^2 + 125,00$$
Maximum area = 125,000 sq. ft.

2.39

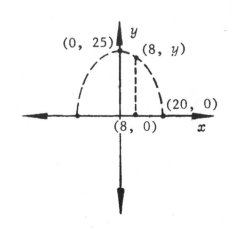

2.39 cont.

$$(x - h)^2 = 4p(y - k)$$
$$(x - 0)^2 = 4p(y - 25)$$
$$x^2 = 4p(y - 25)$$

Substitute (20, 0) into the equation:
$$20^2 = 4p(0 - 25)$$
$$20^2 = 4p(-25)$$
$$20^2 = -100p$$
$$p = \frac{20^2}{-100} = \frac{400}{-100} = -4$$
$$x^2 = 4(-4)(y - 25)$$
$$x^2 = -16(y - 25)$$

Find y when $x = 8$:
$$8^2 = -16(y - 25)$$
$$64 = -16(y - 25)$$
$$-4 = y - 25$$
$$y = 21 \text{ ft.}$$

2.40 Let x = one number
$2x + 4$ = the other number

$$p = x(2x + 4)$$
$$p = 2x^2 + 4x$$
$$p = 2(x^2 + 2x + 1) - 2$$
$$p = 2(x + 1)^2 - 2$$
Minimum product = -2 when $x = -1$.
No maximum product exists.

2.41 Let x = change in number of people
p = profit
p = (cost)(number of people)
$$p = (3 + 0.10x)(100 - x)$$
$$p = 300 - 3x + 10x - 0.10x^2$$
$$p = -0.10x^2 + 7x + 300$$
$$p = -0.10(x^2 - 70x + 35^2) + 300 + 122.5$$
$$p = -0.10(x - 35)^2 + 422.5$$
x = 35 more people
Price = \$3 + 0.10(35) = \$3 + 3.50
= \$6.50

2.42 Position: I
Center = (0, 0)
$a = \sqrt{16} = 4$
$b = \sqrt{25} = 5$
$c = \sqrt{4^2 + 5^2} = \sqrt{16 + 25} = \sqrt{41}$
Foci = $(\pm\sqrt{41}, 0)$
L.R. = $\frac{2(5)^2}{4} = \frac{2(25)}{4} = \frac{25}{2}$
$e = \frac{\sqrt{41}}{4}$

Domain: $x \geq 4$ or $x \leq -4$
Range: all real y

2.42 cont.

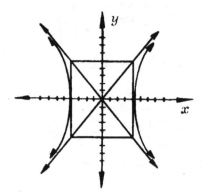

2.43 Position: I
Center = (1, 3)
$a = \sqrt{9} = 3$
$b = \sqrt{4} = 2$
$c = \sqrt{3^2 + 2^2} = \sqrt{9 + 4} = \sqrt{13}$
Foci = $(1 \pm \sqrt{13}, 3)$
L.R. $= \dfrac{2(2)^2}{3} = \dfrac{2(4)}{3} = \dfrac{8}{3}$

$e = \dfrac{\sqrt{13}}{3}$

Domain: $x \geq 4$ or $x \leq -2$
Range: all real y

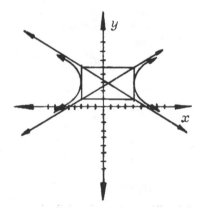

2.44 Position: II
Center = (0, 0)
$a = \sqrt{1} = 1$
$b = \sqrt{1} = 1$
$c = \sqrt{1^2 + 1^2} = \sqrt{2}$
Foci = $(0, \pm\sqrt{2})$
L.R. $= \dfrac{2(1)^2}{1} = 2$

$e = \dfrac{\sqrt{2}}{1}$

2.44 cont.

Domain: all real x
Range: $y \geq 1$ or $y \leq -1$

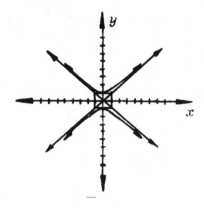

2.45

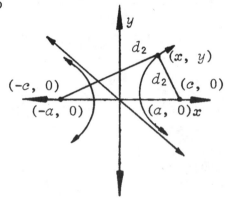

$|d_1 - d_2| = k$
When $(x, y) = (a, 0)$, then
$d_2 = a + c$ and $d_1 = c - a$.
$|d_1 - d_2| = |c - a - (a + c)| = 2a$
$d_1 = \sqrt{(x - c)^2 + (y - 0)^2}$
$d_2 = \sqrt{(x + c)^2 + (y - 0)^2}$

220

2.45 cont.

$$\sqrt{(x - c)^2 + y^2} - \sqrt{(x + c)^2 + y^2} = 2a$$

$$\left(\sqrt{(x - c)^2 + y^2}\right)^2 = \left(2a + \sqrt{(x + c)^2 + y^2}\right)^2$$

$$(x - c)^2 + y^2 = 4a^2 + 4a\sqrt{(x + c)^2 + y^2} + (x + c)^2 + y^2$$

$$x^2 - 2cx + c^2 + y^2 = 4a^2 + 4a\sqrt{(x + c)^2 + y^2} + x^2 + 2cx + c^2 + y^2$$

$$-4cx - 4a^2 = 4a\sqrt{(x + c)^2 + y^2}$$

$$(-cx - a^2)^2 = \left(a\sqrt{(x + c)^2 + y^2}\right)^2$$

$$c^2x^2 + 2a^2cx + a^4 = a^2[x^2 + 2cx + c^2 + y^2]$$

$$c^2x^2 + \cancel{2a^2cx} + a^4 = a^2x^2 + \cancel{2a^2cx} + a^2c^2 + a^2y^2$$

$$c^2x^2 - a^2x^2 - a^2y^2 = a^2c^2 - a^4$$

$$(c^2 - a^2)x^2 - a^2y^2 = a^2(c^2 - a^2)$$

Let $b^2 = c^2 - a^2$.

$$b^2x^2 - a^2y^2 = a^2b^2$$

$$\frac{x^2}{a^2} - \frac{y^2}{b^2} = 1$$

2.46 For $Ax^2 + Bxy + Cy^2 + Dx + Ey + F = 0$, $B = 0$, and A and C must be opposite in sign and $\neq 0$. If D and $E = 0$, the center is at the origin.

2.47

$$\frac{(y - 3)^2}{10} - \frac{(x - 2)^2}{5} = 1$$

$$(y - 3)^2 - 2(x - 2)^2 = 10$$

$$y^2 - 6y + 9 - 2x^2 + 8x - 8 = 10$$

$$-2x^2 + y^2 + 8x - 6y - 9 = 0$$

2.48

$$x^2 - y^2 - 10x + 6y + 15 = 0$$

$$x^2 - 10x - (y^2 - 6y) = -15$$

$$(x^2 - 10x + 25) - (y^2 - 6y + 9) = -15 + 25 - 9$$

$$(x - 5)^2 - (y - 3)^2 = 1$$

2.49

$$x^2 - 4y^2 + 6x + 32y - 59 = 0$$

$$x^2 + 6x - 4y^2 + 32y = 59$$

$$x^2 + 6x + 9 - 4(y^2 - 8y + 16) = 59 + 9 - 64$$

$$(x + 3)^2 - 4(y - 4)^2 = 4$$

$$\frac{(x + 3)^2}{4} - \frac{(y - 4)^2}{1} = 1$$

$$(h, k) = (-3, 4)$$

2.50

$$(h, k) = (0, 0)$$

$$a = 3$$

$$2x - 3y = 0$$

$$y = \pm\frac{b}{a}x$$

$$y = \frac{2}{3}x$$

$$\frac{b}{a} = \frac{2}{3}; \quad b = 2$$

$$\frac{x^2}{9} - \frac{y^2}{4} = 1 \text{ or } 4x^2 - 9y^2 = 36$$

2.51

$$\frac{x^2}{a^2} - \frac{y^2}{b^2} = 1$$

$(3, 1)$:

$$\frac{3^2}{a^2} - \frac{1^2}{b^2} = 1$$

$$\frac{9}{a^2} - \frac{1}{b^2} = 1$$

$$\frac{81}{a^2} - \frac{9}{b^2} = 9$$

$(9, 5)$:

$$\frac{9^2}{a^2} - \frac{5^2}{b^2} = 1$$

$$\frac{81}{a^2} - \frac{25}{b^2} = 1$$

2.51 cont.

Subtract:

$$\frac{81}{a^2} - \frac{9}{b^2} = 9$$

$$\frac{81}{a^2} - \frac{25}{b^2} = 1$$

$$\frac{16}{b^2} = 8$$

$$b^2 = 2$$

Substitute:

$$\frac{9}{a^2} - \frac{1}{2} = 1$$

$$\frac{9}{a^2} = \frac{3}{2}$$

$$3a^2 = 18$$

$$a^2 = 6$$

Therefore,

$$\frac{x^2}{6} - \frac{y^2}{2} = 1 \text{ and}$$

$$x^2 - 3y^2 = 6$$

2.52

$$49x^2 - 36y^2 = 1{,}764$$

$$\frac{49x^2}{1{,}764} - \frac{36y^2}{1{,}764} = \frac{1{,}764}{1{,}764}$$

$$\frac{x^2}{36} - \frac{y^2}{49} = 1$$

$$a = \sqrt{36} = 6$$

$$b = \sqrt{49} = 7$$

$$y = \pm\frac{b}{a}x$$

$$y = \pm\frac{7}{6}x$$

2.53 When the cutting plane passes through the vertex of the cone, no equation exists. Since $a = 0$ and $b = 0$, $\frac{x^2}{a^2} - \frac{y^2}{b^2} = 1$ is undefined.

III. SECTION THREE

3.1 $(h, k) = (5, 4)$ and
$(x, y) = (10, 9)$
$x' = x - h = 10 - 5 = 5$
$y' = y - k = 9 - 4 = 5$
$(x', y') = (5, 5)$

3.2 $(h, k) = (5, 4)$ and
$(x, y) = (8, 8)$
$x' = x - h = 8 - 5 = 3$
$y' = y - k = 8 - 4 = 4$
$(x', y') = (3, 4)$

3.3 $(h, k) = (5, 4)$ and
$(x, y) = (1, 3)$
$x' = x - h = 1 - 5 = -4$
$y' = y - k = 3 - 4 = -1$
$(x', y') = (-4, -1)$

3.4 $(h, k) = (5, 4)$ and
$(x, y) = (-3, 2)$
$x' = x - h = -3 - 5 = -8$
$y' = y - k = 2 - 4 = -2$
$(x', y') = (-8, -2)$

3.5 $(h, k) = (5, 4)$ and
$(x, y) = (-8, -6)$
$x' = x - h = -8 - 5 = -13$
$y' = y - k = -6 - 4 = -10$
$(x', y') = (-13, -10)$

3.6 $(h, k) = (5, 4)$ and
$(x, y) = (-9, 9)$
$x' = x - h = -9 - 5 = -14$
$y' = y - k = 9 - 4 = 5$
$(x', y') = (-14, 5)$

3.7 $(h, k) = (-3, -3)$ and
$(x, y) = (5, 5)$
$x' = x - h = 5 - (-3) = 8$
$y' = y - k = 5 - (-3) = 8$
$(x', y') = (8, 8)$

3.8 $(h, k) = (-3, -3)$ and
$(x, y) = (-3, 4)$
$x' = x - h = -3 - (-3) = 0$
$y' = y - k = 4 - (-3) = 7$
$(x', y') = (0, 7)$

3.9 $(h, k) = (-3, -3)$ and
$(x, y) = (-3, -3)$
$x' = x - h = -3 - (-3) = 0$
$y' = y - k = -3 - (-3) = 0$
$(x', y') = (0, 0)$

3.10 $(h, k) = (-3, -3)$ and
$(x, y) = (-8, -8)$
$x' = x - h = -8 - (-3) = -5$
$y' = y - k = -8 - (-3) = -5$
$(x', y') = (-5, -5)$

3.11 $(h, k) = (-3, -3)$ and
$(x, y) = (-9, 10)$
$x' = x - h = -9 - (-3) = -6$
$y' = y - k = 10 - (-3) = 13$
$(x', y') = (-6, 13)$

3.12 $(h, k) = (-3, -3)$ and
$(x, y) = (7, -12)$
$x' = x - h = 7 - (-3) = 10$
$y' = y - k = -12 - (-3) = -9$
$(x', y') = (10, -9)$

3.13 $(x', y') = (6, 2)$ and
$(h, k) = (-3, 4)$
$x' = x - h$
$6 = x - (-3)$
$x = 3$
$y' = y - k$
$2 = y - (4)$
$y = 6$
$(x, y) = (3, 6)$

3.14 $(x', y') = (0, 0)$ and
$(h, k) = (-3, 4)$
$x' = x - h$
$0 = x - (-3)$
$x = -3$
$y' = y - k$
$0 = y - 4$
$y = 4$
$(x, y) = (-3, 4)$

3.15 $(x', y') = (-3, 4)$ and
$(h, k) = (-3, 4)$
$x' = x - h$
$-3 = x - (-3)$
$x = -6$
$y' = y - k$
$4 = y - (4)$
$y = 8$
$(x, y) = (-6, 8)$

3.16 $(x - 8)^2 + (y + 3)^2 = 40$
Center is $(8, -3)$.
$x' = x - 8$
$x = x' + 8$
$y' = y + 3$
$y = y' - 3$

$(x' + 8 - 8)^2 + (y' - 3 + 3)^2 = 40$
$(x')^2 + (y')^2 = 40$

3.17 $x^2 + y^2 + 8x - 6y - 15 = 0$
$x^2 + 8x + y^2 - 6y = 15$
$x^2 + 8x + 16 + y^2 - 6y + 9 = 15 + 16 + 9$
$(x + 4)^2 + (y - 3)^2 = 40$

Center is $(-4, 3)$.
$x = x' - 4$ and $y = y' + 3$
$(x' - 4 + 4)^2 + (y' + 3 - 3)^2 = 40$
$(x')^2 + (y')^2 = 40$

3.18 $\dfrac{(x - 1)^2}{4} + \dfrac{(y - 2)^2}{1} = 1$
Center is $(1, 2)$.
$x = x' + 1$ and $y = y' + 2$

$\dfrac{(x' + 1 - 1)^2}{4} + \dfrac{(y' + 2 - 2)^2}{1} = 1$
$\dfrac{(x')^2}{4} + \dfrac{(y')^2}{1} = 1$

3.19 $9x^2 + 4y^2 + 54x - 8y + 49 = 0$
$9x^2 + 54x + 4y^2 - 8y = -49$
$9(x^2 + 6x + 9) + 4(y^2 - 2y + 1) = -49 + 81 + 4$
$9(x + 3)^2 + 4(y - 1)^2 = 36$
$\dfrac{9(x + 3)^2}{36} + \dfrac{4(y - 1)^2}{36} = 1$
$\dfrac{(x + 3)^2}{4} + \dfrac{(y - 1)^2}{9} = 1$

3.19 cont.

Center is $(-3, 1)$.
$x = x' - 3$ and $y = y' + 1$

$$\frac{(x' - 3 + 3)^2}{4} + \frac{(y' + 1 - 1)^2}{9} = 1$$

$$\frac{(x')^2}{4} + \frac{(y')^2}{9} = 1$$

3.20

$$4x^2 - 25y^2 - 8x - 100y - 196 = 0$$
$$4x^2 - 8x - 25y^2 - 100y = 196$$
$$4(x^2 - 2x) - 25(y^2 + 4y) = 196$$
$$4(x^2 - 2x + 1) - 25(y^2 + 4y + 4) = 196 + 4 - 100$$
$$\frac{4(x - 1)^2}{100} - \frac{25(y + 2)^2}{100} = \frac{100}{100}$$
$$\frac{(x - 1)^2}{25} - \frac{(y + 2)^2}{4} = 1$$

Center is $(1, -2)$.
$x = x' + 1$ and $y = y' - 2$

$$\frac{(x' + 1 - 1)^2}{25} - \frac{(y' - 2 + 2)^2}{4} = 1$$

$$\frac{(x')^2}{25} - \frac{(y')^2}{4} = 1$$

3.21 $4x^2 - y^2 + 24x + 4y + 28 = 0$
$$4x^2 + 24x - y^2 + 4y = -28$$
$$4(x^2 + 6x + 9) - (y^2 - 4y + 4) = -28 + 36 - 4$$
$$4(x + 3)^2 - (y - 2)^2 = 4$$
$$\frac{(x + 3)^2}{1} - \frac{(y - 2)^2}{4} = 1$$

Center is $(-3, 2)$.
$x = x' - 3$ and $y = y' + 2$

$$\frac{(x' - 3 + 3)^2}{1} + \frac{(y' + 2 - 2)^2}{4} = 1$$

$$\frac{(x')^2}{1} - \frac{(y')^2}{4} = 1$$

3.22 $x^2 + 6x + 4y + 5 = 0$
$$x^2 + 6x + 4y = -5$$
$$x^2 + 6x + 9 + 4y = -5 + 9$$
$$(x + 3)^2 = -4y + 4$$
$$(x + 3)^2 = -4(y - 1)$$

Center is $(-3, 1)$.
$x = x' - 3$ and $y = y' + 1$
$$(x' - 3 + 3)^2 = -4(y' + 1 - 1)$$
$$(x')^2 = -4(y')$$

3.23 $y^2 + 6y - 8x - 31 = 0$
$$y^2 + 6y = 8x + 31$$
$$y^2 + 6y + 9 = 8x + 31 + 9$$
$$(y + 3)^2 = 8x + 40$$
$$(y + 3)^2 = 8(x + 5)$$

Center is $(-5, -3)$.
$x = x' - 5$ and $y = y' - 3$
$$(y' - 3 + 3)^2 = 8(x' - 5 + 5)$$
$$(y')^2 = 8(x')$$

3.24 $x' = x \cos \theta + y \sin \theta$
$$= x(\cos 45°) + y(\sin 45°)$$
$$= 1(\frac{\sqrt{2}}{2}) + 1(\frac{\sqrt{2}}{2})$$
$$= \sqrt{2}$$

$y' = x \sin \theta - y \cos \theta$
$$= x(\sin 45°) - y(\cos 45°)$$
$$= 1(\frac{\sqrt{2}}{2}) - 1(\frac{\sqrt{2}}{2})$$
$$= 0$$

$(x', y') = (\sqrt{2}, 0)$

3.25 $x' = x \cos \theta + y \sin \theta$
$$= 3(\cos 60°) + 8(\sin 60°)$$
$$= 3(\frac{1}{2}) + 8(\frac{\sqrt{3}}{2})$$
$$= \frac{3}{2} + 4\sqrt{3}$$

$y' = x \sin \theta - y \cos \theta$
$$= 3(\sin 60°) - 8(\cos 60°)$$
$$= 3(\frac{\sqrt{3}}{2}) - 8(\frac{1}{2})$$
$$= \frac{3\sqrt{3}}{2} - 4$$

$(x', y') = (\frac{3}{2} + 4\sqrt{3}, \frac{3\sqrt{3}}{2} - 4)$

3.26 $x' = x \cos \theta + y \sin \theta$
$= -2(\cos 30°) + 6(\sin 30°)$
$= -2(\frac{\sqrt{3}}{2}) + 6(\frac{1}{2})$
$= -\sqrt{3} + 3$

$y' = x \sin \theta - y \cos \theta$
$= -2(\sin 30°) - 6(\cos 30°)$
$= -2(\frac{1}{2}) - 6(\frac{\sqrt{3}}{2})$
$= -1 - 3\sqrt{3}$

$(x', y') = (-\sqrt{3} + 3, -1 - 3\sqrt{3})$

3.27 $x' = x \cos \theta + y \sin \theta$
$= 5(\cos 90°) + 4(\sin 90°)$
$= 5(0) + 4(1)$
$= 4$

$y' = x \sin \theta - y \cos \theta$
$= 5(\sin 90°) - 4(\cos 90°)$
$= 5(1) - 4(0)$
$= 5$

$(x', y') = (4, 5)$

3.28 $x' = x \cos \theta + y \sin \theta$
$= -5(\cos 45°) - 5(\sin 45°)$
$= -5(\frac{\sqrt{2}}{2}) - 5(\frac{\sqrt{2}}{2})$
$= -\frac{5\sqrt{2}}{2} - \frac{5\sqrt{2}}{2}$
$= -5\sqrt{2}$

$y' = x \sin \theta - y \cos \theta$
$= -5(\sin 45°) + 5(\cos 45°)$
$= -5(\frac{\sqrt{2}}{2}) + 5(\frac{\sqrt{2}}{2})$
$= -\frac{5\sqrt{2}}{2} + \frac{5\sqrt{2}}{2}$
$= 0$

$(x', y') = (-5\sqrt{2}, 0)$

3.29 $x' = x \cos \theta + y \sin \theta$
$= 3(\cos 10°) + 0(\sin 10°)$
$= 3(.9848)$
$= 2.954$

$y' = x \sin \theta - y \cos \theta$
$= 3(\sin 10°) - 0(\cos 10°)$
$= 3(.1736)$
$= .5208$

$(x', y') = (2.954, 0.521)$

3.30 $8x^2 - 4xy + 5y^2 = 36$
$\tan 2\theta = \frac{B}{A - C} = \frac{-4}{8 - 5} = -\frac{4}{3}$
$\cos 2\theta = -\frac{3}{5}$

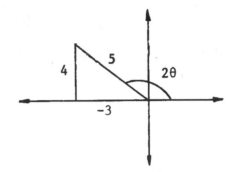

3.31 $\sin \theta = \sqrt{\frac{1 - \cos 2\theta}{2}} = \sqrt{\frac{1 - (-\frac{3}{5})}{2}}$
$= \sqrt{\frac{8}{10}} = \sqrt{\frac{4}{5}} = \frac{2}{\sqrt{5}}$
$= \frac{2}{5}\sqrt{5}$

$\cos \theta = \sqrt{\frac{1 + \cos 2\theta}{2}} = \sqrt{\frac{1 - \frac{3}{5}}{2}}$
$= \sqrt{\frac{1}{5}} = \frac{1}{\sqrt{5}} = \frac{\sqrt{5}}{5}$

3.32 $x = x' \cos \theta - y' \sin \theta$
$= \frac{\sqrt{5}}{5}x' - \frac{2\sqrt{5}}{5}y' = \frac{\sqrt{5}}{5}(x - 2y')$

$y = x' \sin \theta + y' \cos \theta$
$= \frac{2\sqrt{5}}{5}x' + \frac{\sqrt{5}}{5}y' = \frac{\sqrt{5}}{5}(2x' + y')$

3.33 $\quad 8[\frac{\sqrt{5}}{5}(x' - 2y')]^2 - 4[\frac{\sqrt{5}}{5}(x' - 2y')][\frac{\sqrt{5}}{5}(2x' + y')] + 5[\frac{\sqrt{5}}{5}(2x' + y')]^2 = 36$

$$8[\frac{1}{5}(x'^2 - 4x'y' + 4y'^2)] - 4[\frac{1}{5}(2x'^2 - 3x'y' - 2y'^2)] +$$

$$5[\frac{1}{5}(4x'^2 + 4x'y' + y'^2)] = 36$$

$$8(x'^2 - 4x'y' + 4y'^2) - 4(2x'^2 - 3x'y' - 2y'^2) + 5(4x'^2 + 4x'y' + y'^2) = 180$$

$$8x'^2 - 32x'y' + 32y'^2 - 8x'^2 + 12x'y' + 8y'^2 + 20x'^2 + 20x'y' + 5y'^2 = 180$$

$$20x'^2 + 45y'^2 = 180$$

$$\frac{x'^2}{9} + \frac{y'^2}{4} = 1$$

3.34 $\quad \tan 2\theta = \dfrac{B}{A - C} = \dfrac{4}{1 - 1} = \dfrac{4}{0} = \text{undefined}$

$2\theta = 90°; \; \theta = 45°$

3.35 $\quad \sin \theta = \sin 45° = \dfrac{\sqrt{2}}{2}$

$\cos \theta = \cos 45° = \dfrac{\sqrt{2}}{2}$

3.36 $\quad x = x' \cos \theta - y' \sin \theta = \dfrac{\sqrt{2}}{2}x' - \dfrac{\sqrt{2}}{2}y' = \dfrac{\sqrt{2}}{2}(x' - y')$

$y = x' \sin \theta + y' \cos \theta = \dfrac{\sqrt{2}}{2}x' + \dfrac{\sqrt{2}}{2}y' = \dfrac{\sqrt{2}}{2}(x' + y')$

3.37 $\quad [\frac{\sqrt{2}}{2}(x' - y')]^2 + 4[\frac{\sqrt{2}}{2}(x' - y')][\frac{\sqrt{2}}{2}(x' + y')] + [\frac{\sqrt{2}}{2}(x' + y')]^2 = 16$

$$\frac{1}{2}(x'^2 - 2x'y' + y'^2) + 4(\frac{1}{2})(x'^2 - y'^2) + \frac{1}{2}(x'^2 + 2x'y' + y'^2) = 16$$

$$x'^2 - 2x'y' + y'^2 + 4(x'^2 - y'^2) + x'^2 + 2x'y' + y'^2 = 32$$

$$6x'^2 - 2y'^2 = 32$$

$$3x'^2 - y'^2 = 16$$

$$\frac{x'^2}{\frac{16}{3}} - \frac{y'^2}{16} = 1$$

3.38 $9x^2 + 4xy + 6y^2 + 12x + 36y + 44 = 0$

$$\tan 2\theta = \frac{B}{A - C} = \frac{4}{9 - 6} = \frac{4}{3}$$

$$\cos 2\theta = \frac{3}{5}$$

$$\sin \theta = \sqrt{\frac{1 - \frac{3}{5}}{2}} = \sqrt{\frac{1}{5}} = \frac{1}{\sqrt{5}} = \frac{\sqrt{5}}{5}$$

$$\cos \theta = \sqrt{\frac{1 + \frac{3}{5}}{2}} = \sqrt{\frac{4}{5}} = \frac{2}{\sqrt{5}} = \frac{2\sqrt{5}}{5}$$

$$x = x'\cos\theta - y'\sin\theta = \frac{2\sqrt{5}}{5}x' - \frac{\sqrt{5}}{5}y' = \frac{\sqrt{5}}{5}(2x' - y')$$

$$y = x'\sin\theta + y'\cos\theta = \frac{\sqrt{5}}{5}x' + \frac{2\sqrt{5}}{5}y' = \frac{\sqrt{5}}{5}(x' + 2y')$$

Substitute term by term:

$$9x^2 = 9[\frac{\sqrt{5}}{5}(2x' - y')]^2 = 9[\frac{1}{5}(4x'^2 - 4x'y' + y'^2] =$$

$$= \frac{36}{5}(x')^2 - \frac{36}{5}(x')(y') + \frac{9}{5}(y')^2$$

$$4xy = 4[\frac{\sqrt{5}}{5}(2x' - y')][\frac{\sqrt{5}}{5}(x' + 2y')] = 4[\frac{1}{5}(2x'^2 + 3x'y' - 2y'^2]$$

$$= \frac{8}{5}(x')^2 + \frac{12}{5}(x')(y') - \frac{8}{5}(y')^2$$

$$6y^2 = 6[\frac{\sqrt{5}}{5}(x' + 2y')]^2 = 6[\frac{1}{5}(x'^2 + 4x'y' + 4y'^2] = \frac{6}{5}(x')^2 + \frac{24}{5}(x')(y') + \frac{24}{5}(y')^2$$

$$12x = 12[\frac{\sqrt{5}}{5}(2x' - y')] = \frac{24\sqrt{5}}{5}(x') - \frac{12\sqrt{5}}{5}(y')$$

$$36y = 36[\frac{\sqrt{5}}{5}(x' + 2y')] = \frac{36\sqrt{5}}{5}(x') + \frac{72\sqrt{5}}{5}(y')$$

Collect terms:

$$\frac{50(x')^2}{5} + \frac{25(y')^2}{5} + \frac{60\sqrt{5}}{5}(x') + \frac{60\sqrt{5}}{5}(y') + 44 = 0$$

$$10x'^2 + 5y'^2 + 12\sqrt{5}x' + 12\sqrt{5}y' + 44 = 0$$

Complete the squares:

$$10(x')^2 + 12\sqrt{5}(x') + 5(y')^2 + 12\sqrt{5}(y') = -44$$

$$10[(x')^2 + \frac{12\sqrt{5}}{10}(x') + (\frac{12\sqrt{5}}{20})^2] +$$

$$5[y'^2 + \frac{12}{5}\sqrt{5}y' + (\frac{12}{10}\sqrt{5}y')^2] = 10(\frac{12\sqrt{5}}{20})^2 + 5(\frac{12}{10}\sqrt{5})^2 - 44$$

$$10[x' + \frac{12\sqrt{5}}{20}]^2 + 5[y' + \frac{12\sqrt{5}}{10}]^2 = 10$$

3.38 cont.

Center: $h = -\frac{3}{5}\sqrt{5}$, $k = -\frac{6}{5}\sqrt{5}$ or $(-\frac{3}{5}\sqrt{5}, -\frac{6}{5}\sqrt{5})$

$$10(x'')^2 + 5(y'')^2 = 10$$
$$(x'')^2 + \frac{(y'')^2}{2} = 1$$

3.39 $xy = 1$

$$\tan 2\theta = \frac{B}{A - C} = \frac{1}{0 - 0} = \frac{1}{0} = \text{undefined}$$

$2\theta = 90°$; $\theta = 45°$

$$\sin \theta = \sin 45° = \frac{\sqrt{2}}{2}$$
$$\cos \theta = \cos 45° = \frac{\sqrt{2}}{2}$$

$$
\begin{aligned}
x &= x' \cos \theta - y' \cos \theta \\
&= \frac{\sqrt{2}}{2}x' - \frac{\sqrt{2}}{2}y' \\
&= \frac{\sqrt{2}}{2}(x' - y')
\end{aligned}
$$

$$
\begin{aligned}
y &= x' \sin \theta + y' \cos \theta \\
&= \frac{\sqrt{2}}{2}x' + \frac{\sqrt{2}}{2}y' \\
&= \frac{\sqrt{2}}{2}(x' + y')
\end{aligned}
$$

$$\frac{\sqrt{2}}{2}(x' - y')\frac{\sqrt{2}}{2}(x' + y') = 1$$
$$\frac{1}{2}[(x')^2 - (y')^2] = 1$$
$$\frac{(x')^2}{2} - \frac{(y')^2}{2} = 1$$

MATHEMATICS 1209
SOLUTION KEY

I. SECTION ONE

1.1 $P(A') = 1 - \frac{3}{8}$
$= \frac{5}{8}$ or 0.625

1.2 $P(A') = 100\% - 20\%$
$= 80\%$ or 0.8

1.3 $P(A) = \frac{300}{500}$
$= \frac{3}{5}$
$= 60\%$ or 0.6

1.4 a. Sample space =
{a, b, c, d, e, f, g,
h, i, j, k, l, m, n,
o, p, q, r, s, t, u,
v, w, x, y, z}.
b. $P(\text{letter is } w) = \frac{1}{26}$
or 0.038
c. $P(\text{vowel}) = a, e, i, o,$
$u = \frac{5}{26}$ or 0.19
d. $P(\text{consonant}) = \frac{21}{26}$ or 0.81

1.5 a. $P(A \text{ is selected}) = \frac{1}{6}$ or 0.167
b. $P(B \text{ is not selected}) = \frac{5}{6}$
or 0.83
Also, $P(B \text{ is selected}) = \frac{1}{6}$
$P(B \text{ is not selected}) =$
$1 - \frac{1}{6}$
$= \frac{5}{6}$

1.6 a. Sample space is the numbers
from 1 to 50 inclusive.
The numbers divisible by 3 are
{3, 6, 9, 12, 15, 18, 21,
24, 27, 30, 33, 36, 39,
42, 45, 48}.
$P(\text{divisible by 3}) = \frac{16}{50} =$
$\frac{8}{25}$ or 0.32
b. The numbers divisible by
5 are {5, 10, 15, 20, 25,
30, 35, 40, 45, 50}.
$P(\text{divisible by 5}) = \frac{10}{50}$
$= \frac{1}{5}$ or 0.2
c. The numbers not divisible
by 2 are {1, 3, 5, 7, 9,
11, 13, 15, 17, 19, 21,
23, 25, 27, 29, 31, 33,
35, 37, 39, 41, 43, 45,
47, 49}.

The numbers not divisible
by 7 are {1, 2, 3, 4, 5,
6, 8, 9, 10, 11, 12, 13,
15, 16, 17, 18, 19, 20,
22, 23, 24, 25, 26, 27,
29, 30, 31, 32, 33, 34,
36, 37, 38, 39, 40, 41,
43, 44, 45, 46, 47, 48,
50}.

The numbers not divisible
by 9 are {1, 2, 3, 4, 5,
6, 7, 8, 10, 11, 12, 13,
14, 15, 16, 17, 19, 20,
21, 22, 23, 24, 25, 26,
28, 29, 30, 31, 32, 33,
34, 35, 37, 38, 39, 40,
41, 42, 43, 44, 46, 47,
48, 49, 50}.

The numbers that are not
divisible by 2 and 7 and
9 are {1, 3, 5, 11, 13,
15, 17, 19, 23, 25, 29,
31, 33, 37, 39, 41, 43,
47}.
$P(\text{not divisible by 2,}$
7, and 9) $= \frac{18}{50} = \frac{9}{25}$ or 0.36

Note: Another way to
determine the solution is
to consider the probability
of the numbers that are
divisible by 2, 7, and 9
and then subtract that
probability from 1.

The numbers divisible by
2 are {2, 4, 6, 8, 10, 12,
14, 16, 18, 20, 22, 24, 26,
28, 30, 32, 34, 36, 38,
40, 42, 44, 46, 48, 50}.

The numbers divisible by
7 are {7, 14, 21, 28, 35,
42, 49}.

The numbers divisible by
9 are {9, 18, 27, 36, 45}.

Removing the duplicate numbers, the solution set is {2, 4, 6, 7, 8, 9, 10, 12, 14, 16, 18, 20, 21, 22, 24, 26, 27, 28, 30, 32, 34, 35, 36, 38, 40, 42, 44, 45, 46, 48, 49, 50}.

P(divisible by 2, 7, and 9) = $\frac{32}{50}$ = $\frac{16}{25}$

P(not divisible by 2, 7, and 9) = $1 - \frac{16}{25} = \frac{9}{25}$ or 0.36

1.7 Sample space:

(a, b);	(c, a);	(e, a)
(a, c);	(c, b);	(e, b)
(a, d);	(c, d);	(e, c)
(a, e);	(c, e);	(e, d)
(a, f);	(c, f);	(e, f)
(b, a);	(d, a);	(f, a)
(b, c);	(d, b);	(f, b)
(b, d);	(d, c);	(f, c)
(b, e);	(d, e);	(f, d)
(b, f);	(d, f);	(f, e)

P(at least one vowel) = $\frac{18}{30} = \frac{3}{5}$ or 0.6

1.8   a. P(red) = $\frac{8}{20}$
= $\frac{2}{5}$ or 0.4

   b. P(white) = $\frac{2}{20}$
= $\frac{1}{10}$ or 0.1

   c. P(black) = $\frac{10}{20}$
= $\frac{1}{2}$ or 0.5

   d. $P = 1$ (certainty)

1.9 Sample space:

{a, a}	{c, a};	{e, a}
{a, b}	{c, b};	{e, b}
{a, c}	{c, c};	{e, c}
{a, i}	{c, i};	{e, e}
{a, e}	{c, e};	{e, i}
{b, a}	{i, a};	
{b, b}	{i, b};	
{b, c}	{i, c};	
{b, i}	{i, e};	
{b, e}	{i, i};	

   a. P(both vowels) = $\frac{9}{25}$
= .36

   b. P(one is a vowel and other is a consonant = $\frac{12}{25}$
= .48

1.10 P(six cylinders) = $\frac{205,000}{550,000}$
= $\frac{41}{110}$ or 0.37

1.11   Probability of drawing an odd number on the first draw is $\frac{10}{20} = \frac{1}{2}$.
Probability of drawing an even number on the first draw is $\frac{10}{20} = \frac{1}{2}$.

   a.   odd + odd = even;
$\frac{1}{2} \cdot \frac{1}{2} = \frac{1}{4}$
even + even = even;
$\frac{1}{2} \cdot \frac{1}{2} = \frac{1}{4}$
∴ The probability of getting an even number is $\frac{1}{4} + \frac{1}{4} = \frac{1}{2}$ or 0.5.

   b. P(odd) = $1 - P$(even)
= $1 - \frac{1}{2}$
= $\frac{1}{2}$ or 0.5

1.12 P(being called) = $\frac{1}{1,000,000}$ or 0.000001

1.13   a. P(white) = $\frac{8}{28}$
= $\frac{2}{7}$ or 0.286

   b. P(black) = $\frac{20}{28}$
= $\frac{5}{7}$ or 0.71

1.14   a. P(red) = $\frac{3}{12}$
= $\frac{1}{4}$ or 0.25

   b. P(not blue) = P(red and white)
= $\frac{5}{12}$ or 0.42

   c. P(white) = $\frac{2}{12}$
= $\frac{1}{6}$ or 0.167

1.15 P(money) = $\frac{2}{6}$
= $\frac{1}{3}$ or 0.33

1.16 P(of a worm) = $\frac{3}{12}$
= $\frac{1}{4}$

P(no worm) = $1 - \frac{3}{12} = \frac{9}{12}$
= $\frac{3}{4}$ or 0.75

1.17   The probability of odd or even is equally likely. See Problem 1.11.

1.18 a. $P(A) = \frac{4}{16}$
$= \frac{1}{4}$ or 0.25

b. $P(B) = \frac{6}{16}$
$= \frac{3}{8}$ or 0.375

c. $P(C) = \frac{4}{16}$
$= \frac{1}{4}$ or 0.25

d. $P(D) = \frac{1}{16}$ or 0.0625

e. $P(E) = \frac{1}{16}$ or 0.0625

f. 1

1.19 a. Event =
{2, 3, 5, 7, 11, 13, 17, 19, 23, 29, 31, 37, 41, 43, 47, 53, 59, 61, 67, 71, 73, 79, 83, 89, 97}.
$P(A) = \frac{25}{100}$
$= \frac{1}{4}$ or 0.25

b. Event =
{5, 10, 15, 20, 25, 30, 35, 40, 45, 50, 55, 60, 65, 70, 75, 80, 85, 90, 95, 100}.
$P(B) = \frac{20}{100}$
$= \frac{1}{5}$ or 0.2

c. Event =
{7, 14, 21, 28, 35, 42, 49, 56, 63, 70, 77, 84, 91, 98}.
$P(C) = \frac{14}{100}$
$= \frac{7}{50}$ or 0.14

d. $P(A) = \frac{1}{4}$
$P(\text{perfect square}) = P(D)$
Event = {1, 4, 9, 16, 25, 36, 49, 64, 81, 100}.
$P(D) = \frac{10}{100} = \frac{1}{10}$ or 0.1
$P(A \cup D) = P(A) + P(D) - P(A \cap D)$
$= \frac{25}{100} + \frac{10}{100} - 0$
$= \frac{35}{100} = \frac{7}{20}$ or 0.35

e. Event of numbers
divisible by 10 = {10, 20, 30, 40, 50, 60, 70, 80, 90, 100}.
Let $P(E) = P(\text{divisible by 10})$
$= \frac{10}{100}$
$= \frac{1}{10}$ or 0.1
Event of numbers
divisible by 3 = {3, 6, 9, 12, 15, 18, 21, 24, 27, 30, 33, 36, 39, 42, 45, 48, 51, 54, 57, 60, 63, 66, 69, 72, 75, 78, 81, 84, 87, 90, 93, 96, 99}.

Let $P(F) = P(\text{divisible by 3})$
$= \frac{33}{100}$ or 0.33
$E \cap F = \{30, 60, 90\}$
$P(E \cap F) = \frac{3}{100}$
$P(E \cup F) = P(E) + P(F) - P(E \cap F)$
$= \frac{1}{10} + \frac{33}{100} - \frac{3}{100}$
$= \frac{10}{100} + \frac{30}{100}$
$= \frac{40}{100}$
$= \frac{2}{5}$ or 0.4
$P(\text{not divisible by 10 or 3}) = 1 - \frac{2}{5} = \frac{3}{5}$ or 0.6

1.20 Event of numbers
divisible by 6 = {6, 12, 18, 24, 30, 36}.
Let $P(A) = P(\text{divisible by 6})$
$= \frac{6}{40} = \frac{3}{20}$
Event of numbers
divisible by 8 = {8, 16, 24, 32, 40}.
Let $P(B) = P(\text{divisible by 8})$
$= \frac{5}{40}$
$= \frac{1}{8}$
$A \cap B = \{24\}$
$P(A \cap B) = \frac{1}{40}$
$P(A \cup B) = P(A) + P(B) - P(A \cap B)$
$= \frac{6}{40} + \frac{5}{40} - \frac{1}{40}$
$= \frac{10}{40}$
$= \frac{1}{4}$ or 0.25

1.21 Since 80 out of 160 students are not involved in sports and are not honor students, 80 students are honor students and athletes. Twenty students are therefore both honor students and athletes.

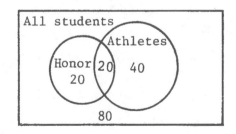

a. Let $P(A)$ = P(honor student and athlete)
$$= \frac{20}{160} = \frac{1}{8} \text{ or } 0.125$$

b. Let $P(B)$ = P(honor student)
$$= \frac{40}{160}$$
$$= \frac{1}{4}$$

Let $P(C)$ = P(athlete) =
$$= \frac{60}{160} = \frac{3}{8}$$

$B \cap C = \frac{20}{160}$
$$= \frac{1}{8}$$

$P(B \cup C) = P(B) + P(C) - P(B \cap C)$
$$= \frac{40}{160} + \frac{60}{160} - \frac{20}{160}$$
$$= \frac{80}{160}$$
$$= \frac{1}{2} \text{ or } 0.5$$

1.22

a. Event (< 29) = {1, 2, 3, 5, 15, 21}.
Let $P(A) = P(< 29)$
$$= \frac{6}{9}$$
$$= \frac{2}{3}$$

Event (odd) = {1, 3, 5, 15, 21, 29}.
Let $P(B)$ = P(odd)
$$= \frac{6}{9}$$
$$= \frac{2}{3}$$

$A \cap B$ = {1, 3, 5, 15, 21}.
$P(A \cap B) = \frac{5}{9}$
$P(A \cup B) = P(A) + P(B) - P(A \cap B)$
$$= \frac{6}{9} + \frac{6}{9} - \frac{5}{9}$$
$$= \frac{7}{9} \text{ or } 0.778$$

b. $P(21) = \frac{1}{9}$ or 0.11

c. Event (divisible by 5) = {5, 15, 500}.
Let $P(C)$ = P(divisible by 5)
$$= \frac{3}{9}$$
$$= \frac{1}{3}.$$

Event (divisible by 7) = {21}.
Let $P(D)$ = P(divisible by 7)
$$= \frac{1}{9}.$$

$C \cap D = \phi$
$P(C \cap D) = 0$
$P(C \cup D) = P(C) + P(D) - P(C \cap D)$
$$= \frac{3}{9} + \frac{1}{9} - 0$$
$$= \frac{4}{9} \text{ or } 0.44$$

1.23

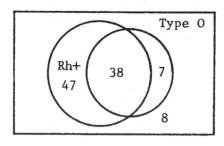

a. Let $P(A)$ = P(Type 0)
$$= \frac{38}{100}$$
$$= \frac{19}{50} \text{ or } 0.38$$

b. Let $P(B)$ = P(not 0)
$$= \frac{100 - 45}{100}$$
$$= \frac{55}{100}$$
$$= \frac{11}{20} \text{ or } 0.55$$

c. Let $P(C)$ = P(Rh negative)
$$= \frac{7 + 8}{100}$$
$$= \frac{15}{100}$$
$$= \frac{3}{20} \text{ or } 0.15$$

d. Let $P(D)$ = P(0 and Rh negative)
$$= \frac{7}{100} \text{ or } 0.07$$

e. Let $P(E)$ = P(Rh +)
$$= \frac{85}{100}$$
$$= \frac{17}{20} \text{ or } 0.85$$

f. $P(\text{not } 0) = P(B) = \frac{55}{100}$
$P(\text{Rh+}) = P(E) = \frac{85}{100}$
$B \cap E$:
$$\begin{array}{r} 55 \\ + 85 \\ \hline 140 \\ - 93 \\ \hline 47 \end{array}$$
$P(B \cap E) = \frac{47}{100}$
$P(B \cup E) = P(B) + P(E) - P(B \cap E)$
$$= \frac{55}{100} + \frac{85}{100} - \frac{47}{100}$$
$$= \frac{93}{100} \text{ or } 0.93$$

1.24 From Problem 1.21, the class has 20 honor students, 40 athletes, and 20 students who are both honor students and athletes.
Let $P(A)$ = P(honor student)
$P(B)$ = P(athlete)
$A \cap B$ = 20 students
$$P(A) = \frac{40}{160}$$
$$P(B) = \frac{60}{160}$$
$$P(A' \cap B') = \frac{80}{160}$$
$$P(A \cap B) = \frac{20}{160}$$

a. $P(B|A) = \dfrac{P(A \cap B)}{P(A)} = \dfrac{\frac{20}{160}}{\frac{40}{160}}$

$= \dfrac{20}{40}$

$= \dfrac{1}{2}$ or 0.5

b. $P(A|B) = \dfrac{P(A \cap B)}{P(B)} = \dfrac{\frac{20}{160}}{\frac{60}{160}}$

$= \dfrac{20}{60}$

$= \dfrac{1}{3}$ or 0.33

c. Does $P(A \cap B) = P(A) \cdot P(B)$?

$\dfrac{20}{160} \stackrel{?}{=} \dfrac{40}{160} \cdot \dfrac{60}{160}$

$\dfrac{1}{8} \stackrel{?}{=} \dfrac{1}{4} \cdot \dfrac{3}{8}$

$\dfrac{1}{8} \neq \dfrac{3}{32}$

No, the events are not independent.

1.25　a. Let $P(W) = P(\text{woman})$

$= \dfrac{40}{100}$

$= \dfrac{2}{5}$ or 0.4

b. Let $P(R) = P(\text{Republican})$

$= \dfrac{35}{100}$

$= \dfrac{7}{20}$ or 0.35

c. Let $P(WD) = P(\text{woman Democrat})$

$= \dfrac{26}{100}$

$= \dfrac{13}{50}$ or 0.26

d. Does $P(D \cap M) = P(D) \cdot P(M)$?

$\dfrac{39}{100} \stackrel{?}{=} \dfrac{65}{100} \cdot \dfrac{60}{100}$

$\dfrac{39}{100} \stackrel{?}{=} \dfrac{13}{20} \cdot \dfrac{12}{20}$

$\dfrac{39}{100} = \dfrac{39}{100}$

Yes, the events D and M are independent.

1.26　$P(A) \cdot P(B) = \dfrac{2}{3} \cdot \dfrac{1}{4}$

$= \dfrac{1}{6}$ or 0.167

1.27　$P(A) \cdot P(B) = 0.352 \cdot 0.500$

$= 0.176$

1.28　a. $P(A) \cdot P(B) \cdot P(C) =$
$\dfrac{1}{2} \cdot \dfrac{1}{5} \cdot \dfrac{2}{3} = \dfrac{1}{15}$ or 0.067

b. $P(A') \cdot P(B') \cdot P(C') =$
$\dfrac{1}{2} \cdot \dfrac{4}{5} \cdot \dfrac{1}{3} = \dfrac{2}{15}$ or 0.13

1.29　a. $P(A) = \dfrac{1}{100}$ or 0.01

b. Let $P(A) = $ first draw
$= \dfrac{6}{100} = \dfrac{3}{50}$.
Let $P(B) = $ second draw
$= \dfrac{5}{99}$.

$P(A) \cdot P(B) = \dfrac{\cancel{6}^{1}}{\cancel{10}} \cdot \dfrac{5^{1}}{\cancel{99}_{33}}$
$ {}_{10} {}^{\cancel{50}}$

$= \dfrac{1}{330}$ or 0.003

1.30　a. $P(A) \cdot P(B) = \dfrac{\cancel{6}^{1}}{\cancel{8}_{4}} \cdot \dfrac{\cancel{6}^{3}}{\cancel{10}_{2}}$

$= \dfrac{3}{8}$ or 0.375

b. $P(\text{both black}) = \dfrac{3}{8}$

$P(\text{both white}) = P(A) \cdot P(B)$

$= \dfrac{3}{\cancel{8}_{2}} \cdot \dfrac{\cancel{4}^{1}}{10}$

$= \dfrac{3}{20}$ or 0.15

Since the events are mutually exclusive, add the probabilities.

$\dfrac{3}{8} + \dfrac{3}{20} = \dfrac{15}{40} + \dfrac{6}{40}$

$= \dfrac{21}{40}$ or 0.525

1.31　a. $P(A) = \dfrac{1}{100}$

b. $P(B) = \dfrac{99}{100}$

c. $P(B) \cdot P(B) = \dfrac{99}{100} \cdot \dfrac{99}{100}$
$= \dfrac{9,801}{10,000}$ or 0.9801

d. $[P(B) \cdot P(B)]^{30} = (0.9801)^{30}$

1.32　a. $P(A) \cdot P(B) = \dfrac{1}{\cancel{2}_{1}} \cdot \dfrac{\cancel{2}^{1}}{3}$

$= \dfrac{1}{3}$ or 0.33

b. Sample space

	A	B
solve =	$\frac{1}{2}$	not solve = $\frac{1}{3}$
not solve =	$\frac{1}{2}$	solve = $\frac{2}{3}$

$P(A \text{ and } B') = \dfrac{1}{2} \cdot \dfrac{1}{3} = \dfrac{1}{6}$

$P(A' \text{ and } B) = \dfrac{1}{\cancel{2}_{1}} \cdot \dfrac{\cancel{2}^{1}}{3} = \dfrac{1}{3}$

Since these events are mutually exclusive, add the probabilities.

$\dfrac{1}{6} + \dfrac{1}{3} = \dfrac{1}{6} + \dfrac{2}{6} = \dfrac{3}{6} = \dfrac{1}{2}$ or 0.5

c. $P(A') \cdot P(B') = \frac{1}{2} \cdot \frac{1}{3}$
$\qquad = \frac{1}{6}$ or 0.167

1.33 a. Let + represent the problem solved and − represent the problem not solved.

Tom: P(solving problem)
$\qquad = \frac{2}{3}$
P(not solving problem)
$\qquad = 1 - \frac{2}{3}$
$\qquad = \frac{1}{3}$

Sue: P(solving problem)
$\qquad = \frac{1}{2}$
P(not solving problem)
$\qquad = 1 - \frac{1}{2}$
$\qquad = \frac{1}{4}$

Joe: P(solving problem)
$\qquad = \frac{1}{4}$
P(not solving problem)
$\qquad = 1 - \frac{1}{4}$
$\qquad = \frac{3}{4}$

Tom	Sue	Joe
+	+	+
+	+	−
+	−	+
−	+	+
+	−	−
−	+	−
−	−	+
−	−	−

b. $\frac{1\!\!\!\!/2}{3} \cdot \frac{1}{2\!\!\!/1} \cdot \frac{1}{4} = \frac{1}{12}$ or 0.083

$\frac{1\!\!\!\!/2}{1\!\!\!\!/3} \cdot \frac{1}{2\!\!\!/1} \cdot \frac{3\!\!\!/1}{4} = \frac{1}{4}$ or 0.25

$\frac{1\!\!\!\!/2}{3} \cdot \frac{1}{2\!\!\!/1} \cdot \frac{1}{4} = \frac{1}{12}$ or 0.083

$\frac{1}{3} \cdot \frac{1}{2} \cdot \frac{1}{4} = \frac{1}{24}$ or 0.042

$\frac{1\!\!\!\!/2}{1\!\!\!\!/3} \cdot \frac{1}{2\!\!\!/1} \cdot \frac{3\!\!\!/1}{4} = \frac{1}{4}$ or 0.25

$\frac{1}{1\!\!\!\!/3} \cdot \frac{1}{2} \cdot \frac{3\!\!\!/1}{4} = \frac{1}{8}$ or 0.125

$\frac{1}{3} \cdot \frac{1}{2} \cdot \frac{1}{4} = \frac{1}{24}$ or 0.042

$\frac{1}{1\!\!\!\!/3} \cdot \frac{1}{2} \cdot \frac{3\!\!\!/1}{4} = \frac{1}{8}$ or 0.125

c. $P = \frac{1}{4} + \frac{1}{12} + \frac{1}{24}$
$\qquad = \frac{6}{24} + \frac{2}{24} + \frac{1}{24}$
$\qquad = \frac{9}{24}$
$\qquad = \frac{3}{8}$ or 0.375

d. $P = \frac{1}{4} + \frac{1}{8} + \frac{1}{24}$
$\qquad = \frac{6}{24} + \frac{3}{24} + \frac{1}{24}$
$\qquad = \frac{10}{24}$
$\qquad = \frac{5}{12}$ or 0.417

e. P(problem not being solved)
$\qquad = \frac{1}{1\!\!\!\!/3} \cdot \frac{1}{2} \cdot \frac{3\!\!\!/1}{4}$
$\qquad = \frac{1}{8}$ or 0.125

P (problem being solved)
$1 - P$(not being solved)
$\qquad = 1 - .125$
$\qquad = .875$

II. SECTION TWO

2.1 $5 \cdot 4 \cdot 3 = 60$

2.2 a. $24 \cdot 24 = 576$
b. $24 \cdot 23 \cdot 22 = 12{,}144$

2.3 The tens' digit has 4 possibilities and the ones' digit has 3 possibilities.
$\underline{4} \cdot \underline{3} = 12$

2.4 First place has 10 possibilities, second place has 9 possibilities, and third place has 8 possibilities.
$\underline{10} \cdot \underline{9} \cdot \underline{8} = 720$

2.5 $5 \cdot 1 \cdot 6 \cdot 2 = 60$

2.6 $3 \cdot 5 \cdot 3 = 45$

2.7 2^{20}

2.8 $2 \cdot 5 \cdot 7 = 70$

2.9   a.   Each digit has 6 possibilities.
$6 \cdot 6 \cdot 6 = 216$

b.   The hundreds' digit has 6 possibilities, the tens' digit has 5 possibilities, and the units' digit has 4 possibilities.
$6 \cdot 5 \cdot 4 = 120$

c.   Consider the units' digit first. For the number to be odd the units' digit must be odd. The units' digit has 5 possibilities, the tens' digit has 6 possibilities, and the hundreds' digit has 6 possibilities.
$5 \cdot 6 \cdot 6 = 180$

d.   Consider the units' digit first. For the number to be even the units' digit must be even. The units' digit has 1 possibility, the tens' digit has 6 possibilities, and the hundreds' digit has 6 possibilities.
$1 \cdot 6 \cdot 6 = 36$

2.10 $4^5 + 4^4 + 4^3 + 4^2 + 4^1$
$= 1{,}024 + 256 + 64 + 16 + 4$
$= 1{,}364$

2.11 $8 \cdot 8 \cdot 9 \cdot 10 \cdot 10 \cdot 10 \cdot 10 = 5{,}760{,}000$
    letters   nonzero
                 number

2.12 $26 \cdot 25 \cdot 24 = 15{,}600$

2.13   a. $_7P_2 = 7 \cdot 6$
$= 42$

b. $_{30}P_3 = 30 \cdot 29 \cdot 28$
$= 24{,}360$

c. $_5P_5 = 5!$
$= 5 \cdot 4 \cdot 3 \cdot 2 \cdot 1$
$= 120$

d. $_8P_3 = 8 \cdot 7 \cdot 6$
$= 336$

e. $_9P_5 = 9 \cdot 8 \cdot 7 \cdot 6 \cdot 5$
$= 15{,}120$

f. $_7P_7 = 7!$
$= 7 \cdot 6 \cdot 5 \cdot 4 \cdot 3 \cdot 2 \cdot 1$
$= 5{,}040$

g. $_6P_4 = 6 \cdot 5 \cdot 4 \cdot 3$
$= 360$

h. $_8P_4 = 8 \cdot 7 \cdot 6 \cdot 5$
$= 1{,}680$

i. $_5P_4 = 5 \cdot 4 \cdot 3 \cdot 2$
$= 120$

j. $_3P_1 = 3$

2.14 $_4P_4 = 4!$
$= 4 \cdot 3 \cdot 2 \cdot 1$
$= 24$

2.15 $_8P_8 = 8!$
$= 8 \cdot 7 \cdot 6 \cdot 5 \cdot 4 \cdot 3 \cdot 2 \cdot 1$
$= 40{,}320$

2.16 $_4P_2 = 4 \cdot 3$
$= 12$

2.17 $_8P_3 = 8 \cdot 7 \cdot 6$
$= 336$

2.18 $_8P_8 = 8!$
$= 40{,}320$

2.19 $_6P_2 = 6 \cdot 5$
$= 30$

2.20 $_6P_6 = 6!$
$= 6 \cdot 5 \cdot 4 \cdot 3 \cdot 2 \cdot 1$
$= 720$

2.21 $_9P_6 = 9 \cdot 8 \cdot 7 \cdot 6 \cdot 5 \cdot 4$
$= 60{,}480$

2.22   The hundred thousands' digit can be any one of the digits 3, 4, 5, or 9.
$4 \cdot 5 \cdot 4 \cdot 3 \cdot 2 \cdot 1 = 480$

2.23 $_5P_5 + {_5P_3} + {_5P_1}$
$= 5! + 5 \cdot 4 \cdot 3 + 5$
$= 5 \cdot 4 \cdot 3 \cdot 2 \cdot 1 + 60 + 5$
$= 120 + 65$
$= 185$

2.24 $_nP_r = n(n - 1)(n - 2)(n - 3)$
$\cdots (n - r + 1)$

Multiply the right member of this equation by $\dfrac{(n - r)!}{(n - r)!}$.

$(n - r)!$ is the number that completes the numerator factors to 1. Hence, the numerator is $n!$.

$_nP_r = n(n - 1)(n - 2) \cdots$
$(n - r + 1)\dfrac{(n - r)!}{(n - r)!}$

$= \dfrac{n!}{(n - r)!}$

2.25 $_xP_4 = x(x - 1)(x - 2)(x - 3)$
$_xP_3 = x(x - 1)(x - 2)$

Therefore,

$x(x - 1)(x - 2) \cdot$
$\quad (x - 3) = 7[x(x - 1)(x - 2)]$
$\quad\quad x - 3 = 7$
$\quad\quad\quad x = 7 + 3$
$\quad\quad\quad x = 10$

2.26 $_nP_5 = n(n - 1)(n - 2)(n - 3) \cdot$
$\quad (n - 4)$
$_nP_3 = n(n - 1)(n - 2)$

Therefore,

$(n - 1)(n - 2)(n - 3) \cdot$
$\quad (n - 4) = 12[n(n - 1) \cdot$
$\quad\quad\quad (n - 2)]$
$(n - 3)(n - 4) = 12$
$n^2 - 7n + 12 = 12$
$n^2 - 7n = 12 - 12$
$n^2 - 7n = 0$
$n(n - 7) = 0$
$\quad\quad n = 0; \text{ reject}$
$\quad n - 7 = 0$
$\quad\quad n = 7$

2.27 Since the word has 4 *e*'s, 2 *n*'s, and 2 *s*'s, the number of different, distinguishable permutations is

$\dfrac{9!}{4!2!2!} = \dfrac{9 \cdot 8^4 \cdot 7 \cdot 6^3 \cdot 5 \cdot 4!}{4! \cdot 2 \cdot 1 \cdot 2 \cdot 1}$
$= 9 \cdot 4 \cdot 7 \cdot 3 \cdot 5$
$= 3,780.$

2.28 $\dfrac{10!}{3!} = \dfrac{10 \cdot 9 \cdot 8 \cdot 7 \cdot 6 \cdot 5 \cdot 4 \cdot 3!}{3!}$
$= 604,800$

2.29 $\dfrac{17!}{6!5!2!4!}$

2.30 a. $_3P_3 = 3!$
$= 3 \cdot 2 \cdot 1$
$= 6$

b. $\dfrac{3!}{2!} = \dfrac{3 \cdot 2!}{2!} = 3$

c. $_5P_5 = 5!$
$= 5 \cdot 4 \cdot 3 \cdot 2 \cdot 1$
$= 120$

d. $\dfrac{5!}{2!2!} = \dfrac{5 \cdot 4^2 \cdot 3 \cdot 2!}{2 \cdot 1 \cdot 2!}$
$= 5 \cdot 2 \cdot 3$
$= 30$

e. $\dfrac{11!}{2!3!2!} = \dfrac{11 \cdot 10 \cdot 9 \cdot 8 \cdot 7 \cdot 6 \cdot 5 \cdot 4 \cdot 3!}{2 \cdot 1 \cdot 2 \cdot 1 \cdot 3!}$
$= 1,663,200$

2.31 $\dfrac{8!}{3!2!2!} = \dfrac{8 \cdot 7 \cdot 6 \cdot 5 \cdot 4 \cdot 3!}{2 \cdot 1 \cdot 2 \cdot 1 \cdot 3!}$
$= 1,680$

2.32 $(8 - 1)! = 7! = 5,040$

2.33 $(7 - 1)! = 6! = 720$

2.34 $(10 - 1)! = 9!$

2.35 $(4 - 1)!(4)! = 3!4!$
$= 6 \cdot 24 = \mathbf{144}$

2.36 $(5 - 1)!(5)! = 4!5!$
$= 24 \cdot 120 = 2,880$

2.37 $n! = 6(n - 1)!$
$n(n - 1)! = 6(n - 1)!$
$\quad\quad n = 6 \quad$ [divide both sides by $(n - 1)!$]

2.38 $(6 - 1)! = 5! = 120$

2.39 $2 \cdot (5 - 1)! = 2 \cdot 4!$
$= 48$

2.40 a. $_7C_2 = \dfrac{7!}{2!5!} = \dfrac{7 \cdot 6 \cdot 5!}{2 \cdot 1 \cdot 5!}$

$= 7 \cdot 3$

$= 21$

b. $_{30}C_3 = \dfrac{30!}{3!27!} = \dfrac{\overset{5}{30} \cdot 29 \cdot 28 \cdot 27!}{3 \cdot 2 \cdot 1 \cdot 27!}$

$= 5 \cdot 29 \cdot 28$

$= 4{,}060$

c. $_5C_5 = \dfrac{5!}{5!0!} = \dfrac{5!}{5!} = 1$

d. $_{13}C_5 = \dfrac{13!}{5!8!} = \dfrac{13 \cdot 12 \cdot 11 \cdot 10 \cdot 9 \cdot 8!}{5 \cdot 4 \cdot 3 \cdot 2 \cdot 1 \cdot 8!}$

$= 13 \cdot 11 \cdot 9$

$= 1{,}287$

e. $_{16}C_{14} = \dfrac{16!}{14!2!} = \dfrac{\overset{8}{16} \cdot 15 \cdot 14!}{2 \cdot 1 \cdot 14!}$

$= 8 \cdot 15$

$= 120$

f. $_{21}C_3 = \dfrac{21!}{3!18!} = \dfrac{\overset{7}{21} \cdot \overset{10}{20} \cdot 19 \cdot 18!}{3 \cdot 2 \cdot 1 \cdot 18!}$

$= 7 \cdot 10 \cdot 19$

$= 1{,}330$

g. $_8C_6 = \dfrac{8!}{6!2!} = \dfrac{\overset{4}{8} \cdot 7 \cdot 6!}{2 \cdot 1 \cdot 6!}$

$= 4 \cdot 7$

$= 28$

h. $_{10}C_0 = \dfrac{10!}{0!10!} = \dfrac{10!}{10!} = 1$

i. $_7C_7 = \dfrac{7!}{7!0!} = \dfrac{7!}{7!} = 1$

j. $_9C_4 = \dfrac{9!}{4!5!} = \dfrac{9 \cdot 8 \cdot 7 \cdot 6 \cdot 5!}{4 \cdot 3 \cdot 2 \cdot 1 \cdot 5!}$

$= 9 \cdot 2 \cdot 7$

$= 126$

2.41 $_{15}C_4 = \dfrac{15!}{4!11!} = \dfrac{15 \cdot 14 \cdot 13 \cdot 12 \cdot 11!}{4 \cdot 3 \cdot 2 \cdot 1 \cdot 11!}$

$= 15 \cdot 7 \cdot 13$

$= 1{,}365$

2.42 $_{20}C_2 = \dfrac{20!}{2!18!} = \dfrac{\overset{10}{20} \cdot 19 \cdot 18!}{2 \cdot 1 \cdot 18!}$

$= 10 \cdot 19$

$= 190$

2.43 $_8C_5 = \dfrac{8!}{5!3!} = \dfrac{8 \cdot 7 \cdot 6 \cdot 5!}{3 \cdot 2 \cdot 1 \cdot 5!}$

$= 8 \cdot 7$

$= 56$

2.44 $_{10}C_2 = \dfrac{10!}{2!8!} = \dfrac{\overset{5}{10} \cdot 9 \cdot 8!}{2 \cdot 1 \cdot 8!}$

$= 5 \cdot 9$

$= 45$

2.45 $_xC_4 = \dfrac{x(x - 1)(x - 2)(x - 3)}{4!}$

$_xC_3 = \dfrac{x(x - 1)(x - 2)}{3!}$

$\dfrac{x(x - 1)(x - 2)(x - 3)}{4!} =$

$\dfrac{7(x)(x - 1)(x - 2)}{3!} \qquad = \dfrac{x - 3}{4!} = \dfrac{7}{3!}$

[divide both sides by $x(x - 1)(x - 2)$]

$\dfrac{x - 3}{24} = \dfrac{7}{6}$

$6(x - 3) = 24 \cdot 7$

$6x - 18 = 168$

$6x = 168 + 18$

$6x = 186$

$\dfrac{6x}{6} = \dfrac{186}{6}$

$x = 31$

2.46 $\qquad _xC_2 = 66$

$\dfrac{x(x - 1)}{2} = 66$

$x(x - 1) = 2 \cdot 66$ (cross-multiply)

$x^2 - x = 132$

$x^2 - x - 132 = 0$

$(x + 11)(x - 12) = 0$

$x + 11 = 0$

$x = -11;\ \text{reject}$

$x - 12 = 0$

$x = 12$

2.47

$$_nC_5 = 19[_{n-2}C_3]$$

$$\frac{n(n-1)(n-2)(n-3)(n-4)}{5!} = $$

$$\frac{19[(n-2)(n-3)(n-4)]}{3!}$$

$$\frac{n(n-1)}{5!} = \frac{19}{3!} \text{ [divide both sides}$$

by $(n-2)(n-3)(n-4)$]

$$\frac{n(n-1)}{120} = \frac{19}{6}$$

$$\frac{n^2-n}{120} = \frac{19}{6}$$

$$n^2 - n = \frac{120 \cdot 19}{6}$$

(multiply
both sides
by 120)

$$n^2 - n = 20 \cdot 19$$
$$n^2 - n = 380$$
$$n^2 - n - 380 = 0$$
$$(n+19)(n-20) = 0$$
$$n + 19 = 0$$
$$n = -19; \text{ reject}$$
$$n - 20 = 0$$
$$n = 20$$

2.48 Cows: $_7C_3 = \frac{7!}{3!4!} = \frac{7 \cdot 6 \cdot 5 \cdot 4!}{3 \cdot 2 \cdot 1 \cdot 4!}$

$$= 7 \cdot 5 = 35$$

Pigs: $_4C_2 = \frac{4!}{2!2!} = \frac{4 \cdot 3 \cdot 2!}{2 \cdot 1 \cdot 2!}$

$$= 2 \cdot 3 = 6$$

Sheep: $_{10}C_{10} = \frac{10!}{10!0!} = \frac{10!}{10!} = 1$

$$35 \cdot 6 \cdot 1 = 210$$

2.49 Men: $_8C_4 = \frac{8!}{4!4!} = \frac{8 \cdot 7 \cdot 6 \cdot 5 \cdot 4!}{4 \cdot 3 \cdot 2 \cdot 1 \cdot 4!}$

$$= 2 \cdot 7 \cdot 5 = 70$$

Women: $_5C_3 = \frac{5!}{3!2!} = \frac{5 \cdot 4 \cdot 3!}{2 \cdot 1 \cdot 3!}$

$$= 5 \cdot 2 = 10$$

$$70 \cdot 10 = 700$$

2.50
$$N = 2^n - 1$$
$$= 2^{10} - 1$$
$$= 1,024 - 1$$
$$= 1,023$$
or

$$N = {}_{10}C_1 + {}_{10}C_2 + {}_{10}C_3 + {}_{10}C_4 + {}_{10}C_5 + {}_{10}C_6 + {}_{10}C_7 + {}_{10}C_8 + {}_{10}C_9 + {}_{10}C_{10}$$

$$= \frac{10!}{1!9!} + \frac{10!}{2!8!} + \frac{10!}{3!7!} + \frac{10!}{4!6!} + \frac{10!}{5!5!} + \frac{10!}{6!4!} + \frac{10!}{7!3!} + \frac{10!}{8!2!} + \frac{10!}{9!1!} + \frac{10!}{10!0!}$$

$$= \frac{10 \cdot 9!}{1 \cdot 9!} + \frac{10 \cdot 9 \cdot 8!}{2 \cdot 1 \cdot 8!} + \frac{10 \cdot 9 \cdot 8 \cdot 7!}{3 \cdot 2 \cdot 1 \cdot 7!} +$$

$$\frac{10 \cdot 9 \cdot 8 \cdot 7 \cdot 6!}{4 \cdot 3 \cdot 2 \cdot 1 \cdot 6!} + \frac{10 \cdot 9 \cdot 8 \cdot 7 \cdot 6 \cdot 5!}{5 \cdot 4 \cdot 3 \cdot 2 \cdot 1 \cdot 5!} +$$

$$\frac{10 \cdot 9 \cdot 8 \cdot 7 \cdot 6!}{4 \cdot 3 \cdot 2 \cdot 1 \cdot 6!} + \frac{10 \cdot 9 \cdot 8 \cdot 7!}{3 \cdot 2 \cdot 1 \cdot 7!} +$$

$$\frac{10 \cdot 9 \cdot 8!}{2 \cdot 1 \cdot 8!} + \frac{10 \cdot 9!}{1 \cdot 9!} + \frac{10!}{10!}$$

$$= 10 + 45 + 120 + 210 + 252 + 210 + 120 + 45 + 10 + 1$$

$$= 1,023$$

2.51
$$N = 2^n - 1$$
$$= 2^8 - 1$$
$$= 256 - 1$$
$$= 255$$
or

$$N = {}_8C_1 + {}_8C_2 + {}_8C_3 + {}_8C_4 + {}_8C_5 + {}_8C_6 + {}_8C_7 + {}_8C_8$$

$$= \frac{8!}{1!7!} + \frac{8!}{2!6!} + \frac{8!}{3!5!} + \frac{8!}{4!4!} + \frac{8!}{5!3!} + \frac{8!}{6!2!} + \frac{8!}{7!1!} + \frac{8!}{8!0!}$$

$$= \frac{8 \cdot 7!}{1 \cdot 7!} + \frac{8 \cdot 7 \cdot 6!}{2 \cdot 1 \cdot 6!} + \frac{8 \cdot 7 \cdot 6 \cdot 5!}{3 \cdot 2 \cdot 1 \cdot 5!} +$$

$$\frac{8 \cdot 7 \cdot 6 \cdot 5 \cdot 4!}{4 \cdot 3 \cdot 2 \cdot 1 \cdot 4!} + \frac{8 \cdot 7 \cdot 6 \cdot 5!}{3 \cdot 2 \cdot 1 \cdot 5!} +$$

$$\frac{8 \cdot 7 \cdot 6!}{2 \cdot 1 \cdot 6!} + \frac{8 \cdot 7!}{1 \cdot 7!} + \frac{8!}{8!}$$

$$= 8 + 28 + 56 + 70 + 56 + 28 + 8 + 1$$

$$= 255$$

2.52 Use 8 members. See Problem 2.51.

2.53 $N = 2^n - 1$
  $= 2^6 - 1$
  $= 64 - 1$
  $= 63$

or

$N = {_6}C_1 + {_6}C_2 + {_6}C_3 + {_6}C_4 + {_6}C_5 + {_6}C_6$

$= \dfrac{6!}{1!5!} + \dfrac{6!}{2!4!} + \dfrac{6!}{3!3!} + \dfrac{6!}{4!2!} + \dfrac{6!}{5!1!} + \dfrac{6!}{6!0!}$

$= \dfrac{6 \cdot 5!}{1 \cdot 5!} + \dfrac{6 \cdot 5 \cdot 4!}{2 \cdot 1 \cdot 4!} + \dfrac{6 \cdot 5 \cdot 4 \cdot 3!}{3 \cdot 2 \cdot 1 \cdot 3!} + \dfrac{6 \cdot 5 \cdot 4!}{2 \cdot 1 \cdot 4!} + \dfrac{6 \cdot 5!}{1 \cdot 5!} + \dfrac{6!}{6!}$

$= 6 + 15 + 20 + 15 + 6 + 1$
$= 63$

III. SECTION THREE

3.1 Let p = probability of getting a head = $\frac{1}{2}$
  q = probability of getting a tail = $\frac{1}{2}$

$(p + q)^6 = \binom{6}{0}\left(\frac{1}{2}\right)^6 + \binom{6}{1}\left(\frac{1}{2}\right)^5 \cdot \left(\frac{1}{2}\right)^1 + \binom{6}{2}\left(\frac{1}{2}\right)^4\left(\frac{1}{2}\right)^2 + \binom{6}{3}\left(\frac{1}{2}\right)^3\left(\frac{1}{2}\right)^3 + \binom{6}{4}\left(\frac{1}{2}\right)^2 \cdot \left(\frac{1}{2}\right)^4 + \binom{6}{5}\left(\frac{1}{2}\right)^1\left(\frac{1}{2}\right)^5 + \binom{6}{6}\left(\frac{1}{2}\right)^6$

$P(2$ or more heads$) = \binom{6}{0}\left(\frac{1}{2}\right)^6 + \binom{6}{1}\left(\frac{1}{2}\right)^5 \cdot \left(\frac{1}{2}\right)^1 + \binom{6}{2}\left(\frac{1}{2}\right)^4 \cdot \left(\frac{1}{2}\right)^2 + \binom{6}{3}\left(\frac{1}{2}\right)^3 \cdot \left(\frac{1}{2}\right)^3 + \binom{6}{4}\left(\frac{1}{2}\right)^2\left(\frac{1}{2}\right)^4$

$= \left(\frac{1}{2}\right)^6 + 6\left(\frac{1}{2}\right)^5\left(\frac{1}{2}\right)^1 + 15\left(\frac{1}{2}\right)^4\left(\frac{1}{2}\right)^2 + 20\left(\frac{1}{2}\right)^3\left(\frac{1}{2}\right)^3 + 15\left(\frac{1}{2}\right)^2\left(\frac{1}{2}\right)^4$

Another way of solving the problem is to subtract from 1 the probability of getting 1 or fewer heads.

$P(2$ or more heads$) = 1 - P(1$ or fewer heads$)$
  $= 1 - [\binom{6}{5}\left(\frac{1}{2}\right)^1 \cdot \left(\frac{1}{2}\right)^5 + \binom{6}{6}\left(\frac{1}{2}\right)^6]$
  $= 1 - [6\left(\frac{1}{2}\right)^1\left(\frac{1}{2}\right)^5 + \left(\frac{1}{2}\right)^6]$

3.2 Let p = probability that the disease is fatal = $\frac{3}{5}$
  q = probability that the disease is not fatal = $1 - \frac{3}{5} = \frac{2}{5}$

$(p + q)^{10} = \binom{10}{0}\left(\frac{3}{5}\right)^{10} + \binom{10}{1}\left(\frac{3}{5}\right)^9\left(\frac{2}{5}\right)^1 + \binom{10}{2}\left(\frac{3}{5}\right)^8\left(\frac{2}{5}\right)^2 + \binom{10}{3}\left(\frac{3}{5}\right)^7\left(\frac{2}{5}\right)^3 + \binom{10}{4}\left(\frac{3}{5}\right)^6\left(\frac{2}{5}\right)^4 + \binom{10}{5}\left(\frac{3}{5}\right)^5\left(\frac{2}{5}\right)^5 + \binom{10}{6}\left(\frac{3}{5}\right)^4\left(\frac{2}{5}\right)^6 + \binom{10}{7}\left(\frac{3}{5}\right)^3\left(\frac{2}{5}\right)^7 + \binom{10}{8}\left(\frac{3}{5}\right)^2\left(\frac{2}{5}\right)^8 + \binom{10}{9}\left(\frac{3}{5}\right)^1\left(\frac{2}{5}\right)^9 + \binom{10}{10}\left(\frac{2}{5}\right)^{10}$

$P($at least 4 patients will recover$) = \binom{10}{4}\left(\frac{3}{5}\right)^6\left(\frac{2}{5}\right)^4 + \binom{10}{5}\left(\frac{3}{5}\right)^5\left(\frac{2}{5}\right)^5 + \binom{10}{6}\left(\frac{3}{5}\right)^4\left(\frac{2}{5}\right)^6 + \binom{10}{7}\left(\frac{3}{5}\right)^3\left(\frac{2}{5}\right)^7 + \binom{10}{8}\left(\frac{3}{5}\right)^2\left(\frac{2}{5}\right)^8 + \binom{10}{9}\left(\frac{3}{5}\right)^1\left(\frac{2}{5}\right)^9 + \binom{10}{10}\left(\frac{2}{5}\right)^{10}$

$= 210\left(\frac{3}{5}\right)^6\left(\frac{2}{5}\right)^4 + 252\left(\frac{3}{5}\right)^5\left(\frac{2}{5}\right)^5 + 210\left(\frac{3}{5}\right)^4\left(\frac{2}{5}\right)^6 + 120\left(\frac{3}{5}\right)^3\left(\frac{2}{5}\right)^7 + 45\left(\frac{3}{5}\right)^2\left(\frac{2}{5}\right)^8 + 10\left(\frac{3}{5}\right)^1\left(\frac{2}{5}\right)^9 + \left(\frac{2}{5}\right)^{10}$

3.3 a. $\left(\frac{1}{4}\right)^{10}$

  b. Let p = probability of getting a correct answer = $\frac{1}{4}$
  q = probability of getting an incorrect answer = $1 - \frac{1}{4} = \frac{3}{4}$

$(p + q)^{10} = \binom{10}{0}(\frac{1}{4})^{10} +$
$\binom{10}{1}(\frac{1}{4})^9(\frac{3}{4})^1 +$
$\binom{10}{2}(\frac{1}{4})^8(\frac{3}{4})^2 +$
$\binom{10}{3}(\frac{1}{4})^7(\frac{3}{4})^3 +$
$\binom{10}{4}(\frac{1}{4})^6(\frac{3}{4})^4 +$
$\binom{10}{5}(\frac{1}{4})^5(\frac{3}{4})^5 +$
$\binom{10}{6}(\frac{1}{4})^4(\frac{3}{4})^6 +$
$\binom{10}{7}(\frac{1}{4})^3(\frac{3}{4})^7 +$
$\binom{10}{8}(\frac{1}{4})^2(\frac{3}{4})^8 +$
$\binom{10}{9}(\frac{1}{4})^1(\frac{3}{4})^9 +$
$\binom{10}{10}(\frac{3}{4})^{10}$

P(at least half correct) $= \binom{10}{0}(\frac{1}{4})^{10} +$
$\binom{10}{1}(\frac{1}{4})^9(\frac{3}{4})^1 +$
$\binom{10}{2}(\frac{1}{4})^8(\frac{3}{4})^2 +$
$\binom{10}{3}(\frac{1}{4})^7(\frac{3}{4})^3 +$
$\binom{10}{4}(\frac{1}{4})^6(\frac{3}{4})^4 +$
$\binom{10}{5}(\frac{1}{4})^5(\frac{3}{4})^5$

$= (\frac{1}{4})^{10} +$
$10(\frac{1}{4})^9(\frac{3}{4})^1 +$
$45(\frac{1}{4})^8(\frac{3}{4})^2 +$
$120(\frac{1}{4})^7(\frac{3}{4})^3 +$
$210(\frac{1}{4})^6(\frac{3}{4})^4 +$
$252(\frac{1}{4})^5(\frac{3}{4})^5$

3.4   Let p = probability that he will get a hit = 0.3 $= \frac{3}{10}$

q = probability that he will not get a hit = $1 - 0.3 = 0.7 = \frac{7}{10}$

$(p + q)^4 = \binom{4}{0}(\frac{3}{10})^4 +$
$\binom{4}{1}(\frac{3}{10})^3(\frac{7}{10})^1 +$
$\binom{4}{2}(\frac{3}{10})^2(\frac{7}{10})^2 +$
$\binom{4}{3}(\frac{3}{10})^1(\frac{7}{10})^3 +$
$\binom{4}{4}(\frac{7}{10})^4$

a. $P(2$ hits$) = \binom{4}{2}(\frac{3}{10})^2(\frac{7}{10})^2$
$= 6(\frac{9}{100})(\frac{49}{100})$
$= \frac{2,646}{10,000}$
$= \frac{1,323}{5,000}$ or 0.265 (rounded to three places)

b. P(at least 1 hit) $= \binom{4}{0}(\frac{3}{10})^4 +$
$\binom{4}{1}(\frac{3}{10})^3(\frac{7}{10})^1 +$
$\binom{4}{2}(\frac{3}{10})^2(\frac{7}{10})^2 +$
$\binom{4}{3}(\frac{3}{10})^1(\frac{7}{10})^3$

$= (\frac{3}{10})^4 +$
$4(\frac{3}{10})^3(\frac{7}{10})^1 +$
$6(\frac{3}{10})^2(\frac{7}{10})^2 +$
$4(\frac{3}{10})^1(\frac{7}{10})^3$

Another way of solving the problem is to subtract from 1 the probability of no hits.

P(at least 1 hit) $= 1 - P$(no hits)
$= 1 - [\binom{4}{4}(\frac{7}{10})^4]$
$= 1 - (\frac{7}{10})^4$

3.5   Let p = probability of winning = $\frac{2}{3}$

q = probability of losing = $1 - \frac{2}{3} = \frac{1}{3}$

$(p + q)^5 = \binom{5}{0}(\frac{2}{3})^5 +$
$\binom{5}{1}(\frac{2}{3})^4(\frac{1}{3})^1 +$
$\binom{5}{2}(\frac{2}{3})^3(\frac{1}{3})^2 +$
$\binom{5}{3}(\frac{2}{3})^2(\frac{1}{3})^3 +$
$\binom{5}{4}(\frac{2}{3})^1(\frac{1}{3})^4 +$
$\binom{5}{5}(\frac{1}{3})^5$

a. P(winning exactly 4 games) $= \binom{5}{1}(\frac{2}{3})^4(\frac{1}{3})^1$
$= 5(\frac{16}{81})(\frac{1}{3})$
$= \frac{80}{243}$ or 0.33

b. P(winning exactly 2 games) $= \binom{5}{3}(\frac{2}{3})^2(\frac{1}{3})^3$
$= 10(\frac{4}{9})(\frac{1}{27})$
$= \frac{40}{243}$ or 0.16

c. P(winning at least 3 games) $= \binom{5}{0}(\frac{2}{3})^5 +$
$\binom{5}{1}(\frac{2}{3})^4(\frac{1}{3})^1 +$
$\binom{5}{2}(\frac{2}{3})^3(\frac{1}{3})^2$
$= \frac{32}{243} + 5(\frac{16}{81})(\frac{1}{3}) +$
$10(\frac{8}{27})(\frac{1}{9})$
$= \frac{32}{243} + \frac{80}{243} + \frac{80}{243}$
$= \frac{192}{243}$
$= \frac{64}{81}$ or 0.79

3.6   Let p = probability of good fuse = 80% = $\frac{8}{10}$

q = probability of defective fuse = 100% - 80% = 20% = $\frac{2}{10}$

$$(p + q)^{10} = \binom{10}{0}\left(\frac{8}{10}\right)^{10} +$$
$$\binom{10}{1}\left(\frac{8}{10}\right)^{9}\left(\frac{2}{10}\right)^{1} +$$
$$\binom{10}{2}\left(\frac{8}{10}\right)^{8}\left(\frac{2}{10}\right)^{2} +$$
$$\binom{10}{3}\left(\frac{8}{10}\right)^{7}\left(\frac{2}{10}\right)^{3} +$$
$$\binom{10}{4}\left(\frac{8}{10}\right)^{6}\left(\frac{2}{10}\right)^{4} +$$
$$\binom{10}{5}\left(\frac{8}{10}\right)^{5}\left(\frac{2}{10}\right)^{5} +$$
$$\binom{10}{6}\left(\frac{8}{10}\right)^{4}\left(\frac{2}{10}\right)^{6} +$$
$$\binom{10}{7}\left(\frac{8}{10}\right)^{3}\left(\frac{2}{10}\right)^{7} +$$
$$\binom{10}{8}\left(\frac{8}{10}\right)^{2}\left(\frac{2}{10}\right)^{8} +$$
$$\binom{10}{9}\left(\frac{8}{10}\right)^{1}\left(\frac{2}{10}\right)^{9} +$$
$$\binom{10}{10}\left(\frac{2}{10}\right)^{10}$$

a. $P(\text{no defectives}) = \binom{10}{0}\left(\frac{8}{10}\right)^{10}$
$$= \left(\frac{8}{10}\right)^{10}$$

b. $P(2 \text{ defectives}) = \binom{10}{2}\left(\frac{8}{10}\right)^{8} \cdot$
$$\left(\frac{2}{10}\right)^{2}$$
$$= 45\left(\frac{8}{10}\right)^{8} \cdot$$
$$\left(\frac{2}{10}\right)^{2}$$

c. $P(\text{at least 7}$
$\text{defectives}) = \binom{10}{7}\left(\frac{8}{10}\right)^{3} \cdot$
$$\left(\frac{2}{10}\right)^{7} +$$
$$\binom{10}{8}\left(\frac{8}{10}\right)^{2}\left(\frac{2}{10}\right)^{8} +$$
$$\binom{10}{9}\left(\frac{8}{10}\right)^{1}\left(\frac{2}{10}\right)^{9} +$$
$$\binom{10}{10}\left(\frac{2}{10}\right)^{10}$$
$$= 120\left(\frac{8}{10}\right)^{3}\left(\frac{2}{10}\right)^{7} +$$
$$45\left(\frac{8}{10}\right)^{2}\left(\frac{2}{10}\right)^{8} +$$
$$10\left(\frac{8}{10}\right)^{1}\left(\frac{2}{10}\right)^{9} +$$
$$\left(\frac{2}{10}\right)^{10}$$

d. $P(\text{all}$
$\text{defectives}) = \binom{10}{10}\left(\frac{2}{10}\right)^{10}$
$$= \left(\frac{2}{10}\right)^{10}$$

3.7 a. $P(x \le 5) = \frac{1}{45} + \frac{2}{45} + \frac{3}{45} + \frac{4}{45}$
$$= \frac{10}{45}$$
$$= \frac{2}{9} \text{ or } 0.22$$

b. $P(5 < x < 9)$
$$= \frac{4}{45} + \frac{5}{45} + \frac{6}{45} + \frac{7}{45} + \frac{8}{45}$$
$$= \frac{30}{45}$$
$$= \frac{2}{3} \text{ or } 0.67$$

c. $P(3 \le x \le 6) = \frac{2}{45} + \frac{3}{45} +$
$$\frac{4}{45} + \frac{5}{45}$$
$$= \frac{14}{45} \text{ or } 0.31$$

d. $P(8 \le x \le 10) = \frac{7}{45} + \frac{8}{45} + \frac{9}{45}$
$$= \frac{24}{45}$$
$$= \frac{8}{15} \text{ or } 0.53$$

e. $P(x = 7) = \frac{6}{45}$
$$= \frac{2}{15} \text{ or } 0.13$$

f. $P(2 \le x \le 4) = \frac{1}{45} + \frac{2}{45}$
$$= \frac{3}{45}$$
$$= \frac{1}{15} \text{ or } 0.07$$

g. $P(4 \le x \le 5) = \frac{4}{45} \text{ or } 0.09$

3.8 Sample space = {(H H H), (H H T), (H T H), (T H H), (H T T), (T H T), (T T H), (T T T)}.

$P(\text{heads}) = \frac{1}{2}$
$P(\text{tails}) = \frac{1}{2}$

$P(\text{H H H}) = \frac{1}{2} \cdot \frac{1}{2} \cdot \frac{1}{2} = \frac{1}{8}$
$P(\text{H H T}) = \frac{1}{2} \cdot \frac{1}{2} \cdot \frac{1}{2} = \frac{1}{8}$
$P(\text{H T H}) = \frac{1}{2} \cdot \frac{1}{2} \cdot \frac{1}{2} = \frac{1}{8}$
$P(\text{T H H}) = \frac{1}{2} \cdot \frac{1}{2} \cdot \frac{1}{2} = \frac{1}{8}$
$P(\text{H T T}) = \frac{1}{2} \cdot \frac{1}{2} \cdot \frac{1}{2} = \frac{1}{8}$
$P(\text{T H T}) = \frac{1}{2} \cdot \frac{1}{2} \cdot \frac{1}{2} = \frac{1}{8}$
$P(\text{T T H}) = \frac{1}{2} \cdot \frac{1}{2} \cdot \frac{1}{2} = \frac{1}{8}$
$P(\text{T T T}) = \frac{1}{2} \cdot \frac{1}{2} \cdot \frac{1}{2} = \frac{1}{8}$

$P(0 \text{ tails}) = \frac{1}{8}$
$P(1 \text{ tail}) = \frac{1}{8} + \frac{1}{8} + \frac{1}{8} = \frac{3}{8}$
$P(2 \text{ tails}) = \frac{1}{8} + \frac{1}{8} + \frac{1}{8} = \frac{3}{8}$
$P(3 \text{ tails}) = \frac{1}{8}$

$x =$	0	1	2	3
$P(x) =$	$\frac{1}{8}$	$\frac{3}{8}$	$\frac{3}{8}$	$\frac{1}{8}$

3.9 Let x = number of defective transistors.
Random variable values:
x = 0, 1, 2, 3.

Probability distribution:

x	$P(x)$
0	$\frac{\binom{7}{4}\binom{3}{0}}{\binom{10}{4}} = \frac{35}{210}$
1	$\frac{\binom{7}{3}\binom{3}{1}}{\binom{10}{4}} = \frac{105}{210}$
2	$\frac{\binom{7}{2}\binom{3}{2}}{\binom{10}{4}} = \frac{63}{210}$
3	$\frac{\binom{7}{1}\binom{3}{3}}{\binom{10}{4}} = \frac{7}{210}$

$E(x) = 0\left(\frac{35}{210}\right) + 1\left(\frac{105}{210}\right)$
$$+ 2\left(\frac{63}{210}\right) + 3\left(\frac{7}{210}\right)$$
$$= 1.2$$

3.10 a. $P(1 \leq x \leq 2) = \frac{105}{210} + \frac{63}{210}$

     $= \frac{168}{210}$ or .8

   b. $P(2 \leq x \leq 3) = \frac{63}{210} + \frac{7}{210}$

     $= \frac{70}{210}$

     $= .33$

   c. $P(x = 3) = \frac{7}{210}$ or .03

   d. $P(1 \leq x \leq 3) = \frac{105}{210} + \frac{63}{210} + \frac{7}{210}$

     $= \frac{175}{210}$ or .83

3.11 Let y = result after three steps.

   a. P(walking upward) = $\frac{1}{2}$
   P(walking downward) = $\frac{1}{2}$
   Let 1 unit upward = 1 and
   1 unit downward = -1.

   3 units upward = 1 + 1 + 1
       = 3
   2 units upward, 1 downward =
   1 + 1 - 1 = 1 (can also be 1
   unit upward, 1 downward,
   1 upward, or 1 unit
   downward, 2 upward)
   1 unit upward, 2 downward =
   1 - 1 - 1 = -1 (can also be
   1 unit downward, 1 upward,
   1 downward or 2 units downward, 1 upward)
   3 units downward = -1 - 1 -
   1 = -3

   After three steps the
   possibilities are 3 units,
   1 unit, -1 unit and -3
   units from the x-axis.
   Two choices (upward and
   downward) = 2^3 = 8
   possibilities.

y	Number of Possibilities	$P(y)$
3	1	$\frac{1}{8}$
1	3	$\frac{3}{8}$
-1	3	$\frac{3}{8}$
-3	1	$\frac{1}{8}$

   b. $P(-1 \leq x \leq 1) = \frac{3}{8} + \frac{3}{8}$

     $= \frac{6}{8}$

     $= \frac{3}{4}$ or 0.75

3.12 4 units upward = 1 + 1 + 1 +
   1 = 4
   3 units upward, 1 downward =
   1 + 1 + 1 - 1 = 2
     (can also be 1 + 1 - 1 + 1
     or 1 - 1 + 1 + 1 or
     -1 + 1 + 1 + 1)
   2 units upward, 2 downward =
   1 + 1 - 1 - 1 = 0
     (can also be 1 - 1 + 1 - 1
     or -1 + 1 - 1 + 1 or
     -1 - 1 + 1 + 1 or
     1 - 1 - 1 + 1 or
     -1 + 1 + 1 - 1)
   1 unit upward, 3 downward =
   1 - 1 - 1 - 1 = -2
     (can also be -1 + 1 - 1 - 1
     or - 1 - 1 + 1 - 1 or
     - 1 - 1 - 1 + 1)
   4 units downward = -1 - 1 -
   1 - 1 = -4

   After four steps the
   possibilities are 4 units,
   2 units, 0 units, -2 units,
   and -4 units from the x-axis.

   Two choices (upward and
   downward) = 2^4 = 16
   possibilities.

y	Number of Possibilities	$P(y)$
-4	1	$\frac{1}{16}$
-2	4	$\frac{4}{16}$
0	6	$\frac{6}{16}$
2	4	$\frac{4}{16}$
4	1	$\frac{1}{16}$
		$\frac{16}{16} = 1$

   Yes, the sum of the
   Probabilities equals 1.

3.13 Let x = number of bulbs
         tested.

   $\binom{6}{2} = \frac{6!}{2!4!} = \frac{6^3 \cdot 5 \cdot 4!}{2 \cdot 1 \cdot 4!}$

     = 15 elements in
       the sample space

x	$P(x)$
2	$\binom{1}{1}\binom{1}{1} = \frac{1}{15}$
3	$\binom{2}{1}\binom{1}{1} = \frac{2}{15}$
4	$\binom{3}{1}\binom{1}{1} = \frac{3}{15}$
5	$\binom{4}{1}\binom{1}{1} = \frac{4}{15}$
6	$\binom{5}{1}\binom{1}{1} = \frac{5}{15}$

$$E(x) = 2(\tfrac{1}{15}) + 3(\tfrac{2}{15}) + 4(\tfrac{3}{15}) + 5(\tfrac{4}{15}) + 6(\tfrac{5}{15})$$
$$= \tfrac{2}{15} + \tfrac{6}{15} + \tfrac{12}{15} + \tfrac{20}{15} + \tfrac{30}{15}$$
$$= \tfrac{70}{15}$$
$$= 4\tfrac{2}{3} \text{ or } 4.67, \text{ or}$$
5 bulbs

3.14 The sample space consists of $\binom{20}{2}$ or 190 elements.
Let x = amounts of money.

x	$P(x)$
0	$\dfrac{\binom{10}{2}}{\binom{20}{2}} = \dfrac{45}{190}$
1	$\dfrac{\binom{5}{1}\binom{10}{1}}{\binom{20}{2}} = \dfrac{5\cdot10}{190} = \dfrac{50}{190}$
2	$\dfrac{\binom{5}{2}}{\binom{20}{2}} = \dfrac{10}{190}$
5	$\dfrac{\binom{3}{1}\binom{10}{1}}{\binom{20}{2}} = \dfrac{3\cdot10}{190} = \dfrac{30}{190}$
6	$\dfrac{\binom{3}{1}\binom{5}{1}}{\binom{20}{2}} = \dfrac{3\cdot5}{190} = \dfrac{15}{190}$
10	$\dfrac{\binom{3}{2} + \binom{2}{1}\binom{10}{1}}{\binom{20}{2}} = \dfrac{3+2\cdot10}{190} = \dfrac{23}{190}$
11	$\dfrac{\binom{2}{1}\binom{5}{1}}{\binom{20}{2}} = \dfrac{2\cdot5}{190} = \dfrac{10}{190}$
15	$\dfrac{\binom{2}{1}\binom{3}{1}}{\binom{20}{2}} = \dfrac{2\cdot3}{190} = \dfrac{6}{190}$
20	$\dfrac{\binom{2}{2}}{\binom{20}{2}} = \dfrac{1}{190}$

$$E(x) = 0(\tfrac{45}{190}) + 1(\tfrac{50}{190}) + 2(\tfrac{10}{190}) + 5(\tfrac{30}{190}) + 6(\tfrac{15}{190}) + 10(\tfrac{23}{190}) + 11(\tfrac{10}{190}) + 15(\tfrac{6}{190}) + 20(\tfrac{1}{190})$$
$$= 0 + \tfrac{50}{190} + \tfrac{20}{190} + \tfrac{150}{190} + \tfrac{90}{190} + \tfrac{230}{190} + \tfrac{110}{190} + \tfrac{90}{190} + \tfrac{20}{190}$$
$$= \tfrac{760}{190}$$
$$= 4$$

3.15 Seniors: $_{20}C_2$
Juniors: $_{15}C_1$
Sophomores: $_{10}C_1$
Freshmen: $_{5}C_1$
Total: $_{50}C_5$

$$P = \frac{_{20}C_2 \cdot {}_{15}C_1 \cdot {}_{10}C_1 \cdot {}_{5}C_1}{_{50}C_5}$$

3.16 Let p = probability of winning = $\frac{3}{5}$
q = probability of losing = $\frac{2}{5}$

$$(p+q)^{10} = \binom{10}{0}(\tfrac{3}{5})^{10} + \binom{10}{1}(\tfrac{3}{5})^9(\tfrac{2}{5})^1 + \binom{10}{2}(\tfrac{3}{5})^8(\tfrac{2}{5})^2 + \binom{10}{3}(\tfrac{3}{5})^7(\tfrac{2}{5})^3 + \binom{10}{4}(\tfrac{3}{5})^6(\tfrac{2}{5})^4 + \ldots \binom{10}{10}(\tfrac{2}{5})^{10}$$

a. P(winning exactly 6 games) = $\binom{10}{4}(\tfrac{3}{5})^6(\tfrac{2}{5})^4$
$$= 210(\tfrac{729}{15,625})(\tfrac{16}{625})$$
$$= \tfrac{2,449,440}{9,765,625}$$
$$= \tfrac{489,888}{1,953,125} \text{ or } 0.251$$

b. P(winning exactly 7 games) = $\binom{10}{3}(\tfrac{3}{5})^7(\tfrac{2}{5})^3$
$$= 120(\tfrac{2,187}{78,125})(\tfrac{8}{125})$$
$$= \tfrac{2,099,520}{9,765,625}$$
$$= \tfrac{419,904}{1,953,125} \text{ or } 0.215$$

3.17 $2(\frac{1}{\binom{10}{5}}) = 2(\frac{5!5!}{10!})$

3.18   Let p = probability of
       female = 40% = $\frac{2}{5}$
       q = probability of
       male = 60% = $\frac{3}{5}$

$(p + q)^5 = \binom{5}{0}\left(\frac{2}{5}\right)^5 +$
$\binom{5}{1}\left(\frac{2}{5}\right)^4\left(\frac{3}{5}\right)^1 +$
$\binom{5}{2}\left(\frac{2}{5}\right)^3\left(\frac{3}{5}\right)^2 +$
$\binom{5}{3}\left(\frac{2}{5}\right)^2\left(\frac{3}{5}\right)^3 +$
$\binom{5}{4}\left(\frac{2}{5}\right)^1\left(\frac{3}{5}\right)^4 +$
$\binom{5}{5}\left(\frac{3}{5}\right)^5$

a. $P(\text{no males}) = \binom{5}{0}\left(\frac{2}{5}\right)^5$
     $= \left(\frac{2}{5}\right)^5$

b. $P(\text{at least one male}) = \binom{5}{1}\left(\frac{2}{5}\right)^4\left(\frac{3}{5}\right)^1 +$
     $\binom{5}{2}\left(\frac{2}{5}\right)^3\left(\frac{3}{5}\right)^2 +$
     $\binom{5}{3}\left(\frac{2}{5}\right)^2\left(\frac{3}{5}\right)^3 +$
     $\binom{5}{4}\left(\frac{2}{5}\right)^1\left(\frac{3}{5}\right)^4 +$
     $\binom{5}{5}\left(\frac{3}{5}\right)^5$

     $= 5\left(\frac{2}{5}\right)^4\left(\frac{3}{5}\right)^1 +$
     $10\left(\frac{2}{5}\right)^3\left(\frac{3}{5}\right)^2 +$
     $10\left(\frac{2}{5}\right)^2\left(\frac{3}{5}\right)^3 +$
     $5\left(\frac{2}{5}\right)^1\left(\frac{3}{5}\right)^4 +$
     $\left(\frac{3}{5}\right)^5$

     Another way of solving the
     problem is to subtract
     from 1 the probability of
     no males.
     $P(\text{at least one male}) = 1 - P(\text{no males})$
     $= 1 - [\binom{5}{0}\left(\frac{2}{5}\right)^5]$
     $= 1 - \left(\frac{2}{5}\right)^5$

c. $P(\text{exactly one male}) = \binom{5}{1}\left(\frac{2}{5}\right)^4\left(\frac{3}{5}\right)^1$
     $= 5\left(\frac{2}{5}\right)^4\left(\frac{3}{5}\right)^1$

d. $P(\text{all males}) = \binom{5}{5}\left(\frac{3}{5}\right)^5$
     $= \left(\frac{3}{5}\right)^5$

3.19   a.   0.7
       b. $P(Y) = 1 - 0.5 = 0.5$
       c. $P(X) \cdot P(Y) = (0.77)(0.5)$
            $= 0.35$
       d. $P(X') \cdot P(Y') = (1 - 0.7) \cdot$
            (0.5)
            $= (0.3)(0.5)$
            $= 0.15$
       e. $P(X) \cdot P(Y) +$
            $P(X') \cdot P(Y') = (0.7)(0.5) +$
            $(0.3)(0.5)$
            $= 0.35 + 0.15$
            $= 0.50 \text{ or } 0.5$

3.20 $P(2 \text{ black}) = \frac{4}{12} \cdot \frac{3}{11} = \frac{12}{132}$
       $P(2 \text{ brown}) = \frac{6}{12} \cdot \frac{5}{11} = \frac{30}{132}$
       $P(2 \text{ blue}) = \frac{2}{12} \cdot \frac{1}{11} = \frac{2}{132}$

       $\frac{12}{132} + \frac{30}{132} + \frac{2}{132} = \frac{44}{132}$
       $= \frac{1}{3} \text{ or } 0.33$

3.21   Start with one person. The
       probability that another
       person does not have the same
       birthday as the first person
       is $\frac{364}{365}$. The probability that
       a third person does not have
       the same birthday as the
       previous two is $\frac{363}{365}$, and so on.

       The probability that all six
       of the people have different
       birthdays is the product of
       independent probabilities.

       $\frac{364}{365} \cdot \frac{363}{365} \cdot \frac{362}{365} \cdot \frac{361}{365} \cdot \frac{360}{365} =$
       $\frac{6.2162 \times 10^{12}}{6.4783 \times 10^{12}} = 0.9595$

       Hence, the probability that
       two people have the same
       birthday is $1 - 0.9595 = 0.04$.

3.22   Let p = probability of same
       birthday = $\frac{1}{365}$
       q = probability of
       different birthday =
       $1 - \frac{1}{365} = \frac{364}{365}$

       $(p + q)^5 = \binom{5}{0}\left(\frac{1}{365}\right)^5 +$
       $\binom{5}{1}\left(\frac{1}{365}\right)^4\left(\frac{364}{365}\right)^1 +$
       $\binom{5}{2}\left(\frac{1}{365}\right)^3\left(\frac{364}{365}\right)^2 +$
       $\binom{5}{3}\left(\frac{1}{365}\right)^2\left(\frac{364}{365}\right)^3 +$
       $\binom{5}{4}\left(\frac{1}{365}\right)^1\left(\frac{364}{365}\right)^4 +$
       $\binom{5}{5}\left(\frac{364}{365}\right)^5$

       $P(\text{at least one}) = 1 - P(\text{none})$
       $= 1 - [\binom{5}{5} \cdot$
       $\left(\frac{364}{365}\right)^5]$
       $= 1 - \left(\frac{364}{365}\right)^5$

3.23   a. $\dfrac{\binom{5}{3}\binom{45}{0}}{\binom{50}{3}} = \dfrac{\frac{5!}{3!2!}\cdot\frac{45!}{0!45!}}{\frac{50!}{3!47!}}$

$= \dfrac{\frac{5\cdot4\cdot\overset{2}{3!}}{2\cdot1\cdot3!}\cdot\frac{45!}{45!}}{\frac{50\cdot49\cdot\overset{8}{48}\cdot47!}{3\cdot2\cdot1\cdot47!}}$

$= \dfrac{10\cdot1}{50\cdot49\cdot8}$

$= \dfrac{10}{19,600}$

$= \dfrac{1}{19,600}$ or 0.0005

b. $\dfrac{\binom{5}{0}\binom{45}{3}}{\binom{50}{3}} = \dfrac{\frac{5!}{0!5!}\cdot\frac{45!}{3!42!}}{\frac{50!}{3!47!}}$

$= \dfrac{\frac{5!}{5!}\cdot\frac{\overset{15}{45}\cdot\overset{22}{44}\cdot43\cdot42!}{3\cdot2\cdot1\cdot42!}}{\frac{50\cdot49\cdot\overset{8}{48}\cdot47!}{3\cdot2\cdot1\cdot47!}}$

$= \dfrac{1\cdot15\cdot22\cdot43}{50\cdot49\cdot8}$

$= \dfrac{14,190}{19,600}$

$= \dfrac{1,419}{1,960}$ or 0.724

c. $P(1\text{ is defective}) = \dfrac{\binom{5}{1}\binom{45}{2}}{\binom{50}{3}}$

$= \dfrac{\frac{5!}{1!4!}\cdot\frac{43!}{2!43!}}{\frac{50!}{3!47!}}$

$= \dfrac{\frac{5\cdot4!}{4!}\cdot\frac{45\cdot\overset{22}{44}\cdot43!}{2\cdot1\cdot43!}}{\frac{50\cdot49\cdot\overset{9}{48}\cdot47!}{3\cdot2\cdot1\cdot47!}}$

$= \dfrac{\overset{}{5}\cdot45\cdot\overset{11}{22}}{\underset{2}{\underset{10}{50}}\cdot49\cdot\underset{4}{8}}$

$= \dfrac{99}{392}$ or 0.2526

3.23   cont.

$P(2\text{ are defective}) = \dfrac{\binom{5}{2}\binom{45}{1}}{\binom{50}{3}}$

$= \dfrac{\frac{5!}{2!3!}\cdot\frac{45!}{1!44!}}{\frac{50!}{3!47!}}$

$= \dfrac{\frac{5\cdot4\cdot\overset{2}{3!}}{2\cdot1\cdot3!}\cdot\frac{45\cdot44!}{1\cdot44!}}{\frac{50\cdot49\cdot\overset{8}{48}\cdot47!}{3\cdot2\cdot1\cdot47!}}$

$= \dfrac{3\cdot2\cdot\overset{9}{45}}{3\cdot50\cdot49\cdot8}$

$= \dfrac{9}{392}$ or 0.023

$P(3\text{ are defective}) = \dfrac{\binom{5}{3}\binom{45}{0}}{\binom{50}{3}}$

$= \dfrac{1}{1,960}$ or 0.0005 (from part a.)

Add the probabilities:
0.2526 + 0.023 + 0.0005 =
0.2761 = 0.276 (rounded to
three decimal places)

3.24   Let F represent owners of Fords

C represent owners of Chevrolets

P represent owners of Plymouths

$F \cap C \cap P = 80$

$F \cap C = 380 - 80$
      $= 300$

$F \cap P = 270 - 80$
      $= 190$

$C \cap P = 350 - 80$
      $= 270$

$F = 600 - (300 + 80 + 190)$
  $= 600 - 570$
  $= 30$

$C = 720 - (300 + 80 + 270)$
  $= 720 - 650$
  $= 70$

$P = 560 - (190 + 80 + 270)$
  $= 560 - 540$
  $= 20$

3.24 cont.

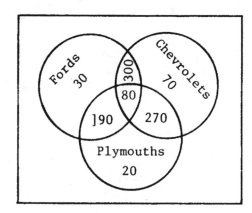

a. $P(F \text{ and } C) = \frac{300}{1,000}$
$= \frac{3}{10}$ or 0.3

b. $P(F \text{ and } P) = \frac{190}{1,000}$
$= \frac{19}{100}$ or 0.19

c. $P(P) = \frac{20}{1,000}$
$= \frac{1}{50}$ or 0.02

d. $P(C) = \frac{70}{1,000}$
$= \frac{7}{100}$ or 0.07

3.25 $P(A) \cdot P(B) \cdot P(C) = (0.1)(0.2) \cdot$
(0.01)
$= 0.0002$

3.26 Let $P(1) = P(\text{average arrives by}$
Channel 1$) = \frac{3}{5}$
Let $P(2) = P(\text{average arrives by}$
Channel 2$) = \frac{4}{5}$
Let $P(3) = P(\text{average arrives by}$
Channel 3$) = \frac{1}{2}$

$P(1') = 1 - \frac{3}{5} = \frac{2}{5}$
$P(2') = 1 - \frac{4}{5} = \frac{1}{5}$
$P(3') = 1 - \frac{1}{2} = \frac{1}{2}$

a. $P(1) = \frac{3}{5}$
$P(2) = \frac{4}{5}$
$P(3) = \frac{1}{2}$
$P(\text{message arrives by all}$
3 channels$) = (\frac{3}{5})(\frac{4}{5})(\frac{1}{2}) = \frac{12}{50}$

$P(1) = \frac{3}{5}$
$P(2') = \frac{1}{5}$
$P(3') = \frac{1}{2}$
$P(\text{message arrives by Channel 1}$
only$) = (\frac{3}{5})(\frac{1}{5})(\frac{1}{2}) = \frac{3}{50}$

$P(1') = \frac{2}{5}$
$P(2) = \frac{4}{5}$
$P(3') = \frac{1}{2}$
$P(\text{message arrives by Channel}$
2 only$) = (\frac{2}{5})(\frac{4}{5})(\frac{1}{2}) = \frac{8}{50}$

$P(1') = \frac{2}{5}$
$P(2') = \frac{1}{5}$
$P(3) = \frac{1}{2}$
$P(\text{message arrives by Channel}$
3 only$) = (\frac{2}{5})(\frac{1}{5})(\frac{1}{2}) = \frac{2}{50}$

$P(1) = \frac{3}{5}$
$P(2) = \frac{4}{5}$
$P(3') = \frac{1}{2}$
$P(\text{message arrives by Channels 1}$
and 2 only$) = (\frac{3}{5})(\frac{4}{5})(\frac{1}{2}) = \frac{12}{50}$

$P(1) = \frac{3}{5}$
$P(2') = \frac{1}{5}$
$P(3) = \frac{1}{2}$
$P(\text{message arrives by Channels 1}$
and 3 only$) = (\frac{3}{5})(\frac{1}{5})(\frac{1}{2}) = \frac{3}{50}$

$P(1') = \frac{2}{5}$
$P(2) = \frac{4}{5}$
$P(3) = \frac{1}{2}$
$P(\text{message arrives by Channels 2}$
and 3 only$) = (\frac{2}{5})(\frac{4}{5})(\frac{1}{2}) = \frac{8}{50}$

Add the probabilities:
$\frac{12}{50} + \frac{3}{50} + \frac{8}{50} + \frac{2}{50} + \frac{12}{50} +$
$\frac{3}{50} + \frac{8}{50} = \frac{48}{50}$
$= \frac{24}{25}$ or 0.96

b. $P(\text{message arrives by all 3}$
channels$) = (\frac{3}{5})(\frac{4}{5})(\frac{1}{2})$
$= \frac{12}{50}$
$= \frac{6}{25}$ or 0.24

3.27 $60 for all A's:
$\overset{15}{\underset{1}{\cancel{60}}}(\frac{\cancel{2}}{\cancel{8}})(\frac{1}{\cancel{2}})(\frac{\cancel{3}}{\cancel{4}}) + \$15$

$10 for each A:
$\frac{2}{3}(10) = \frac{20}{3}$
$\frac{1}{2}(10) = 5$
$\frac{3}{4}(10) = \frac{15}{2}$

$$\frac{20}{3} + 5 + \frac{15}{2} =$$
$$\frac{40}{6} + \frac{30}{6} + \frac{45}{6} =$$
$$\frac{115}{6} = \$19.17$$

Jeff should choose the latter choice, \$10 for each A: \$19.17 versus \$15.

3.28 $N = 2^n - 1$
     $= 2^4 - 1$
     $= 16 - 1$
     $= 15$

or

$N = {}_4C_1 + {}_4C_2 + {}_4C_3 + {}_4C_4$

$= \frac{4!}{1!3!} + \frac{4!}{2!2!} + \frac{4!}{3!1!} + \frac{4!}{4!0!}$

$= \frac{4 \cdot 3!}{1 \cdot 3!} + \frac{4 \cdot 3 \cdot 2!}{2 \cdot 1 \cdot 2!} + \frac{4 \cdot 3!}{1 \cdot 3!} + \frac{4!}{4!}$

$= 4 + 6 + 4 + 1$

$= 15$

3.29 ${}_7C_7 + {}_7C_6 + {}_7C_5 + {}_7C_4 + {}_7C_3 +$

${}_7C_2 = \frac{7!}{7!0!} + \frac{7!}{6!1!} + \frac{7!}{5!2!} +$

$\frac{7!}{4!3!} + \frac{7!}{3!4!} + \frac{7!}{2!5!}$

$= \frac{7!}{7!} + \frac{7 \cdot 6!}{1 \cdot 6!} + \frac{7 \cdot 6 \cdot 5!}{2 \cdot 1 \cdot 5!} +$

$\frac{7 \cdot 6 \cdot 5 \cdot 4!}{3 \cdot 2 \cdot 1 \cdot 4!} + \frac{7 \cdot 6 \cdot 5 \cdot 4!}{3 \cdot 2 \cdot 1 \cdot 4!} +$

$\frac{7 \cdot 6 \cdot 5!}{2 \cdot 1 \cdot 5!}$

$= 1 + 7 + 21 + 35 + 35 +$
21

$= 120$

3.30 $\binom{12}{2}\binom{8}{2} = \left(\frac{12!}{2!10!}\right)\left(\frac{8!}{2!6!}\right)$

$= \left(\frac{12^6 \cdot 11 \cdot 10!}{2 \cdot 1 \cdot 10!}\right)\left(\frac{8^4 \cdot 7 \cdot 6!}{2 \cdot 1 \cdot 6!}\right)$

$= (66)(28)$

$= 1,848$

MATHEMATICS 1210
SOLUTION KEY

I. SECTION ONE

1.1 $\displaystyle\sum_{i=1}^{5} 2i + 1$ = (2·1 + 1) +
(2·2 + 1) +
(2·3 + 1) +
(2·4 + 1) +
(2·5 + 1)

= (2 + 1) +
(4 + 1) +
(6 + 1) +
(8 + 1) +
(10 + 1)

= 3 + 5 + 7 +
9 + 11
= 35

1.2 $\displaystyle\sum_{i=1}^{7} i - 1$ = (1 − 1) + (2 − 1) +
(3 − 1) + (4 − 1) +
(5 − 1) + (6 − 1) +
(7 − 1)

= 0 + 1 + 2 + 3 + 4 +
5 + 6
= 21

1.3 $\displaystyle\sum_{i=1}^{3} i^3$ = $1^3 + 2^3 + 3^3$
= 1 + 8 + 27
= 36

1.4 $\displaystyle\sum_{i=1}^{4} i^{-1}$ = $1^{-1} + 2^{-1} + 3^{-1} + 4^{-1}$

= $\frac{1}{1} + \frac{1}{2} + \frac{1}{3} + \frac{1}{4}$
= $\frac{12}{12} + \frac{6}{12} + \frac{4}{12} + \frac{3}{12}$
= $\frac{25}{12}$ or $2\frac{1}{12}$

1.5 $\displaystyle\sum_{i=1}^{5} 2^i$ = $2^1 + 2^2 + 2^3 + 2^4 + 2^5$
= 2 + 4 + 8 + 16 + 32
= 62

1.6 $\displaystyle\sum_{i=1}^{3} 2^{-i}$ = $2^{-1} + 2^{-2} + 2^{-3}$

= $\frac{1}{2^1} + \frac{1}{2^2} + \frac{1}{2^3}$

= $\frac{1}{2} + \frac{1}{4} + \frac{1}{8}$

= $\frac{4}{8} + \frac{2}{8} + \frac{1}{8}$

= $\frac{7}{8}$

1.7 $\displaystyle\sum_{i=3}^{6} (i - 1)^2$ = $(3 - 1)^2 +$
$(4 - 1)^2 +$
$(5 - 1)^2 +$
$(6 - 1)^2$

= $2^2 + 3^2 + 4^2 + 5^2$

= 4 + 9 + 16 + 25
= 54

1.8 $\displaystyle\sum_{i=0}^{3} 3^i$ = $3^0 + 3^1 + 3^2 + 3^3$
= 1 + 3 + 9 + 27
= 40

1.9 $\displaystyle\sum_{i=1}^{3} i^2 + 3i + 2$ =

$(1^2 + 3·1 + 2) +$
$(2^2 + 3·2 + 2) +$
$(3^2 + 3·3 + 2)$ =
(1 + 3 + 2) +
(4 + 6 + 2) +
(9 + 9 + 2)   =
6 + 12 + 20   = 38

1.10 $\displaystyle\sum_{i=1}^{5} ai$ = a(1) + a(2) +
a(3) + a(4) + a(5)
= a + 2a + 3a + 4a + 5a
= 15a

1.11 $\displaystyle\sum_{i=1}^{2}\sum_{j=1}^{6}(i,\,j) =$ $(1,\,1) +$
$(1,\,2) +$
$(1,\,3) +$
$(1,\,4) +$
$(1,\,5) +$
$(1,\,6) +$
$(2,\,1) +$
$(2,\,2) +$
$(2,\,3) +$
$(2,\,4) +$
$(2,\,5) +$
$(2,\,6)$

1.12 $\displaystyle\sum_{i=1}^{6}\sum_{j=1}^{6}a(i,\,j) = a_{11},\,a_{12},$
$a_{13},\,a_{14},$
$a_{15},\,a_{16},$
$a_{21},\,a_{22},$
$a_{23},\,a_{24},$
$a_{25},\,a_{26},$
$a_{31},\,a_{32},$
$a_{33},\,a_{34},$
$a_{35},\,a_{36},$
$a_{41},\,a_{42},$
$a_{43},\,a_{44},$
$a_{45},\,a_{46},$
$a_{51},\,a_{52},$
$a_{53},\,a_{54},$
$a_{55},\,a_{56},$
$a_{61},\,a_{62},$
$a_{63},\,a_{64},$
$a_{65},\,a_{66}$

1.13 $\displaystyle\sum_{i=1}^{n}k = k + k + k + \dots$
(n times)
$= nk$

1.14 $\displaystyle\sum_{i=1}^{n}ki = k(1) + k(2) +$
$k(3) + \dots$
$= k(1 + 2 + 3 + \dots)$
$= k\displaystyle\sum_{i=1}^{n}i$

1.15 $\displaystyle\sum_{i=1}^{n}f(i) + g(i) = f(1) + g(1) +$
$f(2) + g(2) +$
$f(3) + g(3) +$
$\dots +$
$f(n) + g(n)$

Use the commutative property to regroup the terms.

$\displaystyle\sum_{i=1}^{n}f(i) + g(i) = f(1) + f(2) +$
$f(3) + \dots +$
$f(n) + g(1) +$
$g(2) + g(3) +$
$\dots + g(n)$
$= \displaystyle\sum_{i=1}^{n}f(i) +$
$\displaystyle\sum_{i=1}^{n}g(i)$

1.16 a. When $n = 1$, $n(n + 2)$
$= 1(1 + 2) = 3$.
b. Assume $3 + 5 + 7 + \dots$
$+ (2k + 1) = k(k + 2)$.
c. Then $3 + 5 + 7 + \dots$
$+ (2k + 1) + (2k + 3)$
$= k(k + 2) + 2k + 3$
$\displaystyle\sum_{i=1}^{k+1}2k + 1 = k^2 + 4k + 3$
$= (k + 1)\cdot$
$(k + 1 + 2)$

1.17 a. When $n = 1$, $\displaystyle\sum_{j=1}^{1}2^j =$
$2^1 = 2(2^1 - 1) = 2$.
b. Assume $\displaystyle\sum_{j=1}^{k}2^j = 2(2^k - 1)$.

c. Then $\displaystyle\sum_{j=1}^{k} 2^j + 2^{k+1} =$

$2(2^k - 1) + 2^{k+1}$
by substitution.

$\displaystyle\sum_{j=1}^{k+1} 2^j = 2^{k+1} - 2 + 2^{k+1}$
$= 2(2^{k+1} - 1)$

1.18 a. When $n = 1$, $\dfrac{1}{1(3)} = \dfrac{1}{2(1) + 1}$
$= \dfrac{1}{3}$

b. Assume $\dfrac{1}{1(3)} + \dfrac{1}{3(5)} + \dfrac{1}{5(7)} +$
$\cdots + \dfrac{1}{(2k - 1)(2k + 1)} =$
$\dfrac{k}{2k + 1}$

c. $\dfrac{1}{1(3)} + \dfrac{1}{3(5)} + \dfrac{1}{5(7)} + \cdots +$
$\dfrac{1}{(2k - 1)(2k + 1)} +$
$\dfrac{1}{(2k + 1)(2k + 3)} = \dfrac{k}{2k + 1} +$
$\dfrac{1}{(2k + 1)(2k + 3)}$

LCD $= (2k + 1)(2k + 3)$

$\dfrac{k}{2k + 1} + \dfrac{1}{(2k + 1)(2k + 3)} =$
$\dfrac{k(2k + 3)}{(2k + 1)(2k + 3)} +$
$\dfrac{1}{(2k + 1)(2k + 3)} =$
$\dfrac{k(2k + 3) + 1}{(2k + 1)(2k + 3)} =$
$\dfrac{2k^2 + 3k + 1}{(2k + 1)(2k + 3)} =$
$\dfrac{(2k + 1)(k + 1)}{(2k + 1)(2k + 3)} =$
$\dfrac{k + 1}{2(k + 1) + 1}$

1.19 Let $t = 2n - 1$.
a. For $n = 1$ and $t = 1$,
$a + b$ divide evenly into
$a + b$ is true ($1 = 2 \cdot 1 - 1$).

b. Assume $n = k$ is true.
That is, $a^{2k-1} + b^{2k-1}$ is
divisible by $a + b$. We
need to show that $n = k + 1$
is true. That is, $a^{2k+1} +$
b^{2k+1} is divisible by
$a + b$.
Let $a^{2k+1} + b^{2k+1} =$
$a^{2k+1} + a^2 b^{2k-1} -$
$a^2 b^{2k-1} + b^{2k+1} =$
$a^2(a^{2k-1} + b^{2k-1}) -$
$b^{2k-1}(a^2 - b^2) =$
$a^2(a^{2k-1} + b^{2k-1}) -$
$b^{2k-1}(a - b)(a + b)$.

Since both terms of the
right member are divisible
by $a + b$, the proposition
is proved to be true.

1.20 a. When $n = 2$,
$[1 + na < (1 + a)^n] =$
$[1 + 2a < (1 + a)^2] =$
$[1 + 2a < 1 + 2a + a^2]$.

b. Assume $1 + 2a < (1 + a)^k$
is true. Multiply both
sides by $1 + a$.
$(1 + 2a)(1 + a) < (1 + a)^k \cdot$
$(1 + a)$
Since $(1 + 2a)(1 + a) >$
$1 + 2a$, $1 + 2a < (1 + a)^{k+1}$.

1.21 a. When $n = 1$,
$1 = \dfrac{1^2(1 + 1)^2}{4} = \dfrac{4}{4} = 1$.

b. Assume $\displaystyle\sum_{i=1}^{k} i^3 = \dfrac{k^2(k + 1)^2}{4}$.

c. Then $\sum\limits_{i=1}^{k} i^3 + (k+1)^3 =$

$\dfrac{k^2(k+1)^2}{4} + (k+1)^3 =$

$\dfrac{k^2(k+1)^2}{4} +$

$\dfrac{4(k+1)(k+1)^2}{4}.$

$\sum\limits_{i=1}^{k+1} i^3 =$

$\dfrac{(k+1)^2}{4}[k^2 + 4(k+1)]$

(factor out $\dfrac{(k+1)^2}{4}$ from

preceding equation) $=$

$\dfrac{(k+1)^2}{4}[k^2 + 4k + 4] =$

$\dfrac{(k+1)^2}{4}[k+2]^2 =$

$\dfrac{(k+1)^2}{4}[(k+1)+1]^2$

1.22 a. When $n = 1$, $1 = \frac{1}{2}(1)\cdot$
$(3\cdot 1 - 1) = \frac{1}{2}(2) = 1.$

b. Assume $\sum\limits_{i=1}^{k} 3i - 2 =$
$\frac{1}{2}k(3k - 1).$

c. Then $\sum\limits_{i=1}^{k} 3i - 2 +$
$3(k+1) - 2 =$
$\frac{1}{2}k(3k - 1) + 3(k+1) - 2 =$
$\frac{1}{2}(3k^2 - k) + 3k + 3 - 2 =$

$\sum\limits_{i=1}^{k+1} 3i - 1 =$
$\frac{1}{2}(3k^2 - k + 6k + 6 - 4) =$
$\frac{1}{2}(3k^2 + 5k + 2) =$
$\frac{1}{2}(k+1)(3k+2) =$
$\frac{1}{2}(k+1)[3(k+1) - 1]$

1.23 a. When $n = 1$, $1(2) =$
$\frac{1}{3}(1+1)(1+2) = \frac{1}{3}(2)(3) =$
$\frac{1}{3}\cdot 6 = 2.$

b. Assume $1\cdot 2 + 2\cdot 3 + 3\cdot 4 +$
$\ldots + k(k+1) =$
$\frac{k}{3}(k+1)(k+2).$

c. Then $\sum\limits_{i=1}^{k} i(i+1) +$
$(k+1)(k+2) =$
$\frac{k}{3}(k+1)(k+2) +$
$(k+1)(k+2) =$
$\frac{k}{3}(k+1)(k+2) +$
$\dfrac{3(k+1)(k+2)}{3}$ (LCD is 3).

$\sum\limits_{i=1}^{k+1} i(i+1) =$
$\dfrac{(k+1)}{3}[k(k+2) +$
$3(k+2)]$ (factor out $\dfrac{k+1}{3}$
from the preceding
equation) $=$
$\dfrac{(k+1)}{3}[(k+2)(k+3)] =$
$\dfrac{(k+1)}{3}[(k+1+1)\cdot$
$(k+1+2)].$

1.24 a. When $n = 1$, $2^{2(1)} + 5 =$
$4 + 5 = 9$, which is
divisible by 3.

b. Assume $2^{2k} + 5$ is
divisible by 3.

c. We must show that
$2^{2(k+1)} + 5$ is also
divisible by 3.

$2^{2(k+1)} + 5 =$

$2^{2k+2} + 5 =$

$2^2 \cdot 2^{2k} + 5 + 2^2 \cdot 5 -$

$2^2 \cdot 5 =$

$2^2 \cdot 2^{2k} + 2^2 \cdot 5 -$

$2^2 \cdot 5 + 5 =$

$2^2(2^{2k} + 5) -$

$5(2^2 - 1) =$

$4(2^{2k} + 5) - 5(4 - 1) =$

$4(2^{2k} + 5) - 15$

Since both terms of the right member are divisible by 3, the proposition is proved to be true.

1.25 a. When $n = 1$, $\frac{1}{2^1} = 1 - \frac{1}{2^1} - \frac{1}{2}$.

b. Assume $\displaystyle\sum_{i=1}^{k} \frac{1}{2^i} = 1 - \frac{1}{2^k}$.

c. Then $\displaystyle\sum_{i=1}^{k} \frac{1}{2^i} + \frac{1}{2^{k+1}} =$

$1 - \frac{1}{2^k} + \frac{1}{2^{k+1}}$.

$\displaystyle\sum_{i=1}^{k+1} \frac{1}{2^i} = 1 - \frac{2}{2^{k+1}} +$

$\frac{1}{2^{k+1}} =$

$1 - \frac{1}{2^{k+1}}$

II. SECTION TWO

2.1 $F(0) = 0^2 - 3(0) + 1$
$= 0 - 0 + 1$
$= 1$

2.2 $F(1) = 1^2 - 3(1) + 1$
$= 1 - 3 + 1$
$= -1$

2.3 $F(a) = a^2 - 3(a) + 1$
$= a^2 - 3a + 1$

2.4 $F(a - 1) = (a - 1)^2 - 3(a - 1) + 1$
$= a^2 - 2a + 1 - 3a + 3 + 1$
$= a^2 - 5a + 5$

2.5 $F(\frac{a}{b}) = (\frac{a}{b})^2 - 3(\frac{a}{b}) + 1$

2.6 $F(-3) = (-3)^2 - 3(-3) + 1$
$= 9 + 9 + 1$
$= 19$

2.7 $G(0) = \sqrt{2 \cdot 0 - 1}$
$= \sqrt{-1}$
$= i$

2.8 $G(1) = \sqrt{2 \cdot 1 - 1}$
$= \sqrt{1}$
$= 1$

2.9 $G(-4) = \sqrt{2(-4) - 1}$
$= \sqrt{-9}$
$= 3i$

2.10 $G(5) = \sqrt{2 \cdot 5 - 1}$
$= \sqrt{9}$
$= 3$

2.11 $G(a + 1) = \sqrt{2(a + 1) - 1}$
$= \sqrt{2a + 2 - 1}$
$= \sqrt{2a + 1}$

2.12 $G(1 - P) = \sqrt{2(1 - P) - 1}$
$= \sqrt{2 - 2P - 1}$
$= \sqrt{1 - 2P}$

2.13 $H(2) = 3 \cdot 2 - 1$
$= 5$

2.14 $H(a) = 3(a) - 1$
$= 3a - 1$

2.15 $H(a + h) = 3(a + h) - 1$
$= 3a + 3h - 1$

2.16 $\dfrac{2(a + h) - 2a}{h} =$

$\dfrac{2a + 2h - 2a}{h} =$

$\dfrac{2h}{h} = 2$

2.17 $\dfrac{2(a + h) - 1 - (2a - 1)}{h} =$

$\dfrac{2a + 2h - 1 - 2a + 1}{h} =$

$\dfrac{2h}{h} = 2$

2.18 $\dfrac{\dfrac{3(a + h) + 2}{5} - \dfrac{(3a + 2)}{5}}{h} =$

$\dfrac{3a + 3h + 2 - 3a - 2}{5h} =$

$\dfrac{3h}{5h} = \dfrac{3}{5}$

2.19 $\dfrac{5 - 7(a + h) - (5 - 7a)}{h} =$

$\dfrac{5 - 7a - 7h - 5 + 7a}{h} =$

$\dfrac{-7h}{h} = -7$

2.20 $\dfrac{\dfrac{3 - 8(a + h)}{5} - \dfrac{(3 - 8a)}{5}}{h} =$

$\dfrac{3 - 8a - 8h - 3 + 8a}{5h} =$

$\dfrac{-8h}{5h} = -\dfrac{8}{5}$

2.21 $\dfrac{(a + h)^2 - (a + h) - (a^2 - a)}{h} =$

$\dfrac{a^2 + 2ah + h^2 - a - h - a^2 + a}{h} =$

$\dfrac{2ah + h^2 - h}{h} = 2a + h - 1$

2.22 $\dfrac{3(a + h)^2 + 1 - (3a^2 + 1)}{h} =$

$\dfrac{3(a^2 + 2ah + h^2) + 1 - 3a^2 - 1}{h} =$

$\dfrac{3a^2 + 6ah + 3h^2 + 1 - 3a^2 - 1}{h} =$

$\dfrac{6ah + 3h^2}{h} = 6a + 3h$

2.23 $\dfrac{(a + h)^3 - a^3}{h} =$

$\dfrac{a^3 + 3a^2h + 3ah^2 + h^3 - a^3}{h} =$

$\dfrac{3a^2h + 3ah^2 + h^3}{h} =$

$3a^2 + 3ah + h^2$

2.24 $\dfrac{3(a + h)^3 + 2(a + h)^2 - (3a^3 + 2a^2)}{h} =$

$\dfrac{3(a^3 + 3a^2h + 3ah^2 + h^3) + 2(a^2 + 2ah + h^2) - 3a^3 - 2a^2}{h} =$

$\dfrac{3a^3 + 9a^2h + 9ah^2 + 3h^3 + 2a^2 + 4ah + 2h^2 - 3a^3 - 2a^2}{h} =$

$\dfrac{9a^2h + 9ah^2 + 3h^3 + 4ah + 2h^2}{h} = 9a^2 + 9ah + 3h^2 + 4a + 2h$

2.25 $\dfrac{(a + h)^3 + 3(a + h)^2 + 5(a + h) + 1 - (a^3 + 3a^2 + 5a + 1)}{h} =$

$\dfrac{a^3 + 3a^2h + 3ah^2 + h^3 + 3(a^2 + 2ah + h^2) + 5a + 5h + 1 - a^3 - 3a^2 - 5a - 1}{h} =$

$\dfrac{a^3 + 3a^2h + 3ah^2 + h^3 + 3a^2 + 6ah + 3h^2 + 5a + 5h + 1 - a^3 - 3a^2 - 5a - 1}{h} =$

$\dfrac{3a^2h + 3ah^2 + h^3 + 6ah + 3h^2 + 5h}{h} = 3a^2 + 3ah + h^2 + 6a + 3h + 5$

2.26 0

2.27 0

2.28 $\lim\limits_{x\to\infty} x + 2 = \lim\limits_{x\to\infty} x + \lim\limits_{x\to\infty} 2$

$= \infty + 2$

$= \infty$

2.29 $\lim\limits_{x\to 4} x^2 + 2x + 1 = \lim\limits_{x\to 4} x^2 +$

$\lim\limits_{x\to 4} 2x +$

$\lim\limits_{x\to 4} 1$

$= \lim\limits_{x\to 4} x \cdot \lim\limits_{x\to 4} x +$

$\lim\limits_{x\to 4} 2 \cdot \lim\limits_{x\to 4} x +$

$\lim\limits_{x\to 4} 1$

$= 4 \cdot 4 + 2 \cdot 4 + 1$

$= 16 + 8 + 1$

$= 25$

2.30 $\lim\limits_{x\to -1} x^3 = \lim\limits_{x\to -1} x \cdot \lim\limits_{x\to -1} x \cdot \lim\limits_{x\to -1} x$

$= -1(-1)(-1)$

$= -1$

2.31 $\lim\limits_{x\to -2} x^2 + 5x + 6 = \lim\limits_{x\to -2} x^2 +$

$\lim\limits_{x\to -2} 5x +$

$\lim\limits_{x\to -2} 6$

$= \lim\limits_{x\to -2} x \cdot \lim\limits_{x\to -2} x +$

$\lim\limits_{x\to -2} 5 \cdot \lim\limits_{x\to -2} x +$

$\lim\limits_{x\to -2} 6$

$= -2(-2) +$
$5(-2) + 6$

$= 4 - 10 + 6$

$= 0$

2.32 6

2.33 $\lim\limits_{x\to 5} 5x - 2 = \lim\limits_{x\to 5} 5x - \lim\limits_{x\to 5} 2$

$= \lim\limits_{x\to 5} 5 \cdot \lim\limits_{x\to 5} x - \lim\limits_{x\to 5} 2$

$= 5 \cdot 5 - 2$

$= 23$

2.34 $\lim\limits_{x\to\infty} \dfrac{2}{x} - \dfrac{3}{x^2} = \lim\limits_{x\to\infty} \dfrac{2}{x} - \lim\limits_{x\to\infty} \dfrac{3}{x^2}$

$= 0 - 0$

$= 0$

2.35 $\lim\limits_{x\to 0} \dfrac{5}{x + 1} = \dfrac{\lim\limits_{x\to 0} 5}{\lim\limits_{x\to 0} x + \lim\limits_{x\to 0} 1}$

$= \dfrac{5}{0 + 1}$

$= 5$

2.36 Divide the numerator and the denominator by x.

$\lim\limits_{x\to\infty} \dfrac{x}{x + 2} = \lim\limits_{x\to\infty} \dfrac{1}{1 + \dfrac{2}{x}}$

$= \dfrac{\lim\limits_{x\to\infty} 1}{\lim\limits_{x\to\infty} 1 + \lim\limits_{x\to\infty} \dfrac{2}{x}}$

$= \dfrac{1}{1 + 0}$

$= 1$

2.37 Divide the numerator and the denominator by x.

$$\lim_{x \to \infty} \frac{x + 2}{x^2 + 3x + 3} =$$

$$\lim_{x \to \infty} \frac{1 + \frac{2}{x}}{x + 3 + \frac{3}{x}} =$$

$$\frac{\lim\limits_{x \to \infty} 1 + \lim\limits_{x \to \infty} \frac{2}{x}}{\lim\limits_{x \to \infty} x + \lim\limits_{x \to \infty} 3 + \lim\limits_{x \to \infty} \frac{3}{x}} =$$

$$\frac{1 + 0}{\infty + 3 + 0} = 0$$

2.38 ∞

2.39 Divide the numerator and the denominator by x^2.

$$\lim_{x \to \infty} \frac{5x^2 + 3x + 5}{x^2} = \lim_{x \to \infty} 5 + \frac{3}{x}$$

$$+ \frac{5}{x^2}$$

$$= \lim_{x \to \infty} 5 +$$

$$\lim_{x \to \infty} \frac{3}{x} +$$

$$\lim_{x \to \infty} \frac{5}{x^2}$$

$$= 5 + 0 + 0$$

$$= 5$$

2.40 Divide the numerator and the denominator by x^2.

$$\lim_{x \to \infty} \frac{2x^2 + 6x + 9}{x^2 + 2x + 3} =$$

$$\lim_{x \to \infty} \frac{2 + \frac{6}{x} + \frac{9}{x^2}}{1 + \frac{2}{x} + \frac{3}{x^2}} =$$

$$\frac{\lim\limits_{x \to \infty} 2 + \lim\limits_{x \to \infty} \frac{6}{x} + \lim\limits_{x \to \infty} \frac{9}{x^2}}{\lim\limits_{x \to \infty} 1 + \lim\limits_{x \to \infty} \frac{2}{x} + \lim\limits_{x \to \infty} \frac{3}{x^2}} =$$

$$\frac{2 + 0 + 0}{1 + 0 + 0} = 2$$

III. SECTION THREE

3.1
$$m = \lim_{h \to 0} \frac{f(x + h) - f(x)}{h}$$

$$= \lim_{h \to 0} \frac{2(x + h) + 3 - (2x + 3)}{h}$$

$$= \lim_{h \to 0} \frac{2x + 2h + 3 - 2x - 3}{h}$$

$$= \lim_{h \to 0} \frac{2h}{h}$$

$$= \lim_{h \to 0} 2$$

$$= 2$$

3.2
$$m = \lim_{h \to 0} \frac{f(x + h) - f(x)}{h}$$

$$= \lim_{h \to 0} \frac{3 - 2(x + h) - (3 - 2x)}{h}$$

$$= \lim_{h \to 0} \frac{3 - 2x - 2h - 3 + 2x}{h}$$

$$= \lim_{h \to 0} \frac{-2h}{h}$$

$$= -2$$

3.3
$$m = \lim_{h \to 0} \frac{f(x + h) - f(x)}{h}$$

$$= \lim_{h \to 0} \frac{\frac{5}{2}(x + h) + 3 - (\frac{5x}{2} + 3)}{h}$$

$$= \lim_{h \to 0} \frac{\frac{5x}{2} + \frac{5h}{2} + 3 - \frac{5x}{2} - 3}{h}$$

$$= \lim_{h \to 0} \frac{\frac{5h}{2}}{h}$$

$$= \lim_{h \to 0} \frac{5}{2}$$

$$= \frac{5}{2}$$

3.4

$$m = \lim_{h \to 0} \frac{f(x + h) - f(x)}{h}$$

$$= \lim_{h \to 0} \frac{\frac{7(x + h) + 2}{3} - \frac{7x + 2}{3}}{h}$$

$$= \lim_{h \to 0} \frac{7x + 7h + 2 - 7x - 2}{3h}$$

$$= \lim_{h \to 0} \frac{7h}{3h}$$

$$= \lim_{h \to 0} \frac{7}{3}$$

$$= \frac{7}{3}$$

3.5

$$m = \lim_{h \to 0} \frac{f(x + h) - f(x)}{h}$$

$$= \lim_{h \to 0} \frac{10(x + h) - 5 - (10x - 5)}{h}$$

$$= \lim_{h \to 0} \frac{10x + 10h - 5 - 10x + 5}{h}$$

$$= \lim_{h \to 0} \frac{10h}{h}$$

$$= \lim_{h \to 0} 10$$

$$= 10$$

3.6

$$m = \lim_{h \to 0} \frac{f(x + h) - f(x)}{h}$$

$$= \lim_{h \to 0} \frac{10 - 5(x + h) - (10 - 5x)}{h}$$

$$= \lim_{h \to 0} \frac{10 - 5x - 5h - 10 + 5x}{h}$$

$$= \lim_{h \to 0} \frac{-5h}{h}$$

$$= \lim_{h \to 0} -5$$

$$= -5$$

3.7

$$m = \lim_{h \to 0} \frac{f(x + h) - f(x)}{h}$$

$$= \lim_{h \to 0} \frac{3 - \frac{3(x + h)}{4} - (3 - \frac{3x}{4})}{h}$$

$$= \lim_{h \to 0} \frac{3 - \frac{3x}{4} - \frac{3h}{4} - 3 + \frac{3x}{4}}{h}$$

$$= \lim_{h \to 0} \frac{-\frac{3h}{4}}{h}$$

$$= \lim_{h \to 0} -\frac{3}{4}$$

$$= -\frac{3}{4}$$

3.8

$$m = \lim_{h \to 0} \frac{f(x + h) - f(x)}{h}$$

$$= \lim_{h \to 0} \frac{\frac{-7(x + h) + 4}{2} - \frac{-7x + 4}{2}}{h}$$

$$= \lim_{h \to 0} \frac{-7x - 7h + 4 + 7x - 4}{2h}$$

$$= \lim_{h \to 0} \frac{-7h}{2h}$$

$$= \lim_{h \to 0} -\frac{7}{2}$$

$$= -\frac{7}{2}$$

3.9

$$m = \lim_{h \to 0} \frac{f(x + h) - f(x)}{h}$$

$$= \lim_{h \to 0} \frac{\frac{-8(x + h) + 5}{7} - \frac{-8x + 5}{7}}{h}$$

$$= \lim_{h \to 0} \frac{-8x - 8h + 5 + 8x - 5}{7h}$$

$$= \lim_{h \to 0} \frac{-8h}{7h}$$

$$= \lim_{h \to 0} -\frac{8}{7}$$

$$= -\frac{8}{7}$$

3.10 $m = \lim\limits_{h\to 0} \dfrac{f(x + h) - f(x)}{h}$

$= \lim\limits_{h\to 0} \dfrac{6(x + h) - 6 - (6x - 6)}{h}$

$= \lim\limits_{h\to 0} \dfrac{6x + 6h - 6 - 6x + 6}{h}$

$= \lim\limits_{h\to 0} \dfrac{6h}{h}$

$= \lim\limits_{h\to 0} 6$

$= 6$

3.11 $m = \lim\limits_{h\to 0} \dfrac{f(x + h) - f(x)}{h}$

$= \lim\limits_{h\to 0} \dfrac{(x + h)^2 + 2 - (x^2 + 2)}{h}$

$= \lim\limits_{h\to 0} \dfrac{x^2 + 2xh + h^2 + 2 - x^2 - 2}{h}$

$= \lim\limits_{h\to 0} \dfrac{2xh + h^2}{h}$

$= \lim\limits_{h\to 0} 2x + h$

$= \lim\limits_{h\to 0} 2x$

$= 2x$

The slope at $x = 3$ is
$m = 2 \cdot 3 = 6.$

3.12 $m = \lim\limits_{h\to 0} \dfrac{f(x + h) - f(x)}{h}$

$= \lim\limits_{h\to 0} \dfrac{(x + h)^2 - 8 - (x^2 - 8)}{h}$

$= \lim\limits_{h\to 0} \dfrac{x^2 + 2xh + h^2 - 8 - x^2 + 8}{h}$

$= \lim\limits_{h\to 0} \dfrac{2xh + h^2}{h}$

$= \lim\limits_{h\to 0} 2x + h$

$= \lim\limits_{h\to 0} 2x$

$= 2x$

The slope at $x = 5$ is
$m = 2 \cdot 5 = 10.$

3.13 $m = \lim\limits_{h\to 0} \dfrac{f(x + h) - f(x)}{h}$

$= \lim\limits_{h\to 0} \dfrac{(x + h)^3 - x^3}{h}$

$= \lim\limits_{h\to 0} \dfrac{x^3 + 3x^2h + 3xh^2 + h^3 - x^3}{h}$

$= \lim\limits_{h\to 0} \dfrac{3x^2h + 3xh^2 + h^3}{h}$

$= \lim\limits_{h\to 0} 3x^2 + 3xh + h^2$

$= \lim\limits_{h\to 0} 3x^2$

$= 3x^2$

The slope at $x = -2$ is
$m = 3(-2)^2 = 3(4) = 12.$

3.14 $m = \lim\limits_{h\to 0} \dfrac{f(x + h) - f(x)}{h}$

$= \lim\limits_{h\to 0} \dfrac{(x + h)^2 - 8(x + h) - \ldots}{h}$
$\dfrac{(x^2 - 8x)}{h}$

$= \lim\limits_{h\to 0} \dfrac{x^2 + 2xh + h^2 - 8x - \ldots}{h}$
$\dfrac{8h - x^2 + 8x}{h}$

$= \lim\limits_{h\to 0} \dfrac{2xh + h^2 - 8h}{h}$

$= \lim\limits_{h\to 0} 2x + h - 8$

$= \lim\limits_{h\to 0} 2x - 8$

The slope at $x = 0$ is
$m = 2 \cdot 0 - 8 = -8$

3.15 $m = \lim\limits_{h\to 0} \dfrac{f(x + h) - f(x)}{h}$

$= \lim\limits_{h\to 0} \dfrac{(x + h)^2 + 8(x + h) + \ldots}{h}$
$\dfrac{2 - (x^2 + 8x + 2)}{h}$

$= \lim\limits_{h\to 0} \dfrac{x^2 + 2xh + h^2 + 8x + \ldots}{h}$
$\dfrac{8h + 2 - x^2 - 8x - 2}{h}$

$= \lim\limits_{h\to 0} \dfrac{2xh + h^2 + 8h}{h}$

$= \lim\limits_{h\to 0} 2x + h + 8$

$= \lim\limits_{h\to 0} 2x + 8$

$= 2x + 8$

The slope at $x = 4$ is
$m = 2 \cdot 4 + 8 = 8 + 8 = 16.$

3.16 $m = \lim\limits_{h \to 0} \dfrac{f(x + h) - f(x)}{h}$

$= \lim\limits_{h \to 0} \dfrac{2(x + h)^2 - 1 - (2x^2 - 1)}{h}$

$= \lim\limits_{h \to 0} \dfrac{2(x^2 + 2xh + h^2) - \cancel{1} - 2x^2 + \cancel{1}}{h}$

$= \lim\limits_{h \to 0} \dfrac{\cancel{2x^2} + 4xh + 2h^2 - \cancel{2x^2}}{h}$

$= \lim\limits_{h \to 0} \dfrac{4x\cancel{h} + 2h^{\cancel{2}}}{\cancel{h}}$

$= \lim\limits_{h \to 0} 4x + 2h$

$= \lim\limits_{h \to 0} 4x$

$= \mathbf{4x}$

The slope at $x = -3$ is
$m = 4(-3) = -12$.

3.17 $m = \lim\limits_{h \to 0} \dfrac{f(x + h) - f(x)}{h}$

$= \lim\limits_{h \to 0} \dfrac{(x + h)^3 + 3(x + h)^2 - (x^3 + 3x^2)}{h}$

$= \lim\limits_{h \to 0} \dfrac{\cancel{x^3} + 3x^2h + 3xh^2 + h^3 + 3(x^2 + 2xh + h^2) - \cancel{x^3} - 3x^2}{h}$

$= \lim\limits_{h \to 0} \dfrac{3x^2h + 3xh^2 + h^3 + \cancel{3x^2} + 6xh + 3h^2 - \cancel{3x^2}}{h}$

$= \lim\limits_{h \to 0} \dfrac{3x^2\cancel{h} + 3xh^{\cancel{2}} + h^{\cancel{3}\,2} + 6x\cancel{h} + 3h^{\cancel{2}}}{\cancel{h}}$

$= \lim\limits_{h \to 0} 3x^2 + 3xh + h^2 + 6x + 3h$

$= \lim\limits_{h \to 0} 3x^2 + 6x$

$= \mathbf{3x^2 + 6x}$

The slope at $x = 10$ is $m = 3(10)^2 + 6(10) =$
$3(100) + 60 = 360$.

3.18 $m = \lim\limits_{h \to 0} \dfrac{f(x + h) - f(x)}{h}$

$= \lim\limits_{h \to 0} \dfrac{2(x + h)^3 - 2(x + h)^2 + 3(x + h) + 1 - (2x^3 - 2x^2 + 3x + 1)}{h}$

$= \lim\limits_{h \to 0} \dfrac{2(x^3 + 3x^2h + 3xh^2 + h^3) - 2(x^2 + 2xh + h^2) + \cancel{3x} + 3h + \cancel{1} - 2x^3 + 2x^2 - \cancel{3x} - \cancel{1}}{h}$

$= \lim\limits_{h \to 0} \dfrac{\cancel{2x^3} + 6x^2h + 6xh^2 + 2h^3 - \cancel{2x^2} - 4xh - 2h^2 + 3h - \cancel{2x^3} + \cancel{2x^2}}{h}$

$$= \lim_{h \to 0} \frac{6x^2 h + 6xh^2 + 2h^3 - 4xh - 2h^2 + 3h}{h}$$

$$= \lim_{h \to 0} 6x^2 + 6xh + 2h^2 - 4x - 2h + 3$$

$$= \lim_{h \to 0} 6x^2 - 4x + 3$$

$$= 6x^2 - 4x + 3$$

The slope at $x = 0$ is $m = 6(0)^2 - 4(0) + 3 = 3$.

3.19 $$m = \lim_{h \to 0} \frac{f(x + h) - f(x)}{h}$$

$$= \lim_{h \to 0} \frac{\sqrt{2(x + h)} - \sqrt{2x}}{h}$$

$$= \lim_{h \to 0} \frac{\sqrt{2(x + h)} - \sqrt{2x}}{h} \cdot \frac{\sqrt{2(x + h)} + \sqrt{2x}}{\sqrt{2(x + h)} + \sqrt{2x}}$$

$$= \lim_{h \to 0} \frac{2(x + h) - 2x}{h(\sqrt{2(x + h)} + \sqrt{2x})}$$

$$= \lim_{h \to 0} \frac{2x + 2h - 2x}{h(\sqrt{2(x + h)} + \sqrt{2x})}$$

$$= \lim_{h \to 0} \frac{2h}{h(\sqrt{2(x + h)} + \sqrt{2x})}$$

$$= \lim_{h \to 0} \frac{2}{\sqrt{2x + 2h} + \sqrt{2x}}$$

$$= \lim_{h \to 0} \frac{2}{\sqrt{2x} + \sqrt{2x}}$$

$$= \lim_{h \to 0} \frac{2}{2\sqrt{2x}}$$

$$= \lim_{h \to 0} \frac{1}{\sqrt{2x}}$$

$$= \frac{1}{\sqrt{2x}}$$

The slope at $x = 1$ is $m = \dfrac{1}{\sqrt{2(1)}} = \dfrac{1}{\sqrt{2}}$ or $\dfrac{\sqrt{2}}{2}$.

3.20 $$m = \lim_{h \to 0} \frac{f(x + h) - f(x)}{h}$$

$$= \lim_{h \to 0} \frac{\sqrt{3(x + h) + 1} - \sqrt{3x + 1}}{h}$$

$$= \lim_{h \to 0} \frac{\sqrt{3(x + h) + 1} - \sqrt{3x + 1}}{h} \cdot \frac{\sqrt{3(x + h) + 1} + \sqrt{3x + 1}}{\sqrt{3(x + h) + 1} + \sqrt{3x + 1}}$$

$$= \lim_{h \to 0} \frac{3(x + h) + 1 - (3x + 1)}{h(\sqrt{3(x + h) + 1} + \sqrt{3x + 1})}$$

$$= \lim_{h \to 0} \frac{3x\!\!\!/ + 3h + 1\!\!\!/ - 3x\!\!\!/ - 1\!\!\!/}{h(\sqrt{3(x + h) + 1} + \sqrt{3x + 1})}$$

$$= \lim_{h \to 0} \frac{3h\!\!\!/}{h\!\!\!/(\sqrt{3(x + h) + 1} + \sqrt{3x + 1})}$$

$$= \lim_{h \to 0} \frac{3}{\sqrt{3x + 3h + 1} + \sqrt{3x + 1}}$$

$$= \lim_{h \to 0} \frac{3}{\sqrt{3x + 1} + \sqrt{3x + 1}}$$

$$= \lim_{h \to 0} \frac{3}{2(\sqrt{3x + 1})}$$

The slope at $x = 1$ is

$$m = \frac{3}{2(\sqrt{3(1) + 1})} = \frac{3}{2\sqrt{4}} =$$

$$\frac{3}{2(2)} = \frac{3}{4}.$$

3.21 Let m_2 = slope of $f(x)$
 m_1 = slope of $g(x)$

$$m_2 = \lim_{h \to 0} \frac{2(x + h) + 3 - (2x + 3)}{h}$$

$$= \lim_{h \to 0} \frac{2x\!\!\!/ + 2h + 3\!\!\!/ - 2x\!\!\!/ - 3\!\!\!/}{h}$$

$$= \lim_{h \to 0} \frac{2h\!\!\!/}{h\!\!\!/}$$

$$= \lim_{h \to 0} 2$$

$$= 2$$

$$m_1 = \lim_{h \to 0} \frac{-3(x + h) + 1 - (-3x + 1)}{h}$$

$$= \lim_{h \to 0} \frac{-3x\!\!\!/ - 3h + 1\!\!\!/ + 3x\!\!\!/ - 1\!\!\!/}{h}$$

$$= \lim_{h \to 0} \frac{-3h\!\!\!/}{h\!\!\!/}$$

$$= \lim_{h \to 0} -3$$

$$= -3$$

Point of intersection:

$$2x + 3 = -3x + 1$$
$$2x + 3 + 3x = 1$$
$$5x + 3 = 1$$
$$5x = 1 - 3$$
$$5x = -2$$
$$\frac{5x}{5} = \frac{-2}{5}$$
$$x = -\frac{2}{5}$$

$$y = 2x + 3$$
$$= 2(-\frac{2}{5}) + 3$$
$$= -\frac{4}{5} + 3$$
$$= 2\frac{1}{5}$$

Point of intersection is $(-\frac{2}{5}, 2\frac{1}{5})$.

The x- and y-intercepts of $f(x) = 2x + 3$ are $(-\frac{3}{2}, 0)$ and $(0, 3)$.

The x- and y-intercepts of $g(x) = -3x + 1$ are $(\frac{1}{3}, 0)$ and $(0, 1)$.

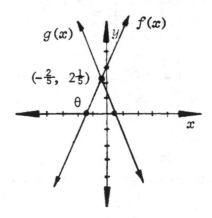

The slope of $f(x)$ at $x = -\frac{2}{5}$ is $m_2 = 2$.
The slope of $g(x)$ at $x = -\frac{2}{5}$ is $m_1 = -3$.

$$\tan \theta = \frac{m_2 - m_1}{1 + m_2 m_1}$$

$$= \frac{2 - (-3)}{1 + (2)(-3)}$$

$$= \frac{2 + 3}{1 - 6}$$

$$= \frac{5}{-5}$$

$$= -1$$

$$\theta = \text{arc tan } (-1) = 135°$$

3.22 Let m_2 = slope of $f(x)$
m_1 = slope of $g(x)$

$$m_2 = \lim_{h \to 0} \frac{2(x + h)^2 - 2x^2}{h}$$

$$= \lim_{h \to 0} \frac{2(x^2 + 2xh + h^2) - 2x^2}{h}$$

$$= \lim_{h \to 0} \frac{2x^2 + 4xh + 2h^2 - 2x^2}{h}$$

$$= \lim_{h \to 0} \frac{4xh + 2h^2}{h}$$

$$= \lim_{h \to 0} 4x + 2h$$

$$= \lim_{h \to 0} 4x$$

$$= 4x$$

$$m_1 = \lim_{h \to 0} \frac{7(x + h) - 5 - (7x - 5)}{h}$$

$$= \lim_{h \to 0} \frac{7x + 7h - 5 - 7x + 5}{h}$$

$$= \lim_{h \to 0} \frac{7h}{h}$$

$$= \lim_{h \to 0} 7$$

$$= 7$$

Points of intersection:

$$2x^2 = 7x - 5$$
$$2x^2 - 7x + 5 = 0$$
$$(2x - 5)(x - 1) = 0$$
$$2x - 5 = 0$$
$$2x = 5$$
$$\frac{2x}{2} = \frac{5}{2}$$
$$x = \frac{5}{2}$$

$$x - 1 = 0$$
$$x = 1$$

$$x = \frac{5}{2}: \quad y = 2x^2$$
$$= 2\left(\frac{5}{2}\right)^2$$
$$= 2\left(\frac{25}{4}\right)_2$$
$$= \frac{25}{2}$$

$$x = 1: \quad y = 2x^2$$
$$= 2(1)^2$$
$$= 2$$

Points of intersection are $\left(\frac{5}{2}, \frac{25}{2}\right)$ and $(1, 2)$.

Points to graph $f(x) = 2x^2$ are $(0, 0)$, $(\pm 1, 2)$, $(\pm 2, 8)$.
Points to graph $g(x) = 7x - 5$ are $(0, -5)$ and $\left(\frac{5}{7}, 0\right)$.

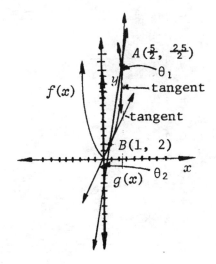

For point A:
$m_2 = 4\left(\frac{5}{2}\right) = 10$
$m_1 = 7$

$$\tan \theta_1 = \frac{m_2 - m_1}{1 + m_2 m_1}$$

$$= \frac{10 - 7}{1 + 10(7)}$$

$$= \frac{3}{1 + 70}$$

$$= \frac{3}{71}$$

$$= 0.0423$$

261

$\theta_1 = $ arc tan $0.0423 = 2.4°$
approximately

For point B:
$m_2 = 4(1) = 4$
$m_1 = 7$

$$\tan \theta_2 = \frac{4 - 7}{1 + 4(7)}$$

$$= \frac{-3}{1 + 28}$$

$$= -\frac{3}{29}$$

$$= -0.1034$$

$\theta_2 = $ arc tan $(-0.1034) = $
$5.9°$ approximately

3.23   Let $m_2 = $ slope of $f(x)$
           $m_1 = $ slope of $g(x)$

$$m_2 = \lim_{h \to 0} \frac{(x + h)^2 - x^2}{h}$$

$$= \lim_{h \to 0} \frac{x^2 + 2xh + h^2 - x^2}{h}$$

$$= \lim_{h \to 0} \frac{2xh + h^2}{h}$$

$$= \lim_{h \to 0} 2x + h$$

$$= \lim_{h \to 0} 2x$$

$$= 2x$$

$$m_1 = \lim_{h \to 0} \frac{\sqrt{x + h} - \sqrt{x}}{h}$$

$$= \lim_{h \to 0} \frac{\sqrt{x + h} - \sqrt{x}}{h} \cdot \frac{\sqrt{x + h} + \sqrt{x}}{\sqrt{x + h} + \sqrt{x}}$$

$$= \lim_{h \to 0} \frac{x + h - x}{h(\sqrt{x + h} + \sqrt{x})}$$

$$= \lim_{h \to 0} \frac{h}{h(\sqrt{x + h} + \sqrt{x})}$$

$$= \lim_{h \to 0} \frac{1}{\sqrt{x} + \sqrt{x}}$$

$$= \lim_{h \to 0} \frac{1}{2\sqrt{x}}$$

$$= \frac{1}{2\sqrt{x}}$$

Points of intersection:
$$x^2 = \sqrt{x}$$
$$(x^2)^2 = (\sqrt{x})^2$$
$$x^4 = x$$
$$x^4 - x = 0$$
$$x(x^3 - 1) = 0$$
$$x = 0$$

$$x^3 - 1 = 0$$
$$x^3 = 1$$
$$\sqrt[3]{x^3} = \sqrt[3]{1}$$
$$x = 1$$

$x = 0$: $y = x^2$
              $= 0^2$
              $= 0$

$x = 1$: $y = x^2$
              $= 1^2$
              $= 1$

Points of intersection are
$(0, 0)$ and $(1, 1)$.

Points to graph $f(x) = x^2$ are
$(0, 0)$, $(\pm 1, 1)$, $(\pm 2, 4)$,
$(\pm 3, 9)$.
Points to graph $g(x) = \sqrt{x}$ are
$(0, 0)$, $(1, 1)$, $(4, 2)$, $(9, 3)$.

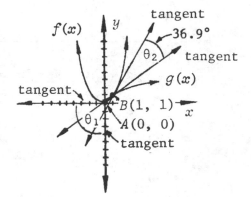

For point A:
$m_2 = 2(0) = 0$
$$m_1 = \frac{1}{2\sqrt{0}} = \frac{1}{0} = \text{undefined}$$

Since $m_2 = 0$ and m_1 is undefined,
the tangents are perpendicular
and the angle of intersection
$(\theta_1) = 90°$.

For point B:

$m_2 = 2(1) = 2$

$m_1 = \dfrac{1}{2\sqrt{1}} = \dfrac{1}{2}$

$\tan \theta_2 = \dfrac{m_2 - m_1}{1 + m_2 m_1}$

$= \dfrac{2 - \dfrac{1}{2}}{1 + 2\left(\dfrac{1}{2}\right)}$

$= \dfrac{\dfrac{3}{2}}{1 + 1}$

$= \dfrac{\dfrac{3}{2}}{2}$

$= \dfrac{3}{4}$

$= 0.75$

$\theta_2 = \text{arc tan } 0.75$
$\quad = 36.9°$ approximately

VI. SECTION FOUR

4.1　all real numbers; $x \in R$

4.2　For x equals any real number, y will always be negative. Therefore, the range is all real numbers less than or equal to zero; $y \leq 0$.

4.3　$F[G(x)] - F(x) =$
$2(3x + 2) - 1 - (2x - 1) =$
$6x + 4 - \cancel{1} - 2x + \cancel{1} =$
$\mathbf{4x + 4}$

4.4　$H(1) = 1^2 = 1$

$G[H(1)] = G(1)$
$\qquad = 3(1) + 2$
$\qquad = 3 + 2$
$\qquad = \mathbf{5}$

4.5　$H(2) = 2^2 = \mathbf{4}$

$G[H(2)] = G(4)$
$\qquad = 3(4) + 2$
$\qquad = 12 + 2$
$\qquad = \mathbf{14}$

$F\{G[H(2)]\} = F(14)$
$\qquad = 2(14) - 1$
$\qquad = 28 - 1$
$\qquad = 27$

4.6　$H(x + a) - H(x) =$
$(x + a)^2 - x^2 =$
$\cancel{x^2} + 2xa + a^2 - \cancel{x^2} =$
$2xa + a^2 =$
$a^2 + 2xa$

4.7　$\dfrac{H(x + a) - H(x)}{a} =$

$\dfrac{(x + a)^2 - x^2}{a} =$

$\dfrac{\cancel{x^2} + 2xa + a^2 - \cancel{x^2}}{a} =$

$\dfrac{2xa + a^{\cancel{2}}}{\cancel{a}} =$

$2x + a$

4.8　$F(x) + G(x) + H(x) =$
$(2x - 1) + (3x + 2) + (x^2) =$
$5x + 1 + x^2 =$
$x^2 + 5x + 1$

4.9　Let $y = G(x)$. Then $y = \dfrac{1}{x - 1}$.

Interchange x and y: $x = \dfrac{1}{y - 1}$.

Solve for y: $x(y - 1) = 1$
$\qquad$ (cross-multiply)

$\qquad y - 1 = \dfrac{1}{x}$

(divide both sides by x)

$\qquad\qquad y = \dfrac{1}{x} + 1$

4.10　$y - y_1 = m(x - x_1)$

$y - 5 = \dfrac{2}{3}(x + 3)$

$3y - 15 = 2(x + 3)$ (multiply both
$\qquad\qquad\qquad\qquad$ sides by 3)

$3y - 15 = 2x + 6$

$0 = 2x + 6 - 3y + 15$

$0 = 2x - 3y + 21$

4.11
$$2x^2 + 5x - 3 \leq 0$$
$$(2x - 1)(x + 3) \leq 0$$
$$2x - 1 \geq 0$$
$$2x \geq 1$$
$$\frac{2x}{2} \geq \frac{1}{2}$$
$$x \geq \frac{1}{2}$$

and $x + 3 \leq 0$
$$x \leq -3$$
empty set
or
$2x - 1 \leq 0$ and $x + 3 \geq 0$
$$2x \leq 1 \qquad x \geq -3$$
$$\frac{2x}{2} \leq \frac{1}{2}$$
$$x \leq \frac{1}{2}$$
$$-3 \leq x \leq \frac{1}{2}$$

4.12 $y \geq 2x^2 + 5x - 3$

x	y
0	-3
$\frac{1}{2}$	0
1	4
-1	-6
$-\frac{5}{4}$	$-\frac{49}{8}$
$-\frac{3}{2}$	-6
-2	-5

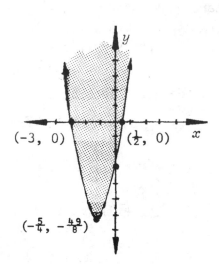

The point (0, 0) satisfies the inequality; therefore, the inside of the curve is shaded.

4.13 By synthetic division:

$$\begin{array}{r|rrrr} 3 & 2 & -11 & +12 & +9 \\ & & 0+6 & -15 & -9 \\ \hline & 2 & -5 & -3 & +0 \end{array}$$

$$\begin{array}{r|rrrr} -\frac{1}{2} & 2 & -11 & +12 & +9 \\ & & 0-1 & +6 & -9 \\ \hline & 2 & -12 & +18 & +0 \end{array}$$

The zeros are 3 and $-\frac{1}{2}$.

4.14
$$\begin{array}{r|rrrrr} 2 & 2 & +0 & -1 & +3 & -1 \\ & & 0+4 & +8 & +14 & +34 \\ \hline & 2 & +4 & +7 & +17 & +33 \end{array}$$

$P(2) = 33$

4.15 $f^{-1}(x) = 3^x$

4.16 $H^{-1}(x) = \frac{1}{2} \log_e x$

4.17

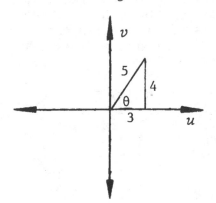

$$\sin \theta = \frac{4}{5}$$

$$\tan \theta = \frac{4}{3}$$

$$\csc \theta = \frac{1}{\frac{4}{5}} = \frac{5}{4}$$

$\sec \theta = \dfrac{1}{\frac{3}{5}} = \dfrac{5}{3}$

$\cot \theta = \dfrac{1}{\frac{4}{3}} = \dfrac{3}{4}$

4.18 Subtract multiples of 360° from 800°.
800° − 720° = 80°
Angle terminates in Quadrant I.

4.19 From the trigonometric table, sin 28° 20' = 0.4746.

4.20 From the trigonometric table, cos 18° 20' = 0.9492.

4.21 From the trigonometric table, θ = 31° 10'.

4.22 340° is located in Quadrant IV.
$\cos 340° = \cos(360° - 340°)$
$= \cos 20°$
$= 0.9397$

4.23 sec 180° + sin 270° − tan 180° + cot 270° =
−1 + (−1) − 0 + 0 = −2

4.24 $\cos 120° = \cos(180° - 120°) =$
$-\cos 60° = -\dfrac{1}{2}$
$\sin 300° = \sin(360° - 300°) =$
$-\sin 60° = -\dfrac{\sqrt{3}}{2}$
$\cos 240° = \cos(180° + 240°) =$
$-\cos 420° = -\cos(420° -$
$360°) = -\cos 60° = -\dfrac{1}{2}$

$\cos^2 120° \cdot \sin^2 300° +$
$\sin^2 300° \cdot \cos^2 240° =$
$\left(-\dfrac{1}{2}\right)^2 \left(-\dfrac{\sqrt{3}}{2}\right)^2 + \left(-\dfrac{\sqrt{3}}{2}\right)^2 \left(-\dfrac{1}{2}\right)^2 =$
$\dfrac{1}{4}\left(\dfrac{3}{4}\right) + \dfrac{3}{4}\left(\dfrac{1}{4}\right) =$
$\dfrac{3}{16} + \dfrac{3}{16} =$
$\dfrac{6}{16} =$
$\dfrac{3}{8}$

4.25 $18° = \dfrac{18° \pi}{180°}$
$= \dfrac{\pi}{10} \text{ rad}$

4.26 amplitude = −2
period $= \dfrac{2\pi}{\frac{\pi}{4}} = 2\pi\left(\dfrac{4}{\pi}\right) = 8$
phase shift $= -\dfrac{\pi}{2}$
$y = -2 \cos 8\left(x + \dfrac{\pi}{2}\right)$

4.27 $F(x) = 2 \sin (2x + \pi)$
$= 2 \sin 2\left(x + \dfrac{\pi}{2}\right)$
amplitude = 2
period $= \dfrac{2\pi}{2} = \pi$
phase shift $= -\dfrac{\pi}{2}(\dfrac{\pi}{2}$ units to the left)

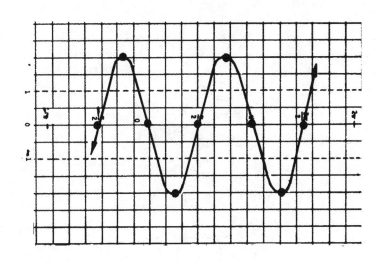

4.28 $G(x) = \frac{1}{2} \cos (x - \frac{\pi}{4})$

amplitude = $\frac{1}{2}$

period = $\frac{2\pi}{1} = 2\pi$

phase shift = $\frac{\pi}{4}$ units to the
right

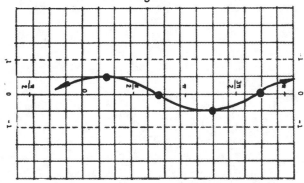

4.29 $f(x) = 3 \sin (2x - 2)$
$= 3 \sin 2(x - 1)$
phase shift = 1 unit to
the right

4.30 $60° = \frac{60°\pi}{180°}$

$= \frac{\pi}{3}$ rad per hour

$\frac{\pi}{3} \cdot 24 = 8\pi$ rad

4.31 $r = \frac{28}{2} = 14$ in.

$16(14) = 224$ inches per
second

4.32 $\sin 2\theta = 2 \sin \theta$
$2 \sin \theta \cos \theta = 2 \sin \theta$
$\cos \theta = 1$ (divide both
sides by
$2 \sin \theta$)
$\theta = 0°, 360°$

4.33 $\cos \beta = \sin \frac{\beta}{2}$

$\cos \beta = \sqrt{\frac{1 - \cos \beta}{2}}$

$(\cos \beta)^2 = \left(\sqrt{\frac{1 - \cos \beta}{2}}\right)^2$

$\cos^2 \beta = \frac{1 - \cos \beta}{2}$

$2 \cos^2 \beta = 1 - \cos \beta$ (multiply
both sides by 2)

$2 \cos^2 \beta + \cos \beta - 1 = 0$
$(2 \cos \beta - 1)(\cos \beta + 1) = 0$
$2 \cos \beta - 1 = 0$
$2 \cos \beta = 1$
$\frac{2 \cos \beta}{2} = \frac{1}{2}$

$\cos \beta = \frac{1}{2}$

$\cos \beta$ is positive in Quadrants I
and IV. Therefore,
$\beta = 60°, 300°$.

$\cos \beta + 1 = 0$
$\cos \beta = -1$
$\beta = 180°$

Check:
$\beta = 60°$: $\cos 60° \overset{?}{=} \sin \frac{60°}{2}$

$\cos 60° \overset{?}{=} \sin 30°$

$\frac{1}{2} = \frac{1}{2}$

$\beta = 300°$: $\cos 300° \overset{?}{=} \sin \frac{300°}{2}$

$\cos 300° \overset{?}{=} \sin 150°$

$\frac{1}{2} = \frac{1}{2}$

$\beta = 180°$: $\cos 180° \overset{?}{=} \sin \frac{180°}{2}$

$\cos 180° \overset{?}{=} \sin 90°$

$-1 \neq 1$

$\beta = 60°, 300°$

4.34 $\sin^2 \theta = 1 - \sin 2\theta$
$\sin^2 \theta = \sin^2 \theta + \cos^2 \theta - 2 \sin \theta \cos \theta$

$\cancel{\sin^2 \theta} - \cancel{\sin^2 \theta} - \cos^2 \theta + 2 \sin \theta \cos \theta = 0$
$\cos \theta(2 \sin \theta - \cos\theta) = 0$

$\cos \theta = 0$
$\theta = 90°, 270°$

$$2 \sin \theta - \cos \theta = 0$$
$$2 \sin \theta = \cos \theta$$
$$4 \sin^2 \theta = \cos^2 \theta$$
$$\text{(square sides)}$$
$$4 \sin^2 \theta - \cos^2 \theta = 0$$
$$4 \sin^2 \theta - (1 - \sin^2 \theta) = 0$$
$$4 \sin^2 \theta - 1 + \sin^2 \theta = 0$$
$$5 \sin^2 \theta - 1 = 0$$
$$5 \sin^2 \theta = 1$$
$$\frac{5 \sin^2 \theta}{5} = \frac{1}{5}$$
$$\sin^2 \theta = \frac{1}{5}$$
$$\sqrt{\sin^2 \theta} = \pm\sqrt{\frac{1}{5}}$$
$$\sin \theta = \pm\frac{\sqrt{5}}{5}$$
$$\sin \theta = \pm 0.4472$$
$$\theta = 27°, 153°, 207°, 333°$$

Check:

$\theta = 90°$: $\quad \sin^2 90° \overset{?}{=} 1 - \sin 180°$

$$1 \overset{?}{=} 1 - 0$$
$$1 = 1$$

$\theta = 270°$: $\quad \sin^2 270° \overset{?}{=} 1 - \sin 540°$

$$1 \overset{?}{=} 1 - 0$$
$$1 = 1$$

$\theta = 27°$: $\quad \sin^2 27° \overset{?}{=} 1 - \sin 54°$

$$0.2 \overset{?}{=} 1 - 0.8$$
$$0.2 = 0.2$$

$\theta = 153°$: $\quad \sin^2 153° \overset{?}{=} 1 - \sin 306°$

$$0.5 \overset{?}{=} 1 - (0.8)$$
$$0.5 \overset{?}{=} 1 + 0.8$$
$$0.5 \neq 1.8$$

$\theta = 207°$: $\quad \sin^2 207° \overset{?}{=} 1 - \sin 414°$

$$0.2 \overset{?}{=} 1 - 0.8$$
$$0.2 = 0.2$$

$\theta = 333°$: $\quad \sin^2 333° \overset{?}{=} 1 - \sin 666°$

$$0.2 \overset{?}{=} 1 - (-0.8)$$
$$0.2 \overset{?}{=} 1 + 0.8$$
$$0.2 \neq 1.8$$

$$\theta = 27°, 90°, 207°, 270°$$

4.35
$$\cos 2\alpha + \sin \alpha = 1$$
$$\cos^2 \alpha - \sin^2 \alpha + \sin \alpha = 1$$
$$\cancel{1} - \sin^2 \alpha - \sin^2 \alpha + \sin \alpha = \cancel{1}$$
$$-2 \sin^2 \alpha + \sin \alpha = 0$$
$$\sin \alpha(-2 \sin \alpha + 1) = 0$$

$$\sin \alpha = 0$$
$$\alpha = 0°, 180°, 360°$$

$$-2 \sin \alpha + 1 = 0$$
$$-2 \sin \alpha = -1$$
$$\frac{-2 \sin \alpha}{-2} = \frac{-1}{-2}$$
$$\sin \alpha = \frac{1}{2}$$

$\sin \alpha$ is positive in Quadrants I and II. Therefore,
$$\alpha = 30°, 150°.$$

$$\alpha = 0°, 30°, 150°, 180°, 360°$$

4.36
$$\tan \alpha \tan 2\alpha = 1$$
$$\tan \alpha\left(\frac{2 \tan \alpha}{1 - \tan^2 \alpha}\right) = 1$$
$$\frac{2 \tan^2 \alpha}{1 - \tan^2 \alpha} = 1$$
$$2 \tan^2 \alpha = 1 - \tan^2 \alpha$$
$$\text{(cross-multiply)}$$
$$2 \tan^2 \alpha + \tan^2 \alpha = 1$$
$$3 \tan^2 \alpha = 1$$
$$\frac{3 \tan^2 \alpha}{3} = \frac{1}{3}$$
$$\tan^2 \alpha = \frac{1}{3}$$
$$\sqrt{\tan^2 \alpha} = \pm\sqrt{\frac{1}{3}}$$
$$\tan \alpha = \pm\frac{1}{\sqrt{3}}$$

$\alpha = 30°, 150°, 210°, 330°$

4.37 Yes. $\sin \frac{\pi}{3} \cos \theta + \cos \frac{\pi}{3}$.

$\sin \theta - (\cos \frac{\pi}{6} \cos \theta -$

$\sin \frac{\pi}{6} \sin \theta) = \sin \theta$

$\frac{\sqrt{3}}{2} \cos \theta + \frac{1}{2} \sin \theta -$

$\frac{\sqrt{3}}{2} \cos \theta + \frac{1}{2} \sin \theta = \sin \theta$

$\qquad\qquad \sin \theta = \sin \theta$

4.38 $\sin (\theta + \phi) = \sin \theta \cos \phi +$
$\qquad\qquad\qquad \cos \theta \sin \phi$

$\cos \theta = \frac{-4}{5} \qquad \sin \phi = \frac{-12}{13}$

$\sin \theta = \frac{-3}{5} \qquad \cos \phi = \frac{5}{13}$

$\sin (\theta + \phi) = (\frac{-3}{5})(\frac{5}{13}) +$

$\qquad\qquad\qquad (\frac{-4}{5})(\frac{-12}{13})$

$\qquad\qquad = -\frac{15}{65} + \frac{48}{65}$

$\qquad\qquad = \frac{33}{65}$

4.39 $\cos (\theta - \phi) = \cos \theta \cos \phi +$
$\qquad\qquad\qquad \sin \theta \sin \phi$

$\cos \theta = \frac{-4}{5} \qquad \sin \phi = \frac{-12}{13}$

$\sin \theta = \frac{-3}{5} \qquad \cos \phi = \frac{5}{13}$

$\cos (\theta - \phi) = (\frac{-4}{5})(\frac{5}{13}) +$

$\qquad\qquad\qquad (\frac{-3}{5})(\frac{-12}{13})$

$\qquad\qquad = -\frac{20}{65} + \frac{36}{65}$

$\qquad\qquad = \frac{16}{65}$

4.40 $\tan (\theta + \phi) = \frac{\tan \theta + \tan \phi}{1 - \tan \theta \tan \phi}$

$\tan \theta = \frac{3}{4}$

$\tan \phi = \frac{-12}{5}$

$\tan (\theta + \phi) = \frac{\frac{3}{4} - \frac{12}{5}}{1 - (\frac{3}{4})(-\frac{12}{5})}$

$\qquad\qquad = \frac{\frac{15}{20} - \frac{48}{20}}{\frac{20}{20} + \frac{36}{20}}$

$\qquad\qquad = \frac{-\frac{33}{20}}{\frac{56}{20}}$

$\qquad\qquad = -\frac{33}{56}$

4.41 $\sin 2\theta = 2 \sin \theta \cos \theta$

$\sin \theta = \frac{-3}{5}$

$\cos \theta = \frac{-4}{5}$

$\sin 2\theta = 2(\frac{-3}{5})(\frac{-4}{5})$

$\qquad\quad = \frac{24}{25}$

4.42 $\cos 2\phi = \cos^2 \phi - \sin^2 \phi$

$\cos \phi = \frac{5}{13}$

$\sin \phi = \frac{-12}{13}$

$\cos 2\phi = (\frac{5}{13})^2 - (-\frac{12}{13})^2$

$\qquad\quad = \frac{25}{169} - \frac{144}{169}$

$\qquad\quad = -\frac{119}{169}$

4.43 $\tan \frac{1}{2}\theta = \sqrt{\frac{1 - \cos \theta}{1 + \cos \theta}}$

$\cos \theta = \frac{-4}{5}$

$\tan \frac{1}{2}\theta = \sqrt{\frac{1 - (-\frac{4}{5})}{1 + (-\frac{4}{5})}}$

$$= \sqrt{\frac{\frac{5}{5} + \frac{4}{5}}{\frac{5}{5} - \frac{4}{5}}}$$

$$= \sqrt{\frac{\frac{9}{5}}{\frac{1}{5}}}$$

$$= \sqrt{\frac{9}{1}}$$

$$= \sqrt{9}$$

$$= 3$$

4.44

$\cot \alpha \sin 2\alpha$	$1 + \cos 2\alpha$
$\frac{\cos \alpha}{\sin \alpha} \cdot 2 \sin \alpha \cos \alpha$	$1 + 2 \cos^2 \alpha$
$2 \cos^2 \alpha$	$2 \cos^2 \alpha$

4.45

$$\frac{\cos^2 x}{\sin^2 x} - \cos^2 x =$$

$$\frac{\cos^2 x}{\sin^2 x} - \frac{\cos^2 x \sin^2 x}{\sin^2 x} =$$

$$\frac{\cos^2 x - \cos^2 x \sin^2 x}{\sin^2 x} =$$

$$\frac{\cos^2 x (1 - \sin^2 x)}{\sin^2 x} =$$

$$\cos^2 x \, \frac{\cos^2 x}{\sin^2 x} =$$

$$\cos^2 x \cot^2 x$$

4.46

$$\frac{1}{\tan^2 x} + \frac{\tan^2 x}{\tan^2 x} =$$

$$\cot^2 x + 1 =$$

$$\csc^2 x = \csc^2 x$$

4.47

$$\frac{\sin^2 x}{\sin x (1 + \cos x)} +$$

$$\frac{(1 + \cos x)^2}{\sin x (1 + \cos x)} =$$

$$\frac{\sin^2 x + (1 + \cos x)^2}{\sin x (1 + \cos x)} =$$

$$\frac{\sin^2 x + 1 + 2 \cos x + \cos^2 x}{\sin x (1 + \cos x)} =$$

$$\frac{2 + 2 \cos x}{\sin x (1 + \cos x)} =$$

$$\frac{2 (1 + \cos x)}{\sin \ (1 + \cos x)} =$$

$$\frac{2}{\sin x} =$$

$$2 \csc x$$

4.48

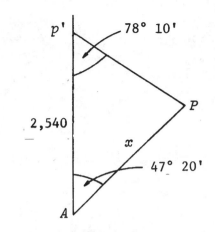

$\angle P = 180° - 78° \ 10' - 47° \ 20'$
     $= 54° \ 30'$

$$\frac{x}{\sin 78° \ 10'} = \frac{2,540}{\sin 54° \ 30'}$$

$$x = \frac{2,540 \sin 78° \ 10'}{\sin 54° \ 30'}$$

(multiply both sides by sin 78° 10')

$$x = \frac{2,540 (0.9787)}{0.8141}$$

$x = 3,053.6$ or
   $3,050$ ft.
   (rounded to the nearest ten)

4.49

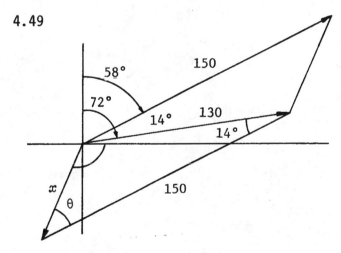

a. $x^2 = 130^2 + 150^2 -$
      $2(130)(150) \cos 14°$
   $= 16,900 + 22,500 -$
      $37,842$
   $= 1,558$

$$\sqrt{x^2} = \sqrt{1,558}$$

$x = 39.48$ or 39 mph

$$\frac{130}{\sin \theta} = \frac{39}{\sin 14°}$$

$$\sin \theta = \frac{130 \sin 14°}{39}$$

$$\sin \theta = \frac{130(0.2419)}{39}$$
$$\sin \theta = 0.8063$$
$$\theta = 54°$$

b. direction
  of wind = 72° + 180° - 14° - 54°
  = 72° + 114°
  = 184°

4.50

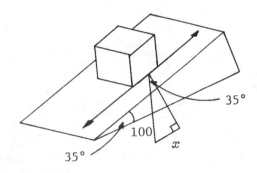

$$\sin 35° = \frac{x}{100}$$
$$x = 100 \sin 35° \text{ (multiply both sides by 100)}$$
$$= 100(0.5736)$$
$$= 57.4 \text{ lbs.}$$

4.51

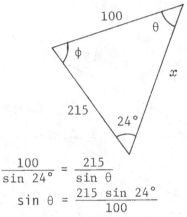

$$\frac{100}{\sin 24°} = \frac{215}{\sin \theta}$$
$$\sin \theta = \frac{215 \sin 24°}{100}$$
$$= \frac{215(0.4067)}{100}$$
$$= 0.8744$$
$$\theta = 61°$$
$$\phi = 180° - 61° - 24°$$
$$= 95°$$

$$\frac{x}{\sin 95°} = \frac{100}{\sin 24°}$$
$$x = \frac{100 \sin 95°}{\sin 24°}$$
$$= \frac{100(.9962)}{.4067} = 244.8 \doteq 245 \text{ yds.}$$

4.52 a. $\angle A = 90° - 30°$
        $= 60°$

b. $\sin 30° = \frac{x}{2}$
    $\frac{1}{2} = \frac{x}{2}$
    $x = 2(\frac{1}{2})$ (multiply both sides by 2)
    $x = 1$

c. $\sin B = \frac{1}{2}$
    $\cos B = \frac{\sqrt{3}}{3}$
    $\tan B = \frac{1}{\sqrt{3}} = \frac{\sqrt{3}}{3}$

d. $\csc A = \frac{1}{\frac{\sqrt{3}}{2}} = \frac{2}{\sqrt{3}} = \frac{2\sqrt{3}}{3}$

    $\sec A = \frac{1}{\frac{1}{2}} = 2$

    $\cot A = \frac{1}{\sqrt{3}} = \frac{\sqrt{3}}{3}$

4.53

a. $\frac{84}{\sin \angle B} = \frac{126}{\sin 74°}$
    $\sin \angle B = \frac{84 \sin 74°}{126}$
    $= \frac{84(0.9613)}{126}$
    $= 0.6408$
    $\angle B = 39.85°$ or 39° 51'

b. $\angle C = 180° - 74° - 39° 51'$
    $= 66° 9'$

c. $\frac{c}{\sin 66° 9'} = \frac{126}{\sin 74°}$
    $c = \frac{126 \sin 66° 9'}{\sin 74°}$
    (multiply both sides by sin 66° 9')
    $= \frac{126(0.9146)}{0.9613}$
    $= 119.88$

270

4.54 and 4.55

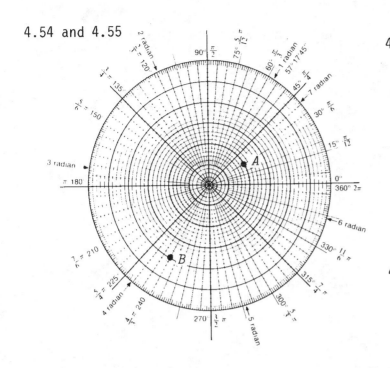

4.56 $\quad x = r \cos \theta$
$\quad\quad = 3 \cos 2\pi$
$\quad\quad = 3(1)$
$\quad\quad = 3$
$\quad y = r \sin \theta$
$\quad\quad = 3 \sin 2\pi$
$\quad\quad = 3(0)$
$\quad\quad = 0$
$\quad (3, 0)$

4.57 $\quad x = r \cos \theta$
$\quad\quad = 1 \cos 130°$
$\quad\quad = 1(-\cos 50°)$
$\quad\quad = -0.6428$
$\quad y = r \sin \theta$
$\quad\quad = 1 \sin 130°$
$\quad\quad = 1(\sin 50°)$
$\quad\quad = 0.7660$
$\quad (-0.6428, 0.7660)$

4.58 The point is in Quadrant II.
$$\theta = \tan^{-1}\left(\frac{y}{x}\right)$$
$$= \tan^{-1}\left(\frac{3}{-3}\right)$$
$$= \tan^{-1}(-1)$$
$\tan \theta = -1$ and $\theta = 135°$ or $\frac{3\pi}{4}$
$$r = \sqrt{x^2 + y^2}$$
$$= \sqrt{(-3)^2 + 3^2}$$
$$= \sqrt{9 + 9}$$
$$= 3\sqrt{2}$$
$\left(3\sqrt{2}, \frac{3\pi}{4}\right)$

4.59 The point is in Quadrant II.
$$\theta = \tan^{-1}\left(\frac{y}{x}\right)$$
$$= \tan^{-1}\left(\frac{\frac{\sqrt{2}}{2}}{\frac{-\sqrt{2}}{2}}\right)$$
$$= \tan^{-1}(-1)$$
$\tan \theta = -1$ and $\theta = 135°$ or $\frac{3\pi}{4}$
$$r = \sqrt{x^2 + y^2}$$
$$= \sqrt{\left(\frac{-\sqrt{2}}{2}\right)^2 + \left(\frac{\sqrt{2}}{2}\right)^2}$$
$$= \sqrt{\frac{2}{4} + \frac{2}{4}}$$
$$= \sqrt{1}$$
$$= 1$$
$\left(1, \frac{3\pi}{4}\right)$

4.60 $\quad x = r \cos \theta$
$\quad\quad y = r \sin \theta$
$$(r \cos \theta)^2 + (r \sin \theta)^2 +$$
$$4(r \cos \theta) - 6(r \sin \theta) = 3$$
$$r^2 \cos^2 \theta + r^2 \sin^2 \theta +$$
$$4r \cos \theta - 6r \sin \theta = 3$$
$$r^2(\cos^2 \theta + \sin^2 \theta) +$$
$$2r(2 \cos \theta - 3 \sin \theta) = 3$$
$$r^2(1) + 2r(2 \cos \theta - 3 \sin \theta) = 3$$
$$r^2 + 2r(2 \cos \theta - 3 \sin \theta) = 3$$

4.61 $r \sin \theta - 3 = 0$
$r \sin \theta = 3$
$$\frac{r \sin \theta}{\sin \theta} = \frac{3}{\sin \theta}$$
$r = 3 \csc \theta$

θ	0	$\frac{\pi}{6}$	$\frac{\pi}{4}$	$\frac{\pi}{3}$	$\frac{\pi}{2}$	$\frac{2\pi}{3}$	$\frac{3\pi}{4}$	$\frac{5\pi}{6}$	π
r	und	2	1.4	1.2	1	1.2	1.4	2	und

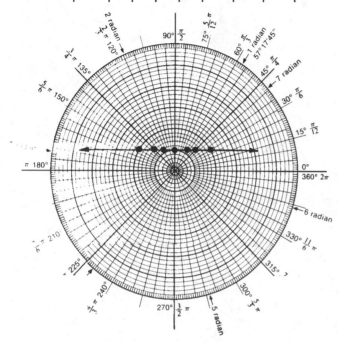

4.62   Let $\theta = \text{arc sin } \frac{5}{13}$ and
$\phi = \text{arc sin } \frac{4}{5}$.
$\sin (\theta + \phi) = \sin \theta \cos \phi +$
$\cos \theta \sin \phi$
$= \frac{5}{13} \cdot \frac{3}{5} + \frac{12}{13} \cdot \frac{4}{5}$
$= \frac{15}{65} + \frac{48}{65}$
$= \frac{63}{65}$

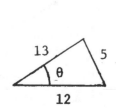   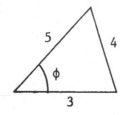

4.63   Let $x = \text{arc tan } (-\frac{5}{12})$; then
$\tan x = -\frac{5}{12}$.
$\cos x = -\frac{12}{13}$

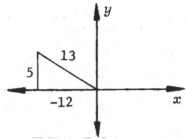

4.64 $\sec \pi = -1$
Let $x = \text{arc tan } (-1)$; then
$\tan x = -1$.
$x = \frac{3\pi}{4}$ or $\frac{7\pi}{4}$

4.65   circle

4.66   ellipse

4.67   hyperbola

4.68   hyperbola

4.69   circle

4.70   parabola

4.71   ellipse

4.72   hyperbola

4.73   no graph
$2x^2 + 2y^2 = -2$ (cannot have a negative radius)

4.74   parabola

4.75 $x^2 + y^2 - 10x - 8y + 1 = 0$
$x^2 - 10x + y^2 - 8y = -1$
$(x^2 - 10x + 25) +$
$(y^2 - 8y + 16) = -1 +$
$25 + 16$
$(x - 5)^2 + (y - 4)^2 = 40$
Center is (5, 4) and
radius is $\sqrt{40} = 2\sqrt{10}$

4.76 $8x^2 + 6y^2 - 32x + 24y + 8 = 0$

$8x^2 - 32x + 6y^2 + 24y = -8$

$(x^2 - 4x + 4) +$

$6(y^2 + 4y + 4) = -8 +$

$32 +$

24

$8(x - 2)^2 + 6(y + 2)^2 = 48$

$\dfrac{(x - 2)^2}{6} + \dfrac{(y + 2)^2}{8} = 1$

(divide both sides by 48)

center (2, -2)

eccentricity $= \dfrac{c}{a}$

$a = \sqrt{8}$ or $2\sqrt{2}$

$b = \sqrt{6}$

$c = \sqrt{a^2 - b^2}$

$= \sqrt{(\sqrt{8})^2 - (\sqrt{6})^2}$

$= \sqrt{8 - 6}$

$= \sqrt{2}$

eccentricity $= \dfrac{\sqrt{2}}{2\sqrt{2}} = \dfrac{1}{2}$

4.77 $x^2 - 10x + y = 0$

$x^2 - 10x = -y$

$x^2 - 10x + 25 = -y + 25$

$(x - 5)^2 = -1(y - 25)$

The maximum height is the value of k in $(y - k)$, which is 25.

4.78 $4x^2 + 9y^2 + 16x - 18y - 11 = 0$

$4x^2 + 16x + 9y^2 - 18y = 11$

$4(x^2 + 4x + 4) +$

$9(y^2 - 2y + 1) = 11 +$

$16 +$

9

$4(x + 2)^2 + 9(y - 1)^2 = 36$

$\dfrac{(x + 2)^2}{9} + \dfrac{(y - 1)^2}{4} = 1$

(divide both sides by 36)

Ellipse

Center = (-2, 1)

Position I

$a = \sqrt{9} = 3$

$b = \sqrt{4} = 2$

$c = \sqrt{a^2 - b^2}$

$= \sqrt{3^2 - 2^2}$

$= \sqrt{9 - 4}$

$= \sqrt{5}$

Major axis $= 2a$

$= 2(3)$

$= 6$

Minor axis $= 2b$

$= 2(2)$

$= 4$

L.R. $= \dfrac{2b^2}{a}$

$= \dfrac{2(2)^2}{3}$

$= \dfrac{2(4)}{3}$

$= \dfrac{8}{3}$

$e = \dfrac{c}{a}$

$= \dfrac{\sqrt{5}}{3}$

Domain: $-5 \le x \le 1$

Range: $-1 \le y \le 3$

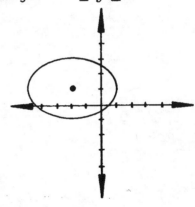

4.79 $x^2 + y^2 + Dx + Ey + F = 0$

For point (9, -1):

$9^2 + (-1)^2 + 9d + (-1)e + f = 0$

$81 + 1 + 9d - e + f = 0$

$82 + 9d - e + f = 0$

$9d - e + f = -82$

For point (0, -4):

$0^2 + (-4)^2 + 0d + (-4)e + f = 0$

$16 - 4e + f = 0$

$-4e + f = -16$

For point $(-1, -1)$:

$$(-1)^2 + (-1)^2 + (-1)d + (-1)e + f = 0$$
$$1 + 1 - d - e + f = 0$$
$$2 - d - e + f = 0$$
$$-d - e + f = -2$$

Solve for d:

$$9d - e + f = -82$$
$$\underline{-d - e + f = -2}$$
$$10d = -80$$
$$\frac{10d}{10} = \frac{-80}{10}$$
$$d = -8$$

Solve for e:

$$-(-8) - e + f = -2$$
$$8 - e + f = -2$$
$$-e + f = -2 - 8$$
$$-e + f = -10$$

$$-4e + f = -16$$
$$\underline{-e + f = -10}$$
$$-3e = -6$$
$$\frac{-3e}{-3} = \frac{-6}{-3}$$
$$e = 2$$

Solve for f:

$$-4(2) + f = -16$$
$$-8 + f = -16$$
$$f = -16 + 8$$
$$f = -8$$

$$x^2 + y^2 - 8x + 2y - 8 = 0$$

4.80   Since the major axis is parallel to the x-axis, the hyperbola is in Position I with general equation $\frac{(x - h)^2}{a^2} - \frac{(y - k)^2}{b^2} = 1$.

$(h, k) = (1, 3)$

A vertex is at $(3, 3)$ and a focus is at $(4, 3)$.

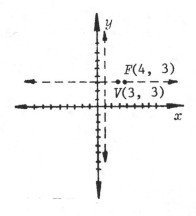

The distance from the center $(1, 3)$ to focus $(4, 3) = 3$, which is the value of c.

The distance from the center $(1, 3)$ to vertex $(3, 3) = 2$, which is the value of a.

$$c^2 = a^2 + b^2$$
$$3^2 = 2^2 + b^2$$
$$9 = 4 + b^2$$
$$9 - 4 = b^2$$
$$b^2 = 5$$

$$\frac{(x - 1)^2}{4} - \frac{(y - 3)^2}{5} = 1$$

4.81   The equation $2xy - x - y + 4 = 0$ passes through the point $(1, -3)$. Let center $(h, k) = (1, -3)$. Since $x = x' + h$ and $y = y' + k$, we know that $x = x' + 1$ and $y = y' - 3$. Substitute these new values of x and y into the original equation to obtain the following equations.

$$2(x' + 1)(y' - 3) - (x' + 1) - (y' - 3) + 4 = 0$$
$$2(x'y' - 3x' + y' - 3) - x' - 1 - y' + 3 + 4 = 0$$
$$2x'y' - 6x' + 2y' - 6 - x' - 1 - y' + 7 = 0$$
$$2x'y' - 7x' + y' = 0$$

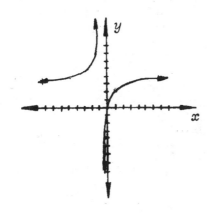

x	-8	-5	-2	-1
y	$3\frac{11}{15}$	$3\frac{8}{9}$	$4\frac{2}{3}$	7

x	$-\frac{8}{23}$	$-\frac{5}{17}$	$-\frac{2}{11}$	$-\frac{1}{9}$	0	1	3	5
y	-8	-5	-2	-1..	0	$2\frac{1}{3}$	3	$3\frac{2}{11}$

4.82 $\tan 2\theta = \dfrac{-6\sqrt{3}}{7 - 13}$

$\qquad\qquad = \dfrac{-6\sqrt{3}}{-6}$

$\qquad\qquad = \sqrt{3}$

$2\theta = 60°; \ \theta = 30°$

$\sin \theta = \dfrac{1}{2}$ and $\cos \theta = \dfrac{\sqrt{3}}{2}$

$x = \dfrac{\sqrt{3}}{2}x' - \dfrac{1}{2}y'$

$\quad = \dfrac{\sqrt{3}x' - y'}{2}$

$y = \dfrac{1}{2}x' + \dfrac{\sqrt{3}}{2}y'$

$\quad = \dfrac{x' + \sqrt{3}y'}{2}$

Substituting these values of x and y into the given equation we obtain the following equations.

$7\left(\dfrac{\sqrt{3}x' - y'}{2}\right)^2 -$

$6\sqrt{3}\left(\dfrac{\sqrt{3}x' - y'}{2}\right) \cdot$

$\left(\dfrac{x' + \sqrt{3}y'}{2}\right) +$

$13\left(\dfrac{x' + \sqrt{3}y'}{2}\right)^2 = 16$

$7\left(\dfrac{3(x')^2 - 2\sqrt{3}x'y' + (y')^2}{4}\right) -$

$6\sqrt{3}\left(\dfrac{\sqrt{3}(x')^2 + 2x'y' - \sqrt{3}(y')^2}{4}\right) +$

$13\left(\dfrac{(x')^2 + 2\sqrt{3}x'y' + 3(y')^2}{4}\right) = 16$

$21(x')^2 - 14\sqrt{3}x'y' + 7(y')^2 -$
$18(x')^2 - 12\sqrt{3}x'y' + 18(y')^2 +$
$13(x')^2 + 26\sqrt{3}x'y' + 39(y')^2 = 64$
   (multiply each term
   and multiply both
   sides by 4)

$16(x')^2 + 64(y')^2 = 64$

$\dfrac{(x')^2}{4} + (y')^2 = 1$ (divide both
   sides by 64)

The graph is an ellipse with center at the origin.

$a = \sqrt{4} = 2$
$b = \sqrt{1} = 1$

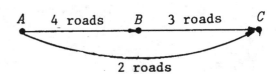

4.83   a. $_5P_2 = 5 \cdot 4 = 20$

b. $_5P_4 = 5 \cdot 4 \cdot 3 \cdot 2 = 120$

c. $_5P_5 = 5 \cdot 4 \cdot 3 \cdot 2 \cdot 1 = 120$

d.   Sample space = {3, 6, 9}.

$P = \dfrac{3}{5}$ or 0.6

e.   Sample space = {6, 9}.

$P = \dfrac{2}{5}$ or 0.4

4.84
```
A    4 roads    B    3 roads    C
```
2 roads

a. $4 \cdot 3 = 12$
b. $12 + 2 = 14$
c.   You can make 14 trips going and 14 returning; $14 \cdot 14 = 196$

4.85   a. $_{10}P_3 = 10 \cdot 9 \cdot 8 = 720$

b. $\dfrac{_9P_4}{_4P_4} = \dfrac{9 \cdot 8 \cdot 7 \cdot 6}{4 \cdot 3 \cdot 2 \cdot 1}$

$\qquad = 126$

275

c. $\quad _9C_4 = \dfrac{9!}{4!5!}$

$\qquad = \dfrac{9 \cdot 8 \cdot 7 \cdot 6 \cdot 5!}{4 \cdot 3 \cdot 2 \cdot 1 \cdot 5!}$

$\qquad = 126$

d. $\quad _8C_5 = \dfrac{8!}{5!3!}$

$\qquad = \dfrac{8 \cdot 7 \cdot 6 \cdot 5!}{3 \cdot 2 \cdot 1 \cdot 5!}$

$\qquad = 56$

e. $\quad _{1,000}C_{999} = \dfrac{1,000!}{999!1!}$

$\qquad = \dfrac{1,000 \cdot 999!}{1 \cdot 999!}$

$\qquad = 1,000$

f. $\quad _{20}C_{20} = \dfrac{20!}{20!0!}$

$\qquad = \dfrac{20!}{20!}$

$\qquad = 1$

g. $\quad _{10}P_{10} = 10!$

h. $\quad _{16}P_1 = 16$

i. $\quad _{16}C_1 = \dfrac{16!}{1!15!}$

$\qquad = \dfrac{16 \cdot 15!}{1 \cdot 15!}$

$\qquad = 16$

j. $\quad \binom{8}{2}\binom{6}{3}\binom{4}{1}\binom{2}{0} =$

$\dfrac{8!}{2!6!} \cdot \dfrac{6!}{3!3!} \cdot \dfrac{4!}{1!3!} \cdot \dfrac{2!}{0!2!} =$

$\dfrac{8 \cdot 7 \cdot 6!}{2 \cdot 1 \cdot 6!} \cdot \dfrac{6 \cdot 5 \cdot 4 \cdot 3!}{3 \cdot 2 \cdot 1 \cdot 3!} \cdot \dfrac{4 \cdot 3!}{1 \cdot 3!} \cdot \dfrac{2!}{2!} =$

$28 \cdot 20 \cdot 4 \cdot 1 = 2,240$

k. $\quad _4P_3 + {_6P_2} + {_5P_1} =$

$4 \cdot 3 \cdot 2 + 6 \cdot 5 + 5 =$

$24 + 30 + 5 = 59$

l. $\quad \binom{6}{2} + \binom{8}{3} =$

$\dfrac{6!}{2!4!} + \dfrac{8!}{3!5!} =$

$\dfrac{6 \cdot 5 \cdot 4!}{2 \cdot 1 \cdot 4!} + \dfrac{8 \cdot 7 \cdot 6 \cdot 5!}{3 \cdot 2 \cdot 1 \cdot 5!} =$

$15 + 56 = 71$

4.86 a. $\quad _{10}C_2 = \dfrac{10!}{2!8!}$

$\qquad = \dfrac{10 \cdot 9 \cdot 8!}{2 \cdot 1 \cdot 8!}$

$\qquad = 45$

b. Let x = number of defectives. The sample space = $\binom{10}{2}$ = 45 elements.

x	Number of Possibilities	$P(x)$
0	$\binom{7}{2}$	$= \dfrac{21}{45}$
1	$\binom{7}{1}\binom{3}{1}$	$= \dfrac{7 \cdot 3}{45} = \dfrac{21}{45}$
2	$\binom{3}{2}$	$= \dfrac{3}{45}$

$P(2\text{ defectives}) = \dfrac{3}{45}$

$\qquad = \dfrac{1}{45}$ or 0.067

c. From (b),
$P(\text{one defective}) = \dfrac{21}{45}$

$\qquad = \dfrac{7}{15}$ or 0.47

d. From (b),
$P(\text{no defectives}) = \dfrac{21}{45}$

$\qquad = \dfrac{7}{15}$ or 0.47

4.87 Let p = probability of winning = $\dfrac{2}{3}$
q = probability of losing = $1 - \dfrac{2}{3} = \dfrac{1}{3}$

$(p + q)^5 = \binom{5}{0}\left(\dfrac{2}{3}\right)^5 +$
$\binom{5}{1}\left(\dfrac{2}{3}\right)^4\left(\dfrac{1}{3}\right)^1 +$
$\binom{5}{2}\left(\dfrac{2}{3}\right)^3\left(\dfrac{1}{3}\right)^2 +$
$\binom{5}{3}\left(\dfrac{2}{3}\right)^2\left(\dfrac{1}{3}\right)^3 +$
$\binom{5}{4}\left(\dfrac{2}{3}\right)^1\left(\dfrac{1}{3}\right)^4 +$
$\binom{5}{5}\left(\dfrac{1}{3}\right)^5$

a. $P(\text{winning 4 out of 5 games}) = \binom{5}{1}\left(\dfrac{2}{3}\right)^4\left(\dfrac{1}{3}\right)^1$

$\qquad = 5\left(\dfrac{16}{81}\right)\left(\dfrac{1}{3}\right)$

$\qquad = \dfrac{80}{243}$ or 0.33

b. $P(\text{winning at most 4 out of 5 games})$ means winning 4 or 3 or 2 or 1 or 0 games.

$P = \binom{5}{1}\left(\frac{2}{3}\right)^4\left(\frac{1}{3}\right)^1 +$
$\binom{5}{2}\left(\frac{2}{3}\right)^3\left(\frac{1}{3}\right)^2 +$
$\binom{5}{3}\left(\frac{2}{3}\right)^2\left(\frac{1}{3}\right)^3 +$
$\binom{5}{4}\left(\frac{2}{3}\right)^1\left(\frac{1}{3}\right)^4 +$
$\binom{5}{5}\left(\frac{2}{3}\right)^5$

$= 5\left(\frac{2}{3}\right)^4\left(\frac{1}{3}\right)^1 +$
$10\left(\frac{2}{3}\right)^3\left(\frac{1}{3}\right)^2 +$
$10\left(\frac{2}{3}\right)^2\left(\frac{1}{3}\right)^3 +$
$5\left(\frac{2}{3}\right)^1\left(\frac{1}{3}\right)^4 + \left(\frac{1}{3}\right)^5$

Another way of solving the problem is to subtract from 1 the probability of winning 5 games.

P(winning at most 4 out of 5 games) $= 1 - P$(winning 5 games)

$= 1 - [\binom{5}{0}\left(\frac{2}{3}\right)^5]$

$= 1 - \left(\frac{2}{3}\right)^5$

c. P(winning no games $= \binom{5}{5}\left(\frac{1}{3}\right)^5$

$= \left(\frac{1}{3}\right)^5$

$= \frac{1}{243}$ or 0.004

4.88 Let p = probability of American League winning = $\frac{1}{2}$

q = probability of American League losing = $1 - \frac{1}{2} = \frac{1}{2}$

a. P(American League will win in 4 games) $= \left(\frac{1}{2}\right)\left(\frac{1}{2}\right)\left(\frac{1}{2}\right)\left(\frac{1}{2}\right)$

$= \left(\frac{1}{2}\right)^4$

$= \frac{1}{16}$ or 0.06

b. The American League must win the fifth game. Therefore, the National League can win any of the other four games.

Sample space (A = American League wins; N = National League wins):

First Game	Second Game	Third Game	Fourth Game	Fifth Game		
A	A	A	N	A	$= \left(\frac{1}{2}\right)^5 =$	$\frac{1}{32}$
A	A	N	A	A	$= \left(\frac{1}{2}\right)^5 =$	$\frac{1}{32}$
A	N	A	A	A	$= \left(\frac{1}{2}\right)^5 =$	$\frac{1}{32}$
N	A	A	A	A	$= \left(\frac{1}{2}\right)^5 =$	$\frac{1}{32}$

P(American League will win in 5 games) $= \frac{1}{32} + \frac{1}{32} + \frac{1}{32} + \frac{1}{32}$

$= \frac{4}{32}$

$= \frac{1}{8}$ or 0.125

4.89 Let p = probability of a girl = $\frac{1}{2}$

q = probability of a boy = $\frac{1}{2}$

$(p + q)^6 = \binom{6}{0}\left(\frac{1}{2}\right)^6 +$
$\binom{6}{1}\left(\frac{1}{2}\right)^5\left(\frac{1}{2}\right)^1 +$
$\binom{6}{2}\left(\frac{1}{2}\right)^4\left(\frac{1}{2}\right)^2 +$
$\binom{6}{3}\left(\frac{1}{2}\right)^3\left(\frac{1}{2}\right)^3 +$
$\binom{6}{4}\left(\frac{1}{2}\right)^2\left(\frac{1}{2}\right)^4 +$
$\binom{6}{5}\left(\frac{1}{2}\right)^1\left(\frac{1}{2}\right)^5 +$
$\binom{6}{6}\left(\frac{1}{2}\right)^6$

a. P(4 girls and 2 boys) $= \binom{6}{2}\left(\frac{1}{2}\right)^4\left(\frac{1}{2}\right)^2$

$= 15\left(\frac{1}{16}\right)\left(\frac{1}{4}\right)$

$= \frac{15}{64}$ or 0.23

b. P(3 boys and 3 girls) $= \binom{6}{3}\left(\frac{1}{2}\right)^3\left(\frac{1}{2}\right)^3$

$= 20\left(\frac{1}{8}\right)\left(\frac{1}{8}\right)$

$= \frac{20}{64}$

$= \frac{5}{16}$ or 0.31

4.90 $10 \cdot 10 = 100$

4.91   a. $_5C_3 \cdot _4C_2 = \dfrac{5!}{3!2!} \cdot \dfrac{4!}{2!2!}$

$= \dfrac{5 \cdot \overset{2}{\cancel{4}} \cdot \cancel{3!}}{\cancel{2} \cdot \cancel{1} \cdot \cancel{3!}} \cdot \dfrac{\overset{2}{\cancel{4}} \cdot 3 \cdot \cancel{2!}}{\cancel{2} \cdot \cancel{1} \cdot \cancel{2!}}$

$= 10 \cdot 6$

$= 60$

b.   3 Democrats and
2 Republicans = 60 (from a.)
4 Democrats and
1 Republican:

$_5C_4 \cdot _4C_1 = \dfrac{5!}{4!1!} \cdot \dfrac{4!}{1!3!}$

$= \dfrac{5 \cdot \cancel{4!}}{1 \cdot \cancel{4!}} \cdot \dfrac{4 \cdot \cancel{3!}}{1 \cdot \cancel{3!}}$

$= 5 \cdot 4$

$= 20$

5 Democrats and
0 Republicans:

$_5C_5 \cdot _4C_0 = \dfrac{5!}{5!0!} \cdot \dfrac{4!}{0!4!}$

$= \dfrac{5!}{5!} \cdot \dfrac{4!}{4!}$

$= 1 \cdot 1$

$= 1$

60 + 20 + 1 = 81 ways

4.92   a. $E(x) = 2\left(\frac{1}{6}\right)$

$= \frac{1}{3}$ or 0.33

b. $P(x \neq 1) = \frac{1}{6} + \frac{1}{3} + \frac{1}{4}$

$= \frac{2}{12} + \frac{4}{12} + \frac{3}{12}$

$= \frac{9}{12}$

$= \frac{3}{4}$ or 0.75

c. $P(x < 3) = \frac{1}{4} + \frac{1}{6}$

$= \frac{3}{12} + \frac{2}{12}$

$= \frac{5}{12}$ or 0.42

4.93   The number of possible
letters is 23. The number
of possible digits is 9 for
the first digit and 10 for
each of the remaining three
digits.
$\underline{23} \cdot \underline{23} \cdot \underline{9} \cdot \underline{10} \cdot \underline{10} \cdot \underline{10} = 4{,}761{,}000$

4.94 $(n - 1)! = (4 - 1)!$

$= 3!$

$= 3 \cdot 2 \cdot 1$

$= 6$

4.95   a.   Sample space = {2, 4, 6,
8, 10, 12, 14, 16, 18,
20, 22, 24, 26, 28, 30,
32, 34, 36, 38, 40, 42,
44, 46, 48, 50}.

b.   Let A = numbers divisible
by 5.
Sample space (A) = {10, 20,
30, 40, 50}.
$P(A) = \frac{5}{25}$

$= \frac{1}{5}$

Let B = numbers divisible
by 8.
Sample space (B) = {8, 16,
24, 32, 40, 48}.

$P(B) = \frac{6}{25}$

$A \cap B = \{40\}$

$P(A \cap B) = \frac{1}{25}$

$A(A \cap B) = P(A) + P(B) - $
$\qquad\qquad\quad P(A \cap B)$

$= \frac{5}{25} + \frac{6}{25} - \frac{1}{25}$

$= \frac{10}{25}$

$= \frac{2}{5}$ or 0.4

MATHEMATICS 1201
SELF TEST
SOLUTION KEY

SELF TEST 1

1.01 no

1.02 yes

1.03 ϕ; No, range, because x is not a set of ordered-pair numbers.

1.04 No, not all are pairs.

1.05 {2}

1.06 {4}

1.07 yes

1.08 yes

1.09 no

1.010 yes

1.011 $y = 4x - 4$

1.012 $y = x^3$

1.013 $y = \dfrac{x + 4}{2}$

1.014 $y = \dfrac{x}{2} + 3$

SELF TEST 2

2.01 {-3, 0, 2, 5}

2.02 {-2, 1, 3}

2.03 yes

2.04 No, there is no set of ordered-pair numbers.

2.05 all real numbers; $x \in R$

2.06 all real numbers less than or equal to zero; $y \leq 0$

2.07 $g[f(x)] = g(3 - x)$
$= -2(3 - x) = -6 + 2x$
$= 2x - 6$

2.08 $f]g(2)] = f(-4) = 3 - (-4) = 7$

2.09 $g[f(-1)] = g(4) = -2(4) = -8$

2.010 $F[G(x)] - F(x)$
$= F(3x + 2) - F(2x - 1)$
$= 2(3x + 2) - 1 - (2x - 1)$
$= 6x + 4 - 1 - 2x + 1$
$= 4x + 4$

2.011 $G[H(1)] = G(1) = 3(1) + 2 = 5$

2.012 $F\{G[H(2^2)]\} = F[G(4)] = F(14)$
$= 2(14) - 1$
$= 28 - 1$
$= 27$

2.013 $H(x + a) - H(x)$
$= (x + a)^2 - x^2$
$= x^2 + 2ax + a^2 - x^2$
$= a^2 + 2ax$

2.014 $\dfrac{H(x + a) - H(x)}{a}$
$= \dfrac{(x + a)^2 - x^2}{a}$
$= \dfrac{x^2 + 2ax + a^2 - x^2}{a}$
$= \dfrac{2ax + a^2}{a} = \dfrac{a(2x + a)}{a} = 2x + a$

2.015 $F(x) + G(x) + H(x)$
$= (2x - 1) + (3x + 2) + (x^2)$
$= x^2 + 5x + 1$

2.016 a. The second element is one-half the first element:
$y = \frac{1}{2}x$ or $y = \frac{x}{2}$.
b. yes
c. $y = \frac{1}{2}x$
$2y = x$
$x = 2y$
The inverse is $y = 2x$.

2.017 a. In each case the second
          element is a square root
          of the first element:
          $y = \sqrt{x}$.
       b. no
       c. not a function

2.018 no

2.019 {(2, 1), (0, 1), (1, 1),
        (3, 0), (0, 0), (1, 2)}

MATHEMATICS 1202
SELF TEST
SOLUTION KEY

SELF TEST 1

1.01 The second element is $\frac{1}{2}$ of the first element decreased by 3:

$y = \frac{x}{2} - 3.$

1.02 For $x + 4 = 0$
$x = -4$

1.03 $F^{-1}(x) = \frac{x + 1}{2}$

$0 = \frac{x + 1}{2}; \ x = -1$

1.04 $y - y_1 = m(x - x_1)$

$y - 5 = \frac{2}{3}[x - (-3)]$

$y = \frac{2}{3}x + 2 + 5$

$y = \frac{2}{3}x + 7$

1.05 Given $(-1, 0), (0, 3)$

$m = \frac{3}{1} = 3$

$y - 3 = 3(x - 0)$

$y = 3x + 3$

1.06

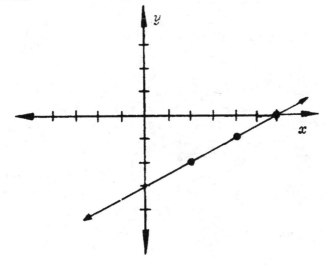

1.07 $y = \frac{x^2 - 16}{x + 4} = \frac{(x + 4)(x - 4)}{x + 4}$

$= x - 4$ for $x \neq -4$

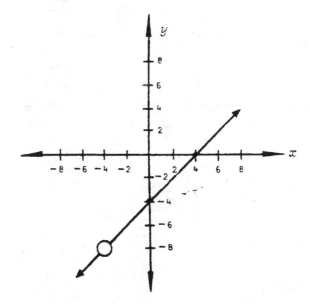

1.08 Let $y = F(x); \ y = 2x - 1$

Solve for x: $\ x = \frac{y + 1}{2}$

Interchange the variables:

$y = \frac{x + 1}{2}$

Then $F^{-1}(x) = \frac{x + 1}{2}$

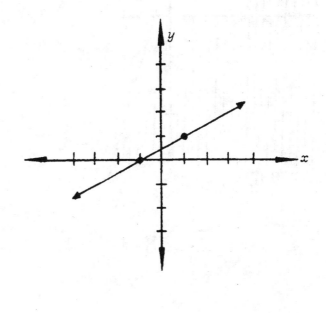

1.09

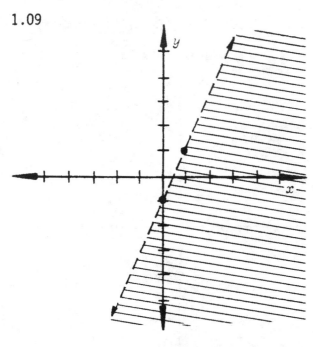

1.010 $x + y < -3$ $-3x > y - 2$
          $y < -x - 3$ $y < -3x + 2$

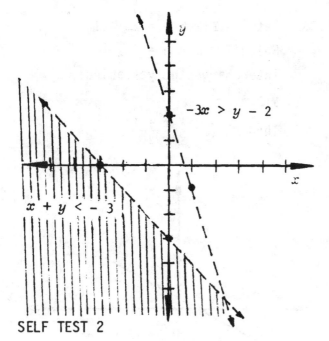

SELF TEST 2

2.01 $f(x) = 4x^2 + 5x - 21$
         $4x^2 + 5x - 21 = 0$
         $(4x - 7)(x + 3) = 0$
    $4x - 7 = 0$ $x + 3 = 0$
       $x = \dfrac{7}{4}$ $x = -3$

    $\{\dfrac{7}{4}, -3\}$

2.02 $f(x) = 9x^4 - 37x^2 + 4$
         $9x^4 - 37x^2 + 4 = 0$
         $(9x^2 - 1)(x^2 - 4) = 0$
  $9x^2 - 1 = 0$ $x^2 - 4 = 0$
     $x^2 = \dfrac{1}{9}$ $x^2 = 4$
     $x = \pm\dfrac{1}{3}$ $x = \pm 2$

  $\{\pm\dfrac{1}{3}, \pm 2\}$

2.03   a. $G(x) = x^2 + 4x$
       $G(x) = x^2 + 4x + 4 - 4$
       $G(x) = (x + 2)^2 - 4$
     The vertex is (h, k)
     $= (-2, -4)$.
    b. The axis of symmetry is
     $x = h$, $x = -2$.

2.04 $G(x) = 5x - 2$; let
    $y = 5x - 2$.
    Solve for x: $x = \dfrac{y + 2}{5}$.
    Interchange the variables:
    $y = \dfrac{x + 2}{5}$.   Therefore,

    $G^{-1}(x) = \dfrac{x + 2}{5}$.

2.05   Let $y = x^2 - 4x + 1$
         $y = (x^2 - 4x + 4) + 1 - 4$
         $y = (x - 2)^2 - 3$
   $(h, k) = (2, -3)$. Since the
   curve opens upward, -3 is
   the smallest value of y;
   therefore, the range is
   $y \geq -3$.
   $\{y: \ y \geq -3\}$

2.06 $2x^2 + 5x - 3 \leq 0$
       $(2x - 1)(x + 3) \leq 0$
  $(2x - 1 \leq 0 \cap x + 3 \geq 0) \cup$
  $(2x - 1 \geq 0 \cap x + 3 \leq 0)$
    $(x \leq \dfrac{1}{2} \cap x \geq -3) \cup$
    $(x \geq \dfrac{1}{2} \cap x \leq -3)$
    $(x \leq \dfrac{1}{2} \cap x \geq -3) \cup \phi$
    $x \leq \dfrac{1}{2} \cap x \geq -3$

    $\{-3 \leq x \leq \dfrac{1}{2}\}$

2.07 $y = -3x^2$

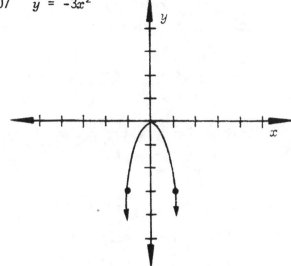

2.010 $y \leq x^2 - 3$
$y \geq 2x + 1$

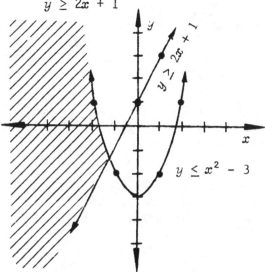

2.08 $y \geq 2x^2 \div 5x - 3$

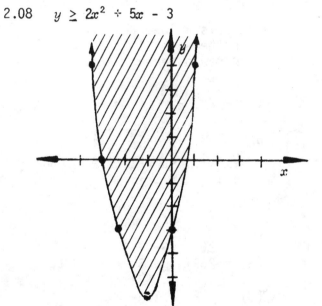

SELF TEST 3

3.01 $f(x) = 2x^5 - 11x^4 + 14x^3$
$- 2x^2 + 12x + 9$
Try all possible elements
of the subset of $\pm\frac{9}{2}$.

$$
\begin{array}{r|rrrrrr}
3 & 2 & -11 & +14 & -2 & +12 & +9 \\
& 0 & +6 & -15 & -3 & -15 & -9 \\
\hline
-\frac{1}{2} & 2 & -5 & -1 & -5 & -3 & +0 \\
& 0 & -1 & +3 & -1 & +3 & \\
\hline
3 & 2 & -6 & +2 & -6 & +0 & \\
& 0 & +6 & +0 & +6 & & \\
\hline
& 2 & +0 & +2 & +0 & &
\end{array}
$$

$2x^2 + 2 = 0$
$x^2 = -1$
$x = \pm i$

The rational roots are
$\{-\frac{1}{2}, 3\}$.

2.09 $36 \leq x^2 + y^2 \leq 49$

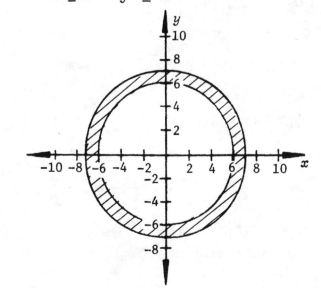

3.02 $P(y) = 2y^3 - 11y^2 + 12y + 9$

If $y - 3$ is a factor, then $y = 3$ must be a root.

$$
\begin{array}{r|rrrr}
3 & 2 & -11 & +12 & +9 \\
  & 0 & +6 & -15 & -9 \\
\hline
  & 2 & -5 & -3 & +0
\end{array}
$$

yes, $y - 3$ is a factor; remainder = 0

3.03 $2x^3 - 11x^2 + 12x + 9 = 0$
Any zeros, or roots, must be a member of the subset of factors of $\pm\frac{9}{2}$:

$\{\pm\frac{9}{2}, \pm9, \pm\frac{3}{2}, \pm3, \pm\frac{1}{2}, \pm1\}$

$$
\begin{array}{r|rrrr}
3 & 2 & -11 & +12 & +9 \\
  & 0 & +6 & -15 & -9 \\
\hline
  & 2 & -5 & -3 & +0
\end{array}
$$

$2x^2 - 5x - 3 = 0$
$(2x + 1)(x - 3) = 0$
$2x + 1 = 0 \qquad x - 3 = 0$
$\qquad x = -\frac{1}{2} \qquad x = 3$

The roots are $\{3, -\frac{1}{2}\}$.

3.04 Let $f(x) = v^4 + 16v^3 + 8v^2 - 725.$
$f(-5) = (-5)^4 + 16(-5)^3 + 8(-5)^2 - 725$
$\qquad = -1,900$

no, $v + 5$ is not a factor; remainder is not 0

3.05 $f(x) = \dfrac{4x^2 - 49}{2x + 7}$ for $x \neq -\frac{7}{2}$

$\dfrac{4x^2 - 49}{2x + 7} = 0$

$4x^2 - 49 = 0$

$\qquad x^2 = \dfrac{49}{4}, \quad x = \dfrac{7}{2}$

3.06 $2x^4 - 7x^3 + 4x^2 + 7x - 6 = 0$
Let $r = 1, 2, 3, \ldots$

$$
\begin{array}{r|rrrrr}
4 & 2 & -7 & +4 & +7 & -6 \\
  & 0 & +8 & +4 & +32 & +156 \\
\hline
  & 2 & +1 & +8 & +39 & +150
\end{array}
$$

$r = 4$ is an upper limit since the signs in the third row are all positive.

Let $r = -1, -2, -3, \ldots$

$$
\begin{array}{r|rrrrr}
-1 & 2 & -7 & +4 & +7 & -6 \\
   & 0 & -2 & +9 & -13 & +6 \\
\hline
   & 2 & -9 & +13 & -6 & +0
\end{array}
$$

$r = -1$ is a lower limit since the signs in the third row alternate.

3.07 $P(x) = 2x^4 - x^2 + 3x - 1$

$$
\begin{array}{r|rrrrr}
2 & 2 & +0 & -1 & +3 & -1 \\
  & 0 & +4 & +8 & +14 & +34 \\
\hline
  & 2 & +4 & +7 & +17 & +33
\end{array}
$$

$P(2) = 33$

3.08 $f(x) = 2x^2 - 3x + 1$
$f(3) = 2(9) - 3(3) + 1 = 10$
$f(2) = 2(4) - 3(2) + 1 = 3$
$f(3) - f(2) = 10 - 3 = 7$

3.09 $x^4 - 11x^2 + 18 = 0$
$(x^2 - 9)(x^2 - 2) = 0$
$x^2 - 9 = 0 \qquad x^2 - 2 = 0$
$\quad x^2 = 9 \qquad\quad x^2 = 2$
$\quad x = \pm3 \qquad\quad x = \pm\sqrt{2}$

$\{\pm3, \pm\sqrt{2}\}$

3.010 a. $P(x) = x^5 + 1$

$$
\begin{array}{r|rrrrrr}
-1 & 1 & +0 & +0 & +0 & +0 & +1 \\
   & 0 & -1 & +1 & -1 & +1 & -1 \\
\hline
   & 1 & -1 & +1 & -1 & +1 & +0
\end{array}
$$

$Q(x) = x^4 - x^3 + x^2 - x + 1$

b. remainder = 0

SELF TEST 4

4.01 [2.7] (greatest integer) = 2

4.02 all values of x

4.03 $H(x) = F[G(x)] - G(x)$,
$F(x) = 3x - 3$, $G(x) = x^2$
$H(x) = F(x^2) - x^2$
$= 3x^2 - 3 - x^2 = 2x^2 - 3$
$H(2) = 2(2)^2 - 3 = 5$

4.04 Use the table: 0.74.

4.05 $\dfrac{e^x - e^{-x}}{2} = \dfrac{e^{1.5} - e^{-1.5}}{2}$

$= \dfrac{4.48 - 0.22}{2} = 2.24 - 0.11$

$= 2.13$

4.06 Use the table: $(-2, 0.37)$,
$(-1, 0.61)$, $(0, 1)$, $(1, 1.64)$,
$(2, 2.72)$, $(4, 7.39)$.

4.07 a. Let $y = F(x)$.
$y = \log_8 64$
$8^y = 64$
$y = 2$
b. $y = F(x)$
$y = \log_8 1$
$8^y = 1$
$y = 0$
c. $y = F(x)$
$3 = \log_8 x$
$8^3 = x$
$x = 512$

4.08 Let $y = F(x)$.
$y = \log_3 x$
Solve for x: $x = 3^y$

Interchange variables: $y = 3^x$

$f^{-1}(x) = 3^x$

4.09 $F(x) = x^2 + 1$ and $G(x) = \log_{10} x$
$(G \circ F)(x) = G[F(x)] = G(x^2 + 1)$
$G(x^2 + 1) = \log_{10}(x^2 + 1)$

4.010 $f(x) = x^2 - \dfrac{2}{x}$ and
$g(x) = \sqrt{x - 1}$
$(f \circ g)(x) = f[g(x)]$
$= f(\sqrt{x - 1}) = (\sqrt{x - 1})^2$
$- \dfrac{2}{\sqrt{x - 1}} = x - 1 - \dfrac{2}{\sqrt{x - 1}}$

4.011 x is any real number such
that $x > 1$.

4.012

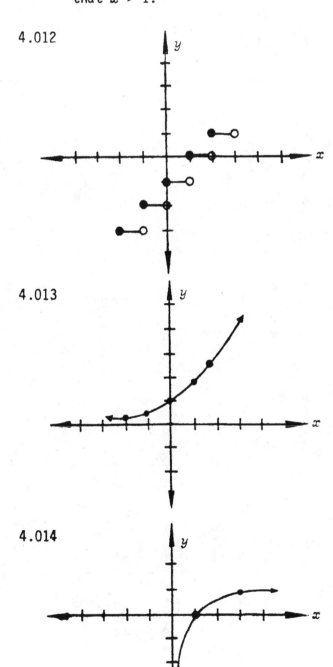

4.013

4.014

MATHEMATICS **1203**
SELF TEST
SOLUTION KEY

SELF TEST 1

1.01   true

1.02   true

1.03   false

1.04   false

1.05   true

1.06   false

1.07   false

1.08   true

1.09   false

1.010 true

1.011 a. IV
      b. I
      c. III
      d. IV
      e. II

SELF TEST 2

2.01   Sin is positive in Quadrants I and II.

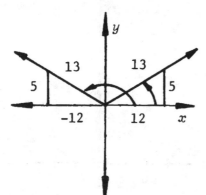

2.02   Quadrant I
$x = 12$
$y = 5$
$r = \sqrt{12^2 + 5^2}$
$ = \sqrt{144 + 25}$
$ = \sqrt{169}$
$ = 13$

a. $\dfrac{5}{13}$

b. $\dfrac{12}{13}$

c. $\dfrac{5}{12}$

d. $\dfrac{13}{5}$

e. $\dfrac{13}{12}$

f. $\dfrac{12}{5}$

Quadrant II
$x = -12$
$y = 5$
$r = \sqrt{(-12)^2 + 5^2}$
$ = \sqrt{144 + 25}$
$ = \sqrt{169}$
$ = 13$

g. $\dfrac{5}{13}$

h. $\dfrac{-12}{13} = -\dfrac{12}{13}$

i. $\dfrac{5}{-12} = -\dfrac{5}{12}$

j. $\dfrac{13}{5}$

k. $\dfrac{13}{-12} = -\dfrac{13}{12}$

l. $\dfrac{-12}{5} = -\dfrac{12}{5}$

2.03 $\cos\theta = \dfrac{-8}{17} = \dfrac{x}{r}$

$x = -8$
$r = 17$

$\sin\theta$ is negative (third quadrant)
$y = -\sqrt{17^2 - (-8)^2}$
$ = -\sqrt{289 - 64}$
$ = -\sqrt{255}$
$ = -15$

2.03 cont.

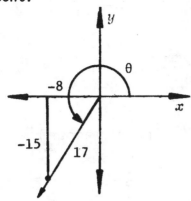

2.04 $x = -8$, $r = 17$, $y = -15$

   a. $\dfrac{-15}{17} = -\dfrac{15}{17}$

   b. $\dfrac{-8}{17} = -\dfrac{8}{17}$

   c. $\dfrac{-15}{-8} = \dfrac{15}{8}$

   d. $\dfrac{17}{-15} = -\dfrac{17}{15}$

   e. $\dfrac{17}{-8} = -\dfrac{17}{8}$

   f. $\dfrac{-8}{-15} = \dfrac{8}{15}$

2.05 a. I
     b. I
     c. IV
     d. II

2.06 a. Sin is negative in Quadrants III and IV.

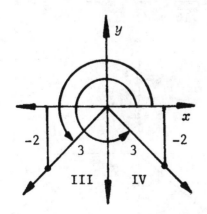

b. Sec is positive in Quadrants I and IV.

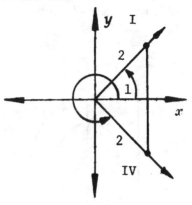

c. Tan is positive in Quadrants I and III.

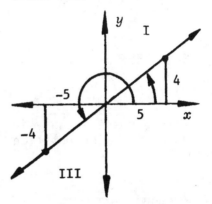

d. Csc is negative in Quadrants III and IV.

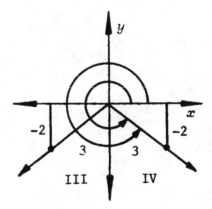

2.06 cont.

   e. Cos is negative in Quadrants II and III.

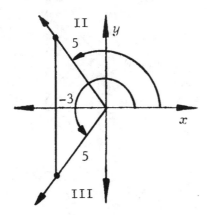

SELF TEST 3

3.01 false

3.02 false; possible only in absolute value notation

3.03 true

3.04 true

3.05 false; must be $270° < \theta < 360°$

3.06 I

3.07 IV

3.08 I

3.09 III, IV

3.010 I

3.011 I

3.012 I, IV

3.013 III

3.014 II

3.015 I, III

3.016
$$= \sqrt{10}$$
$$= 5$$
$$= \sqrt{5^2 - (\sqrt{10})^2}$$
$$= \sqrt{25 - 10}$$
$$= \sqrt{15} \text{ (first quadrant)}$$

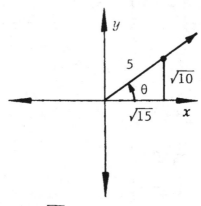

3.017 a. $\dfrac{\sqrt{10}}{5}$

      b. $\dfrac{\sqrt{15}}{5}$

      c. $\dfrac{\sqrt{10}}{\sqrt{15}} = \dfrac{\sqrt{2}}{\sqrt{3}} = \dfrac{\sqrt{2}\sqrt{3}}{\sqrt{3}\sqrt{3}} = \dfrac{\sqrt{6}}{3}$

      d. $\dfrac{5}{\sqrt{10}} = \dfrac{5\sqrt{10}}{10} = \dfrac{\sqrt{10}}{2}$

      e. $\dfrac{5}{\sqrt{15}} = \dfrac{5\sqrt{15}}{15} = \dfrac{\sqrt{15}}{3}$

      f. $\dfrac{\sqrt{15}}{\sqrt{10}} = \dfrac{\sqrt{3}}{\sqrt{2}} = \dfrac{\sqrt{3}\sqrt{2}}{\sqrt{2}\sqrt{2}} = \dfrac{\sqrt{6}}{2}$

3.018 a.

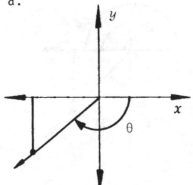

      b. third quadrant

      c. tan, cot

3.019 a.

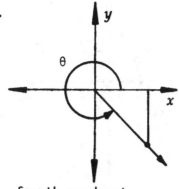

b. fourth quadrant
c. sin, csc, tan, cot

3.020 a.

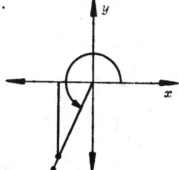

b. third quadrant

c. $\sin \theta = -\frac{12}{13}$ f. $\csc \theta = -\frac{13}{12}$

d. $\cos \theta = -\frac{5}{13}$ g. $\sec \theta = -\frac{13}{5}$

e. $\tan \theta = \frac{12}{5}$ h. $\cot \theta = \frac{5}{12}$

SELF TEST 4

4.01   true

4.02   true

4.03   true

4.04   false

4.05   true

4.06   true

4.07   true

4.08   true

4.09   true

4.010 false

4.011 II   + - - + - -

4.012 IV   - + - - + -

4.013 III   - - + - - +

4.014 IV

4.015 I

4.016 II

4.017 through 4.022

$y = 3$
$r = 5$
$x = -\sqrt{5^2 - 3^2}$
$\quad = -\sqrt{25 - 9}$
$\quad = -\sqrt{16}$
$\quad = -4$ (second quadrant)

4.017 $\frac{3}{5}$

4.018 $\frac{-4}{5} = -\frac{4}{5}$

4.019 $\frac{3}{-4} = -\frac{3}{4}$

4.020 $\frac{5}{3}$

4.021 $\frac{5}{-4} = -\frac{5}{4}$

4.022 $\frac{-4}{3} = -\frac{4}{3}$

4.023 through 4.028

$r = 13$
$x = -12$
$y = \sqrt{13^2 - (-12)^2}$
$\quad = \sqrt{169 - 144}$
$\quad = \sqrt{25}$
$\quad = \pm 5$ (second and third quadrants)

4.023

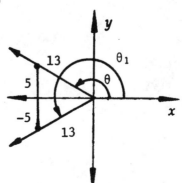

4.024 $\frac{5}{13}$; $\frac{-5}{13} = -\frac{5}{13}$

4.025 $\frac{-12}{13} = -\frac{12}{13}$; $\frac{-12}{13} = -\frac{12}{13}$

4.026 $\frac{5}{-12} = -\frac{5}{12}$; $\frac{-5}{-12} = \frac{5}{12}$

4.027 $\frac{13}{5}$; $\frac{13}{-5} = -\frac{13}{5}$

4.028 $\frac{-12}{5} = -\frac{12}{5}$; $\frac{-12}{-5} = \frac{12}{5}$

4.029   III

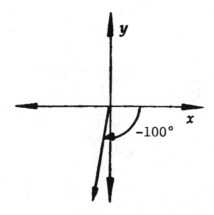

4.030   I

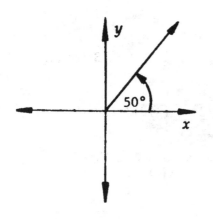

4.031   IV

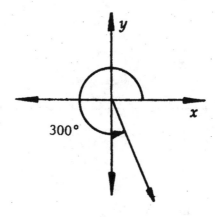

4.032   III

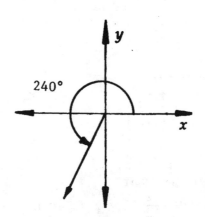

SELF TEST 5

5.01   .5616

5.02   1.570

5.03
$$10\left\{5\left\{\begin{array}{l}\cos 69°\ 40' = .3475 \\ \cos 69°\ 45' = \\ \cos 69°\ 50' = .3448\end{array}\right\}x\right\}.0027$$

$$\frac{5}{10} = \frac{x}{.0027}$$
$$10x = .0135$$
$$x = .00135 \doteq .0014$$
$$\cos 69°\ 45' = .3475 - .0014$$
$$= .3461$$

5.04

$$10\left\{8\left\{\begin{matrix}\sin \\ 13°\ 30' = .2334 \\ \sin \\ 13°\ 38' = \\ \sin \\ 13°\ 40' = .2363\end{matrix}\right\}x\right\}.0029$$

$$\frac{8}{10} = \frac{x}{.0029}$$

$10x = .0232$

$x = .00232 \doteq .0023$

$\sin 13°\ 38' = .2334 + .0023$

$\qquad\qquad = .2357$

5.05   85.95

5.06   29° 20'

5.07   75°

5.08

$$10\left\{x\left\{\begin{matrix}\tan \\ 72°\ 40' = 3.204 \\ \tan\ \theta\ \ = 3.220 \\ \tan \\ 72°\ 50' = 3.237\end{matrix}\right\}.016\right\}.033$$

$$\frac{x}{10} = \frac{.016}{.033}$$

$.033x = .16$

$x = 4.8 \doteq 5$

$\theta = 72°\ 40' + 5' = 72°\ 45'$

5.09

$$10\left\{x\left\{\begin{matrix}\sin \\ 22°\ 20' = .3800 \\ \sin\ \theta\ \ = .3815 \\ \sin \\ 22°\ 30' = .3827\end{matrix}\right\}.0015\right\}.0027$$

$$\frac{x}{10} = \frac{.0015}{.0027}$$

$.0027x = .015$

$x = 5.6 \doteq 6$

$\theta = 22°\ 20' + 6' = 22°\ 26'$

5.010   undefined

5.011   II

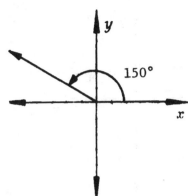

5.012   III

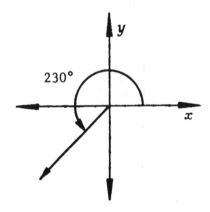

5.013   I

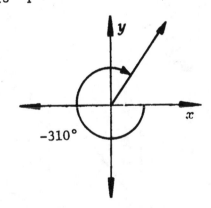

5.014   none--quadrantal angle

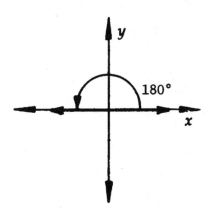

5.015   IV

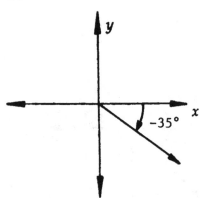

5.016   a.   60
        b.   .8660
        c.   1.732
        d.   1.155
        e.   2.000
        f.   .5774
        g.

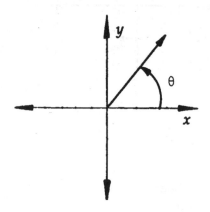

5.017   III

5.018   II

5.019   IV

5.020   I

5.021   IV

5.022   a. $r = \sqrt{(-5)^2 + (12)^2}$
             $= \sqrt{25 + 144}$
             $= \sqrt{169}$
             $= 13$

        b. $\frac{-5}{13} = -\frac{5}{13}$

        c. $\frac{12}{13}$

        d. $\frac{13}{-5} = -\frac{13}{5}$

        e. $\frac{13}{12}$

        f. $\frac{12}{-5} = -\frac{12}{5}$

        g.   IV
        h.

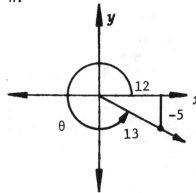

SELF TEST 6

6.01 $\sin 230° = \sin(180° + 50°)$
        $= -\sin 50° = -.7660$

6.02 $\cos 340° = \cos(360° - 20°)$
        $= \cos 20°$
        $= .9397$

6.03 $\tan 99\frac{1}{2}° = \tan(180° - 80\frac{1}{2}°)$
        $= -\tan 80° \; 30'$
        $= -5.976$

6.04   sin 400° = sin(400° - 360°)
                   = sin 40° = .6428

6.05   cot 75° = .2679

6.06   tan θ = $\frac{5}{12}$

   x = 12
   y = 5
   r = $\sqrt{5^2 + 12^2}$
      = $\sqrt{25 + 144}$
      = $\sqrt{169}$
      = 13 (third quadrant)

   a.

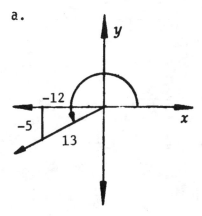

   b. $\frac{-5}{13} = -\frac{5}{13}$

   c. $\frac{-12}{13} = -\frac{12}{13}$

   d. $\frac{-5}{-12} = \frac{5}{12}$

   e. $\frac{13}{-5} = -\frac{13}{5}$

   f. $\frac{13}{-12} = -\frac{13}{12}$

   g. $\frac{-12}{-5} = \frac{12}{5}$

6.07 $10\left\{ 6\left\{ \begin{array}{l} \cos \\ 38°\ 50' = .7790 \\ \cos \\ 38°\ 56' = \\ \cos \\ 39°\ 00' = .7771 \end{array} \right\}x \right\}.0019$

   $\frac{6}{10} = \frac{x}{.0019}$
   $10x = .0114$
   $x = .0014 \doteq .0011$
   cos 38° 56' = .7790 - .0011 =
                  = .7779

6.08 $10\left\{ x\left\{ \begin{array}{l} \tan \\ 82°\ 10' = 7.269 \\ \tan\ \theta\ = 7.280 \\ \tan \\ 82°\ 20' = 7.429 \end{array} \right\}.011 \right\}.160$

   $\frac{x}{10} = \frac{.011}{.160}$
   $.160x = .11$
   $x = .69 \doteq 1$
   θ = 82° 10' + 1' = 82° 11'

6.09   false

6.010   true

6.011   false

6.012   true

6.013   false

6.014   sin θ = $\frac{12}{13}$

   y = 12
   r = 13
   x = $-\sqrt{13^2 - 12^2}$
      = $-\sqrt{169 - 144}$
      = $-\sqrt{25}$
      = -5 (second quadrant)

   a. $\frac{-5}{13} = -\frac{5}{13}$

   b. $\frac{12}{-5} = -\frac{12}{5}$

   c. $\frac{13}{12}$

   d. $\frac{13}{-5} = -\frac{13}{5}$

   e. $\frac{-5}{12} = -\frac{5}{12}$

SELF TEST 7

7.01 $[(\sin 90°)(\cos 180°)]^2 =$
              $[(1)(-1)]^2 =$
                      1

7.02 $[\tan 0°]^3 = (0)^3 = 0$

7.03 $(\sin 90°)^4 \cdot (\cos 0°)^5 +$
              $\tan 0° \cdot \sin 180° =$
                  $1^4 \cdot 1^5 + 0 \cdot 0 =$
                          1

7.04 sec 180° + sin 270° −
      tan 180° + cot 270° =
      −1 + (−1) − 0 + 0 =
                    = −2

7.05   [sin 0° + cos 0° +
      (sin 180°)^2 + (cos 270°)^3]^4 =
              [0 + 2 + 0^2 + 0^3]^4 =
                              1^4 =
                                1

7.06   cos(−25°) =
              cos 335° =
        cos(360° − 25°) =
              cos 25°

7.07   sin(−136°) =
              sin 224° =
        sin(180° + 44°) =
              −sin 44°

7.08   tan(−212$\frac{1}{2}$°) =
              tan 147$\frac{1}{2}$° =
        tan(180° − 32$\frac{1}{2}$°) =
              −tan 32$\frac{1}{2}$°

7.09   sec(−45$\frac{3}{4}$°) =
              sec 314$\frac{1}{4}$° =
        sec(360° − 45$\frac{3}{4}$°) =
              sec 45$\frac{3}{4}$°

7.010 cot(−315°) = cot 45°

7.011 I

7.012 560° − 360° = 200°; III

7.013 −490° + 360° = −130°; III

7.014 IV

7.015 II

7.016 sin 125° = sin(180° − 55°)
              = sin 55°
              = .8192

7.017 cos 125° = cos(180° − 55°)
              = −cos 55°
              = −.5736

7.018 tan 125° = tan(180° − 55°)
              = −tan 55°
              = −1.428

7.019 through 7.025
        $\cos \theta = -\frac{12}{13}$
        $x = -12$
        $r = 13$
        $y = \sqrt{13^2 - (-12)^2}$
          $= \sqrt{169 - 144}$
          $= \sqrt{25}$
          $= 5$

7.019 $\sin \theta = \frac{5}{13}$

7.020 $\cos \theta = \frac{-12}{13} = -\frac{12}{13}$

7.021 $\tan \theta = \frac{5}{-12} = -\frac{5}{12}$

7.022 $\csc \theta = \frac{13}{5}$

7.023 $\sec \theta = \frac{13}{-12} = -\frac{13}{12}$

7.024 $\cot \theta = \frac{-12}{5} = -\frac{12}{5}$

7.025 $r = 13$

SELF TEST 8

8.01

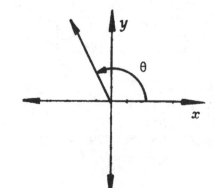

8.02 a. $\sin 120° = \sin 60° = \dfrac{\sqrt{3}}{2}$

b. $\cos 120° = -\cos 60° = -\dfrac{1}{2}$

c. $\tan 120° = -\tan 60° = -\sqrt{3}$

8.03

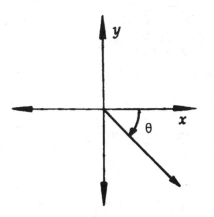

8.04 a. $\csc(-45°) = -\csc 45° = -\sqrt{2}$
b. $\sec(-45°) = \sec 45° = \sqrt{2}$
c. $\cot(-45°) = -\cot 45° = -1$

8.05 $\cos \theta = \dfrac{-11}{61}$

$x = -11$
$r = 61$
$y = \sqrt{61^2 - (-11)^2}$
$\quad = -\sqrt{3,721 - 121}$
$\quad = -\sqrt{3,600}$
$\quad = -60$

a. $\sin \theta = \dfrac{-60}{61} = -\dfrac{60}{61}$

b. $\tan \theta = \dfrac{-60}{-11} = \dfrac{60}{11}$

c. $\csc \theta = \dfrac{61}{-60} = -\dfrac{61}{60}$

d. $\sec \theta = \dfrac{61}{-11} = -\dfrac{61}{11}$

e. $\cot \theta = \dfrac{-11}{-60} = \dfrac{11}{60}$

8.06 $(\sin 30°)^2 \cdot \cos 180° +$
$\quad \tan 0° - \cot(-45°) =$
$(\sin 30°)^2 \cdot \cos 180° +$
$\quad \tan 0° + \cos 45° =$
$(\dfrac{1}{2})^2 (-1) + 0 + 1 =$
$\dfrac{1}{4}(-1) + 1 =$
$-\dfrac{1}{4} + 1 =$
$\dfrac{3}{4}$

8.07 $\cos 150° \cdot \tan 210° +$
$\quad \cos 135° \cdot \tan 240° =$
$-\cos 30° \cdot \tan 30° -$
$\quad \cos 45° \cdot \tan 60° =$
$-\dfrac{\sqrt{3}}{2} \cdot \dfrac{\sqrt{3}}{3} - \dfrac{\sqrt{2}}{2} \cdot \sqrt{3} =$
$-\dfrac{3}{6} - \dfrac{\sqrt{6}}{2} =$
$-\dfrac{1}{2} - \dfrac{\sqrt{6}}{2} =$
$\dfrac{-\sqrt{6} - 1}{2}$

8.08 $(\cos 120°)^2 (\sin 300°)^2 +$
$\quad (\sin 300°)^2 (\cos 240°)^2 =$
$(-\cos 60°)^2 (-\sin 60°)^2 +$
$\quad (-\sin 60°)^2 (-\cos 60°)^2 =$
$(-\dfrac{1}{2})^2 (-\dfrac{\sqrt{3}}{2})^2 + (-\dfrac{\sqrt{3}}{2})^2 (-\dfrac{1}{2})^2 =$
$\dfrac{1}{4}(\dfrac{3}{4}) + \dfrac{3}{4}(\dfrac{1}{4}) =$
$\dfrac{3}{16} + \dfrac{3}{16} =$
$\dfrac{3}{8}$

8.09 $(\tan 135°)^2 (\sin 225°)^2 -$
$\quad (\cot 225°)^2 (\cos 315°)^2 =$
$(-\tan 45°)^2 (-\sin 45°)^2 -$
$\quad (\cot 45°)^2 (\cos 45°)^2 =$
$(-1)^2 (-\dfrac{\sqrt{2}}{2})^2 - (1)^2 (\dfrac{\sqrt{2}}{2})^2 =$
$1(\dfrac{1}{2}) - 1(\dfrac{1}{2}) =$
0

8.010 $\cos 870° - \sin 780° =$
$\cos 150° - \sin 60° =$
$-\cos 30° - \sin 60° =$
$-\dfrac{\sqrt{3}}{2} - \dfrac{\sqrt{3}}{2} =$
$-\dfrac{2\sqrt{3}}{2} =$
$-\sqrt{3}$

8.011 $\sin(-30°) \cdot \cos 45° -$
$\quad \tan(-135°) \cdot \cot(225°) =$
$-\sin 30° \cdot \cos 45° -$
$\quad \tan 45° \cdot \cot 45° =$
$-\dfrac{1}{2} \cdot \dfrac{\sqrt{2}}{2} - 1 \cdot 1 =$
$-\dfrac{\sqrt{2}}{4} - 1$

8.012 $\sec(-45°)\cdot\csc(-135°)$ –
$\tan(-315°)\cdot\cos(-240°) =$
$\sec 45°(-\csc 135°) -$
$(-\tan 315°)\cdot\cos 240° =$
$\sec 45°(-\csc 45°) -$
$\tan 45°(-\cos 60°) =$

$$(\sqrt{2})(-\sqrt{2}) - (1)(-\tfrac{1}{2}) =$$

$$-2 + \tfrac{1}{2} =$$

$$-\tfrac{3}{2}$$

8.013 $[\sec(-60°)]^2[\sin(-135°)]^2 -$
$(\cos 30°)^2[\tan(-210°)]^2 =$
$(\sec 60°)^2(-\sin 135°)^2 -$
$(\cos 30°)^2(-\tan 210°)^2 =$
$(\sec 60°)^2(-\sin 45°)^2 -$
$(\cos 30°)^2(-\tan 30°)^2 =$

$$(2)^2(-\tfrac{\sqrt{2}}{2})^2 - (\tfrac{\sqrt{3}}{2})^2(-\tfrac{\sqrt{3}}{3})^2 =$$

$$4(\tfrac{1}{2}) - \tfrac{3}{4}(\tfrac{1}{3}) =$$

$$2 - \tfrac{1}{4} =$$

$$1\tfrac{3}{4}$$

8.014 $\sin 240°\cdot\sec(-45°)$ –
$\tan(-30°)\cdot\csc(-315°) =$
$-\sin 60°\cdot\sec 45°$ –
$(-\tan 30°)(-\csc 315°) =$
$-\sin 60°\cdot\sec 45°$ –
$\tan 30°\cdot\csc 45° =$

$$-\tfrac{\sqrt{3}}{2}\cdot\sqrt{2} + \tfrac{\sqrt{3}}{3}\cdot\sqrt{2} =$$

$$-\tfrac{\sqrt{6}}{2} + \tfrac{\sqrt{6}}{3} =$$

$$-\tfrac{\sqrt{6}}{6}$$

8.015
$$10\left\{2\left\{\begin{matrix}\sin\\46°\ 30' = .7254\\ \sin\\ 46°\ 32' = \\ \sin \\ 46°\ 40' = .7274\end{matrix}\right\}x\right\}.0020$$

$$\frac{2}{10} = \frac{x}{.0020}$$
$$10x = .0040$$
$$x = .00040 = .0004$$

$$\sin 46°\ 32' = .7254 + .0004$$
$$= .7258$$

8.016
$$10\left\{x\left\{\begin{matrix}\cos\\67°\ 00' = .3907\\ \cos\ \theta\ = .3890\\ \cos\\ 67°\ 10' = .3881\end{matrix}\right\}.0017\right\}.0026$$

$$\frac{x}{10} = \frac{.0017}{.0026}$$
$$.0026x = .017$$
$$x = 6.5 \doteq 7'$$

$$\theta = 67°\ 0' + 7' = 67°\ 7'$$

SELF TEST 9

9.01 a. $\dfrac{2\pi}{3} = \dfrac{2\pi}{3}\cdot\dfrac{180°}{\pi} = 2\cdot60° = 120°$
  b. II

9.02 a. $300° = 300°\cdot\dfrac{\pi}{180°} = \dfrac{5\pi}{3}$
  b. IV

9.03 a. $\dfrac{3\pi}{2} = \dfrac{3\pi}{2}\cdot\dfrac{180°}{\pi} = 3\cdot90° = 270°$
  b. none (quadrantal angle)

9.04 a. $\dfrac{11\pi}{12} = \dfrac{11\pi}{12}\cdot\dfrac{180°}{\pi} = 11\cdot15° = 165°$
  b. II

9.05 a. $675° = 675° - 360° = 315°$
  $315° = 315°\cdot\dfrac{\pi}{180°}\quad \dfrac{7\pi}{4}$
  $675° = \dfrac{8\pi}{4} + \dfrac{7\pi}{4} = \dfrac{15\pi}{4}$
  b. IV

9.06 I, III

9.07 IV

9.08 I

9.09 $\cos\theta = -\dfrac{8}{17}$
  $x = -8$
  $r = 17$
  $y = -\sqrt{17^2 - (-8)^2}$
  $\ = -\sqrt{289 - 64}$
  $\ = -\sqrt{255}$
  $\ = -15$

9.09 cont.

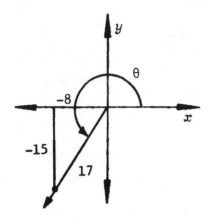

9.010

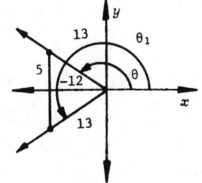

9.011 a.

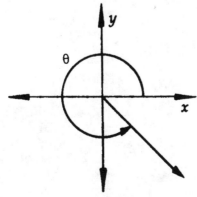

9.011 cont.

b. IV
c. sin, csc, tan, cot

9.012 sin 400° = sin(400° - 430°)
= sin 40°

9.013 cos(-170°) = cos 190°
= cos(180° + 10°)
= -cos 10°

9.014 33°

9.015 sin θ = $\frac{12}{13}$
y = 12
r = 13
x = $-\sqrt{13^2 - 12^2}$
= $-\sqrt{169 - 144}$
= $-\sqrt{25}$
= -5
cos θ = $\frac{x}{r}$ = $\frac{-5}{13}$ = $-\frac{5}{13}$

9.016 .2004

9.017 $10\left\{5\left\{\begin{matrix}\cos 69°\ 40' = 0.3475 \\ \cos 69°\ 45' = \\ \cos 69°\ 50' = 0.3448\end{matrix}\right\}x\right\}.0027$

$\frac{5}{10}$ = $\frac{x}{.0027}$
10x = .0135
x = .00135 = .0014

cos 69° 45' = .3475 - .0014 =
= .3461

9.018 sec 180° + sin 270° -
tan 180° + cot 270° =
-1 + (-1) - 0 + 0 =
-2

297

9.019 $(\sin 30°)^2 \cdot \cos 180° +$
$\tan 0° - \cot(-45°) =$
$(\sin 30°)^2 \cdot \cot 180° +$
$\tan 0° + \cot 45° =$
$(\frac{1}{2})^2 \cdot (-1) + 0 + 1 =$

$-\frac{1}{4} + 1 =$

$\frac{3}{4}$

9.020 $\tan \theta = \frac{-15}{-8} = \frac{15}{8}$

MATHEMATICS 1204
SELF TEST
SOLUTION KEY

SELF TEST 1

1.01   IV

1.02   III

1.03   III

1.04   IV

1.05   I

1.06   IV

1.07

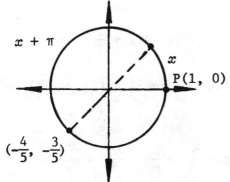

1.08

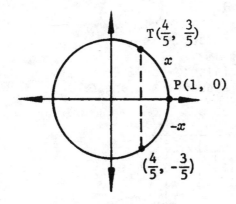

1.09

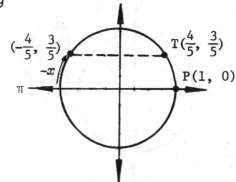

1.010

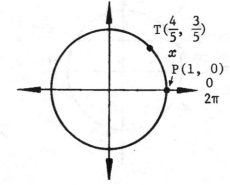

SELF TEST 2

2.01 $\left(\frac{\sqrt{2}}{2}\right)^2 = \frac{2}{4} = \frac{1}{2}$

2.02 $\frac{\sqrt{3}}{2} + \frac{1}{2} = \frac{\sqrt{3}+1}{2}$

2.03 $0 - 0 + \sqrt{3} = \sqrt{3}$

2.04 $\left(\frac{\sqrt{2}}{2}\right)^2 + \left(\frac{\sqrt{2}}{2}\right)^2 = \frac{1}{2} + \frac{1}{2} = 1$

2.05 $1 + \left(\frac{\sqrt{3}}{3}\right)^2 = 1 + \frac{3}{9} = 1\frac{1}{3}$

2.06

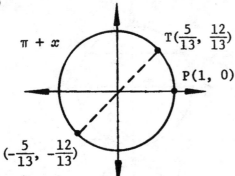

2.07

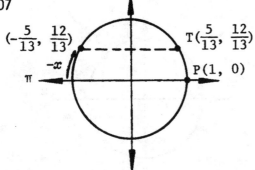

2.08

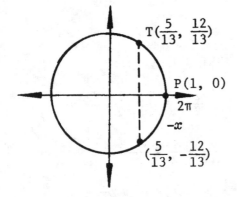

2.09 $1 + (\frac{\sqrt{3}}{3})^2 = (\frac{2}{\sqrt{3}})^2$

$\frac{3}{9} + 1 = \frac{4}{3}$

$1\frac{1}{3} = \frac{4}{3}$ = true

2.010 $(\frac{\sqrt{3}}{2})^2 = 1 - (\frac{1}{2})^2$

$\frac{3}{4} = 1 - \frac{1}{4}$

$\frac{3}{4} = \frac{3}{4}$; true

SELF TEST 3

3.01 $\frac{\sqrt{3}}{2} + \frac{1}{2} = \frac{\sqrt{3} + 1}{2}$

3.02 $1 + (\frac{\sqrt{3}}{3})^2 = 1 + \frac{3}{9} = 1\frac{1}{3}$

3.03 $\sin^2\frac{\pi}{6} + \cos^2\frac{\pi}{3} = (\frac{1}{2})^2 + (\frac{1}{2})^2 =$

$= \frac{1}{4} + \frac{1}{4} = \frac{1}{2}$

3.04 $\pi - \frac{5\pi}{6} = \frac{6}{6}\pi - \frac{5\pi}{6} = \frac{\pi}{6}$

3.05 -1

3.06 1

3.07 false; $\frac{\pi}{8} < \frac{\pi}{2}$

3.08 false; $-5\pi + 4\pi = -\pi$
= quadrantal angle

3.09

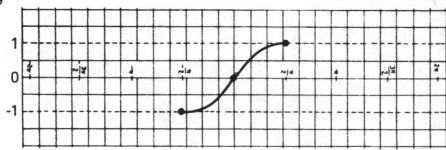

3.010

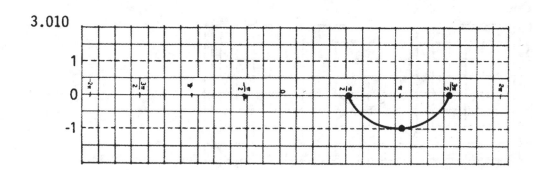

SELF TEST 4

4.01

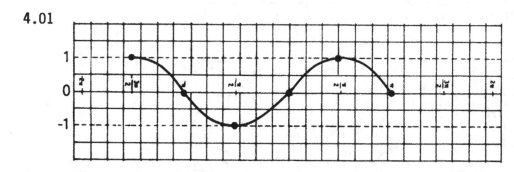

4.02

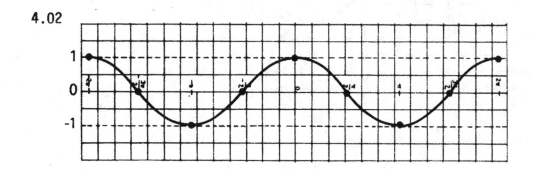

4.03

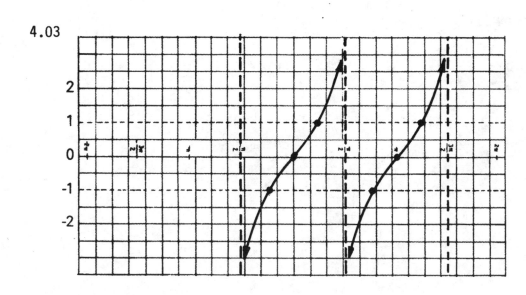

4.04

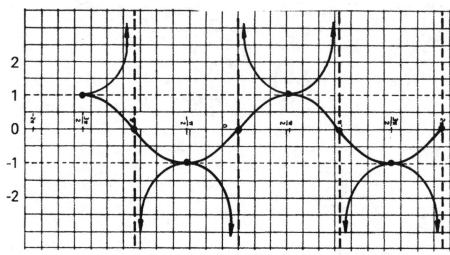

4.05

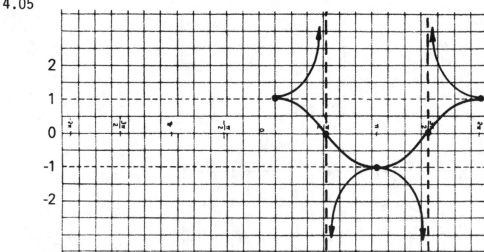

4.06 through 4.011

$$x = \frac{3}{5}, \quad y = \frac{4}{5}, \quad r = \frac{5}{5} = 1$$

4.06 $\sin x = \dfrac{y}{r} = \dfrac{\frac{4}{5}}{1} = \dfrac{4}{5}$

4.07 $\cos x = \dfrac{x}{r} = \dfrac{\frac{3}{5}}{1} = \dfrac{3}{5}$

4.08 $\tan x = \dfrac{y}{r} = \dfrac{\frac{4}{5}}{\frac{3}{5}} = \dfrac{4}{3}$

4.09 $\csc x = \dfrac{r}{y} = \dfrac{1}{\frac{4}{5}} = \dfrac{5}{4}$

4.010 $\sec x = \dfrac{r}{x} = \dfrac{1}{\frac{3}{5}} = \dfrac{5}{3}$

4.011 $\cot x = \dfrac{x}{y} = \dfrac{\frac{3}{5}}{\frac{4}{5}} = \dfrac{3}{4}$

4.012 $\sin 240° \cdot \sec(-45°) - \tan(\frac{-\pi}{6})\csc(-315°) =$

$$-\frac{\sqrt{3}}{2} \cdot \sqrt{2} - (-\frac{\sqrt{3}}{3})(\sqrt{2}) =$$

$$-\frac{\sqrt{6}}{2} + \frac{\sqrt{6}}{3} =$$

$$\frac{-3\sqrt{2} + 2\sqrt{6}}{6} =$$

$$-\frac{\sqrt{6}}{6}$$

4.013 $\sin^2(\frac{2\pi}{3}) + \cos^2(\frac{2\pi}{3}) + \tan^2(\frac{\pi}{4}) =$

$$(\frac{\sqrt{3}}{2})^2 + (-\frac{1}{2})^2 + 1^2 =$$

$$\frac{3}{4} + \frac{1}{4} + 1 =$$

$$2$$

4.014 $\sec^2 \frac{\pi}{3} \cdot \sin^2 \frac{3\pi}{4} -$

$$\cos^2(-\frac{\pi}{6}) \cdot \tan^2 \frac{7\pi}{6} =$$

$$2^2 \cdot (\frac{\sqrt{2}}{2})^2 - (\frac{\sqrt{3}}{2})^2 (\frac{\sqrt{3}}{3})^2 =$$

$$4 \cdot \frac{1}{2} - \frac{3}{4} \cdot \frac{3}{9} =$$

$$2 - \frac{1}{4} =$$

$$1\frac{3}{4}$$

SELF TEST 5

5.01 $v = r\omega$ or $v = \frac{s}{t}$

5.02 $\omega = \frac{v}{r}$ or $\omega = \frac{\theta}{t}$

5.03   a. $14(\frac{\pi}{3}) = \frac{43.982}{3} = 14.66 \doteq 15$

   b. $s = 276(\frac{2\pi}{3}) = \frac{1,734.159}{3}$
   $$\doteq 578$$

5.04 $r = \frac{s}{\theta} = \frac{32}{\pi} \doteq 10$ inches

5.05   a. $\theta = \frac{s}{r} = \frac{3}{8}$ radians
   $$= 0.375 \text{ radians}$$

   b. $\theta = \frac{s}{r} = \frac{4}{8}$ radians
   $$= 0.5 \text{ radians}$$

5.06   3 hours = 3 complete revolutions
   $\therefore 3(2\pi) = 6\pi$ radians

5.07 $v = \omega \cdot r = 8 \cdot 10\pi$
   $$= 80\pi \text{ feet per second}$$

5.08 $\omega = \frac{v}{r} = \frac{200}{4} = 50$ radians per second

SELF TEST 6

6.01

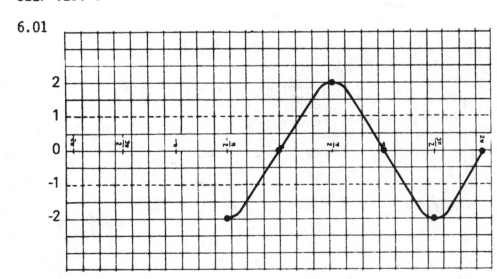

6.02

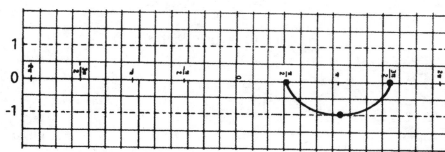

6.03 $\dfrac{\sqrt{3}}{2} + \dfrac{1}{2} = \dfrac{\sqrt{3}+1}{2}$

6.04 $\sin 240° \cdot \sec(-45°) -$
$\tan(\dfrac{-\pi}{6})\csc(-315°) =$

$-\dfrac{\sqrt{3}}{2} \cdot \sqrt{2} - (-\dfrac{\sqrt{3}}{3})(\sqrt{2}) =$

$-\dfrac{\sqrt{6}}{2} + \dfrac{\sqrt{6}}{3} =$

$\dfrac{-3\sqrt{2} + 2\sqrt{6}}{6} =$

$-\dfrac{\sqrt{6}}{6}$

6.05 $A = |-4| = 4$

6.06 No minimum; infinitely small function value for x close to $\dfrac{\pi}{2}$ in second quadrant.

6.07 $-2 \le F(x) \le 2$

6.08 6

6.09 III

6.010 a. $\theta = \dfrac{s}{r} = \dfrac{3}{8}$ radians
$= 0.375$ radians

b. $\theta = \dfrac{s}{r} = \dfrac{4}{8}$ radians
$= 0.5$ radians

SELF TEST 7

7.01

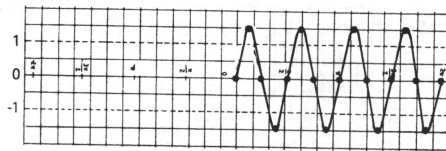

7.02

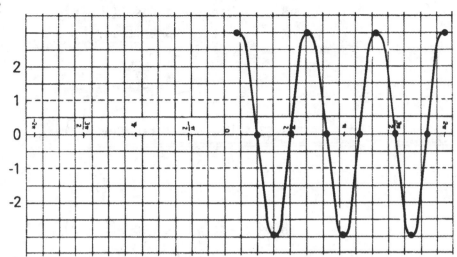

7.03

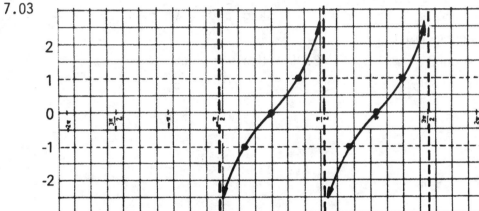

7.04 $(\frac{\sqrt{2}}{2})^2 + (\frac{\sqrt{2}}{2})^2 = \frac{1}{2} + \frac{1}{2} = 1$

7.05 $\sin^2(\frac{2\pi}{3}) + \cos^2(\frac{2\pi}{3}) + \tan^2(\frac{\pi}{4}) =$
$(\frac{\sqrt{3}}{2})^2 + (-\frac{1}{2})^2 + 1^2 =$
$\frac{3}{4} + \frac{1}{4} + 1 =$
2

7.06 $(\frac{\sqrt{3}}{2})^2 = 1 - (\frac{1}{2})^2$
$\frac{3}{4} = 1 - \frac{1}{4}$
$\frac{3}{4} = \frac{3}{4}$; **true**

7.07 **false**; $-5\pi + 4\pi = -\pi$
= quadrantal angle

7.08 $\frac{1}{2}$

7.09 $-\infty < F(x) < \infty$; infinitely
large and small function
values.

7.010 $P = \frac{2\pi}{B}$, $B = 1$; $P = \frac{2\pi}{1} = 2\pi$

7.011 $P = \frac{2\pi}{B}$, $B = 5$; $P = \frac{2\pi}{5}$

7.012 $B = 3$

7.013 -4; amplitude = 4

7.014 3; amplitude = 3

7.015　　$A = 1.5$

　　　　$P = \dfrac{\pi}{2}$

　　　　$\dfrac{2\pi}{B} = \dfrac{\pi}{2}$

　　　　$B = 4$

　　　　$F(x) = 1.5 \sin 4x$

7.016　IV

7.017　III

7.018　1

7.019　$v = \omega \cdot r = 8 \cdot 10\pi$
　　　　　　　　$= 80\pi$ feet per second

7.020　$\omega = \dfrac{v}{r} = \dfrac{12}{14} = \dfrac{6}{7} =$ approximately
　　　　0.86 radians per second

SELF TEST 8

8.01　　Use $y = A \sin B(x - p)$.
　　　　$A = 3$, $B = \dfrac{2\pi}{\pi} = 2$, $p = \pi$
　　　　$y = 3 \sin 2(x - \pi)$

8.02　　Use $y = A \cos B(x - p)$.
　　　　$A = -2$, $B = \dfrac{2\pi}{\frac{\pi}{4}} = 8$, $p = -\dfrac{\pi}{2}$

　　　　$y = -2 \cos 8\left(x + \dfrac{\pi}{2}\right)$

8.03　　Use $y = A \tan B(x - p)$.
　　　　$A = 2$, $B = 3$, $p = \dfrac{\pi}{2}$

　　　　$y = 2 \tan 3\left(x - \dfrac{\pi}{2}\right)$

8.04　　Use $y = A \sec B(x - p)$.
　　　　$A = \dfrac{1}{2}$, $B = \dfrac{1}{3}$, $p = 5$

　　　　$y = \dfrac{1}{2} \sec\dfrac{1}{3}(x - 5)$

8.05　　Use $y = A \csc B(x - p)$.
　　　　$A = 7$, $B = 5$, $p = \dfrac{\pi}{4}$

　　　　$y = 7 \csc 5\left(x - \dfrac{\pi}{4}\right)$

8.06　　$A = 2$, $P = \dfrac{2\pi}{2} = \pi$, $p = -\dfrac{\pi}{2}$　　　Since $F(x) = 2 \sin 2\left(x + \dfrac{\pi}{2}\right)$

8.07 $A = \frac{1}{2}$, $P = 2\pi$, $p = \frac{\pi}{4}$

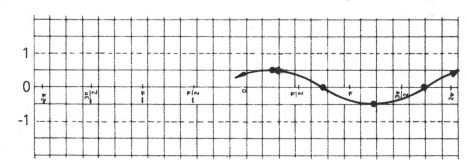

8.08

8.09 $F(x) = 3 \sin(2x - 2)$
           $= 3 \sin 2(x - 1)$
       $p = 1$ unit to the right

8.010 $G(x) = 5 \sin(3x - 3\pi)$
           $= 5 \sin 3(x - \pi)$
       $B = 3$, $P = \frac{2\pi}{3}$

8.011 $3y = \sin 2(x + 1)$
       $y = \frac{1}{3} \sin 2(x + 1)$
       $A = \frac{1}{3}$

8.012 II

8.013 IV

8.014 $120° \cdot \frac{\pi}{180°} = \frac{2\pi}{3}$

8.015 $\left(\frac{\sqrt{3}}{2}\right)^2 = \frac{3}{4}$

8.016 $\sec^2 \frac{\pi}{3} \cdot \sin^2 \frac{3\pi}{4} -$
            $\cos^2\left(-\frac{\pi}{6}\right) \cdot \tan^2 \frac{7\pi}{6} =$
       $2^2 \cdot \left(\frac{\sqrt{2}}{2}\right)^2 - \left(\frac{\sqrt{3}}{2}\right)^2 \left(\frac{\sqrt{3}}{3}\right)^2 =$
              $4 \cdot \frac{1}{2} - \frac{3}{4} \cdot \frac{3}{9} =$
                   $2 - \frac{1}{4} =$
                      $1\frac{3}{4}$

8.017 true

8.018 true

8.019 $60° = \frac{\pi}{3}$ radians per hour

$\frac{\pi}{3} \cdot 24 = 8\pi$ radians per 24-
        hour day

8.020 $v = r\omega = 224$ inches per second

MATHEMATICS 1205
SELF TEST
SOLUTION KEY

SELF TEST 1

1.01 $\sin x \cos x \sec x$
        $= \sin x \cdot 1$
        $= \sin x$

1.02 $3 \tan x \cos x \cot x$
        $= 3 \tan x \cot x \cos x$
        $= 3 \cdot 1 \cdot \cos x$
        $= 3 \cos x$

1.03 $4 \sin x \cos x \csc x$
        $= 4 \sin x \csc x \cos x$
        $= 4 \cdot 1 \cdot \cos x$
        $= 4 \cos x$

1.04 $\dfrac{\cot \theta}{\tan \theta} = \dfrac{\cot \theta}{\frac{1}{\cot \theta}} = \cot^2 \theta$

1.05 $\sin \dfrac{\pi}{3} \cdot \csc \dfrac{\pi}{3}$
        $= \dfrac{\sqrt{3}}{2} \cdot \dfrac{2\sqrt{3}}{3}$
        $= \dfrac{2(3)}{6}$
        $= \dfrac{6}{6}$
        $= 1$

SELF TEST 2

2.01

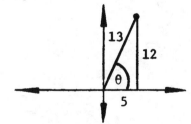

$r = \sqrt{5^2 + 12^2}$
$\ = \sqrt{25 + 144}$
$\ = \sqrt{169}$
$\ = 13$

2.01 cont.

$\sin \theta = \dfrac{y}{r} = \dfrac{12}{13}; \quad \cos \theta = \dfrac{x}{r} = \dfrac{5}{13}$

$\sin^2 \theta + \cos^2 \theta = \left(\dfrac{12}{13}\right)^2 + \left(\dfrac{5}{13}\right)^2$

$\qquad\qquad\qquad = \dfrac{144}{169} + \dfrac{25}{169}$

$\qquad\qquad\qquad = \dfrac{169}{169}$

$\qquad\qquad\qquad = 1$

2.02 $\sin^2 \theta + \cos^2 \theta = 1$
        $\cos^2 \theta = 1 - \sin^2 \theta$
        $\sqrt{\cos^2 \theta} = \pm\sqrt{1 - \sin^2 \theta}$
        $\cos \theta = \pm\sqrt{1 - \sin^2 \theta}$

2.03 $\cot^2 \theta + 1 - \csc^2 \theta = 0$
        $\csc^2 \theta = \cot^2 \theta + 1$
        $\sqrt{\csc^2 \theta} = \pm\sqrt{\cot^2 \theta + 1}$
        $\csc \theta = \pm\sqrt{\cot^2 \theta + 1}$

2.04 $\sin^2 \theta + \sin \theta \csc \theta + \cos^2 \theta$
        $= \sin^2 \theta + \cos^2 \theta + \sin \theta \csc \theta$
        $= 1 + 1$
        $= 2$

2.05 $\dfrac{\sec \theta}{\cos \theta} = \dfrac{\sec \theta}{\frac{1}{\sec \theta}} = \sec^2 \theta$

2.06 $\sec^2 \theta = 1 + \tan^2 \theta$; therefore,
        $\sec^2 \theta - \tan^2 \theta + 1$
        $= 1 + \tan^2 \theta - \tan^2 \theta + 1$
        $= 1 + 0 + 1$
        $= 2$

2.07 $\csc^2 \theta = \cot^2 \theta + 1$; therefore,
        $\csc^2 \theta + \cot^2 \theta - 1$
        $= \cot^2 \theta + 1 + \cot^2 \theta - 1$
        $= 2 \cot^2 \theta$

2.08 $\sin^2 x + \sin x + \cos^2 x - 1$
        $= \sin^2 x + \cos^2 x + \sin x - 1$
        $= 1 + \sin x - 1$
        $= \sin x$

2.09 $\cot^2 x = \csc^2 x - 1$; therefore,

$$= \sqrt{\cot^2 x + 1}$$
$$= \sqrt{\csc^2 x - 1 + 1}$$
$$= \sqrt{\csc^2 x}$$
$$= \csc x$$

2.010 $\sin x \cos x \sec x$
$$= \sin x \cdot 1$$
$$= \sin x$$

SELF TEST 3

3.01 $\dfrac{\sin^2 \theta}{\cos \theta} = \dfrac{\sin \theta}{\cos \theta} \cdot \sin \theta$

$$= \tan \theta \sin \theta \text{ or } \dfrac{\sin^2 \theta}{\cos \theta}$$
$$= \dfrac{1 - \cos^2 \theta}{\cos \theta}$$

3.02 $\cot \theta \tan^3 \theta + 1$
$$= \cot \theta \tan \theta \tan^2 \theta + 1$$
$$= 1 \cdot \tan^2 \theta + 1$$
$$= \sec^2 \theta$$

3.03 $\sin \theta \cos \theta \tan \theta$

$$= \sin \theta \cancel{\cos \theta} \dfrac{\sin \theta}{\cancel{\cos \theta}}$$
$$= \sin^2 \theta$$

3.04 $\dfrac{\sin \theta}{\cos \theta} + \tan \theta$

$$= \tan \theta + \tan \theta$$
$$= 2 \tan \theta$$

3.05 $\sec x - \sec x \sin^2 x$
$$= \sec x(1 - \sin^2 x)$$
$$= \sec x \cos^2 x$$
$$= \sec x \cos x \cos x$$
$$= 1 \cdot \cos x$$
$$= \cos x$$

3.06 $\sin^2 x + \sin x + \cos^2 x - 1$
$$= \sin^2 x + \cos^2 x + \sin x - 1$$
$$= \cancel{1} + \sin x - \cancel{1}$$
$$= \sin x$$

3.07 $\cos x(\tan x + \cot x)$

$$= \cos x\left(\dfrac{\sin x}{\cos x} + \dfrac{\cos x}{\sin x}\right)$$
$$= \cos x\left(\dfrac{\sin^2 x + \cos^2 x}{\cos x \sin x}\right)$$
$$= \cancel{\cos x}\left(\dfrac{1}{\cancel{\cos x} \sin x}\right)$$
$$= \dfrac{1}{\sin x}$$
$$= \csc x$$

3.08 $\sec^2 \theta - \tan^2 \theta + 1$
$$= \cancel{\tan^2 \theta} + 1 - \cancel{\tan^2 \theta} + 1$$
$$= 1 + 1$$
$$= 2$$

3.09 $\tan x \cos x = \dfrac{\sin x}{\cos x} \cdot \cos x = \sin x$

3.010 $\dfrac{1}{\sec x}(\tan x + \cot x)$

$$= \cos x\left(\dfrac{\sin x}{\cos x} + \dfrac{\cos x}{\sin x}\right)$$
$$= \sin x + \dfrac{\cos^2 x}{\sin x}$$
$$= \dfrac{\sin^2 x}{\sin x} + \dfrac{\cos^2 x}{\sin x}$$
$$= \dfrac{\sin^2 x + \cos^2 x}{\sin x}$$
$$= \dfrac{1}{\sin x}$$

SELF TEST 4

4.01 $\dfrac{\sin^2 \theta}{\cos \theta} = \dfrac{\sin \theta \cdot \sin \theta}{\cos \theta} = \dfrac{\sin \theta}{\cos \theta} \cdot$

$\sin \theta = \tan \theta \sin \theta \text{ or } \dfrac{\sin^2 \theta}{\cos \theta} =$

$\dfrac{1 - \cos^2 \theta}{\cos \theta}$

4.02 $\sin^2 \theta + \cos^2 \theta = 1$
$$\cos^2 \theta = 1 - \sin^2 \theta$$
$$\sqrt{\cos^2 \theta} = \pm\sqrt{1 - \sin^2 \theta}$$
$$\cos \theta = \pm\sqrt{1 - \sin^2 \theta}$$

4.03 $\dfrac{\tan \theta}{\cot \theta} = \dfrac{\tan \theta}{\dfrac{1}{\tan \theta}} = \tan^2 \theta$

4.04 $\cos x + \sin x \tan x$

$= \cos x + \sin x \dfrac{\sin x}{\cos x}$

$= \dfrac{\cos^2 x + \sin^2 x}{\cos x}$

$= \dfrac{1}{\cos x}$

$= \sec x$

4.05 $\dfrac{\tan^2 x}{\sec^2 x} + \dfrac{\cot^2 x}{\csc^2 x}$

$= \dfrac{1}{\sec^2 x} \cdot \tan^2 x + \dfrac{1}{\csc^2 x} \cdot \cot^2 x$

$= \cos^2 x \tan^2 x + \sin^2 x \cot^2 x$

$= \cancel{\cos^2 x} \cdot \dfrac{\sin^2 x}{\cancel{\cos^2 x}} + \cancel{\sin^2 x} \cdot \dfrac{\cos^2 x}{\cancel{\sin^2 x}}$

$= \sin^2 x + \cos^2 x$

$= 1$

4.06 $\csc^2 x - \cot^2 x$

$= 1 + \cancel{\cot^2 x} - \cancel{\cot^2 x}$

$= 1$

4.07 $\tan A - \sec A = \dfrac{\sin A}{\cos A} - \dfrac{1}{\cos A} =$

$\dfrac{\sin A - 1}{\cos A}$

4.08 $\tan x \sin x = \sec x - \cos x$

$\dfrac{\sin x}{\cos x} \cdot \sin x =$

$\dfrac{\sin^2 x}{\cos x} =$

$\dfrac{1 - \cos^2 x}{\cos x} =$

$\dfrac{1}{\cos x} - \dfrac{\cos^2 x}{\cos x} =$

$\sec x - \cos x = \sec x - \cos x$

4.09 $\sec x - \cos x = \sin x \tan x$

$\dfrac{1}{\cos x} - \cos x =$

$\dfrac{1}{\cos x} - \dfrac{\cos^2 x}{\cos x} =$

$\dfrac{1 - \cos^2 x}{\cos x} =$

$\dfrac{\sin^2 x}{\cos x} =$

$\sin x \cdot \dfrac{\sin x}{\cos x} =$

$\sin x \tan x = \sin x \tan x$

4.010 $\cot^2 x - \cos^2 x = \cos^2 x \cdot \cot^2 x$

$\dfrac{\cos^2 x}{\sin^2 x} - \cos^2 x =$

$\dfrac{\cos^2 x - \cos^2 x \sin^2 x}{\sin^2 x} =$

$\dfrac{\cos^2 x(1 - \sin^2 x)}{\sin^2 x} =$

$\cos^2 x \dfrac{\cos^2 x}{\sin^2 x} =$

$\cos^2 x \cot^2 x = \cos^2 x \cdot \cot^2 x$

SELF TEST 5

5.01 $\cos \alpha \cos \beta - \sin \alpha \sin \beta$

5.02 $\cos \alpha \cos \beta + \sin \alpha \sin \beta$

5.03 $\sin \alpha = \dfrac{3}{5}$

$x = 4$

$\cos \alpha = \dfrac{4}{5}$

$\sin \beta = \dfrac{5}{13}$

$x = 12$

$\cos \beta = \dfrac{12}{13}$

$\cos(\alpha + \beta) = \cos \alpha \cos \beta -$
$\qquad\qquad \sin \alpha \sin \beta$

$= \dfrac{4}{5} \cdot \dfrac{12}{13} - \dfrac{3}{5} \cdot \dfrac{5}{13}$

$= \dfrac{48}{65} - \dfrac{15}{65}$

$= \dfrac{33}{65}$

5.04 $\cos(\alpha - \beta) = \cos \alpha \cos \beta +$
$\qquad\qquad \sin \alpha \sin \beta$

$= \dfrac{4}{5} \cdot \dfrac{12}{13} + \dfrac{3}{5} \cdot \dfrac{5}{13}$

$= \dfrac{48}{65} + \dfrac{15}{65}$

$= \dfrac{63}{65}$

5.05 $\frac{\pi}{12} = \frac{\pi}{3} - \frac{\pi}{4}$; therefore, $\cos \frac{\pi}{12} =$

$\cos(\frac{\pi}{3} - \frac{\pi}{4})$

$$\cos(\frac{\pi}{3} - \frac{\pi}{4}) = \cos \frac{\pi}{3} \cos \frac{\pi}{4} +$$

$$\sin \frac{\pi}{3} \sin \frac{\pi}{4}$$

$$= \frac{1}{2} \cdot \frac{\sqrt{2}}{2} + \frac{\sqrt{3}}{2} \cdot \frac{\sqrt{2}}{2}$$

$$= \frac{\sqrt{2}}{4} + \frac{\sqrt{6}}{4}$$

$$= \frac{\sqrt{2} + \sqrt{6}}{4}$$

5.06 $\cos(\frac{\pi}{2} - t) = \cos \frac{\pi}{2} \cos t +$

$$\sin \frac{\pi}{2} \sin t$$

$$= 0 \cdot \cos t + 1 \cdot \sin t$$

$$= 0 + \sin t$$

$$= \sin t$$

5.07 $\cos(\alpha - \beta) + \cos(\alpha + \beta)$

$= (\cos \alpha \cos \beta + \sin \alpha \sin \beta) +$

$(\cos \alpha \cos \beta - \sin \alpha \sin \beta)$

$= \cos \alpha \cos \beta + \cos \alpha \cos \beta$

$= 2 \cos \alpha \cos \beta$

5.08 $1 - 2 \cos^2 r = 2 \sin^2 r - 1$

$1 - 2(1 - \sin^2 r) =$

$1 - 2 + 2 \sin^2 r =$

$-1 + 2 \sin^2 r =$

$2 \sin^2 r - 1 = 2 \sin^2 r - 1$

5.09 $\frac{\sin \theta}{\cos \theta \tan \theta} = \frac{\sin \theta}{\cos \theta} \cdot \frac{1}{\tan \theta} =$

$\tan \theta \cdot \frac{1}{\tan \theta} = 1$

5.010 $\frac{\sin \theta}{\cos \theta} + \frac{\sin \theta}{\cos \theta} = \tan \theta + \tan \theta =$

$2 \tan \theta$

SELF TEST 6

6.01 through 6.03

$$\sin \theta = -\frac{3}{5}$$

$$x = 4$$

$$\cos \theta = -\frac{4}{5}$$

$$\tan \theta = \frac{3}{4}$$

$$\tan \phi = -\frac{7}{24}$$

$$r = 25$$

$$\sin \phi = \frac{7}{25}$$

$$\cos \phi = -\frac{24}{25}$$

6.01 $\sin(\theta + \phi) = \sin \theta \cos \phi +$

$$\cos \theta \sin \phi$$

$$= -\frac{3}{5} \cdot (-\frac{24}{25}) + (-\frac{4}{5}) \cdot \frac{7}{25}$$

$$= \frac{72}{125} - \frac{28}{125}$$

$$= \frac{44}{125}$$

6.02 $\cos(\theta + \phi) = \cos \theta \cos \phi -$

$$\sin \theta \sin \phi$$

$$= -\frac{4}{5} \cdot (-\frac{24}{25}) - (-\frac{3}{5}) \cdot \frac{7}{25}$$

$$= \frac{96}{125} + \frac{21}{125}$$

$$= \frac{117}{125}$$

6.03 $\tan(\theta + \phi) = \frac{\tan \theta + \tan \phi}{1 - \tan \theta \tan \phi}$

$$= \frac{\frac{3}{4} + (-\frac{7}{24})}{1 - \frac{3}{4}(-\frac{7}{24})} \quad \text{Multiply by 96.}$$

$$= \frac{72 - 28}{96 + 21}$$

$$= \frac{44}{117}$$

6.04 through 6.06

$$\cos \alpha = -\frac{24}{25}$$
$$y = 7$$
$$\sin \alpha = \frac{7}{25}$$
$$\tan \alpha = -\frac{7}{24}$$

$$\sin \beta = \frac{3}{5}$$
$$x = -4$$
$$\cos \beta = -\frac{4}{5}$$
$$\tan \beta = -\frac{3}{4}$$

6.04 $\sin(\alpha - \beta) = \sin \alpha \cos \beta -$
  $\cos \alpha \sin \beta$
$$= \frac{7}{25} \cdot \left(-\frac{4}{5}\right) - \left(-\frac{24}{25}\right) \cdot \frac{3}{5}$$
$$= -\frac{28}{125} + \frac{72}{125}$$
$$= \frac{44}{125}$$

6.05 $\cos(\alpha - \beta) = \cos \alpha \cos \beta +$
  $\sin \alpha \sin \beta$
$$= -\frac{24}{25} \cdot \left(-\frac{4}{5}\right) + \frac{7}{25} \cdot \frac{3}{5}$$
$$= \frac{96}{125} + \frac{21}{125}$$
$$= \frac{117}{125}$$

6.06 $\tan(\alpha - \beta) = \dfrac{\tan \alpha - \tan \beta}{1 + \tan \alpha \tan \beta}$
$$= \frac{\frac{7}{24} - \left(-\frac{3}{4}\right)}{1 + \left(-\frac{7}{24}\right)\left(-\frac{3}{4}\right)}$$
$$= \frac{-\frac{7}{24} + \frac{3}{4}}{1 + \frac{21}{96}} \quad \text{Multiply by 96.}$$
$$= \frac{-28 + 72}{96 + 21}$$
$$= \frac{44}{117}$$

6.07 $\sin 75° =$
$\sin(45° + 30°) = \sin 45° \cos 30° +$
  $\cos 45° \sin 30°$
$$= \frac{\sqrt{2}}{2} \cdot \frac{\sqrt{3}}{2} + \frac{\sqrt{2}}{2} \cdot \frac{1}{2}$$
$$= \frac{\sqrt{6}}{4} + \frac{\sqrt{2}}{4}$$
$$= \frac{\sqrt{6} + \sqrt{2}}{4}$$

6.08 $\sin(\frac{\pi}{4} - \beta) = \sin \frac{\pi}{4} \cos \beta -$
  $\cos \frac{\pi}{4} \sin \beta$
$$= \frac{\sqrt{2}}{2} \cos \beta - \frac{\sqrt{2}}{2} \sin \beta$$
$$= \frac{\sqrt{2}}{2}(\cos \beta - \sin \beta)$$

6.09 $\cos(\frac{\pi}{3} + \beta) = \cos \frac{\pi}{3} \cos \beta -$
  $\sin \frac{\pi}{3} \sin \beta$
$$= \frac{1}{2} \cos \beta - \frac{\sqrt{3}}{2} \sin \beta$$
$$= \frac{1}{2}(\cos \beta - \sqrt{3} \sin \beta)$$

6.010 $\tan(45° - \alpha) = \dfrac{\tan 45° - \tan \alpha}{1 + \tan 45° \tan \alpha}$
$$= \frac{1 - \tan \alpha}{1 + \tan \alpha}$$

6.011 $3 \tan x \cos x \cot x$
$= 3 \tan x \cot x \cos x$
$= 3 \cdot 1 \cdot \cos x$
$= 3 \cos x$

6.012 $\dfrac{\cot \theta}{\tan \theta} = \dfrac{\cot \theta}{\frac{1}{\cot \theta}} = \cot^2 \theta$

6.013

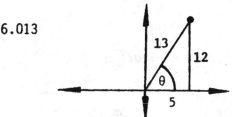

$r = \sqrt{5^2 + 12^2}$
$ = \sqrt{25 + 144}$
$ = \sqrt{169}$
$ = 13$

$\sin \theta = \frac{12}{13}$

$\cos \theta = \frac{5}{13}$

$\sin^2 \theta + \cos^2 \theta = \left(\frac{12}{13}\right)^2 + \left(\frac{5}{13}\right)^2$
$$= \frac{144}{169} + \frac{25}{169}$$
$$= \frac{169}{169}$$
$$= 1$$

6.014 $\dfrac{\sec\theta}{\cos\theta} = \dfrac{\sec\theta}{\dfrac{1}{\sec\theta}} = \sec^2\theta$

6.015 $\dfrac{\sin^2\theta}{\cos\theta} = \dfrac{\sin\theta\cdot\sin\theta}{\cos\theta} = \dfrac{\sin\theta}{\cos\theta}\cdot$

$\sin\theta = \tan\theta\,\sin\theta$ or $\dfrac{\sin^2\theta}{\cos\theta} =$

$\dfrac{1-\cos^2\theta}{\cos\theta}$

6.016 $\dfrac{\sin\theta}{\cos\theta\,\tan\theta} = \dfrac{\sin\theta}{\cos\theta}\cdot\dfrac{1}{\tan\theta} =$

$\cancel{\tan\theta}\cdot\dfrac{1}{\cancel{\tan\theta}} = 1$

6.017 $\dfrac{1}{\sec x}(\tan x + \cot x)$

$= \cos x\left(\dfrac{\sin x}{\cos x} + \dfrac{\cos x}{\sin x}\right)$

$= \sin x + \dfrac{\cos^2 x}{\sin x}$

$= \dfrac{\sin^2 x}{\sin x} + \dfrac{\cos^2 x}{\sin x}$

$= \dfrac{\sin^2 x + \cos^2 x}{\sin x}$

$= \dfrac{1}{\sin x}$

6.018 $\tan x\,\cos x = \dfrac{\sin x}{\cos x}\cdot\cos x = \sin x$

6.019 $\csc^2 x - \cot^2 x$
$= 1 + \cancel{\cot^2 x} - \cancel{\cot^2 x}$
$= 1$

6.020 $\cos\left(\dfrac{3\pi}{2} + x\right) = \cos\dfrac{3\pi}{2}\cos x -$

$\sin\dfrac{3\pi}{2}\sin x = 0\cdot\cos x -$

$(-1)\sin x = \sin x$

SELF TEST 7

7.01 through 7.08

$\cos\theta = \dfrac{3}{5}$
$\quad u = 3$
$\quad v = -4$
$\quad r = 5$

7.01 $\sin\theta = \dfrac{v}{r} = -\dfrac{4}{5}$

7.02 $\tan\theta = \dfrac{v}{u} = -\dfrac{4}{3}$

7.03 $\sin 2\theta = 2\sin\theta\cos\theta$
$= 2\left(-\dfrac{4}{5}\right)\left(\dfrac{3}{5}\right)$
$= -\dfrac{24}{25}$

7.04 $\cos 2\theta = 2\cos^2\theta - 1$
$= 2\left(\dfrac{3}{5}\right)^2 - 1$
$= 2\left(\dfrac{9}{25}\right) - 1$
$= \dfrac{18}{25} - 1$
$= -\dfrac{7}{25}$

7.05 $\tan 2\theta = \dfrac{2\tan\theta}{1-\tan^2\theta}$

$= \dfrac{2\left(-\dfrac{4}{3}\right)}{1-\left(-\dfrac{4}{3}\right)^2}$

$= \dfrac{-\dfrac{8}{3}}{1-\dfrac{16}{9}}$

$= \dfrac{-\dfrac{8}{3}}{-\dfrac{7}{9}}$

$= \dfrac{72}{21}$

$= \dfrac{24}{7}$

7.06 $\sin\dfrac{\theta}{2} = -\sqrt{\dfrac{1-\cos\theta}{2}}$

$= -\sqrt{\dfrac{1-\dfrac{3}{5}}{2}}$

$= -\sqrt{\dfrac{2}{10}}$

$= -\sqrt{\dfrac{1}{5}}$

$= -\dfrac{\sqrt{5}}{5}$

7.07　　$\cos \dfrac{\theta}{2} = \sqrt{\dfrac{1 + \cos \theta}{2}}$

$\quad = \sqrt{\dfrac{1 + \dfrac{3}{5}}{2}}$

$\quad = \sqrt{\dfrac{\dfrac{8}{5}}{2}}$

$\quad = \sqrt{\dfrac{4}{5}}$

$\quad = \dfrac{2}{\sqrt{5}}$

$\quad = \dfrac{2}{5}\sqrt{5}$

7.08　　$\tan \dfrac{\theta}{2} = -\sqrt{\dfrac{1 - \cos \theta}{1 + \cos \theta}}$

$\quad = -\sqrt{\dfrac{1 - \dfrac{3}{5}}{1 + \dfrac{3}{5}}}$

$\quad = -\sqrt{\dfrac{\dfrac{2}{5}}{\dfrac{8}{5}}}$

$\quad = -\sqrt{\dfrac{2}{8}}$

$\quad = -\sqrt{\dfrac{1}{4}}$

$\quad = -\dfrac{1}{2}$

7.09　　Since $\tan \theta = \dfrac{\sin \theta}{\cos \theta}$, $\tan \theta \cos \theta =$
$\sin \theta$. Hence, $\tan(\alpha + \beta) \cdot$
$\cos(\alpha + \beta) = \sin(\alpha + \beta)$.
Now simplify the right member.

$\dfrac{\cos \beta \sec \alpha + \sin \beta \csc \alpha}{\csc \alpha \sec \alpha}$

$= \dfrac{\cos \beta \sec \alpha}{\csc \alpha \sec \alpha} + \dfrac{\sin \beta \csc \alpha}{\csc \alpha \sec \alpha}$

$= \dfrac{\cos \beta}{\csc \alpha} + \dfrac{\sin \beta}{\sec \alpha}$

$= \cos \beta \sin \alpha + \sin \beta \cos \alpha$

$= \sin(\alpha + \beta)$

Therefore, $\tan(\alpha + \beta) \cos(\alpha + \beta) =$
$\dfrac{\cos \beta \sec \alpha + \sin \beta \csc \alpha}{\csc \alpha \sec \alpha}$.

7.010　　$\tan x \sin x = \sec x - \cos x$

$\dfrac{\sin x}{\cos x} \cdot \sin x =$

$\dfrac{\sin^2 x}{\cos x} =$

$\dfrac{1 - \cos^2 x}{\cos x} =$

$\dfrac{1}{\cos x} - \dfrac{\cos^2 x}{\cos x} =$

$\sec x - \cos x = \sec x - \cos x$

7.011　　$1 - \dfrac{\cos^2 x}{1 + \sin x} = \sin x$

$\dfrac{1 + \sin x}{1 + \sin x} - \dfrac{\cos^2 x}{1 + \sin x} =$

$\dfrac{1 + \sin x - \cos^2 x}{1 + \sin x} =$

$\dfrac{1 - \cos^2 x + \sin x}{1 + \sin x} =$

$\dfrac{\sin^2 x + \sin x}{1 + \sin x} =$

$\dfrac{\sin x(\cancel{\sin x + 1})}{\cancel{1 + \sin x}} =$

$\sin x = \sin x$

7.012 through 7.016

Since $\cos \alpha = \dfrac{\sqrt{2}}{2}$ and
$\sin \beta = \dfrac{\sqrt{2}}{2}$, α and β are
first quadrant angles; $\alpha = \beta$.

7.012　　$\cos(\alpha + \beta) = \cos 2\alpha$

$\quad = 2 \cos^2 \alpha - 1$

$\quad = 2\left(\dfrac{\sqrt{2}}{2}\right)^2 - 1$

$\quad = 2 \cdot \dfrac{1}{2} - 1$

$\quad = 0$

7.013　　$\sin(\alpha - \beta) = \sin(\alpha - \alpha)$

$\quad = \sin(0)$

$\quad = 0$

7.014　　$\cos 2\alpha = 0$
(See Problem 7.012.)

7.015 $\sin \frac{1}{2}\alpha = \sqrt{\dfrac{1 - \cos\alpha}{2}} = \sqrt{\dfrac{1 - \frac{\sqrt{2}}{2}}{2}}$

$$= \sqrt{\dfrac{\frac{2}{2} - \frac{\sqrt{2}}{2}}{\frac{4}{2}}}$$

$$= \sqrt{\dfrac{2 - \sqrt{2}}{4}}$$

$$= \dfrac{\sqrt{2 - \sqrt{2}}}{2}$$

7.016 $\tan \frac{1}{2}\beta = \sqrt{\dfrac{1 - \cos\beta}{1 + \cos\beta}} = \sqrt{\dfrac{1 - \frac{\sqrt{2}}{2}}{1 + \frac{\sqrt{2}}{2}}}$

$$= \sqrt{\dfrac{2 - \sqrt{2}}{2 + \sqrt{2}}}$$

$$= \sqrt{\dfrac{2 - \sqrt{2}}{2 + \sqrt{2}} \cdot \dfrac{2 - \sqrt{2}}{2 - \sqrt{2}}}$$

$$= \sqrt{\dfrac{4 - 4\sqrt{2} + 2}{4 - 2}}$$

$$= \sqrt{\dfrac{6 - 4\sqrt{2}}{2}}$$

$$= \sqrt{3 - 2\sqrt{2}}$$

7.017 $\dfrac{\cos^2\theta}{\sin\theta} = \dfrac{\cos\theta \cdot \cos\theta}{\sin\theta} = \dfrac{\cos\theta}{\sin\theta} \cdot$
$\cos\theta = \cot\theta \cos\theta$

7.018 $\cot\theta + \dfrac{1}{\tan\theta} + \dfrac{\cos\theta}{\sin\theta} =$
$\cot\theta + \cot\theta + \cot\theta =$
$\qquad\qquad 3\cot\theta$

7.019 $\sin^2\theta + \sin\theta \csc\theta \cos^2\theta$
$= \sin^2\theta + (\sin\theta \csc\theta)(\cos^2\theta)$
$= \sin^2\theta + (1)\cos^2\theta$
$= 1$

7.020 $\sqrt{\dfrac{\tan^2 x + 1}{\cot^2 x + 1}} = \sqrt{\dfrac{\sec^2 x}{\csc^2 x}} =$

$$\dfrac{\sec x}{\csc x} = \dfrac{\frac{1}{\cos x}}{\frac{1}{\sin x}} = \dfrac{\sin x}{\cos x} = \tan x$$

SELF TEST 8

8.01 through 8.04

$$\sin\theta = \frac{2}{3}$$

$$\cos\theta = -\frac{\sqrt{5}}{3}$$

$$\tan\theta = -\frac{2}{\sqrt{5}}$$

8.01 $\sin 2\theta = 2\sin\theta\cos\theta$
$\qquad = 2\left(\frac{2}{3}\right)\left(-\frac{\sqrt{5}}{3}\right)$
$\qquad = -\dfrac{4\sqrt{5}}{9}$

8.02 $\cos 2\theta = 2\cos^2\theta - 1$
$\qquad = 2\left(-\frac{\sqrt{5}}{3}\right)^2 - 1$
$\qquad = 2\left(\frac{5}{9}\right) - 1$
$\qquad = \dfrac{10}{9} - 1$
$\qquad = \dfrac{1}{9}$

8.03 $\tan 2\theta = \dfrac{2\tan\theta}{1 - \tan^2\theta}$

$$= \dfrac{2\left(-\frac{2}{\sqrt{5}}\right)}{1 - \left(-\frac{2}{\sqrt{5}}\right)^2}$$

$$= \dfrac{-\frac{4}{\sqrt{5}}}{1 - \frac{4}{5}}$$

$$= \dfrac{-\frac{20}{\sqrt{5}}}{1} = -\dfrac{20\sqrt{5}}{5} = -4\sqrt{5}$$

8.04 $\quad \cos \dfrac{\theta}{2} = \sqrt{\dfrac{1 + \cos \theta}{2}} = \sqrt{\dfrac{1 - \dfrac{\sqrt{5}}{3}}{2}}$

$\qquad = \sqrt{\dfrac{\dfrac{3}{3} - \dfrac{\sqrt{5}}{3}}{\dfrac{6}{3}}} = \sqrt{\dfrac{3 - \sqrt{5}}{6}}$

8.05 and 8.06

$\qquad \sin \alpha = \dfrac{5}{13}$

$\qquad x = 12$

$\qquad \cos \alpha = \dfrac{12}{13}$

$\qquad \tan \alpha = \dfrac{5}{12}$

$\qquad \cos \beta = -\dfrac{12}{13}$

$\qquad y = 5$

$\qquad \sin \beta = \dfrac{5}{13}$

$\qquad \tan \beta = -\dfrac{5}{12}$

8.05 $\quad \sin (\alpha + \beta) = \sin \alpha \cos \beta +$
$\qquad \qquad \qquad \quad \cos \alpha \sin \beta$

$\qquad = \dfrac{5}{13} \cdot (-\dfrac{12}{13}) + \dfrac{12}{13} \cdot \dfrac{5}{13}$

$\qquad = -\dfrac{60}{169} + \dfrac{60}{169}$

$\qquad = \mathbf{0}$

8.06 $\quad \tan (\alpha - \beta) = \dfrac{\tan \alpha - \tan \beta}{1 + \tan \alpha \tan \beta}$

$\qquad = \dfrac{\dfrac{5}{12} - (-\dfrac{5}{12})}{1 + (\dfrac{5}{15})(-\dfrac{5}{12})}$

$\qquad = \dfrac{\dfrac{10}{12}}{1 - \dfrac{25}{144}}$

$\qquad = \dfrac{\dfrac{120}{144}}{\dfrac{144}{144} - \dfrac{25}{144}}$

$\qquad = \dfrac{120}{144 - 25}$

$\qquad = \dfrac{120}{119}$

8.07 $\quad \cos 2x + 2 \sin^2 x \qquad\qquad\qquad\qquad$ 1

$\qquad 2 \cos^2 x - 1 + 2 \sin^2 x$

$\qquad 2 \sin^2 x + 2 \cos^2 x - 1$

$\qquad 2(\sin^2 x + \cos^2 x) - 1$

$\qquad 2(1) - 1$

$\qquad 1 \qquad\qquad\qquad\qquad\qquad\qquad\qquad\qquad$ 1

8.08 $\quad \sin 2x \csc x \qquad\qquad\qquad\qquad\qquad$ $2 \cos x$

$\qquad 2 \sin x \cos x \cdot \dfrac{1}{\sin x}$

$\qquad 2 \cos x \qquad\qquad\qquad\qquad\qquad\qquad$ $2 \cos x$

8.09 $\quad \cos(\dfrac{\pi}{2} - \dfrac{x}{2}) \qquad\qquad\qquad\qquad$ $\sin \dfrac{x}{2}$

$\qquad \cos \dfrac{\pi}{2} \cos \dfrac{x}{2} + \sin \dfrac{\pi}{2} \sin \dfrac{x}{2}$

$\qquad 0 \cdot \cos \dfrac{x}{2} + (1) \sin \dfrac{x}{2}$

$\qquad 0 + \sin \dfrac{x}{2}$

$\qquad \sin \dfrac{x}{2} \qquad\qquad\qquad\qquad\qquad\qquad$ $\sin \dfrac{x}{2}$

8.010 sin $3x$ $3 \sin x - 4 \sin^3 x$

sin $(2x + x)$

sin $2x \cos x + \cos 2x \sin x$

$2 \sin x \cos x \cos x + (1 - 2 \sin^2 x)\sin x$

$2 \sin x \cos^2 x + \sin x - 2 \sin^3 x$

$2 \sin x(1 - \sin^2 x) + \sin x - 2 \sin^3 x$

$2 \sin x - 2 \sin^3 x + \sin x - 2 \sin^3 x$

$3 \sin x - 4 \sin^3 x$ $3 \sin x - 4 \sin^3 x$

SELF TEST 9

9.01

$$\sin 2\theta = 2 \sin \theta$$
$$2 \sin \theta \cos \theta = 2 \sin \theta$$
$$2 \sin \theta \cos \theta - 2 \sin \theta = 0$$
$$2 \sin \theta(\cos \theta - 1) = 0$$

$2 \sin \theta = 0$ or $\cos \theta - 1 = 0$

$\sin \theta = 0$ $\cos \theta = 1$

$\theta = 0°, 180°, 360°$ $\theta = 0°, 360°$

$\theta = \{0°, 180°, 360°\}$

9.02

$$\cos \beta = \sin \frac{\beta}{2}$$
$$1 - 2 \sin^2 \frac{\beta}{2} = \sin \frac{\beta}{2}$$
$$2 \sin^2 \frac{\beta}{2} + \sin \frac{\beta}{2} - 1 = 0$$
$$\left(2 \sin \frac{\beta}{2} - 1\right)\left(\sin \frac{\beta}{2} + 1\right) = 0$$

$2 \sin \frac{\beta}{2} - 1 = 0$ or $\sin \frac{\beta}{2} + 1 = 0$

$2 \sin \frac{\beta}{2} = 1$ $\sin \frac{\beta}{2} = -1$

$\sin \frac{\beta}{2} = \frac{1}{2}$ $\frac{\beta}{2} = 270°$

$\frac{\beta}{2} = 30°, 150°$ $\beta = 540°$

$\beta = 60°, 300°$

$\beta = \{60°, 300°\}$

9.03

$$\sin^2 \theta = 1 - \sin 2\theta$$
$$\sin^2 \theta = 1 - 2 \sin \theta \cos \theta$$
$$\sin^2 \theta - 1 = -2 \sin \theta \cos \theta$$
$$\sin^2 \theta - 1 = -2 \sin \theta \sqrt{1 - \sin^2 \theta}$$
$$(\sin^2 \theta - 1)^2 = (-2 \sin \theta \sqrt{1 - \sin^2 \theta})^2$$
$$\sin^4 \theta - 2 \sin^2 \theta + 1 = 4 \sin^2 \theta(1 - \sin^2 \theta)$$
$$\sin^4 \theta - 2 \sin^2 \theta + 1 = 4 \sin^2 \theta - 4 \sin^4 \theta$$
$$5 \sin^4 \theta - 2 \sin^2 \theta + 1 = 4 \sin^2 \theta$$
$$5 \sin^4 \theta - 6 \sin^2 \theta + 1 = 0$$
$$(5 \sin^2 \theta - 1)(\sin^2 \theta - 1) = 0$$

$$5 \sin^2 \theta - 1 = 0 \qquad \text{or} \quad \sin^2 \theta - 1 = 0$$
$$5 \sin^2 \theta = 1 \qquad\qquad \sin^2 \theta = 1$$
$$\sin^2 \theta = \frac{1}{5} \qquad\qquad \sqrt{\sin^2 \theta} = \pm\sqrt{1}$$
$$\qquad\qquad\qquad\qquad \sin \theta = \pm 1$$
$$\sqrt{\sin^2 \theta} = \pm\sqrt{\frac{1}{5}}$$
$$\sin \theta = \pm\frac{\sqrt{5}}{5}$$
$$\theta = 27°, 207° \text{ or } \theta = 90°, 270°$$
$$\theta = \{27°, 90°,$$
$$207°, 270°\}$$

9.04

$$\cos 2\alpha + \sin \alpha = 1$$
$$\cancel{1} - 2 \sin^2 \alpha + \sin \alpha = \cancel{1}$$
$$2 \sin^2 \alpha - \sin \alpha = 0$$
$$\sin \alpha(2 \sin \alpha - 1) = 0$$

$$\sin \alpha = 0 \qquad \text{or} \qquad 2 \sin \alpha - 1 = 0$$
$$\qquad\qquad\qquad\qquad\qquad 2 \sin \alpha = 1$$
$$\alpha = 0°, 180°, \qquad\qquad \sin \alpha = \frac{1}{2}$$
$$360°$$
$$\alpha = \{0°, 30°, 150°, \qquad \alpha = 30°, 150°$$
$$180°, 360°\}$$

9.05

$$\tan \alpha \tan 2\alpha = 1$$
$$\tan \alpha\left[\frac{2 \tan \alpha}{1 - \tan^2 \alpha}\right] = 1$$
$$\frac{2 \tan^2 \alpha}{1 - \tan^2 \alpha} = 1$$
$$2 \tan^2 \alpha = 1 - \tan^2 \alpha$$
$$3 \tan^2 \alpha = 1$$
$$\tan^2 \alpha = \frac{1}{3}$$
$$\sqrt{\tan^2 \alpha} = \pm\sqrt{\frac{1}{3}}$$
$$\tan \alpha = \pm\frac{\sqrt{3}}{3}$$
$$\alpha = \{30°, 150°, 210°, 330°\}$$

9.06

$$\sin(\tfrac{\pi}{3} + \theta) - \cos(\tfrac{\pi}{6} + \theta) = \sin \theta$$

$$\sin \tfrac{\pi}{3} \cos \theta + \cos \tfrac{\pi}{3} \sin \theta - (\cos \tfrac{\pi}{6} \cos \theta - \sin \tfrac{\pi}{6} \sin \theta) = \sin \theta$$

$$\tfrac{\sqrt{3}}{2} \cancel{\cos \theta} + \tfrac{1}{2} \sin \theta - \tfrac{\sqrt{3}}{2} \cancel{\cos \theta} + \tfrac{1}{2} \sin \theta = \sin \theta$$

$$\sin \theta = \sin \theta$$

9.07

$$\cos(\tfrac{\pi}{3} - x) = \sin(\tfrac{\pi}{6} + x)$$

$$\cos \tfrac{\pi}{3} \cos x + \sin \tfrac{\pi}{3} \sin x = \sin \tfrac{\pi}{6} \cos x + \cos \tfrac{\pi}{6} \sin x$$

$$\tfrac{1}{2} \cos x + \tfrac{\sqrt{3}}{2} \sin x = \tfrac{1}{2} \cos x + \tfrac{\sqrt{3}}{2} \sin x$$

9.08 through 9.021

$$\cos \theta = -\tfrac{4}{5}$$
$$y = -3$$
$$\sin \phi = -\tfrac{12}{13}$$
$$x = 5$$

9.08 $\sin \theta = -\tfrac{3}{5}$

9.09 $\tan \theta = \dfrac{-3}{-4} = \dfrac{3}{4}$

9.010 $\cos \phi = \tfrac{5}{13}$

9.011 $\tan \phi = -\tfrac{12}{5}$

9.012 $\sin (\theta + \phi) = \sin \theta \cos \phi + \cos \theta \sin \phi$

$$= (-\tfrac{3}{5})(\tfrac{5}{13}) + (-\tfrac{4}{5})(-\tfrac{12}{13})$$

$$= -\tfrac{15}{65} + \tfrac{48}{65}$$

$$= \tfrac{33}{65}$$

9.013 $\cos (\theta + \phi) = \cos \theta \cos \phi - \sin \theta \sin \phi$

$$= (-\tfrac{4}{5})\tfrac{5}{13} - (-\tfrac{3}{5})(-\tfrac{12}{13})$$

$$= -\tfrac{20}{65} - \tfrac{36}{65}$$

$$= -\tfrac{56}{65}$$

9.014 $\cos (\theta - \phi) = \cos \theta \cos \phi + \sin \theta \sin \phi$

$$= (-\tfrac{4}{5})(\tfrac{5}{13}) + (-\tfrac{3}{5})(-\tfrac{12}{13})$$

$$= -\tfrac{20}{65} + \tfrac{36}{65}$$

$$= \tfrac{16}{65}$$

9.015 $\tan (\theta + \phi) = \dfrac{\tan \theta + \tan \phi}{1 - \tan \theta \tan \phi}$

$$= \dfrac{\tfrac{3}{4} + (-\tfrac{12}{5})}{1 - (\tfrac{3}{4})(-\tfrac{12}{5})}$$

$$= \dfrac{\tfrac{3}{4} - \tfrac{12}{5}}{1 + \tfrac{36}{20}} \quad \text{Multiply by 20.}$$

$$= \dfrac{15 - 48}{20 + 36}$$

$$= -\tfrac{33}{56}$$

9.016 $\sin 2\theta = 2 \sin \theta \cos \theta$

$$= 2(-\tfrac{3}{5})(-\tfrac{4}{5})$$

$$= \tfrac{24}{25}$$

9.017 $\cos 2\phi = \cos^2 \phi - \sin^2 \phi$

$$= (\tfrac{5}{13})^2 - (-\tfrac{12}{13})^2$$

$$= \tfrac{25}{169} - \tfrac{144}{169}$$

$$= -\tfrac{119}{169}$$

9.018 $\tan 2\theta = \dfrac{2\tan\theta}{1-\tan^2\theta}$

$= \dfrac{2\left(\frac{3}{4}\right)}{1-\left(\frac{3}{4}\right)^2}$

$= \dfrac{\frac{6}{4}}{1-\frac{9}{16}}$

$= \dfrac{24}{16-9}$

$= \dfrac{24}{7}$

9.019 $\sin\frac{1}{2}\theta = -\sqrt{\dfrac{1-\cos\theta}{2}}$

$= -\sqrt{\dfrac{1-\left(-\frac{4}{5}\right)}{2}}$

$= -\sqrt{\dfrac{\frac{9}{5}}{\frac{10}{5}}}$

$= -\sqrt{\dfrac{9}{10}}$

$= -\dfrac{3}{\sqrt{10}}$

$= \dfrac{-3\sqrt{10}}{10}$

9.020 $\cos\frac{1}{2}\phi = \sqrt{\dfrac{1+\cos\phi}{2}}$

$= \sqrt{\dfrac{1+\frac{5}{13}}{2}}$

$= \sqrt{\dfrac{\frac{18}{13}}{\frac{26}{13}}}$

$= \sqrt{\dfrac{18}{26}}$

$= \sqrt{\dfrac{9}{13}}$

$= \dfrac{3}{\sqrt{13}}$

$= \dfrac{3\sqrt{13}}{13}$

9.021 $\tan\frac{1}{2}\theta = \sqrt{\dfrac{1-\cos\theta}{1+\cos\theta}}$

$= \sqrt{\dfrac{1-\left(-\frac{4}{5}\right)}{1+\left(-\frac{4}{5}\right)}}$

$= \sqrt{\dfrac{\frac{9}{5}}{\frac{1}{5}}}$

$= \sqrt{\dfrac{9}{1}}$

$= 3$

9.022

$\cos\alpha\ \sin 2\alpha$	$1+\cos 2\alpha$
$\dfrac{\cos\alpha}{\cancel{\sin\alpha}}\cdot 2\ \cancel{\sin\alpha}$	$\cancel{1}+2\cos^2\alpha-\cancel{1}$
$\cos\alpha$	
$2\cos^2\alpha$	$2\cos^2\alpha$

9.023 $\cot^2 x - \cos^2 x = \cos^2 x\cdot\cot^2 x$

$\dfrac{\cos^2 x}{\sin^2 x} - \cos^2 x =$

$\dfrac{\cos^2 x - \cos^2 x \sin^2 x}{\sin^2 x} =$

$\dfrac{\cos^2 x(1-\sin^2 x)}{\sin^2 x} =$

$\cos^2 x\ \dfrac{\cos^2 x}{\sin^2 x} =$

$\cos^2 x\ \cot^2 x = \cos^2 x\cdot\cot^2 x$

9.024 $\dfrac{1+\tan^2 x}{\tan^2 x} = \csc^2 x$

$\dfrac{1}{\tan^2 x} + \dfrac{\tan^2 x}{\tan^2 x} =$

$\cot^2 x + 1 =$

$\csc^2 x = \csc^2 x$

9.025

$$\frac{\sin x}{1 + \cos x} + \frac{1 + \cos x}{\sin x} = 2 \csc x$$

$$\frac{\sin^2 x}{\sin x(1 + \cos x)} + \frac{(1 + \cos x)^2}{\sin x(1 + \cos x)} =$$

$$\frac{\sin^2 x + 1 + 2 \cos x + \cos^2 x}{\sin x(1 + \cos x)} =$$

$$\frac{\sin^2 x + \cos^2 x + 1 + 2 \cos x}{\sin x(1 + \cos x)} =$$

$$\frac{1 + 1 + 2 \cos x}{\sin x(1 + \cos x)} =$$

$$\frac{2 + 2 \cos x}{\sin x(1 + \cos x)} =$$

$$\frac{2\cancel{(1 + \cos x)}}{\sin x\cancel{(1 + \cos x)}} =$$

$$\frac{2}{\sin x} =$$

$$2 \csc x = 2 \csc x$$

MATHEMATICS 1206
SELF TEST
SOLUTION KEY

SELF TEST 1

1.01　a.　$\dfrac{v}{r}$

　　　b.　$\dfrac{u}{r}$

　　　c.　$\dfrac{v}{u}$

　　　d.　$\dfrac{r}{v}$

　　　e.　$\dfrac{r}{u}$

　　　f.　$\dfrac{u}{v}$

1.02　$x = 6$
　　　$y = -5$
　　　$r = \sqrt{6^2 + (-5)^2}$
　　　　$= \sqrt{36 + 25}$
　　　　$= \sqrt{61}$

　　　a.　$\sin \theta = \dfrac{y}{r} = \dfrac{-5}{\sqrt{61}} = -\dfrac{5\sqrt{61}}{61}$

　　　b.　$\cos \theta = \dfrac{x}{r} = \dfrac{6}{\sqrt{61}} = \dfrac{6\sqrt{61}}{61}$

　　　c.　$\tan \theta = \dfrac{y}{x} = \dfrac{-5}{6} = -\dfrac{5}{6}$

1.03　$u = -8$
　　　$v = -6$
　　　$r = \sqrt{(-8)^2 + (-6)^2}$
　　　　$= \sqrt{64 + 36}$
　　　　$= \sqrt{100}$
　　　　$= 10$

　　　a.　$\sin \theta = \dfrac{v}{r} = \dfrac{-6}{10} = -\dfrac{3}{5}$

　　　b.　$\cos \theta = \dfrac{u}{r} = \dfrac{-8}{10} = -\dfrac{4}{5}$

　　　c.　$\tan \theta = \dfrac{v}{u} = \dfrac{-6}{-8} = \dfrac{3}{4}$

　　　d.　$\csc \theta = \dfrac{r}{v} = \dfrac{10}{-6} = -\dfrac{5}{3}$

　　　e.　$\sec \theta = \dfrac{r}{u} = \dfrac{10}{-8} = -\dfrac{5}{4}$

　　　f.　$\cot \theta = \dfrac{u}{v} = \dfrac{-8}{-6} = \dfrac{4}{3}$

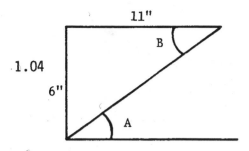

1.04

Angle of elevation is ∠A,
but ∠A = ∠B.

$\tan \angle B = \dfrac{6}{11}$
　　$\angle B = 28.6°$
　　$\angle B = 29°$

1.05

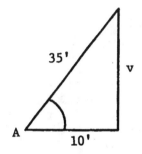

　　a.　$v = \sqrt{35^2 - 10^2}$
　　　　$v = \sqrt{1,225 - 100}$
　　　　$v = \sqrt{1,125}$
　　　　$v = 5\sqrt{45}$
　　　　$v = 34$ ft. (rounded)

　　b.　$\cos \angle A = \dfrac{10}{35}$
　　　　$\cos \angle A = .2857$
　　　　$\angle A = 73°$

1.06

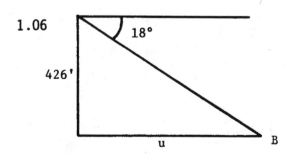

$\angle B = 18°$

$\cot \angle B = \dfrac{u}{426}$
　　$u = 426 \cos 18°$
　　$u = 426(3.08)$
　　$u = 1,312$ ft.

1.07

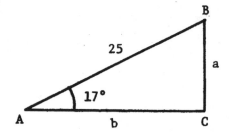

a. $\overline{AC} = b;$

$$\therefore \cos 17° = \frac{b}{25}$$
$$b = 25 \cos 17°$$
$$b = 25(.956)$$
$$b = 23.9$$
$$\underline{b = 24 \text{ cm}}$$
$$\overline{AC} = 24 \text{ cm}$$

b. $\overline{BC} = a;$

$$\therefore \sin 17° = \frac{a}{25}$$
$$a = 25 \sin 17°$$
$$a = 25(.2924)$$
$$\underline{a = 7.3 \text{ cm}}$$
$$\overline{BC} = 7.3 \text{ cm}$$

SELF TEST 2

2.01 $u = -20$
$v = 21$
$r = \sqrt{(-20)^2 + 21^2}$
$= \sqrt{400 + 441}$
$= \sqrt{841}$
$= 29$

a. $\sin \theta = \frac{v}{r} = \frac{21}{29}$

b. $\cos \theta = \frac{u}{r} = \frac{-20}{29} = -\frac{20}{29}$

c. $\tan \theta = \frac{v}{u} = \frac{21}{-20} = -\frac{21}{20}$

2.02

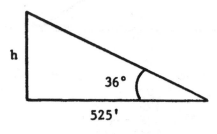

2.02 cont.

$$\tan 36° = \frac{h}{525}$$
$$h = 525 \tan 36°$$
$$h = 525(.7265)$$
$$h = 381 \text{ ft.}$$

2.03

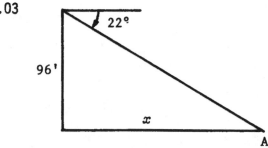

$$\angle A = 22°$$
$$\cos 22° = \frac{x}{96}$$
$$x = 96 \cot 22°$$
$$x = 96(2.48)$$
$$x = 238 \text{ ft.}$$

2.04

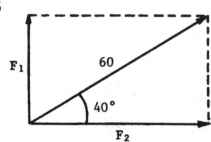

$$\sin 35° = \frac{\overline{GF}}{100}$$
$$\overline{GF} = 100 \sin 35°$$
$$\overline{GF} = 100(.5735)$$
$$\overline{GF} = 57.4 \text{ or } 57 \text{ lbs.}$$
$$\text{(rounded)}$$

2.05

2.05 cont.

a. $\sin 40° = \dfrac{F_1}{60}$

$F_1 = 60 \sin 40°$
$F_1 = 60(.6428)$
$F_1 = 38.56$ or 39 lbs.
(rounded)

b. $\cos 40° = \dfrac{F_2}{60}$

$F_2 = 60 \cos 40°$
$F_2 = 60(.7660)$
$F_2 = 45.96$ or 46 lbs.
(rounded)

2.06

a. $R^2 = 41^2 + 37^2$
$R^2 = 1,681 + 1,369$
$R^2 = 3,050$
$\sqrt{R^2} = \sqrt{3,050}$
$R = 55.2$ or 55 lbs.
(rounded)

b. $\tan \theta = \dfrac{41}{37}$
$\tan \theta = 1.108$
$\theta = 48°$

2.07

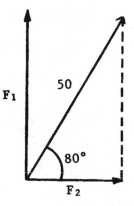

a. $\cos 80° = \dfrac{F_2}{50}$
$F_2 = 50 \cos 80°$
$F_2 = 50(.1736)$
$F_2 = 8.68$ or 9 lbs.
(rounded)

2.07 cont.

b. $\sin 80° = \dfrac{F_1}{50}$
$F_1 = 50 \sin 80°$
$F_1 = 50(.9848)$
$F_1 = 49.2$ or 49 lbs.
(rounded)

2.08

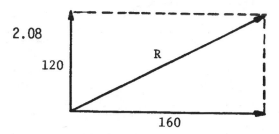

$R^2 = 160^2 + 120^2$
$R^2 = 25,600 + 14,400$
$R^2 = 40,000$
$\sqrt{R^2} = \sqrt{40,000}$
$R = 200$ lbs.

2.09

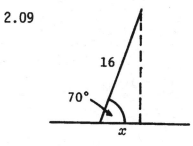

$\cos 70° = \dfrac{x}{16}$
$x = 16 \cos 70°$
$x = 16(.3420)$
$x = 5.4$ or 5 lbs.
(rounded)

2.010

20   F_2 θ F_1

2.010 cont.

a. $F_1^2 + F_2^2 = 20^2$ and $F_1 = F_2$
$$2F_1^2 = 20^2$$
$$2F_1^2 = 400$$
$$F_1^2 = \frac{400}{2} = 200$$
$$\sqrt{F_1^2} = \sqrt{200}$$
$$F_1 = 10\sqrt{2}$$

b. $\theta = 45°$; isoceles rt. $\triangle$

SELF TEST 3

3.01 a.
$$b^2 = a^2 + c^2 - 2ac \cos B$$
$$b^2 = 12^2 + 10^2 - 2(12)(10)\cos 24°$$
$$b^2 = 144 + 100 - 240(.9135)$$
$$b^2 = 244 - 219.25$$
$$b^2 = 24.75$$
$$\sqrt{b^2} = \sqrt{24.75}$$
$$b = 4.97 \text{ or } 5 \text{ (rounded)}$$

b.
$$a^2 = b^2 + c^2 - 2bc \cos A$$
$$12^2 = 5^2 + 10^2 - 2(5) \cdot (10)\cos A$$
$$144 = 25 + 100 - 100 \cos A$$
$$144 = 125 - 100 \cos A$$
$$19 = -100 \cos A$$
$$\cos A = -\frac{19}{100}$$
$$\cos A = -.19$$
$$\angle A = 180° - 79°$$
$$\angle A = 101°$$

c. $\angle C = 180° - \angle B - \angle A$
$$\angle C = 180° - 24° - 101°$$
$$\angle C = 180° - 125°$$
$$\angle C = 55°$$

3.02 $x = 3$
$y = -4$
$r = \sqrt{3^2 + (-4)^2}$
$= \sqrt{9 + 16}$
$= \sqrt{25}$
$= 5$

3.02 cont.

a. $\sin \theta = \frac{-4}{5} = -\frac{4}{5}$

b. $\cos \theta = \frac{3}{5}$

c. $\tan \theta = \frac{-4}{3} = -\frac{4}{3}$

d. $\csc \theta = \frac{5}{-4} = -\frac{5}{4}$

e. $\sec \theta = \frac{5}{3}$

f. $\cot \theta = \frac{3}{-4} = -\frac{3}{4}$

3.03

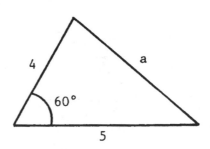

$$a^2 = 4^2 + 5^2 - 2(4)(5)\cos 60°$$
$$a^2 = 16 + 25 - 40(\tfrac{1}{2})$$
$$a^2 = 41 - 20$$
$$a^2 = 21$$
$$\sqrt{a^2} = \sqrt{21}$$
$$a = \sqrt{21} \text{ or } 4.6 \text{ in. (rounded)}$$

3.04

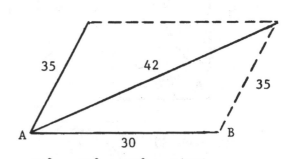

$$42^2 = 30^2 + 35^2 - 2(30) \cdot (35)\cos B$$
$$1{,}764 = 900 + 1{,}225 - 2{,}100 \cos B$$
$$1{,}764 = 2{,}125 - 2{,}100 \cos B$$
$$-361 = -2{,}100 \cos B$$
$$\cos B = \frac{361}{2{,}100}$$
$$\cos B = .1719$$
$$\angle B = 80°$$

3.04 cont.

$\angle A = 180° - \angle B$
$\angle A = 180° - 80°$
$\angle A = 100°$

3.05

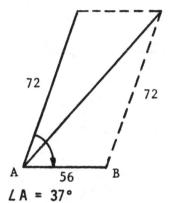

$\angle A = 37°$

$\angle B = 180° - \angle A$
$\angle B = 180° - 37°$
$\angle B = 143°$

$R^2 = 72^2 + 56^2 - 2(72)\cdot$
$\qquad (56)\cos 143°$
$R^2 = 5{,}184 + 3{,}136 -$
$\qquad 8{,}064(-.7986)$
$R^2 = 8{,}320 + 6{,}440$
$R^2 = 14{,}760$
$\sqrt{R^2} = \sqrt{14{,}760}$
$\quad R = 121.5$ lbs. (rounded)

3.06

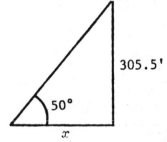

$\cot 50° = \dfrac{x}{305.5}$
$\quad x = 305.5 \cot 50°$
$\quad x = 305.5(.8391)$
$\quad x = 256.3$ ft.

3.07 Let x = height above the
window and
y = height below the
window.

Then $h = x + y$.

$\tan 25° = \dfrac{x}{185}$
$\quad x = 185 \tan 25°$
$\quad x = 185(.4663)$
$\quad x = 86.27$

$\tan 12° = \dfrac{y}{185}$
$\quad y = 185 \tan 12°$
$\quad y = 185(.2126)$
$\quad y = 39.33$

$h = x + y$
$h = 86.27 + 39.33$
$h = 125.6$ ft. (rounded)

SELF TEST 4

4.01 a. $\dfrac{20}{\sin 30°} = \dfrac{b}{\sin 45°}$

$b = \dfrac{20 \sin 45°}{\sin 30°}$

$b = \dfrac{20\left(\frac{\sqrt{2}}{2}\right)}{\frac{1}{2}}$

$b = 20\sqrt{2}$
$b = 28$

b. $\dfrac{c}{\sin 105°} = \dfrac{20}{\sin 30°}$

$c = \dfrac{20 \sin 105°}{\sin 30°}$

$c = \dfrac{20 \sin 75°}{\sin 30°}$

$c = \dfrac{20(.9659)}{\frac{1}{2}}$

$c = 38.636$ or 39
(rounded)

c. $\angle C = 180° - 30° - 45°$
$\angle C = 180° - 75°$
$\angle C = 105°$

4.02

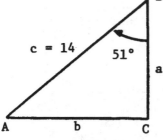

a. $\cos 51° = \dfrac{a}{14}$

     $a = 14 \cos 51°$

     $a = 14(.6293)$

     $a \doteq 8.81$

b. $\sin 51° = \dfrac{b}{14}$

     $b = 14 \sin 51°$

     $b = 14(.7771)$

     $b \doteq 10.88$

c. $\angle A = 180° - 90° - 51°$

     $\angle A = 180° - 141°$

     $\angle A = 39°$

4.03
$x = -8$
$y = 6$
$r = \sqrt{(-8)^2 + 6^2}$
  $= \sqrt{64 + 36}$
  $= \sqrt{100}$
  $= 10$

a. $\sin \theta = \dfrac{6}{10} = \dfrac{3}{5}$

b. $\cos \theta = \dfrac{-8}{10} = -\dfrac{4}{5}$

c. $\tan \theta = \dfrac{6}{-8} = -\dfrac{3}{4}$

d. $\csc \theta = \dfrac{10}{6} = \dfrac{5}{3}$

e. $\sec \theta = \dfrac{10}{-8} = -\dfrac{5}{4}$

f. $\cot \theta = \dfrac{-8}{6} = -\dfrac{4}{3}$

4.04 $\angle B = 180° - 55° - 50°$
     $\angle B = 180° - 105°$
     $\angle B = 75°$

$$\dfrac{b}{\sin 75°} = \dfrac{30}{\sin 50°}$$

$$b = \dfrac{30 \sin 75°}{\sin 50°}$$

$$b = \dfrac{30(.9659)}{.7660}$$

$$b \doteq 37.83$$

4.05

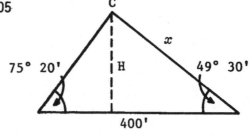

$\angle C = 180° - 75° 20' - 49° 30'$
$\angle C = 180° - 124° 50'$
$\angle C = 55° 10'$

$$\dfrac{x}{\sin 75° 20'} = \dfrac{400}{\sin 55° 10'}$$

$$x = \dfrac{400 \sin 75° 20'}{\sin 55° 10'}$$

$$x = \dfrac{400(.9674)}{.8208}$$

$$x = 471 \text{ (rounded)}$$

$\sin 49° 30' = \dfrac{H}{x}$

     $H = x \sin 49° 30'$

     $H = 471(.7604)$

     $H = 358.4$ ft.

4.06

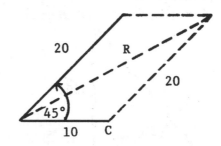

$\angle C = 180° - 45°$
$\angle C = 135°$

$R^2 = 10^2 + 20^2 - 2(10) \cdot$
       $(20)\cos 135°$
$R^2 = 100 + 400 - 400(-\cos 45°)$
$R^2 = 500 + 400(.707)$
$R^2 = 782.8$
$\sqrt{R^2} = \sqrt{782.8}$
   $R = 27.9$ or 28 ft. (rounded)

4.07

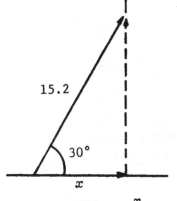

a. $\cos 30° = \dfrac{x}{15.2}$

   $x = 15.2 \cos 30°$

   $x = 15.2(\dfrac{\sqrt{2}}{2})$

   $x \doteq 13.2$ lbs.

b. $\sin 30° = \dfrac{y}{15.2}$

   $y = 15.2 \sin 30°$

   $y = 15.2(\dfrac{1}{2})$

   $y = 7.6$ lbs.

4.08

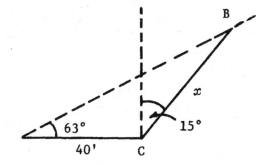

$\angle C = 90° + 15°$
$\angle C = 105°$

$\angle B = 180° - 63° - 105°$
$\angle B = 180° - 168°$
$\angle B = 12°$

$\dfrac{40}{\sin 12°} = \dfrac{x}{\sin 63°}$

   $x = \dfrac{40 \sin 63°}{\sin 12°}$

   $x = \dfrac{40(.8910)}{.2079}$

   $x = 171$ ft. (rounded)

4.09

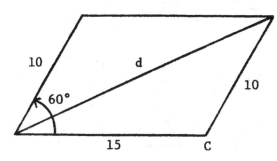

$\angle C = 180° - 60°$
$\angle C = 120°$

$d^2 = 10^2 + 15^2 - 2(10) \cdot$
$\qquad (15)\cos 120°$
$d^2 = 100 + 225 - 300(-\cos 60°)$
$d^2 = 325 + 300(\dfrac{1}{2})$
$d^2 = 325 + 150$
$d^2 = 475$
$\sqrt{d^2} = \sqrt{475}$
$d = 21.8$

4.010

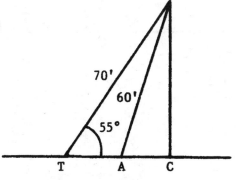

$\dfrac{70}{\sin \angle TAB} = \dfrac{60}{\sin 55°}$

$\sin \angle TAB = \dfrac{70 \sin 55°}{60}$

$\sin \angle TAB = 0.9557$

$\angle TAB = 180° - 73°$

$\angle TAB = 107°$ (second
   quadrant)

$\angle BAC = 180° - \angle TAB$
$\angle BAC = 180° - 107°$
$\angle BAC = 73°$

SELF TEST 5

5.01

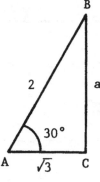

$$\sin 30° = \frac{a}{2}$$
$$a = 2 \sin 30°$$
$$a = 2(\tfrac{1}{2})$$
$$a = 1$$

5.02

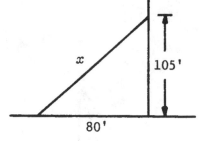

$$x^2 = 105^2 + 80^2$$
$$x^2 = 11,025 + 6,400$$
$$x^2 = 17,425$$
$$\sqrt{x^2} = \sqrt{17,425}$$
$$x = 132 \text{ ft. (rounded)}$$

5.03

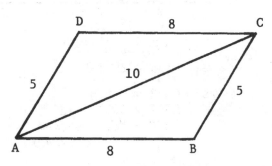

a. $\angle DAB = 180° - \angle B$
$$10^2 = 8^2 + 5^2 - 2(8)(5)\cos B$$
$$100 = 64 + 25 - 80 \cos B$$
$$100 = 89 - 80 \cos B$$
$$11 = -80 \cos B$$
$$\cos B = -\frac{11}{80} = -.1375$$
$$\angle B = 98°$$
$$\angle DAB = 180° - 98°$$
$$\angle DAB = 82°$$

5.03 cont.

b. $\dfrac{5}{\sin \angle CAB} = \dfrac{10}{\sin \angle B}$
$$\sin \angle CAB = \frac{5 \sin \angle B}{10}$$
$$\sin \angle CAB = \frac{5 \sin 98°}{10}$$
$$\sin \angle CAB = \tfrac{1}{2}(.9903)$$
$$\sin \angle CAB = .4952$$
$$\angle CAB = 29.7° \text{ or } 30°$$
$$\text{(rounded)}$$

5.04

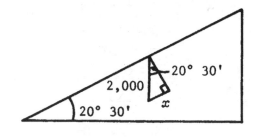

$$\sin 20° \ 30' = \frac{x}{2,000}$$
$$x = 2,000 \sin 20° \ 30'$$
$$x = 2,000(.3502)$$
$$x = 700.4 \text{ or } 700 \text{ lbs.}$$
$$\text{(rounded)}$$

5.05

The smallest angle of a triangle lies opposite the smallest side.

$$250^2 = 300^2 + 420^2 -$$
$$2(300)(420)\cos \theta$$
$$62,500 = 90,000 + 176,400 -$$
$$252,000 \cos \theta$$
$$62,500 = 266,400 - 252,000 \cos \theta$$
$$-203,900 = -252,000 \cos \theta$$
$$\cos \theta = \frac{203,900}{252,000}$$
$$\cos \theta = .8091$$
$$\theta = 36°$$

5.06

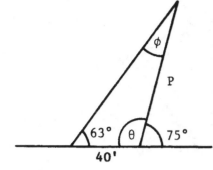

$\angle \theta = 180° - 75°$
$\angle \theta = 105°$

$\angle \phi = 180° - 105° - 63°$
$\angle \phi = 12°$

$\dfrac{P}{\sin 63°} = \dfrac{40}{\sin 12°}$

$P = \dfrac{40 \sin 63°}{\sin 12°}$

$P = \dfrac{40(.8910)}{.2079}$

$P = 171.4$ or 171 ft.
(rounded)

5.07

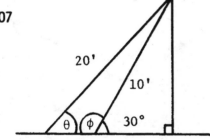

$\angle \phi = 180° - 30°$
$\angle \phi = 150°$

$\dfrac{20}{\sin 150°} = \dfrac{10}{\sin \theta}$

$\sin \theta = \dfrac{10 \sin 150°}{20}$

$\sin \theta = \dfrac{1}{2} \sin 30°$

$\sin \theta = \dfrac{1}{2}(\dfrac{1}{2})$

$\sin \theta = \dfrac{1}{4} = .25$

$\theta = 14°$

5.08

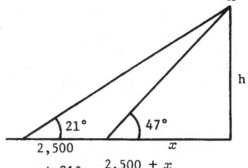

$\cot 21° = \dfrac{2{,}500 + x}{h}$

$2{,}500 + x = h \cot 21°$
$x = h \cot 21° - 2{,}500$

Also, $\cot 47° = \dfrac{x}{h}$ or
$x = h \cot 47°$

Therefore,
$h \cot 21° - 2{,}500 = h \cot 47°$

$h \cot 21° - h \cot 47° = 2{,}500$

$(\cot 21° - \cot 47°)h = 2{,}500$

$h = \dfrac{2{,}500}{\cot 21° - \cot 47°}$

$h = \dfrac{2{,}500}{2.6 - .9}$

$h = \dfrac{2{,}500}{1.7}$

$h = 1{,}470$ ft.
(rounded)

5.09

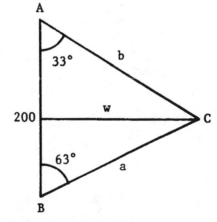

$\angle ACB = 180° - 33° - 63°$
$\angle ACB = 180° - 96°$
$\angle ACB = 84°$

5.09 cont.

a. $\dfrac{200}{\sin 84°} = \dfrac{b}{\sin 63°}$

$b = \dfrac{200 \sin 63°}{\sin 84°}$

$b = \dfrac{200(.8910)}{.9945}$

$b = 179$ ft. (rounded)

b. $\dfrac{200}{\sin 84°} = \dfrac{a}{\sin 33°}$

$a = \dfrac{200 \sin 33°}{\sin 84°}$

$a = \dfrac{200(.5446)}{.9945}$

$a = 110$ ft. (rounded)

c. $\sin 33° = \dfrac{w}{b}$

$w = b \sin 33°$

$w = 179(.5446)$

$w = 97.4$ or 97 ft.
(rounded)

5.010

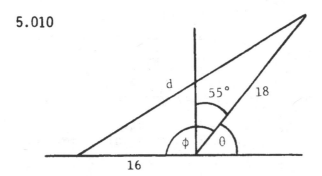

$\angle\theta = 90° - 55°$
$\angle\theta = 35°$

$\angle\phi = 180° - 35°$
$\angle\phi = 145°$

$d^2 = 16^2 + 18^2 - 2(16)\cdot$
$\quad (18)\cos 145°$
$d^2 = 256 + 324 - 576(-.8192)$
$d^2 = 580 + 472$
$d^2 = 1052$
$d = 32.4$ or 32 na. mi. (rounded)

SELF TEST 6

6.01

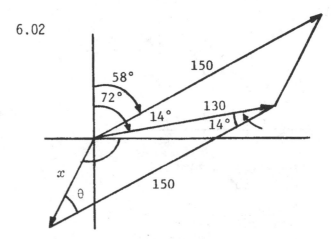

$\angle P = 180° - 78° \ 10' - 47° \ 20'$
$\angle P = 180° - 125° \ 30'$
$\angle P = 54° \ 30'$

$\dfrac{x}{\sin 78° \ 10'} = \dfrac{2,540}{\sin 54° \ 30'}$

$x = \dfrac{2,540 \sin 78° \ 10'}{\sin 54° \ 30'}$

$x = \dfrac{2,540(.9787)}{.8141}$

$x = 3,053.6$ or 3,050 ft.
(rounded to
the nearest
ten)

6.02

a. $x^2 = 130^2 + 150^2 - 2(130)\cdot$
$\quad (150)\cos 14°$
$x^2 = 16,900 + 22,500 -$
$\quad 39,000(.9703)$
$x^2 = 16,900 + 22,500 - 37,842$
$x^2 = 1,558$
$\sqrt{x^2} = \sqrt{1,558}$
$x \doteq 39.47$ or 39 mph

6.02 cont.

b. $\dfrac{130}{\sin \theta} = \dfrac{40}{\sin 14°}$

$\sin \theta = \dfrac{130 \sin 14°}{39}$

$\sin \theta = \dfrac{130(.2419)}{39}$

$\sin \theta = .8063$

$\theta = 54°$

direction of wind = 72° + 180° - 14° - 54°

= 72° + 112°

= 184°

6.03

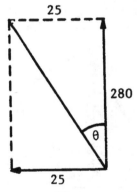

$\sin 35° = \dfrac{x}{100}$

$x = 100 \sin 35°$

$x = 100(.5736)$

$x = 57.4$ lbs.

6.04

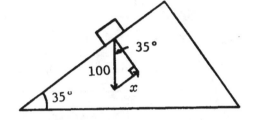

$\tan \theta = \dfrac{25}{280}$

$\theta = .0893$

$\theta = 5°$

course = 360° - 5°

= 355°

6.05

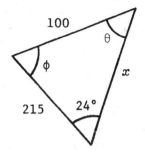

$\dfrac{100}{\sin 24°} = \dfrac{215}{\sin \theta}$

$\sin \theta = \dfrac{215 \sin 24°}{100}$

$\sin \theta = \dfrac{215(.4067)}{100}$

$\sin \theta = .8744$

$\theta = 61°$

$\angle \phi = 180° - 61° - 24°$

$\angle \phi = 180° - 85°$

$\angle \phi = 95°$

$\dfrac{x}{\sin 95°} = \dfrac{215}{\sin 61°}$

$x = \dfrac{215 \sin 95°}{\sin 61°}$

$x = \dfrac{215(.9962)}{.8746}$

$x = 245$ yd. (rounded)

6.06

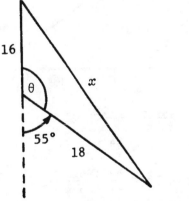

$\angle \theta = 180° - 55°$

$\angle \theta = 125°$

$x^2 = 16^2 + 18^2 - 2(16) \cdot (18)\cos 125°$

$x^2 = 256 + 324 - 576(-.5736)$

$x^2 = 256 + 324 + 330$

$x^2 = 910$

$\sqrt{x^2} = \sqrt{910}$

$x = 30$ na. mi. (rounded)

6.07 a. $\angle A = 90° - 30°$
          $\angle A = 60°$

      b. $\sin 30° = \dfrac{\overline{AC}}{2}$

             $\dfrac{1}{2} = \dfrac{\overline{AC}}{2}$

             $\overline{AC} = 2\left(\tfrac{1}{2}\right)$

             $\overline{AC} = 1$

      c. $\sin B = \dfrac{1}{2}$

          $\cos B = \dfrac{\sqrt{3}}{2}$

          $\tan B = \dfrac{1}{\sqrt{3}} = \dfrac{\sqrt{3}}{3}$

      d. $\csc A = \dfrac{1}{\frac{\sqrt{3}}{2}} = \dfrac{2}{\sqrt{3}} = \dfrac{2\sqrt{3}}{3}$

          $\sec A = \dfrac{1}{\frac{1}{2}} = 2$

          $\cot A = \dfrac{1}{\sqrt{3}} = \dfrac{\sqrt{3}}{3}$

6.08

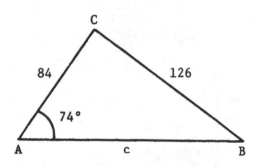

  a. $\dfrac{84}{\sin \angle B} = \dfrac{126}{\sin 74°}$

        $\sin \angle B = \dfrac{84 \sin 74°}{126}$

        $\sin \angle B = \dfrac{84(.9613)}{126}$

        $\sin \angle B = .6408$

           $\angle B = 39.85°$ or $39°\ 51'$

6.08 cont.

  b. $\angle C = 180° - 74° - 39°\ 51'$
        $\angle C = 66°\ 9'$

  c. $\dfrac{c}{\sin 66°\ 9'} = \dfrac{126}{\sin 74°}$

            $c = \dfrac{126 \sin 66°\ 9'}{\sin 74°}$

            $c = \dfrac{126(.9146)}{.9613}$

            $c = 119.88$

6.09

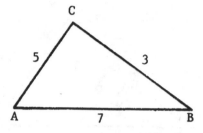

    $3^2 = 5^2 + 7^2 - 2(5)(7)\cos A$
    $9 = 25 + 49 - 70 \cos A$
    $9 = 74 - 70 \cos A$
  $-65 = -70 \cos A$

$\cos \angle A = \dfrac{65}{70}$

$\cos \angle A = .9286$

    $\angle A = 21°\ 47'$ or $22°$
              (rounded)

6.010

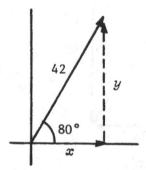

  a. $x = 42 \cos 80°$
      $x = 42(.1736)$
      $x = 7.29$

  b. $y = 42 \sin 80°$
      $y = 42(.9848)$
      $y = 41.36$

MATHEMATICS 1207
SELF TEST
SOLUTION KEY

SELF TEST 1

1.01 $y = \arcsin(-\frac{\sqrt{3}}{2})$, $\sin y = -\frac{\sqrt{3}}{2}$

$y = \frac{4\pi}{3} \pm 2\pi K$ or $\frac{5\pi}{3} \pm 2\pi K$

1.02 Let $y = \arcsin 2$.
Then $2 = \sin y$ and y is an undefined angle ($\sin y < 1$). Hence, $\sin y$ is undefined and the soluiton is ϕ.

1.03 Let $y = \arcsin x$ where $x = \sin 30°$. Then $x = \sin y$ and $\sin 30° = \sin y$
$\therefore y = 30°$

1.04 $\frac{y}{2} = \arcsin \frac{\sqrt{2}}{2}$,

$\sin \frac{y}{2} = \frac{\sqrt{2}}{2}$

$\frac{y}{2} = 45°$

$\therefore y = 90°$ or $\frac{\pi}{2}$

1.05 infinite

SELF TEST 2

2.01 $y = \arcsin(-\frac{\sqrt{2}}{2})$, $\sin y = -\frac{\sqrt{2}}{2}$,

$y = \frac{5\pi}{4} \pm 2\pi K$ or $\frac{7\pi}{4} \pm 2\pi K$

2.02 $y = \arccos(-1)$, $\cos y = -1$,
$y = \pm \pi K$

2.03 Let $\theta = \arccos \frac{4}{5}$; find $\sin \frac{1}{2}\theta$.

$\cos \theta = \frac{4}{5}$

$\sin \frac{1}{2}\theta = \sqrt{\frac{1 - \cos \theta}{2}}$

$= \sqrt{\frac{1 - \frac{4}{5}}{2}}$

$= \sqrt{\frac{1}{10}}$

$= \frac{1}{\sqrt{10}}$

$= \frac{\sqrt{10}}{10}$

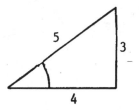

2.04 Let $\theta = \arcsin \frac{1}{2}$ and

$\phi = \arccos \frac{1}{3}$.
Then $\sin(\theta - \phi) = \sin(\arcsin \frac{1}{2}) \cdot$

$\cos(\arccos \frac{1}{3}) -$

$\sin(\arccos \frac{1}{3}) \cdot$

$\cos(\arcsin \frac{1}{2})$.

$\sin(\theta - \phi) = \frac{1}{2} \cdot \frac{1}{3} - \frac{2\sqrt{2}}{3} \cdot \frac{\sqrt{3}}{2}$

$= \frac{1}{6} - \frac{2\sqrt{6}}{6}$

$= \frac{1 - 2\sqrt{6}}{6}$

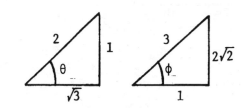

2.05 Let $\theta = \arcsin \frac{5}{13}$ and $\phi = \arcsin \frac{4}{5}$.

$$\begin{aligned}
\sin(\theta + \phi) &= \sin\theta\cos\phi + \cos\theta\sin\phi \\
&= \frac{5}{13}\cdot\frac{3}{5} + \frac{12}{13}\cdot\frac{4}{5} \\
&= \frac{15}{65} + \frac{48}{65} \\
&= \frac{63}{65}
\end{aligned}$$

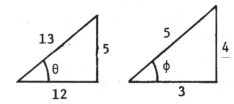

SELF TEST 3

3.01 Let $x = \arcsin \frac{2}{3}$; then $\sin x = \frac{2}{3}$.

$$\tan x = \frac{2}{\sqrt{5}}$$

$$\tan(\pi + x) = \tan x = \frac{2}{\sqrt{5}} = \frac{2\sqrt{5}}{5}$$

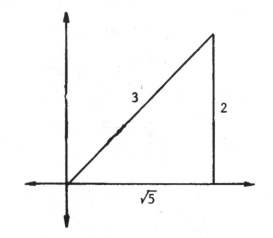

3.02 Let $A = \arcsin\left(-\frac{1}{2}\right)$ and

$B = \arccos\frac{5}{13}$. $\sin A = -\frac{1}{2}$

and $\cos B = \frac{5}{13}$

$$\begin{aligned}
\cos(A + B) &= \cos A\cos B - \sin A\sin B \\
&= \frac{\sqrt{3}}{2}\cdot\frac{5}{13} - \left(-\frac{1}{2}\right)\cdot\frac{12}{13} \\
&= \frac{5\sqrt{3}}{26} + \frac{12}{26} \\
&= \frac{12 + 5\sqrt{3}}{26}
\end{aligned}$$

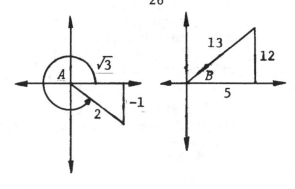

3.03 Let $A = \arccos\left(-\frac{8}{17}\right)$; then

$\cos A = -\frac{8}{17}$. Find $\sin 2A$.

$$\begin{aligned}
\sin 2A &= 2\sin A\cos A \\
&= 2\cdot\frac{15}{17}\cdot\left(-\frac{8}{17}\right) \\
&= -\frac{240}{289}
\end{aligned}$$

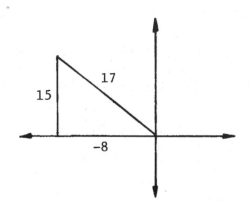

336

3.04   Let $x = \arctan \frac{3}{5}$; then

$\tan x = \frac{3}{5}$.   Find $\sin \frac{1}{2}x$.

$\sin \frac{1}{2}x = \sqrt{\dfrac{1 - \cos x}{2}}$

$= \sqrt{\dfrac{1 - \dfrac{5}{\sqrt{34}}}{2}}$

$= \sqrt{\dfrac{\sqrt{34} - 5}{2 \cdot \sqrt{34}}}$

$= \sqrt{\dfrac{34 - 5\sqrt{34}}{2 \cdot 34}}$

$= \sqrt{\dfrac{34 - 5\sqrt{34}}{68}}$

$= \dfrac{1}{2}\sqrt{\dfrac{34 - 5\sqrt{34}}{17}}$

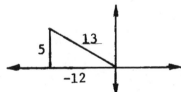

3.05   Let $x = \text{arc tan}\left(-\dfrac{5}{12}\right)$; then

$\tan x = -\dfrac{5}{12}$. $\cos x = -\dfrac{12}{13}$

3.06   Show $\sin\left[\arcsin \dfrac{3}{5} + \arcsin \dfrac{12}{13}\right] =$
$\sin\left[\arccos\left(-\dfrac{16}{65}\right)\right]$.

Let $\theta = \arcsin \dfrac{3}{5}$, $\phi = \arcsin \dfrac{12}{13}$.

3.06 cont.

$\sin(\theta + \phi) = \sin \theta \cos \phi +$
$\cos \theta \sin \phi$

$= \dfrac{3}{5} \cdot \dfrac{5}{13} + \dfrac{4}{5} \cdot \dfrac{12}{13}$

$= \dfrac{15}{65} + \dfrac{48}{65}$

$= \dfrac{63}{65}$

Also, $\sin\left[\arccos\left(-\dfrac{16}{65}\right)\right] = \dfrac{63}{65}$.

Therefore, $\dfrac{63}{65} = \dfrac{63}{65}$.

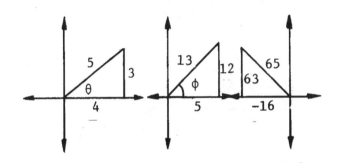

3.07   Show that $\cos\left[\arccos\left(-\dfrac{2}{3}\right) - \arccos\left(\dfrac{2}{3}\right)\right] = \cos\left(\arccos \dfrac{1}{9}\right)$.

If $\theta = \arccos\left(-\dfrac{2}{3}\right)$ and $\phi = \arccos \dfrac{2}{3}$, then $\cos(\theta - \phi) =$

$\cos \theta \cos \phi + \sin \theta \sin \phi$.

$\cos(\theta - \phi) = -\dfrac{2}{3} \cdot \dfrac{2}{3} + \dfrac{\sqrt{5}}{3} \cdot \dfrac{\sqrt{5}}{3}$

$= -\dfrac{4}{9} + \dfrac{5}{9}$

$= \dfrac{1}{9} = \cos\left(\arccos \dfrac{1}{9}\right)$

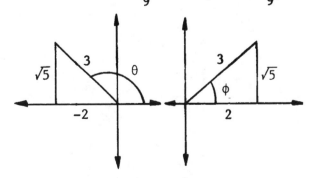

3.08 Show that $\tan[\arctan \frac{4}{3} - \arcsin(-\frac{8}{17})] = \tan(\arctan \frac{84}{13})$.

Let $\theta = \arctan \frac{4}{3}$ and $\phi = \arcsin(-\frac{8}{17})$.

$$\tan(\theta - \phi) = \frac{\tan \theta - \tan \phi}{1 + \tan \theta \tan \phi}$$

$$= \frac{\frac{4}{3} - \frac{8}{15}}{1 + \frac{4}{3} \cdot \frac{8}{15}}$$

$$= \frac{60 - 24}{45 + 32}$$

$$= \frac{36}{77}$$

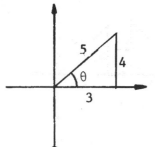

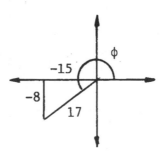

3.09 Let $\theta = \arccos x$; then $\cos \phi = x$.
Then $\sin \theta = \frac{\sqrt{1 - x^2}}{1}$.
Therefore, $\sin(\arccos x) = \sqrt{1 - x^2}$.

3.010 If $y = 3 \tan(2x)$, then $\frac{y}{3} = \tan 2x$ and $2x = \arctan(\frac{y}{3})$.

$$x = \frac{1}{2} \arctan(\frac{y}{3})$$

By definition of inverse, interchange x and y; then
$y = \frac{1}{2} \arctan(\frac{x}{3})$.

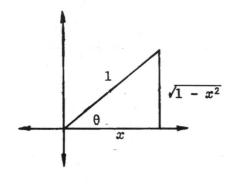

SELF TEST 4

4.01 Let $x = \arcsin \frac{2}{7}$; find $\cot(2x)$.
$\sin x = \frac{2}{7}$

$$\cot 2x = \frac{1 - \tan^2 x}{2 \tan x} = \frac{1 - (\frac{2}{3\sqrt{5}})^2}{2(\frac{2}{3\sqrt{5}})} =$$

$$\frac{1 - \frac{4}{45}}{\frac{4}{3\sqrt{5}}} = \frac{45 - 4}{12\sqrt{5}} = \frac{41\sqrt{5}}{60}$$

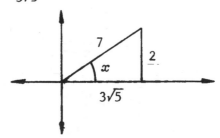

4.02 Let $x = \arctan 6$; find $\cos 2x$.
$\tan x = 6$

$$\cos 2x = 2 \cos^2 x - 1 = 2(\frac{1}{\sqrt{37}})^2 - 1 = \frac{2}{37} - 1 = -\frac{35}{37}$$

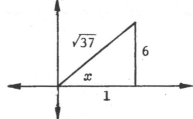

4.03 Let $x = \arccos \frac{1}{2}$; find $\tan \frac{1}{2}x$.

$\cos x = \frac{1}{2}$

$$\tan \frac{1}{2}x = \sqrt{\frac{1 - \cos x}{1 + \cos x}} = \sqrt{\frac{1 - \frac{1}{2}}{1 + \frac{1}{2}}} =$$

$$\sqrt{\frac{\frac{1}{2}}{\frac{3}{2}}} = \sqrt{\frac{1}{3}} = \frac{\sqrt{3}}{3}$$

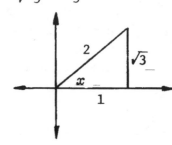

4.04   Let $x = \arctan(-\frac{5}{12})$.

$\tan x = -\frac{5}{12}$; x is in the second or fourth quadrant

$\cos x = \pm\frac{12}{13}$

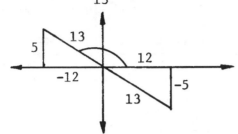

4.05   Let $x = \arctan\frac{3}{4}$; find $\cos\frac{1}{2}x$.

$\tan x = \frac{3}{4}$

$\cos\frac{1}{2}x = \pm\sqrt{\dfrac{1 + \cos x}{2}} = \pm\sqrt{\dfrac{1 + \frac{4}{5}}{2}} =$

$\pm\sqrt{\dfrac{9}{10}} = \pm\dfrac{3}{\sqrt{10}} = \pm\dfrac{3\sqrt{10}}{10}$

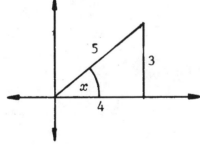

4.06   Let $\theta = \arctan(-\frac{2}{3})$ and

$\phi = \text{arccot}(\frac{2}{3})$. Show $\sin(\theta - \phi) =$

$\sin(-\frac{\pi}{2}) = -1$.

$\sin(\theta - \phi) = \sin\theta\cos\phi -$
$\qquad\qquad\quad \cos\theta\sin\phi$

$= -\dfrac{2}{\sqrt{13}}\cdot\dfrac{2}{\sqrt{13}} - \dfrac{3}{\sqrt{13}}\cdot\dfrac{3}{\sqrt{13}}$

$= -\dfrac{4}{13} - \dfrac{9}{13}$

$= -\dfrac{13}{13}$

$= -1$

4.06 cont.

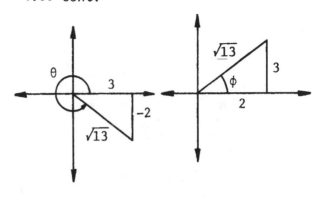

4.07   Let $x = \text{arcsec}\frac{5}{3}$.

Therefore, the problem reduces to show that $\text{arcsec}\frac{5}{3} =$

$\arctan\frac{4}{3}$; $\sec x = \frac{5}{3}$. From the diagram, $\tan x = \frac{4}{3}$; hence, $x =$

$\arctan\frac{4}{3}$ and $\text{arcsec}\frac{5}{3} =$

$\arctan\frac{4}{3}$.

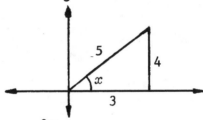

4.08 $\tan\frac{2\pi}{3} = -\sqrt{3}$

Let $x = \text{arccot}(-\sqrt{3})$; then $\cot x = \sqrt{3}$. Therefore, $x = \frac{5\pi}{6}$.

4.09 $\sec\pi = -1$
Let $x = \arctan(-1)$;
then $\tan x = -1$.
$x = \dfrac{3\pi}{4}$ or $\dfrac{7\pi}{4}$

4.010 Domain: $-1 \le x \le 1$
Range: all Real y

SELF TEST 5

5.01   Let $y = \arcsin \frac{\sqrt{3}}{2}$; $\sin y = \frac{\sqrt{3}}{2}$, $-\frac{\pi}{2} \le y \le \frac{\pi}{2}$.   Therefore, $y = \frac{\pi}{3}$.

5.02   Let $y = \arcsin \frac{\sqrt{3}}{2}$; $\sin y = \frac{\sqrt{3}}{2}$.

∴ $y = \frac{\pi}{3} \pm 2\pi K$ or $\frac{2\pi}{3} \pm 2\pi K$.

5.03   Let $y = \arccos 2$; $\cos y = 2$, since $-1 \le x \le 1$
∴ $y = \phi$, no solution

5.04   Let $y = \text{arcsec } 2$; $\sec y = 2$, $0 \le y \le \frac{\pi}{3}$. $y = \frac{\pi}{3}$

5.05   Let $x = \text{arccot } 1$; $\cos x = 1$.
∴ $x = \frac{\pi}{4} \pm 2\pi K$ or $\frac{5\pi}{4} \pm 2\pi K$

5.06   Let $x = \arcsin 0.30$; $\sin x = 0.30$; therefore, $\sin (\arcsin 0.30) = 0.30$.

5.07   Let $\theta = \arctan 2$; $\tan \theta = 2$.
$\cos \theta = \frac{1}{\sqrt{5}} = \frac{\sqrt{5}}{5}$

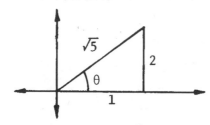

5.08   Let $x = \tan 30$; then $\arctan x = 30$.   Therefore, $\arctan (\tan 30) = \arctan (30) = 30$.

5.09   Let $x = \text{arccot } (-\frac{1}{\sqrt{3}})$; then $\cot x = -\frac{1}{\sqrt{3}}$. x is in the second or fourth quadrant.   The reference angle is $\frac{\pi}{3}$.   Therefore, $x = \pi - \frac{\pi}{3} = \frac{2\pi}{3}$ or $2\pi - \frac{\pi}{3} = \frac{5\pi}{3}$.

5.010   Let $x = \arcsin \frac{2}{3}$; $\sin x = \frac{2}{3}$.
$\tan (\pi + x) = \tan x = \frac{2}{\sqrt{5}} = \frac{2\sqrt{5}}{5}$

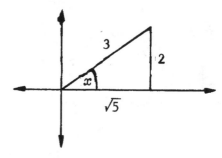

SELF TEST SIX

6.01 through 6.010

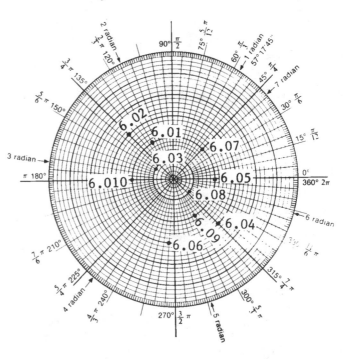

6.011 $y = \arcsin \frac{\sqrt{3}}{2}$, $\sin y = \frac{\sqrt{3}}{2}$, $y = \frac{\pi}{3}$

6.012   Let $x = \arccos (\cos \frac{\pi}{4})$.
Then $\cos x = \cos \frac{\pi}{4}$ and $x = \frac{\pi}{4}$.

6.013 Let $x = \arctan \frac{3}{5}$; then

$\tan x = \frac{3}{5}$. Find $\sin \frac{1}{2}x$.

$\sin \frac{1}{2}x = \sqrt{\dfrac{1 - \cos x}{2}}$

$= \sqrt{\dfrac{1 - \dfrac{5}{\sqrt{34}}}{2}}$

$= \sqrt{\dfrac{\sqrt{34} - 5}{2 \cdot \sqrt{34}}}$

$= \sqrt{\dfrac{34 - 5\sqrt{34}}{2 \cdot 34}}$

$= \sqrt{\dfrac{34 - 5\sqrt{34}}{68}}$

$= \dfrac{1}{2}\sqrt{\dfrac{34 - 5\sqrt{34}}{17}}$

6.014 Let $x = \text{arcsec } \frac{5}{3}$.

Therefore, the problem reduces
to show that $\text{arcsec } \frac{5}{3} = \arctan \frac{4}{3}$;
$\sec x = \frac{5}{3}$. From the diagram,
$\tan x = \frac{4}{3}$; hence, $x = \arctan \frac{4}{3}$ and
$\text{arcsec } \frac{5}{3} = \arctan \frac{4}{3}$.

6.015

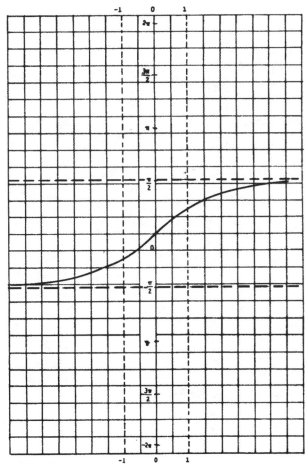

SELF TEST 7

7.01 through 7.06

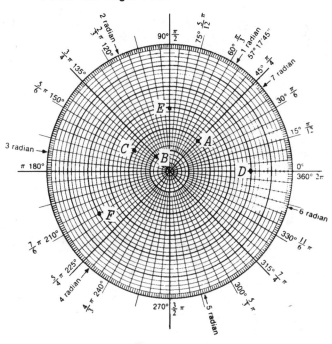

7.07 $x = r \cos \theta$
$x = 3 \cos \pi$
$x = 3(-1)$
$x = -3$

$y = r \sin \theta$
$y = 3 \sin \pi$
$y = 3(0)$
$y = 0$

$(x, y) = (-3, 0)$

7.08 $x = r \cos \theta$
$x = \sqrt{2} \cos(-\frac{3\pi}{4})$
$x = \sqrt{2} \cos \frac{3\pi}{4}$
$x = \sqrt{2}(-\cos \frac{\pi}{4})$
$x = -\sqrt{2}(\frac{\sqrt{2}}{2})$
$x = -1$

$y = r \sin \theta$
$y = \sqrt{2} \sin(-\frac{3\pi}{4})$
$y = -\sqrt{2} \sin \frac{3\pi}{4}$
$y = -\sqrt{2}(\sin \frac{\pi}{4})$
$y = -\sqrt{2}(\frac{\sqrt{2}}{2})$
$y = -1$

$(x, y) = (-1, -1)$

7.09 $x = r \cos \theta$
$x = -4 \cos 120°$
$x = 4 \cos 60°$
$x = 4(\frac{1}{2})$
$x = 2$

$y = r \sin \theta$
$y = -4 \sin 120°$
$y = -4 \sin 60°$
$y = -\frac{4\sqrt{3}}{2}$
$y = -2\sqrt{3}$

$(x, y) = (2, -2\sqrt{3})$

7.010 $x = r \cos \theta$
$x = -2 \cos(-\frac{\pi}{2})$
$x = -2 \cos \frac{\pi}{2}$
$x = -2(0)$
$x = 0$

$y = r \sin \theta$
$y = -2 \sin(-\frac{\pi}{2})$
$y = 2 \sin \frac{\pi}{2}$
$y = 2(1)$
$y = 2$

$(x, y) = (0, 2)$

7.011 $x = r \cos \theta$
$x = -2 \cos 315°$
$x = -2 \cos 45°$
$x = -\frac{2\sqrt{2}}{2}$
$x = -\sqrt{2}$

$y = r \sin \theta$
$y = -2 \sin 315°$
$y = -2(-\sin 45°)$
$y = 2(\frac{\sqrt{2}}{2})$
$y = \sqrt{2}$

$(x, y) = -\sqrt{2}, \sqrt{2})$

7.012 $x = r \cos \theta$
$x = -1 \cos(-\frac{7\pi}{6})$
$x = -1 \cos \frac{7\pi}{6}$
$x = -1(-\frac{\sqrt{3}}{2})$
$x = \frac{\sqrt{3}}{2}$

$y = r \sin \theta$
$y = -1 \sin(-\frac{7\pi}{6})$
$y = \sin \frac{7\pi}{6}$
$y = -\frac{1}{2}$

$(x, y) = (\frac{\sqrt{3}}{2}, -\frac{1}{2})$

7.013 $x = r \cos \theta$

$x = 0 \cos \dfrac{\pi}{2}$

$x = 0$

$y = r \sin \theta$

$y = 0 \sin \dfrac{\pi}{2}$

$y = 0$

$(x, y) = (0, 0)$

7.014 $r = \sqrt{x^2 + y^2}$
$r = \sqrt{1^2 + (-1)^2}$
$r = \sqrt{1 + 1}$
$r = \sqrt{2}$

$\theta = \tan^{-1} \left(\dfrac{y}{x}\right)$

$\theta = \tan^{-1} (-1)$
$\theta = 315°$

$(r, \theta) = (\sqrt{2}, 315°)$

7.015 $r = \sqrt{x^2 + y^2}$
$r = \sqrt{(-\sqrt{3})^2 + (1)^2}$
$r = \sqrt{3 + 1}$
$r = \sqrt{4}$
$r = 2$

$\theta = \tan^{-1} \left(\dfrac{y}{x}\right)$

$\theta = \tan^{-1} \left(-\dfrac{\sqrt{3}}{3}\right)$

$\theta = 150°$

$(r, \theta) = (2, 150°)$

7.016 $r = \sqrt{x^2 + y^2}$
$r = \sqrt{2^2 + 2^2}$
$r = \sqrt{4 + 4}$
$r = \sqrt{8}$
$r = 2\sqrt{2}$

$\theta = \tan^{-1} \left(\dfrac{y}{x}\right)$

$\theta = \tan^{-1} \left(\dfrac{2}{2}\right)$

$\theta = 45°$

$(r, \theta) = (2\sqrt{2}, 45°)$

7.017 $r = \sqrt{x^2 + y^2}$
$r = \sqrt{(-5)^2 + 0^2}$
$r = 5$

$\theta = \tan^{-1} \left(\dfrac{y}{x}\right)$

$\theta = \tan^{-1} \left(\dfrac{0}{-5}\right)$

$\theta = \tan^{-1} (0)$
$\theta = \pi$

$(r, \theta) = (5, \pi)$

7.018 $r = \sqrt{x^2 + y^2}$
$r = \sqrt{0^2 + (-2)^2}$
$r = 2$

$\theta = \tan^{-1} \left(\dfrac{y}{x}\right)$

$\theta = \tan^{-1} \left(-\dfrac{2}{0}\right)$

$\theta = \dfrac{3\pi}{2}$

$(r, \theta) = \left(2, \dfrac{3\pi}{2}\right)$

7.019 $r = \sqrt{x^2 + y^2}$
$r = \sqrt{1^2 + 0^2}$
$r = 1$

$\theta = \tan^{-1} \left(\dfrac{y}{x}\right)$

$\theta = \tan^{-1} \left(\dfrac{0}{1}\right)$

$\theta = 0°$

$(r, \theta) = (1, 0°)$

7.020 $r = \sqrt{x^2 + y^2}$
$r = \sqrt{0^2 + 1^2}$
$r = 1$

$\theta = \tan^{-1} \left(\dfrac{y}{x}\right)$

$\theta = \tan^{-1} \left(\dfrac{1}{0}\right)$

$\theta = \dfrac{\pi}{2}$

$(r, \theta) = \left(1, \dfrac{\pi}{2}\right)$

7.021 Let $y = \arcsin x$ where $x = \sin 30°$. Then $x = \sin y$ and $\sin 30° = \sin y$.
$\therefore y = 30°$

7.022 Let $\theta = \arccos \frac{4}{5}$; find $\sin \frac{1}{2}\theta$.

$\cos \theta = \frac{4}{5}$

$\sin \frac{1}{2}\theta = \sqrt{\dfrac{1 - \cos \theta}{2}}$

$= \sqrt{\dfrac{1 - \frac{4}{5}}{2}}$

$= \sqrt{\dfrac{1}{10}}$

$= \dfrac{1}{\sqrt{10}}$

$= \dfrac{\sqrt{10}}{10}$

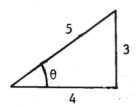

7.023 Let $y = \arctan \frac{1}{3}$; then

$\tan y = \frac{1}{3}$.

7.024 Let $x = \text{arcsec } \frac{1}{2}$. Then $\sec x = \frac{1}{2}$. Therefore, $x = \phi$ since $|\sec x| \geq 1$; no solution

7.025 Domain: all Real x
Range: $-\frac{\pi}{2} < y < \frac{\pi}{2}$

SELF TEST 8

8.01 through 8.05

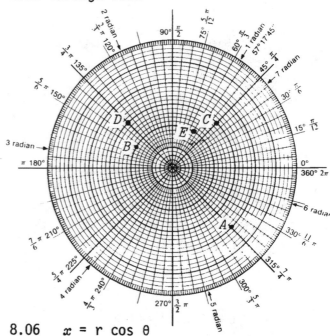

8.06 $x = r \cos \theta$
$x = 4 \cos 315°$
$x = 4 \cos 45°$
$x = 4\left(\dfrac{\sqrt{2}}{2}\right)$
$x = 2\sqrt{2}$

$y = r \sin \theta$
$y = 4 \sin 315°$
$y = -4 \sin 45°$
$y = -2\sqrt{2}$

$(x, y) = (2\sqrt{2}, -2\sqrt{2})$

8.07 $x = r \cos \theta$
$x = -3 \cos \left(-\dfrac{\pi}{4}\right)$
$x = -3 \cos \dfrac{\pi}{4}$
$x = -\dfrac{3\sqrt{2}}{2}$

$y = r \sin \theta$
$y = -3 \sin \left(-\dfrac{\pi}{4}\right)$
$y = 3 \sin \dfrac{\pi}{4}$
$y = \dfrac{3\sqrt{2}}{2}$

8.07 cont.

$(x, y) = (-\frac{3\sqrt{2}}{2}, \frac{3\sqrt{2}}{2})$

8.08

$r = \sqrt{x^2 + y^2}$
$r = \sqrt{(2)^2 + -2^2}$
$r = \sqrt{4 + 4}$
$r = \sqrt{8}$
$r = 2\sqrt{2}$

$\theta = \tan^{-1}(\frac{y}{x})$

$\theta = \tan^{-1}(-\frac{2}{2})$

$\theta = 315°$

$(r, \theta) = (2\sqrt{2}, 315°)$

8.09

$r = \sqrt{x^2 + y^2}$
$r = \sqrt{(-4)^2 + 3^2}$
$r = \sqrt{16 + 9}$
$r = \sqrt{25}$
$r = 5$

$\theta = \tan^{-1}(\frac{y}{x})$

$\theta = \tan^{-1}(-\frac{3}{4})$

$\theta = 143°$

$(r, \theta) = (5, \tan^{-1}(-\frac{3}{4}))$
or $(5, 143°)$

8.010 $y = 4$, $y = r \sin \theta$
$r \sin \theta = 4$ or
$r = \dfrac{4}{\sin \theta}$

8.011 $xy = 1$
$x = r \cos \theta$ and $y = r \sin \theta$
$(r \cos \theta)(r \sin \theta) = 1$
$r^2 \cos \theta \sin \theta = 1$
$r^2 = \dfrac{1}{\sin \theta \cos \theta}$

8.012 $y = x^2$
$y = r \sin \theta$ and $x = r \cos \theta$
$r \sin \theta = (r \cos \theta)^2$
$r \sin \theta = r^2 \cos^2 \theta$
$r^2 \cos^2 \theta - r \sin \theta = 0$
$r(r \cos^2 \theta - \sin \theta) = 0$
$r \cos^2 \theta - \sin \theta = 0$
or
$r \cos^2 \theta = \sin \theta$

8.013 Let $y = \arcsin x$ where $x = \sin 6\pi$. Then $x = \sin y$ and $\sin 6\pi = \sin y$.
$\therefore y = 6\pi = 0°$

8.014 $y = \arccos(\frac{\sqrt{3}}{2})$, $\cos y = \frac{\sqrt{3}}{2}$, $y = \pm\frac{\pi}{6} \pm 2\pi K$

8.015 $y = \arcsin(-\frac{\sqrt{2}}{2})$, $\sin y = -\frac{\sqrt{2}}{2}$, $y = \frac{5\pi}{4} \pm 2\pi K$ or $\frac{7\pi}{4} \pm 2\pi K$

8.016 Let $y = \arctan \frac{1}{3}$; find $\tan 2y$.
$\tan y = \frac{1}{3}$

$\tan 2y = \dfrac{2 \tan y}{1 - \tan^2 y} = \dfrac{2 \cdot \frac{1}{3}}{1 - (\frac{1}{3})^2} =$

$\dfrac{\frac{2}{3}}{1 - \frac{1}{9}} = \dfrac{6}{8} = \dfrac{3}{4}$

8.017 Let $x \arctan \frac{4}{7}$ and $y = \arctan \frac{7}{4}$.

Then $\tan x = \frac{4}{7}$ and $\tan y = \frac{7}{4}$.

Since $\frac{4}{7}$ and $\frac{7}{4}$ are reciprocals

of each other, $x + y = 90°$ or

$\frac{\pi}{2}$ (see diagram).

8.018 Domain: $x \geq 1$ or $x \leq -1$
Range: $y \neq \pi + \pi K$

8.019 Let $x = \arcsin \frac{2}{3}$. Then

$\sin x = \frac{2}{3}$ and $\sec x = \frac{3}{\sqrt{5}}$.

Therefore, $\sec (\arcsin \frac{2}{3}) = \frac{3}{\sqrt{5}} = \frac{3\sqrt{5}}{5}$.

8.020 Let $y = \arcsin \frac{1}{2}$; $\sin y = \frac{1}{2}$,

$-\frac{\pi}{2} \le y \le \frac{\pi}{2}$. Therefore, $y = \frac{\pi}{6}$

or 30°.

SELF TEST 9

9.01 through 9.05

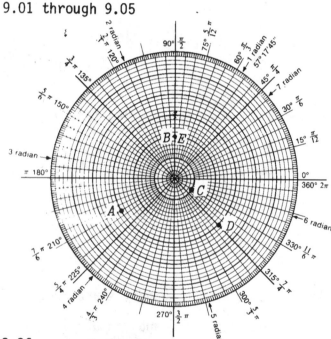

9.06 $x = r \cos \theta$
$x = 1(\cos 90°)$
$x = 0$

$y = r \sin \theta$
$y = 1(\sin 90°)$
$y = 1$

$(x, y) = (0, 1)$

9.07 $x = r \cos \theta$
$x = 2 \cos \frac{5\pi}{6}$
$x = -2 \cos \frac{\pi}{6}$
$x = -2(\frac{\sqrt{3}}{2})$
$x = -\sqrt{3}$

$y = r \sin \theta$
$y = 2 \sin \frac{5\pi}{6}$
$y = 2 \sin \frac{\pi}{6}$
$y = 2(\frac{1}{2})$
$y = 1$

$(x, y) = (-\sqrt{3}, 1)$

9.08 $x = r \cos \theta$
$x = -3 \cos (-60°)$
$x = -3 \cos 60°$
$x = -3(\frac{1}{2})$
$x = -\frac{3}{2}$

$y = r \sin \theta$
$y = -3 \sin (-60°)$
$y = 3 \sin 60°$
$y = 3(\frac{\sqrt{3}}{2})$
$y = \frac{3\sqrt{3}}{2}$

$(x, y) = (-\frac{3}{2}, \frac{3\sqrt{3}}{2})$

9.09 $x = r \cos \theta$
$x = 1 \cos \frac{11\pi}{6}$
$x = \cos \frac{\pi}{6}$
$x = \frac{\sqrt{3}}{2}$

$y = r \sin \theta$
$y = 1 \sin \frac{11\pi}{6}$
$y = -\sin \frac{\pi}{6}$
$y = -\frac{1}{2}$

9.09 cont.

$$(x, y) = (\frac{\sqrt{3}}{2}, -\frac{1}{2})$$

9.010 $x = r \cos \theta$
$x = -2 \cos 0.5236$
$x = -2(0.866)$
$x = -1.732$
$x = -\sqrt{3}$

$y = r \sin \theta$
$y = -2 \sin 0.5236$
$y = -2(0.500)$
$y = -1$

$$(x, y) = (-\sqrt{3}, -1)$$

9.011 $r = \sqrt{(-2)^2 + (2\sqrt{3})^2}$
$r = \sqrt{4 + 12}$
$r = \sqrt{16}$
$r = 4$

$\theta = \tan^{-1} (\frac{-2}{2\sqrt{3}})$

$\theta = \tan^{-1} (-\frac{1}{\sqrt{3}})$

$\theta = 120°$

$$(r, \theta) = (4, 120°)$$

9.012 $r = \sqrt{3^2 + (-4)^2}$
$r = \sqrt{9 + 16}$
$r = \sqrt{25}$
$r = 5$

$\theta = \tan^{-1} (-\frac{4}{3})$
$\theta = \tan^{-1} (-1.333)$
$\theta = 306.86°$

$$(r, \theta) = (5, 306.86°)$$

9.013 $r = \sqrt{(-\frac{\sqrt{3}}{2})^2 + (\frac{1}{2})^2}$

$r = \sqrt{\frac{3}{4} + \frac{1}{4}}$
$r = \sqrt{1}$
$r = 1$

$\theta = \tan^{-1} (\frac{\frac{1}{2}}{-\frac{\sqrt{3}}{2}})$

$\theta = \tan^{-1} (-\frac{\sqrt{3}}{3})$

$\theta = \frac{5\pi}{6}$

$$(r, \theta) = (1, \frac{5\pi}{6})$$

9.014 $r = \sqrt{(-\sqrt{3})^2 + (-1)^2}$
$r = \sqrt{3 + 1}$
$r = \sqrt{4}$
$r = 2$

$\theta = \tan^{-1} (\frac{-1}{-\sqrt{3}})$

$\theta = \tan^{-1} (\frac{\sqrt{3}}{3})$

$\theta = \frac{7\pi}{6}$

$$(r, \theta) = (2, \frac{7\pi}{6}) \text{ or } (2, 210°)$$

9.015 $x^2 + y^2 = 8$
$r^2 = x^2 + y^2$; therefore $r^2 = 8$

9.016 $x^2 + y^2 - 2x = 0$,
$r^2 = x^2 + y^2$,
$x = r \cos \theta$
$r^2 - 2r \cos \theta - 0$; therefore,
$r = 2 \cos \theta$

9.017 $\theta = 60°$

$\tan 60° = \frac{y}{x}$

$\sqrt{3} = \frac{y}{x}$

$y = \sqrt{3}x$

9.018

$$r = \frac{6}{2 - 3\sin\theta}$$

$$r = \frac{6}{2 - \frac{3y}{r}}$$

$$r = \frac{6r}{2r - 3y}$$

$$1 = \frac{6}{2r - 3y}$$

$2r - 3y = 6$ or
$2\sqrt{x^2 + y^2} = 3y + 6$
$4(x^2 + y^2) = 9y^2 + 36y + 36$
$4x^2 + 4y^2 = 9y^2 + 36y + 36$

$4x^2 - 5y^2 - 36y - 36 = 0$

9.019 Let $x = \arctan\frac{1}{3}$ and $y = \arctan\frac{2}{3}$. Then $\tan x = \frac{1}{3}$ and $\tan y = \frac{2}{3}$.

$x = 18°\ 26'$ (approx.)
$y = 33°\ 41'$ (approx.)
$x + y = 18°\ 26' + 33°\ 41' = 52°\ 7'$

9.020 Show that $\tan[\arctan\frac{4}{3} - \arcsin(-\frac{8}{17})] = \tan(\arctan\frac{84}{31})$.

Let $\theta = \arctan\frac{4}{3}$ and $\phi = \arcsin(-\frac{8}{17})$.

$$\tan(\theta - \phi) = \frac{\tan\theta - \tan\phi}{1 + \tan\theta\tan\phi}$$

$$= \frac{\frac{4}{3} - \frac{8}{15}}{1 + \frac{4}{3}\cdot\frac{8}{15}}$$

$$= \frac{60 - 24}{45 + 32}$$

$$= \frac{36}{77}$$

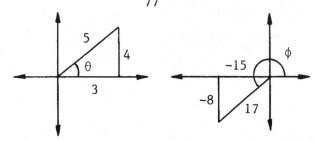

SELF TEST 10

10.01 through 10.04

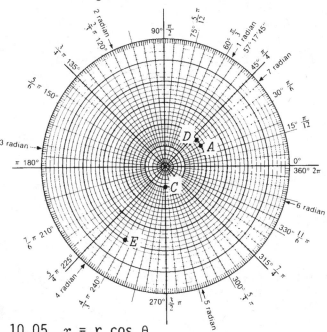

10.05 $x = r\cos\theta$
$x = 3\cos 2\pi$
$x = 3(1)$
$x = 3$

$y = r\sin\theta$
$y = 3\sin 2\pi$
$y = 3(0)$
$y = 0$

$(x, y) = (3, 0)$

10.06 $x = r\cos\theta$
$x = 2\cos 60°$
$x = 2(\frac{1}{2})$
$x = 1$

$y = r\sin\theta$
$y = 2\sin 60°$
$y = 2(\frac{\sqrt{3}}{2})$
$y = \sqrt{3}$

$(x, y) = (1, \sqrt{3})$

10.07 $x = r \cos \theta$
     $x = 1 \cos 130°$
     $x = -1(\cos 50°)$
     $x = -0.643$

     $y = r \sin \theta$
     $y = 1 \sin 130°$
     $y = \sin 50°$
     $y = 0.766$

     $(x, y) = (-0.643, 0.766)$

10.08 $r = \sqrt{x^2 + y^2}$
     $r = \sqrt{1^2 + 0^2}$
     $r = 1$

     $\tan \theta = \dfrac{0}{1} = 0$
       $\theta = 0°$

     $(r, \theta) = (1, 0°)$

10.09 $r = \sqrt{x^2 + y^2}$
     $r = \sqrt{(-3)^2 + (3)^2}$
     $r = 3\sqrt{2}$

     $\tan \theta = \dfrac{y}{x} = -\dfrac{3}{3} = -1$
       $\theta = 135°$ (second quadrant)

     $(r, \theta) = (3\sqrt{2}, 135°)$ or $(3\sqrt{2}, \frac{3\pi}{4})$

10.010 $r = \sqrt{x^2 + y^2}$
     $r = \sqrt{0^2 + 6^2}$
     $r = 6$

     $\tan \theta = \dfrac{y}{x} = \dfrac{6}{0} =$ undefined
       $\theta = 90°$

     $(r, \theta) = (6, 90°)$ or $(6, \frac{\pi}{2})$

10.011 $r = \sqrt{x^2 + y^2}$

     $r = \sqrt{\left(-\dfrac{\sqrt{2}}{2}\right)^2 + \left(\dfrac{\sqrt{2}}{2}\right)^2}$

     $r = \sqrt{\dfrac{2}{4} + \dfrac{2}{4}}$
     $r = \sqrt{1}$
     $r = 1$

$\tan \theta = \dfrac{y}{x} = \dfrac{\frac{\sqrt{2}}{2}}{-\frac{\sqrt{2}}{2}} = -1$

     $\theta = 135°$ (second quadrant)
     $(r, \theta) = (1, 135°)$ or $(1, \frac{3\pi}{4})$

10.012 $2x - 3y + 4 = 0$
     $x = r \cos \theta$ and $y = r \sin \theta$
     $2r \cos \theta - 3r \sin \theta + 4 = 0$
     $r(2 \cos \theta - 3 \sin \theta) + 4 = 0$

10.013 $x^2 + y^2 + 4x - 6y - 3 = 0$
     $r^2 = x^2 + y^2$
     $x = r \cos \theta$ and $y = r \sin \theta$
     $r^2 + 4r \cos \theta - 6r \sin \theta - 3 = 0$
     $r^2 + 2r(2 \cos \theta - 3 \sin \theta) - 3 = 0$

10.014 $x - 5 = 0$
     $x = r \cos$
     $r \cos \theta - 5 = 0$
       $r = \dfrac{5}{\cos \theta}$ or $r = 5 \sec \theta$

10.015 $r = \dfrac{3}{\sin \theta} = 3 \csc \theta$

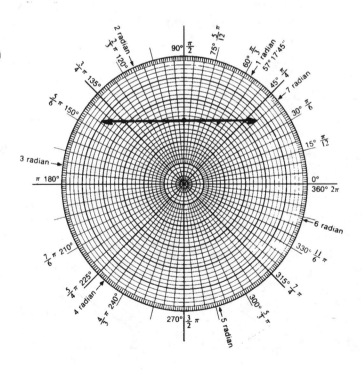

10.016

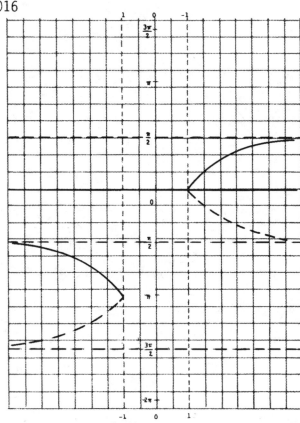

10.017 Let y = arcsin x where x = sin 40°.
Then x = sin y and sin 60° = sin y.
$\therefore$ y = 40°

10.018 Let θ = arcsin $\frac{5}{13}$ and ϕ = arcsin $\frac{4}{5}$.

$\sin(\theta + \phi)$ = sin θ cos ϕ + cos θ sin ϕ

$= \frac{5}{13} \cdot \frac{3}{5} + \frac{12}{13} \cdot \frac{4}{5}$

$= \frac{15}{65} + \frac{48}{65}$

$= \frac{63}{65}$

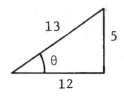 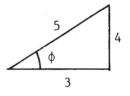

10.019 Let x = arc tan $(-\frac{5}{12})$; then
tan x = $-\frac{5}{12}$.   cos x = $-\frac{12}{13}$

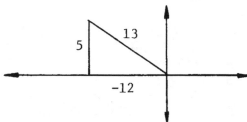

10.020 sec π = -1
Let x = arctan(-1);
than tan x = -1.
$x = \frac{3\pi}{4}$ or $\frac{7\pi}{4}$

350

MATHEMATICS 1208
SELF TEST
SOLUTION KEY

SELF TEST 1

1.01 $(x - 0)^2 + (y - 0)^2 = 5^2$
$x^2 + y^2 = 25$
$x^2 + y^2 - 25 = 0$

1.02 $(x - 2)^2 + (y - 3)^2 = 7^2$
$x^2 - 4x + 4 + y^2 - 6y + 9 = 49$
$x^2 + y^2 - 4x - 6y - 36 = 0$

1.03 $(x + 2)^2 + (y - 5)^2 = 10^2$
$x^2 + 4x + 4 + y^2 - 10y + 25 = 100$
$x^2 + y^2 + 4x - 10y - 71 = 0$

1.04 Center = (0, 0)
$r = \sqrt{36} = 6$

1.05 $x^2 - 6x + y^2 + 10y = 2$
$x^2 - 6x + 9 + y^2 + 10y + 25 = 2 + 9 + 25$
$(x - 3)^2 + (y + 5)^2 = 36$
Center = (3, -5)
$r = \sqrt{36} = 6$

1.06 $x^2 + 5x + y^2 - 4y = 0$
$x^2 + 5x + \frac{25}{4} + y^2 - 4y + 4 = \frac{25}{4} + 4$
$(x + \frac{5}{2})^2 + (y - 2)^2 = \frac{41}{4}$
Center = $(-\frac{5}{2}, 2)$
$r = \sqrt{\frac{41}{4}} = \frac{\sqrt{41}}{2}$

1.07 $x^2 + y^2 + dx + ey + f = 0$
(0, 0): $0 + 0 + 0 + 0 + f = 0$
$f = 0$
(0, 6): $0 + 36 + 0d + 6e + f = 0$
$6e = -36$
$e = -6$
(2, 3): $4 + 9 + 2d + 3e + f = 0$
$13 + 2d + 3e + f = 0$
$2d + 3e + f = -13$
$2d + 3(-6) + 0 = -13$
$2d - 18 = -13$
$2d = 5$
$d = \frac{5}{2}$

1.07 cont.
$x^2 + y^2 + \frac{5}{2}x - 6y = 0$
$2x^2 + 2y^2 + 5x - 12y = 0$

1.08 $h = \frac{-2 + 8}{2} = 3$
$k = \frac{4 - 6}{2} = -1$
$(h, k) = (3, -1)$
$r = \frac{1}{2}\sqrt{(8 + 2)^2 + (-6 - 4)^2}$
$= \frac{1}{2}\sqrt{10^2 + (-10)^2}$
$= \frac{1}{2}\sqrt{100 + 100}$
$= \frac{1}{2}\sqrt{200}$
$= \frac{1}{2}(10)(\sqrt{2})$
$= 5\sqrt{2}$
$(x - 3)^2 + (y + 1)^2 = (5\sqrt{2})^2$
$(x - 3)^2 + (y + 1)^2 = 50$

1.09 $r = \frac{|0 + 0 - 6|}{\sqrt{1 + 1}} = \frac{6}{\sqrt{2}}$
$= \frac{6\sqrt{2}}{2} = 3\sqrt{2}$
$x^2 + y^2 = (3\sqrt{2})^2$
$x^2 + y^2 = 18$

1.010 $r = \sqrt{(5 - 2)^2 + (7 - 2)^2}$
$= \sqrt{3^2 + 5^2}$
$= \sqrt{9 + 25}$
$= \sqrt{34}$
$(x - 2)^2 + (y - 2)^2 = (\sqrt{34})^2$
$(x - 2)^2 + (y - 2)^2 = 34$

1.011 $\frac{(x - 0)^2}{6^2} + \frac{(y - 0)^2}{4^2} = 1$
$\frac{x^2}{36} + \frac{y^2}{16} = 1$

1.012 $\frac{(x + 3)^2}{4^2} + \frac{(y - 5)^2}{7^2} = 1$
$\frac{(x + 3)^2}{16} + \frac{(y - 5)^2}{49} = 1$

1.013 $(h, k) = (2, 3)$
$a = 3$
$c = 2$
$b^2 = 3^2 - 2^2 = 9 - 4 = 5$
$\frac{(x - 2)^2}{9} + \frac{(y - 3)^2}{5} = 1$

1.014 $(h, k) = (2, 2)$

$c = 3$

$e = \dfrac{c}{a} = \dfrac{3}{5}$

$a = 5$

$b^2 = a^2 - c^2$

$\quad = 5^2 - 3^2$

$\quad = 25 - 9$

$\quad = 16$

$\dfrac{(x - 2)^2}{25} + \dfrac{(y - 2)^2}{16} = 1$

1.015 $x^2 + 4y^2 = 4$

$\dfrac{x^2}{4} + \dfrac{y^2}{1} = 1$

$(h, k) = (0, 0)$

$a = \sqrt{4} = 2$

$b = \sqrt{1} = 1$

1.016 $\quad 4x^2 + y^2 + 8x - 5 = 0$

$\quad 4x^2 + 8x + y^2 = 5$

$4(x^2 + 2x + 1) + y^2 = 5 + 4$

$\quad 4(x + 1)^2 + y^2 = 9$

$\quad \dfrac{(x + 1)^2}{\frac{9}{4}} + \dfrac{y^2}{9} = 1$

$(h, k) = (-1, 0);$

Position II

$a = \sqrt{9} = 3$

$b = \sqrt{\frac{9}{2}} = \frac{3}{2}$

1.017 $4x^2 + 3y^2 - 32x + 12y + 64 = 0$

$\quad 4x^2 - 32x + 3y^2 + 12y = -64$

$\quad 4(x^2 - 8x + 16) +$

$\qquad 3(y^2 + 4y + 4) = -64 +$

$\qquad\qquad\qquad\qquad\quad 64 +$

$\qquad\qquad\qquad\qquad\quad 12$

$\quad 4(x - 4)^2 + 3(y + 2)^2 = 12$

$\quad \dfrac{(x - 4)^2}{3} + \dfrac{(y + 2)^2}{4} = 1$

$(h, k) = (4, -2)$

$a = \sqrt{4} = 2$

$b = \sqrt{3}$

1.018 $4x^2 + y^2 = 4$

$\dfrac{x^2}{1} + \dfrac{y^2}{4} = 1$

$a = \sqrt{4} = 2$

$b = \sqrt{1} = 1$

1.019 $9x^2 + 25y^2 = 225$

$\dfrac{x^2}{25} + \dfrac{y^2}{9} = 1$

$a = \sqrt{25} = 5$

$b = \sqrt{9} = 3$

1.020 $9x^2 + 4y^2 - 18x + 8y - 23 = 0$

$\quad 9x^2 - 18x + 4y^2 + 8y = 23$

$\quad 9(x^2 - 2x + 1) +$

$\qquad 4(y^2 + 2y + 1) = 23 +$

$\qquad\qquad\qquad\qquad\quad 9 + 4$

$\quad 9(x - 1)^2 + 4(y + 1)^2 = 36$

$\quad \dfrac{(x - 1)^2}{4} + \dfrac{(y + 1)^2}{9} = 1$

Center $= (1, -1)$

$a = \sqrt{9} = 3$

$b = \sqrt{4} = 2$

1.020 cont.

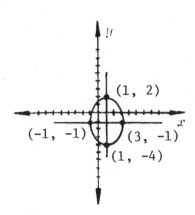

(1, 2)

(-1, -1)   (3, -1)

(1, -4)

SELF TEST 2

2.01   parabola

2.02   line

2.03   parabola

2.04   ellipse

2.05   hyperbola

2.06   ellipse

2.07   line

2.08   circle

2.09   parabola

2.010 point

2.011
$$x^2 + y^2 - 8x - 2y + 7 = 0$$
$$x^2 - 8x + y^2 - 2y = -7$$
$$x^2 - 8x + 16 + y^2 - 2y + 1 = -7 + 16 + 1$$
$$(x - 4)^2 + (y - 1)^2 = 10$$

Circle with center at (4, 1)
and radius = $\sqrt{10}$

2.012
$$5x^2 + 9y^2 - 80x + 54y + 221 = 0$$
$$5x^2 - 80x + 9y^2 + 54y = -221$$
$$5(x^2 - 16x + 64) +$$
$$9(y^2 + 6y + 9) = -221 + 320 + 81$$
$$5(x - 8)^2 + 9(y + 3)^2 = 180$$
$$\frac{(x - 8)^2}{36} + \frac{(y + 3)^2}{20} = 1$$

Ellipse in Position I

2.013
$$y^2 + 8y - 6x + 4 = 0$$
$$y^2 + 8y = 6x - 4$$
$$y^2 + 8y + 16 = 6x - 4 + 16$$
$$(y + 4)^2 = 6(x + 2)$$

Parabola in Position I

2.014
$$16x^2 - 9y^2 + 64x + 18y - 89 = 0$$
$$16x^2 + 64x - 9y^2 + 18y = 89$$
$$16(x^2 + 4x + 4) - 9(y^2 - 2y + 1) = 89 + 64 - 9$$
$$16(x + 2)^2 - 9(y - 1)^2 = 144$$
$$\frac{(x + 2)^2}{9} - \frac{(y - 1)^2}{16} = 1$$

Hyperbola in Position I

2.015 $(h, k) = (3, -1)$
$$(x - h)^2 + (y - k)^2 = r^2$$
$$(x - 3)^2 + (y + 1)^2 = 5^2$$
$$(x - 3)^2 + (y + 1)^2 = 25$$
$$x^2 - 6x + 9 + y^2 + 2y + 1 = 25$$
$$x^2 - 6x + y^2 + 2y + 10 = 25$$
$$x^2 + y^2 - 6x + 2y - 15 = 0$$

2.016 $(y - k)^2 = -4p(x - h)$

$p = \frac{3}{2}$

$$(y - 2)^2 = -4(\tfrac{3}{2})(x - 2)$$
$$(y - 2)^2 = -6(x - 2)$$
$$y^2 - 4y + 4 = -6x + 12$$
$$y^2 - 4y + 6x + 4 = 12$$
$$y^2 - 4y + 6x - 8 = 0$$

2.017 $(h, k) = (-1, -1)$

$a = 6$

$e = \dfrac{c}{a} = \dfrac{2}{3}$;

$c = 4$

$b^2 = a^2 - c^2$

$b^2 = 6^2 - 4^2$

$b^2 = 36 - 16$

$b^2 = 20$

$\dfrac{(x + 1)^2}{36} + \dfrac{(y + 1)^2}{20} = 1$

2.018 $\dfrac{x^2}{a^2} - \dfrac{y^2}{b^2} = 1$

$c = 6$

$18 = \dfrac{2b^2}{a}$

$18a = 2b^2$

$b^2 = 9a$

$c^2 - a^2 = b^2$

$6^2 - a^2 = b^2$

$36 - a^2 = b^2$

$36 - a^2 = 9a$

$a^2 + 9a - 36 = 0$

$(a + 12)(a - 3) = 0$

$a + 12 = 0$

$\qquad a = -12$; reject

$\qquad$ or

$a - 3 = 0$

$\qquad a = 3$

$b^2 = 9a = 9(3) = 27$

$\dfrac{x^2}{3^2} - \dfrac{y^2}{27} = 1$

$\dfrac{x^2}{9} - \dfrac{y^2}{27} = 1$

$3x^2 - y^2 - 27 = 0$

2.019

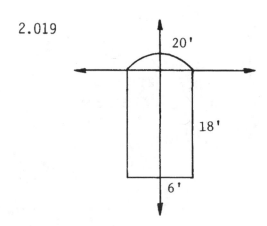

2.019 cont.

$\dfrac{x^2}{a^2} + \dfrac{y^2}{b^2} = 1$

$b = 20 - 18 = 2$

$a = \dfrac{6}{2} = 3$

$\dfrac{x^2}{3^2} + \dfrac{y^2}{2^2} = 1$

$\dfrac{x^2}{9} + \dfrac{y^2}{4} = 1$

$4x^2 + 9y^2 = 36$

$\qquad 9y^2 = 36 - 4x^2$

$y^2 = \dfrac{36 - 4x^2}{9}$

$\sqrt{y^2} = \sqrt{\dfrac{36 - 4x^2}{9}}$

$y = \dfrac{\sqrt{36 - 4x^2}}{3}$

$y = \dfrac{\sqrt{4(9 - x^2)}}{3}$

$y = \dfrac{2}{3}\sqrt{9 - x^2}$

Heights of window starting
at center:

0 ft.: $y = \dfrac{2}{3}\sqrt{9 - 0^2}$

$\qquad = \dfrac{2}{3}\sqrt{9}$

$\qquad = \dfrac{2}{3}(3)$

$\qquad = 2$

$\qquad (0, 2)$

±1 ft.: $y = \dfrac{2}{3}\sqrt{9 - (\pm 1)^2}$

$\qquad = \dfrac{2}{3}\sqrt{9 - 1}$

$\qquad = \dfrac{2}{3}\sqrt{8}$

$\qquad = \dfrac{2}{3}(2\sqrt{2})$

$\qquad = \dfrac{4\sqrt{2}}{3}$

$\qquad (\pm 1, \dfrac{4\sqrt{2}}{3})$

±2 ft.: $y = \dfrac{2}{3}\sqrt{9 - (\pm 2)^2}$

$\qquad = \dfrac{2}{3}\sqrt{9 - 4}$

$\qquad = \dfrac{2}{3}\sqrt{5}$

$\qquad = \dfrac{2\sqrt{5}}{3}$

$\qquad (\pm 2, \dfrac{2\sqrt{5}}{3})$

±3 ft.: $y = \dfrac{2}{3}\sqrt{9 - (\pm 3)^2}$

$\qquad = \dfrac{2}{3}\sqrt{9 - 9}$

$\qquad = \dfrac{2}{3}\sqrt{0}$

$\qquad = 0$

$\qquad (\pm 3, 0)$

SELF TEST 3

3.01 circle

3.02 ellipse

3.03 hyperbola

3.04 hyperbola

3.05 circle

3.06 parabola

3.07 ellipse

3.08 hyperbola

3.09 no graph, circle with negative radius

3.010 parabola

3.011 $x^2 + y^2 - 10x - 8y + 1 = 0$
$x^2 - 10x + y^2 - 8y = -1$
$(x^2 - 10x + 25) +$
$\qquad (y^2 - 8y + 16) = -1 + 25 + 16$
$(x - 5)^2 + (y - 4)^2 = 40$

Center = (5, 4)
radius = $\sqrt{40} = 2\sqrt{10}$

3.012 $8x^2 + 6y^2 - 32x + 24y + 8 = 0$
$8x^2 - 32x + 6y^2 + 24y = -8$
$8(x^2 - 4x) + 6(y^2 + 4y) = -8$
$8(x^2 - 4x + 4) +$
$\qquad 6(y^2 + 4y + 4) = -8 + 32 + 24$
$\dfrac{8(x - 2)^2}{48} + \dfrac{6(y + 2)^2}{48} = \dfrac{48}{48}$
$\dfrac{(x - 2)^2}{6} + \dfrac{(y + 2)^2}{8} = 1$

The equation is an ellipse in Position II.
$a = \sqrt{8} = 2\sqrt{2}$
$b = \sqrt{6}$
$c = \sqrt{a^2 - b^2}$
$\quad = \sqrt{(2\sqrt{2})^2 - (\sqrt{6})^2}$
$\quad = \sqrt{8 - 6}$
$\quad = \sqrt{2}$

3.012 cont.

center = (2, -2)
eccentricity $= \dfrac{c}{a} = \dfrac{\sqrt{2}}{2\sqrt{2}} = \dfrac{1}{2}$

3.013 $\dfrac{3x^2}{15} + \dfrac{5y^2}{15} = \dfrac{15}{15}$
$\dfrac{x^2}{5} + \dfrac{y^2}{3} = 1$

$a^2 = 5$
$\sqrt{a^2} = \sqrt{5}$
$a = \sqrt{5}$

$b^2 = 3$
$\sqrt{b^2} = \sqrt{3}$
$b = \sqrt{3}$

L.R. $= \dfrac{2b^2}{a} = \dfrac{2(\sqrt{3})^2}{\sqrt{5}} = \dfrac{2(3)}{\sqrt{5}} = \dfrac{6}{\sqrt{5}}$
$\qquad = \dfrac{6\sqrt{5}}{5}$

3.014 $y = x^2 - 12x$
$y + 36 = x^2 - 12x + 36$
$(y + 36) = (x - 6)^2$

Vertex = (6, -36)
$4p$ = distance from vertex to focus
$4p = 1$
$p = \frac{1}{4}$

Focus $= -36 + \frac{1}{4} = -35\frac{3}{4}$
Focus = $(6, -35\frac{3}{4})$

3.015 $x^2 - 10x + y = 0$
$x^2 - 10x = -y$
$x^2 - 10x + 25 = -y + 25$
$(x - 5)^2 = -1(y - 25)$

The maximum height is the value of k in $(y - k)$, which is 25.

3.016 $4x^2 + 9y^2 + 16x - 18y - 11 = 0$

$$4x^2 + 16x + 9y^2 - 18y = 11$$
$$4(x^2 + 4x + 4) +$$
$$9(y^2 - 2y + 1) = 11 +$$
$$16 + 9$$
$$4(x + 2)^2 + 9(y - 1)^2 = 36$$
$$\frac{(x + 2)^2}{9} + \frac{(y - 1)^2}{4} = 1$$

Ellipse
Position I
$(h, k) = (-2, 1)$
$a = \sqrt{9} = 3$
$b = \sqrt{4} = 2$
$c = \sqrt{a^2 - b^2}$
  $= \sqrt{3^2 - 2^2}$
  $= \sqrt{9 - 4}$
  $= \sqrt{5}$
Major axis = 2(3) = 6
Minor axis = 2(2) = 4
L.R. $= \dfrac{2b^2}{a} = \dfrac{2(2)^2}{3} = \dfrac{2(4)}{3} = \dfrac{8}{3}$

$e = \dfrac{c}{a} = \dfrac{\sqrt{5}}{3}$

Domain: $-5 \leq x \leq 1$
Range: $-1 \leq y \leq 3$

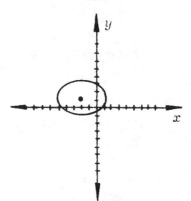

3.017 $x^2 - 2x - 4y - 3 = 0$

$$x^2 - 2x = 4y + 3$$
$$x^2 - 2x + 1 = 4y + 3 + 1$$
$$x^2 - 2x + 1 = 4y + 4$$
$$(x - 1)^2 = 4(y + 1)$$

Parabola
Position II
Vertex = (1, -1)
Focus = p = (1, 0)
L.R. $= |4p| = |4(1)| = 4$
Directrix: $y = -3$
Domain: all real numbers
Range: $y \geq -1$

3.017 cont.

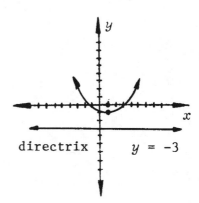

3.018

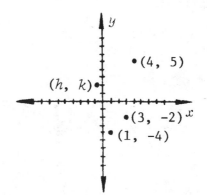

$$d_1 = \sqrt{(4 - h)^2 + (5 - k)^2}$$
$$d_2 = \sqrt{(3 - h)^2 + (-2 - k)^2}$$
$$d_3 = \sqrt{(1 - h)^2 + (-4 - k)^2}$$

3.018 cont.

$$d_1 = d_2$$

$$\sqrt{(4 - h)^2 + (5 - k)^2} = \sqrt{(3 - h)^2 + (-2 - k)^2}$$

$$(\sqrt{(4 - h)^2 + (5 - k)^2})^2 = (\sqrt{(3 - h)^2 + (-2 - k)^2})^2$$

$$(4 - h)^2 + (5 - k)^2 = (3 - h)^2 + (-2 - k)^2$$

$$h^2 - 8h + 16 + k^2 - 10k + 25 = h^2 - 6h + 9 + k^2 + 4k + 4$$

$$-8h - 10k + 41 = -6h + 4k + 13$$

$$-2h - 10k + 41 = 4k + 13$$

$$-2h - 14k + 41 = 13$$

$$-2h - 14k = -28$$

$$2h + 14k = 28$$

$$d_1 = d_2$$

$$\sqrt{(4 - h)^2 + (5 - k)^2} = \sqrt{(1 - h)^2 + (-4 - k)^2}$$

$$(\sqrt{(4 - h)^2 + (5 - k)^2})^2 = (\sqrt{(1 - h)^2 + (-4 - k)^2})^2$$

$$(4 - h)^2 + (5 - k)^2 = (1 - h)^2 + (-4 - k)^2$$

$$h^2 - 8h + 16 + k^2 - 10k + 25 = h^2 - 2h + 1 + k^2 + 8k + 16$$

$$-8h - 10k + 41 = -2h + 8k + 17$$

$$-6h - 10k + 41 = 8k + 17$$

$$-6h - 18k + 41 = 17$$

$$-6h - 18k = -24$$

$$
\begin{array}{r}
6h + 42k = 84 \\
-6h - 18k = -24 \\
\hline
24k = 60 \\
\end{array}
$$

$$k = \frac{60}{24} = \frac{5}{2}$$

$$6h + 42(\tfrac{5}{2}) = 84$$

$$6h + 105 = 84$$

$$6h = -21$$

$$h = \frac{-21}{6} = -\frac{7}{2}$$

Center $= (-\tfrac{7}{2}, \tfrac{5}{2})$

$$r = d_1 = \sqrt{(4 + \tfrac{7}{2})^2 + (5 - \tfrac{5}{2})^2}$$

$$r = \sqrt{(\tfrac{15}{2})^2 + (\tfrac{5}{2})^2}$$

$$r = \sqrt{\tfrac{225}{4} + \tfrac{25}{4}}$$

$$r = \sqrt{\tfrac{250}{4}}$$

$$r = \tfrac{5}{2}\sqrt{10}$$

$$\therefore (x + \tfrac{7}{2})^2 + (y - \tfrac{5}{2})^2 = \left(\tfrac{5\sqrt{10}}{2}\right)^2$$

3.018 cont.

$$x^2 + 7x + \tfrac{49}{4} + y^2 - 5y + \tfrac{25}{4} = \tfrac{250}{4}$$
$$4x^2 + 28x +$$
$$49 + 4y^2 - 20y + 25 = 250$$
$$4x^2 + 4y^2 + 28x - 20y + 74 = 250$$
$$4x^2 + 4y^2 + 28x - 20y - 176 = 0$$
$$x^2 + y^2 + 7x - 5y - 44 = 0$$

3.019 $(x - h)^2 = -4p(y - k)$

$(-2, 1)$:
$$(-2 - h)^2 = -4p(1 - k)$$
$$4 + 4h + h^2 = -4p + 4pk$$

$(1, 2)$:
$$(1 - h)^2 = -4p(2 - k)$$
$$1 - 2h + h^2 = -8p + 4pk$$

$(-1, 3)$:
$$(-1 - h)^2 = -4p(3 - k)$$
$$1 + 2h + h^2 = -12p + 4pk$$

Subtract:
$$4 + 4h + h^2 = -4p + 4pk$$
$$\underline{1 - 2h + h^2 = -8p + 4pk}$$
$$3 + 6h \qquad = 4\,p$$

Subtract:
$$1 - 2h + h^2 = -8p + 4pk$$
$$\underline{1 + 2h + h^2 = -12p + 4pk}$$
$$-4h \qquad = 4p$$
$$-h = p$$

Substitute $-h = p$ into $3 + 6h = 4p$:

$$3 - 6p = 4p$$
$$3 = 10p$$
$$p = \tfrac{3}{10}$$
$$h = -\tfrac{3}{10}$$

Substitute point $(-1, 3)$ and the values for p and h into the general equation:

$$\left(-1 + \tfrac{3}{10}\right)^2 = -4\left(\tfrac{3}{10}\right)(3 - k)$$

$$\left(-1 + \tfrac{3}{10}\right)^2 = -\tfrac{12}{10}(3 - k)$$

$$\left(-\tfrac{7}{10}\right)^2 = -\tfrac{18}{5} + \tfrac{6k}{5}$$

$$\tfrac{49}{100} = -\tfrac{18}{5} + \tfrac{6k}{5}$$

$$49 = -360 + 120k$$
$$409 = 120k$$
$$k = \tfrac{409}{120}$$

3.019 cont.

$$\therefore \left(x + \tfrac{3}{10}\right)^2 = -4\left(\tfrac{3}{10}\right)\left(y - \tfrac{409}{120}\right)$$

$$x^2 + \tfrac{3}{5}x + \tfrac{9}{100} = -\tfrac{6}{5}y + \tfrac{409}{100}$$

$$100x^2 + 60x + 9 = -120y + 409$$
$$100x^2 + 60x + 120y + 9 = 409$$
$$100x^2 + 60x + 120y - 400 = 0$$
$$5x^2 + 3x + 6y - 20 = 0$$

3.020 Since the major axis is parallel to the x-axis, the hyperbola is in Position I with general equation
$$\frac{(x - h)^2}{a^2} - \frac{(y - k)^2}{b^2} = 1.$$

Center $= (1, 3)$

A vertex is at $(3, 3)$ and a focus is at $(4, 3)$.

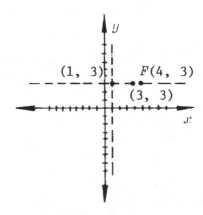

The distance from the center $(1, 3)$ to focus $(4, 3) = 3$, which is the value of c. The distance from the center $(1, 3)$ to vertex $(3, 3) = 2$, which is the value of a.

$$c^2 = a^2 + b^2$$
$$3^2 = 2^2 + b^2$$
$$9 = 4 + b^2$$
$$9 - 4 = b^2$$
$$b^2 = 5$$

$$\frac{(x - 1)^2}{4} - \frac{(y - 3)^2}{5} = 1$$

3.021 $xy = 4$

$\tan 2\theta = \frac{1}{0}$ undefined

$2\theta = 90°; \quad \theta = 45°$

$\sin \theta = \sin 45° = \frac{\sqrt{2}}{2}$

$\cos \theta = \cos 45° = \frac{\sqrt{2}}{2}$

$x = x' \cos \theta - y' \sin \theta$

$\quad = \frac{\sqrt{2}}{2}x' - \frac{\sqrt{2}}{2}y'$

$\quad = \frac{\sqrt{2}}{2}(x' - y')$

$y = x' \sin \theta + y' \cos \theta$

$\quad = \frac{\sqrt{2}}{2}x' + \frac{\sqrt{2}}{2}y'$

$\quad = \frac{\sqrt{2}}{2}(x' + y')$

$\frac{\sqrt{2}}{2}(x' - y')\frac{\sqrt{2}}{2}(x' + y') = 4$

$\quad \frac{1}{2}[(x')^2 - (y')^2] = 4$

$\quad\quad (x')^2 - (y')^2 = 8$

3.022   Focus on $x = -2$

Center at $(-2, 0)$

$e = \frac{4}{5}$

Length of major axis ($2a$) = 20;

$\quad\quad\quad\quad\quad\quad\quad\quad a = 10$

$e = \frac{c}{a}$

$\frac{4}{5} = \frac{c}{10}$

$\therefore \; c = 8$

Since the focus is on $x = -2$, the graph will be in Position II with general equation

$\frac{(x - h)^2}{b^2} + \frac{(y - k)^2}{a^2} = 1.$

$b^2 = a^2 - c^2$

$b^2 = 100 - 64$

$b^2 = 36$

$\sqrt{(b)^2} = \sqrt{36}$

$\quad b = 6$

3.022 cont.

$\frac{(x + 2)^2}{6^2} + \frac{(y - 0)^2}{10^2} = 1$

$\frac{(x + 2)^2}{36} + \frac{(y - 0)^2}{100} = 1$

$\frac{x^2 + 4x + 4}{36} + \frac{y^2}{100} = 1$

$100x^2 + 400x + 400 + 36y^2 = 3{,}600$

$100x^2 + 400x + 36y^2 - 3{,}200 = 0$

$25x^2 + 100x + 9y^2 - 800 = 0$

3.023 $a = \frac{1}{2}(8) = 4$

$b = \frac{1}{2}(4) = 2$

$(h, k) = (3, 5)$

Position I

$\frac{(x' - 3)^2}{4^2} + \frac{(y' - 5)^2}{2^2} = 1$

$\frac{(x' - 3)^2}{16} + \frac{(y' - 5)^2}{4} = 1$

$(x' - 3)^2 + 4(y' - 5)^2 = 16$

$(x')^2 - 6(x')^2 + 9 +$

$4(y')^2 - 40y' + 100 = 16$

$x' = x \cos \theta + y \sin \theta$

$\quad = x \cos 30° + y \sin 30°$

$\quad = \frac{\sqrt{3}}{2}x + \frac{1}{2}y$

$\quad = \frac{1}{2}(\sqrt{3}x + y)$

$y' = x \sin \theta - y \cos \theta$

$\quad = x \sin 30° - y \cos 30°$

$\quad = \frac{1}{2}x - \frac{\sqrt{3}}{2}y$

$\quad = \frac{1}{2}(x - \sqrt{3}y)$

3.023 cont.

Substitute x' and y':

$$\left[\tfrac{1}{2}(\sqrt{3}x + y)\right]^2 - 6\left[\tfrac{1}{2}(\sqrt{3}x + y)\right] + 4\left[\tfrac{1}{2}(x - \sqrt{3}y)\right]^2 - 40\left[\tfrac{1}{2}(x - \sqrt{3}y)\right] + 93 = 0$$

$$\frac{3x^2 + 2\sqrt{3}xy + y^2}{4} - 3\sqrt{3}x - 3y + x^2 - 2\sqrt{3}xy + 3y^2 - 20x + 20\sqrt{3}y + 93 = 0$$

$$3x^2 + 2\sqrt{3}xy + y^2 - 12\sqrt{3}x - 12y + 4x^2 - 8\sqrt{3}xy + 12y^2 - 80x + 80\sqrt{3}y + 372 = 0$$

$$7x^2 - 6\sqrt{3}xy + 13y^2 - (12\sqrt{3} + 80)x - (12 - 80\sqrt{3})y + 372 = 0$$

3.024 $\tan 2\theta = \dfrac{B}{A - C} = \dfrac{24}{9 - 16} = \dfrac{24}{-7}$

$\qquad\qquad = -\dfrac{24}{7}$

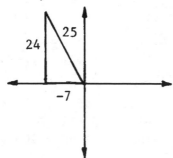

$\sin 2\theta = \dfrac{24}{25}$

$\cos 2\theta = \dfrac{-7}{25}$

$\sin \theta = \sqrt{\dfrac{1 - \cos 2\theta}{2}}$

$\sin \theta = \sqrt{\dfrac{1 + \frac{7}{25}}{2}}$

$\sin \theta = \sqrt{\dfrac{\frac{32}{25}}{2}}$

$\sin \theta = \sqrt{\dfrac{16}{25}}$

$\sin \theta = \dfrac{4}{5}$

$\cos \theta = \sqrt{\dfrac{1 + \cos 2\theta}{2}}$

$\cos \theta = \sqrt{\dfrac{1 - \frac{7}{25}}{2}}$

$\cos \theta = \sqrt{\dfrac{\frac{18}{25}}{2}}$

$\cos \theta = \sqrt{\dfrac{9}{25}}$

$\cos \theta = \dfrac{3}{5}$

3.024 cont.

$x = x' \cos\theta - y' \sin\theta$

$\quad = \frac{3}{5}x' - \frac{4}{5}y'$

$y = x' \sin\theta + y' \cos\theta$

$\quad = \frac{4}{5}x' + \frac{3}{5}y'$

$$9x^2 + 24xy + 16y^2 + 90x - 130y = 0$$

$$9\left(\frac{3}{5}x' - \frac{4}{5}y'\right)^2 + 24\left(\frac{3}{5}x' - \frac{4}{5}y'\right)\left(\frac{4}{5}x' + \frac{3}{5}y'\right) +$$

$$16\left(\frac{4}{5}x' + \frac{3}{5}y'\right)^2 + 90\left(\frac{3}{5}x' - \frac{4}{5}y'\right) - 130\left(\frac{4}{5}x' + \frac{3}{5}y'\right) = 0$$

$$9\left(\frac{9}{25}(x')^2 - \frac{24}{25}x'y' + \frac{16}{25}(y')^2\right) + 24\left(\frac{12}{25}(x')^2 - \frac{7}{25}x'y' - \frac{12}{25}(y')^2\right) +$$

$$16\left(\frac{16}{25}(x')^2 + \frac{24}{25}x'y' + \frac{9}{25}(y')^2\right) + \frac{270}{5}x' - \frac{360}{5}y' - \frac{520}{5}x' - \frac{390}{5}y' = 0$$

$$\frac{81}{25}(x')^2 - \frac{216}{25}x'y' + \frac{144}{25}(y')^2 + \frac{288}{25}(x')^2 - \frac{168}{25}x'y' - \frac{288}{25}(y')^2 +$$

$$\frac{256}{25}(x')^2 + \frac{384}{25}x'y' + \frac{144}{25}(y')^2 + \frac{1,350}{25}x' - \frac{1,800}{25}y' - \frac{2,600}{25}x' - \frac{1,950}{25}y' = 0$$

$$625(x')^2 - 1,250x' - 3,750y' = 0$$

$$25(x')^2 - 50x' - 150y' = 0$$

$$25(x')^2 - 50x' = 150y'$$

$$25[(x')^2 - 2x' + 1] = 150y' + 25$$

$$25(x' - 1)^2 = 150\cdot\left(y' + \frac{1}{6}\right)$$

$$(x' - 1)^2 = 6\left(y' + \frac{1}{6}\right)$$

Let $x' - 1 = x''$

and $y' + \frac{1}{6} = y''$.

$$(x'')^2 = 6y''$$

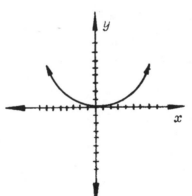

3.025 Circle
$(h, k) = (2, 2)$, $r = 3$

$(x - h)^2 + (y - k)^2 = r^2$
$(x - 2)^2 + (y - 2)^2 = 3^2$
$(x - 2)^2 + (y - 2)^2 = 9$

3.026 Hyperbola in Position II
$a = 2$, $b = 1$

$\dfrac{y^2}{a^2} - \dfrac{x^2}{b^2} = 1$

$\dfrac{y^2}{2^2} - \dfrac{x^2}{1^2} = 1$

$\dfrac{y^2}{4} - \dfrac{x^2}{1} = 1$

3.027 Parabola in Position I
$(h, k) = (2, -4)$, $p = 1$

$(y - k)^2 = -4p(x - h)$
$(y + 4)^2 = -4(x - 2)$

3.028 Ellipse in Position I
$(h, k) = (-3, 2)$
$a = 3$, $b = 2$

$\dfrac{(x - h)^2}{a^2} + \dfrac{(y - k)^2}{b^2} = 1$

$\dfrac{(x + 3)^2}{3^2} + \dfrac{(y - 2)^2}{2^2} = 1$

$\dfrac{(x + 3)^2}{9} + \dfrac{(y - 2)^2}{4} = 1$

MATHEMATICS 1209
SELF TEST
SOLUTION KEY

SELF TEST 1

1.01 $P(A) = \frac{5}{8}$
       $P(A') = 1 - \frac{5}{8} = \frac{3}{8}$

1.02 $P(A) \cdot P(B) = \frac{3}{4} \cdot \frac{3}{8} = \frac{9}{32}$ or 0.28

1.03   a. Event = {3, 6, 9, 12, 15, 18, 21, 24, 27, 30}.
           $P(B) = \frac{10}{30} = \frac{1}{3}$ or 0.33
       b. Event = {2, 3, 5, 7, 11, 13, 17, 19, 23, 29}.
           $P(B) = \frac{10}{30} = \frac{1}{3}$ or 0.33
       c. Event (divisible by 4) = {4, 8, 12, 16, 20, 24, 28}.
           Event $(25 < x < 30)$ = {26, 27, 28, 29}.
           $P(C) = \frac{7}{30}$
           $P(D) = \frac{4}{30} = \frac{2}{15}$
           $C \cap D$ = {28}
           $P(C \cap D) = \frac{1}{30}$
           $P(C \cup D) = P(C) + P(D) - P(C \cap D)$
           $= \frac{7}{30} + \frac{4}{30} - \frac{1}{30}$
           $= \frac{10}{30}$
           $= \frac{1}{3}$ or 0.33
       d. Event = {1, 3, 5, 7, 9, 11, 13, 15, 17, 19, 21, 23, 25, 27, 29}.
           $P(E) = \frac{15}{30} = \frac{1}{2}$ or 0.5

1.04   Sample space = {1, 2, 3, 4, 5, 6, 7, 8, 9, 10, 11, 12, 13, 14, 15}.

       First draw   Second draw
         even   +   even   = even
         odd   +   odd   = even

       $P(\text{2 evens}) = \frac{7}{15} \cdot \frac{7}{15} = \frac{49}{225}$
       $P(\text{2 odds}) = \frac{8}{15} \cdot \frac{8}{15} = \frac{64}{225}$

       Since these events are mutually exclusive, add the probabilities.

       $\frac{49}{225} + \frac{64}{225} = \frac{113}{225}$ or 0.502

1.05   a. $P(\text{red}) = \frac{16}{40} = \frac{2}{5}$ or 0.4
       b. $P(\text{red}) = \frac{2}{5}$
           $P(\text{white}) = \frac{4}{40} = \frac{1}{10}$ or 0.1
           $P(\text{red or white}) = P(\text{red}) + P(\text{white})$
           $= \frac{2}{5} + \frac{1}{10}$
           $= \frac{4}{10} + \frac{1}{10}$
           $= \frac{5}{10}$
           $= \frac{1}{2}$ or 0.5
       c. $P = 1$: certainty

1.06   a. H H T = $\frac{1}{2} \cdot \frac{1}{2} \cdot \frac{1}{2} = \frac{1}{8}$
           H T H = $\frac{1}{2} \cdot \frac{1}{2} \cdot \frac{1}{2} = \frac{1}{8}$
           T H H = $\frac{1}{2} \cdot \frac{1}{2} \cdot \frac{1}{2} = \frac{1}{8}$

           Since the events are mutually exclusive, add the probabilities.

           $\frac{1}{8} + \frac{1}{8} + \frac{1}{8} = \frac{3}{8}$ or 0.375
       b. H H H = $\frac{1}{2} \cdot \frac{1}{2} \cdot \frac{1}{2} = \frac{1}{8}$ or 0.125
       c. H T T = $\frac{1}{2} \cdot \frac{1}{2} \cdot \frac{1}{2} = \frac{1}{8}$
           T H T = $\frac{1}{2} \cdot \frac{1}{2} \cdot \frac{1}{2} = \frac{1}{8}$
           T T H = $\frac{1}{2} \cdot \frac{1}{2} \cdot \frac{1}{2} = \frac{1}{8}$

           Since events are mutually exclusive, add the probabilities.
           $\frac{1}{8} + \frac{1}{8} + \frac{1}{8} = \frac{3}{8}$ or 0.375
       d. T T T = $\frac{1}{2} \cdot \frac{1}{2} \cdot \frac{1}{2} = \frac{1}{8}$ or 0.125
       e. $\frac{3}{8} + \frac{1}{8} + \frac{3}{8} + \frac{1}{8} = \frac{8}{8} = 1$

1.07

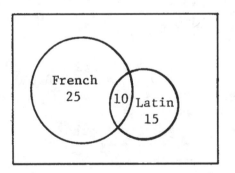

       a. $P(A) = \frac{25}{50} = \frac{1}{2}$ or 0.5
       b. $P(B) = \frac{15}{50} = \frac{3}{10}$ or 0.3
       c. $P(A \cap B) = \frac{10}{50} = \frac{1}{5}$ or 0.2
       d. $P(A \cap B) = \frac{10}{50} = \frac{1}{5}$ or 0.2
           $P(A \cup B) = P(A) + P(B) - P(A \cap B)$
           $= \frac{25}{50} + \frac{15}{50} - \frac{10}{50}$
           $= \frac{30}{50}$
           $= \frac{3}{5}$ or 0.6

1.08 a. Event = {(6, 1), (6, 2), (6, 3), (6, 4), (6, 5), (6, 6)}.
$P(A) = \frac{6}{36} = \frac{1}{6}$ or 0.167

b. $P(B) = \frac{30}{36} = \frac{5}{6}$ or 0.83

c. Event = {(3, 6), (4, 5), (4, 6), (5, 4), (5, 5), (5, 6), (6, 3), (6, 4), (6, 5), (6, 6)}.
$P(C) = \frac{10}{36} = \frac{5}{18}$ or 0.28

d. Event = {(6, 1)}.
$P(D) = \frac{1}{36}$ or 0.03

e. $P(A \cup B) = P(A) + P(B) - P(A \cap B)$
$P(A \cap B) = P(w > 5$ and $g \geq 2)$
Event = {(6, 2), (6, 3), (6, 4), (6, 5), (6, 6)}.
$P(A \cap B) = \frac{5}{36}$
$P(A \cup B) = \frac{6}{36} + \frac{30}{36} - \frac{5}{36}$
$= \frac{31}{36}$ or 0.86

f. $P(C \cup D) = P(C) + P(D) - P(C \cap D)$
Event
$P(C \cap D) = \phi$
$P(C \cap D) = 0$
$P(C \cup D) = \frac{10}{36} + \frac{1}{36} - 0$
$= \frac{11}{36}$ or 0.31

1.09 a. $P(A) \cdot P(B) = \frac{3}{4} \cdot \frac{7}{8} = \frac{21}{32}$ or 0.66

b. $P(B') = 1 - \frac{7}{8} = \frac{1}{8}$ or 0.125

c. $P(B) \cdot P(A') = \frac{7}{8} \cdot \frac{1}{4}$
$= \frac{7}{32}$ or 0.22
$P(A') \cdot P(B') = \frac{1}{4} \cdot \frac{1}{8}$
$= \frac{1}{32}$ or 0.03

e. $P(A) \cdot P(B') + P(A') \cdot P(B) + P(A) \cdot P(B)$
$= \frac{3}{4} \cdot \frac{1}{8} + \frac{1}{4} \cdot \frac{7}{8} + \frac{3}{4} \cdot \frac{7}{8}$
$= \frac{3}{32} + \frac{7}{32} + \frac{21}{32}$
$= \frac{31}{32}$ or 0.97

1.010 Wrong; alternatives are not equally likely.

SELF TEST 2

2.01 a. $_4P_4 = 4! = 4 \cdot 3 \cdot 2 \cdot 1 = 24$

b. $_nC_3 = \frac{n(n - 1)(n - 2)}{3!}$

c. $\frac{5!}{2!3!} = \frac{5 \cdot \overset{2}{\cancel{4}} \cdot \cancel{3!}}{\cancel{2} \cdot \cancel{1} \cdot \cancel{3!}} = 5 \cdot 2 = 10$

d. $\frac{(n + 1)! n!}{(n + 2)!(n - 1)!} =$
$\frac{(n + 1)! n(n - 1)!}{(n + 2)(n + 1)!(n - 1)!} =$
$\frac{n}{n + 2}$

e. $_4C_2$ or $\binom{4}{2} = \frac{4!}{2!2!}$
$= \frac{\overset{2}{\cancel{4}} \cdot 3 \cdot 2!}{\cancel{2} \cdot \cancel{1} \cdot 2!}$
$= 2 \cdot 3$
$= 6$

f. $_6P_4 = 6 \cdot 5 \cdot 4 \cdot 3 = 360$

g. $_{10}C_{10}$ or $\binom{10}{10} = \frac{10!}{10!0!}$
$= \frac{10!}{10!} = 1$

h. $_5P_3 = 5 \cdot 4 \cdot 3 = 60$

2.02 The tens' digit has 4 possibilities and the ones' digit has 3 possibilities.
$\underline{4 \cdot 3} = 12$

2.03 The hundreds' digit has 4 possibilities (2, 6, 7, and 9), the tens' digit has 5 possibilities, and the ones' digit has 5 possibilities.
$4 \cdot 5 \cdot 5 = 100$

2.04 $2^{10} = 1,024$

2.05 a. $_5P_5 = 5! = 5 \cdot 4 \cdot 3 \cdot 2 \cdot 1 = 120$

b. $(5 - 1)! = 4!$
$= 4 \cdot 3 \cdot 2 \cdot 1$
$= 24$

2.06 $_4P_4 + {_5P_3} - {_5P_1} = 4! + 5 \cdot 4 \cdot 3 - 5 = 4 \cdot 3 \cdot 2 \cdot 1 + 60 - 5 = 24 + \underline{55} = 79$

2.07 $_xP_8 = x(x - 1)(x - 2) \ldots$
$(x - 7)$

$_xP_6 = (x - 1)(x - 2) \ldots$
$(x - 5)$

$x(x - 1)(x - 2) \ldots (x - 7) =$
$2x(x - 1)(x - 2) \ldots (x - 5)$

$(x - 6)(x - 7) = 2$ [divide both
sides by
$x(x - 1) \cdot$
$(x - 2) \ldots$
$(x - 5)$]

$x^2 - 13x + 42 = 2$
$x^2 - 13x + 42 - 2 = 0$
$x^2 - 13x + 40 = 0$
$(x - 5)(x - 8) = 0$
$x - 5 = 0$
$x = 5$; reject--
cannot have $_5P_8$
$x - 8 = 0$
$x = 8$

2.08 $(5 - 1)!(5)! = 4!5!$
$= 24 \cdot 120$
$= 2,880$

2.09 $_{10}C_3 = \dfrac{10!}{3!7!} = \dfrac{10 \cdot \overset{3}{9} \cdot \overset{4}{8} \cdot 7!}{3 \cdot 2 \cdot 1 \cdot 7!} = 120$

2.010 $_xC_2 = 66$

$\dfrac{x(x - 1)}{2!} = 66$

$\dfrac{x^2 - x}{2} = 66$

$x^2 - x = 2 \cdot 66$ (cross-
multiply)

$x^2 - x = 132$
$x^2 - x - 132 = 0$
$(x + 11)(x - 12) = 0$
$x + 11 = 0$
$x = -11$; reject
$x - 12 = 0$
$x = 12$

2.011 $_7C_2 \cdot {_4C_3} \cdot {_{10}C_{10}} = \dfrac{7!}{2!5!} \cdot \dfrac{4!}{3!1!} \cdot$

$\dfrac{10!}{10!0!} = \dfrac{7 \cdot \overset{3}{6} \cdot 5!}{2 \cdot 1 \cdot 5!} \cdot \dfrac{4 \cdot 3!}{1 \cdot 3!} \cdot \dfrac{10!}{10!} =$
$21 \cdot 4 \cdot 1 = 84$

2.012 $_5C_4 \cdot {_6C_3} = \dfrac{5!}{4!1!} \cdot \dfrac{6!}{3!3!}$

$= \dfrac{5 \cdot 4!}{1 \cdot 4!} \cdot \dfrac{6 \cdot 5 \cdot 4 \cdot 3!}{3 \cdot 2 \cdot 1 \cdot 3!}$

$= 5 \cdot 20$
$= 100$

2.013 $\dfrac{11!}{4!4!2!} = \dfrac{11 \cdot 10 \cdot 9 \cdot 8 \cdot 7 \cdot 6 \cdot 5 \cdot 4!}{4 \cdot 3 \cdot 2 \cdot 1 \cdot 2 \cdot 1 \cdot 4!} =$
$= 34,650$

2.014 a. Event = {8, 22, 50}.
$P(A) = \frac{3}{10}$ or 0.3
b. Event = {1, 3, 15,
21, 19, 25, 79}.
$P(B) = \frac{7}{10}$ or 0.7
c. Event = {3, 19, 79}.
$P(C) = \frac{3}{10}$ or 0.3
d. Event = {19, 22, 25,
50, 79}.
$P(D) = \frac{5}{10} = \frac{1}{2}$ or 0.5
e. Event = {3, 15, 21}.
$P(E) = \frac{3}{10}$ or 0.3
f. Event = ϕ
$P(F) = 0$
g. $C \cup D$ = {3, 19, 79, 22,
25, 50}
$P(C \cup D) = \frac{6}{10} = \frac{3}{5}$ or 0.6
h. $D \cup E$ = {19, 22, 25, 50,
79, 3, 15, 21}
$P(D \cup E) = \frac{8}{10} = \frac{4}{5}$ or 0.8
i. $C \cap D$ = {19, 79}
$P(C \cap D) = \frac{2}{10} = \frac{1}{5}$ or 0.2
$P(C) = \frac{3}{10}$ or 0.3
$P(D) = \frac{1}{2}$
$\frac{1}{5} \overset{?}{=} \frac{3}{10} \cdot \frac{1}{2}$
$\frac{1}{5} \ne \frac{3}{20}$
No, the probabilities are
not equal.

SELF TEST 3

3.01 a. The tens' digit has 5
possibilities and the
units' digit has 4
possibilities.
$\underline{5} \cdot \underline{4} = 20$
b. The thousands' digit has
5 possibilities, the
hundreds' digit has 4
possibilities, the tens'
digit has 3 possibilities,
and the ones' digit has
2 possibilities.
$\underline{5} \cdot \underline{4} \cdot \underline{3} \cdot \underline{2} = 120$

c. The ten thousands' digit has 5 possibilities, the thousands' digit has 4 possibilities, the hundreds' digit has 3 possibilities, the tens' digit has 2 possibilities, and the ones' digit has 1 possibility.
$5 \cdot 4 \cdot 3 \cdot 2 \cdot 1 = 120$

d. Sample space = {3, 6, 9}.
$P(\text{divisible by 3}) = \frac{3}{5}$ or 0.6

e. Sample space = {6, 9}.
$P(\text{not a prime number}) = \frac{2}{5}$ or 0.4

3.02

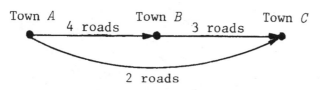

Town A   4 roads   Town B   3 roads   Town C
2 roads

a. $4 \cdot 3 = 12$

b. From Town A to Town C via Town B are 12 routes. From Town A to Town C bypassing Town B are 2 routes.
$12 + 2 = 14$ routes

c. You can make 14 trips going from Town A to Town C and 14 trips returning from Town C to Town A.
$14 \cdot 14 = 196$ **roundtrips**

3.03 a. $_{10}P_3 = 10 \cdot 9 \cdot 8 = 720$

b. $\dfrac{_9P_4}{_4P_4} = \dfrac{9 \cdot \overset{2}{\cancel{8}} \cdot 7 \cdot \cancel{6}}{\cancel{4} \cdot \cancel{3} \cdot \cancel{2} \cdot \cancel{1}} = 126$

c. $_9C_4$ or $\binom{9}{4} = \dfrac{9!}{4!5!} =$
$\dfrac{9 \cdot \overset{2}{\cancel{8}} \cdot 7 \cdot \cancel{6} \cdot \cancel{5}!}{\cancel{4} \cdot \cancel{3} \cdot \cancel{2} \cdot \cancel{1} \cdot \cancel{5}!} = 126$

d. $_8C_5$ or $\binom{8}{5} = \dfrac{8!}{5!3!}$
$= \dfrac{8 \cdot 7 \cdot 6 \cdot 5!}{3 \cdot 2 \cdot 1 \cdot 5!}$
$= 56$

e. $_{1,000}C_{999} = \dfrac{1,000!}{999!1!} =$
$\dfrac{1,000 \cdot \cancel{999!}}{1 \cdot \cancel{999!}} = 1,000$

f. $_{20}C_{20} = \dfrac{20!}{20!0!} = \dfrac{20!}{20!} = 1$

g. $_{10}P_{10} = 10!$

h. $_{16}P_1 = 16$

i. $_{16}C_1$ or $\binom{16}{1} = \dfrac{16!}{1!15!}$
$= \dfrac{16 \cdot \cancel{15!}}{1 \cdot \cancel{15!}}$
$= 16$

j. $\binom{8}{2}\binom{6}{3}\binom{4}{1}\binom{2}{0} =$
$\dfrac{8!}{2!6!} \ \dfrac{6!}{3!3!} \ \dfrac{4!}{1!3!} \ \dfrac{2!}{0!2!} =$
$\left(\dfrac{\overset{4}{\cancel{8}} \cdot 7 \cdot \cancel{6}!}{\cancel{2} \cdot \cancel{1} \cdot \cancel{6}!}\right)\left(\dfrac{\cancel{6} \cdot 5 \cdot 4 \cdot \cancel{3}!}{\cancel{3} \cdot \cancel{2} \cdot \cancel{1} \cdot \cancel{3}!}\right)\left(\dfrac{4 \cdot \cancel{3}!}{1 \cdot \cancel{3}!}\right) \cdot$
$\dfrac{2!}{2!} = (28)(20)(4)(1) = 2,240$

k. $_4P_3 + {_6P_2} + {_5P_1} = 4 \cdot 3 \cdot 2 + 6 \cdot 5 + 5$
$= 24 + 30 + 5$
$= 59$

l. $\binom{6}{2} + \binom{8}{3} = \dfrac{6!}{2!4!} + \dfrac{8!}{3!5!}$
$= \dfrac{\overset{3}{\cancel{6}} \cdot 5 \cdot \cancel{4}!}{\cancel{2} \cdot \cancel{1} \cdot \cancel{4}!} + \dfrac{8 \cdot 7 \cdot \cancel{6} \cdot \cancel{5}!}{\cancel{3} \cdot \cancel{2} \cdot \cancel{1} \cdot \cancel{5}!}$
$= 15 + 56$
$= 71$

3.04

a. $_{10}C_2 = \dfrac{10!}{2!8!}$
$= \dfrac{\overset{5}{\cancel{10}} \cdot 9 \cdot \cancel{8}!}{\cancel{2} \cdot \cancel{1} \cdot \cancel{8}!}$
$= 45$

b. Let x = number of defectives. The sample space = $\binom{10}{2}$ = 45 elements.

3.04 cont.

	Number of	
x	Possibilities	$P(x)$
0	$\binom{7}{2}$	$= \frac{21}{45}$
1	$\binom{7}{1}\binom{3}{1}$	$= \frac{7 \cdot 3}{45} = \frac{21}{45}$
2	$\binom{3}{2}$	$= \frac{3}{45}$

$P(2 \text{ defectives}) = \frac{3}{45}$

$= \frac{1}{15}$

or 0.067

c. From (b), $P(\text{one defective}) = \frac{21}{45}$

$= \frac{7}{15}$ or 0.47

d. From (b), $P(\text{no defectives}) = \frac{21}{45}$

$= \frac{7}{15}$ or 0.47

3.05 Let p = probability of winning $= \frac{2}{3}$

q = probability of losing $= 1 - \frac{2}{3} = \frac{1}{3}$

$(p + q)^5 = \binom{5}{0}\left(\frac{2}{3}\right)^5 +$
$\binom{5}{1}\left(\frac{2}{3}\right)^4\left(\frac{1}{3}\right)^1 +$
$\binom{5}{2}\left(\frac{2}{3}\right)^3\left(\frac{1}{3}\right)^2 +$
$\binom{5}{3}\left(\frac{2}{3}\right)^2\left(\frac{1}{3}\right)^3 +$
$\binom{5}{4}\left(\frac{2}{3}\right)^1\left(\frac{1}{3}\right)^4 +$
$\binom{5}{5}\left(\frac{1}{3}\right)^5$

a. $P(\text{winning 4 out of 5 games}) = \binom{5}{1}\left(\frac{2}{3}\right)^4\left(\frac{1}{3}\right)^1$

$= 5\left(\frac{16}{81}\right)\left(\frac{1}{3}\right)$

$= \frac{80}{243}$ or 0.33

b. $P(\text{winning at most 4 out of 5 games})$ means winning 4 or 3 or 2 or 1 or 0 games.

$P = \binom{5}{1}\left(\frac{2}{3}\right)^4\left(\frac{1}{3}\right)^1 +$
$\binom{5}{2}\left(\frac{2}{3}\right)^3\left(\frac{1}{3}\right)^2 +$
$\binom{5}{3}\left(\frac{2}{3}\right)^2\left(\frac{1}{3}\right)^3 +$
$\binom{5}{4}\left(\frac{2}{3}\right)^1\left(\frac{1}{3}\right)^4 +$
$\binom{5}{5}\left(\frac{1}{3}\right)^5$

$= 5\left(\frac{2}{3}\right)^4\left(\frac{1}{3}\right)^1 +$
$10\left(\frac{2}{3}\right)^3\left(\frac{1}{3}\right)^2 +$
$10\left(\frac{2}{3}\right)^2\left(\frac{1}{3}\right)^3 +$
$5\left(\frac{2}{3}\right)^1\left(\frac{1}{3}\right)^4 + \left(\frac{1}{3}\right)^5$

Another way of solving the problem is to subtract from 1 the probability of winning 5 games.

3.05 cont.

$P(\text{winning at most 4 out of 5 games}) = 1 - P(\text{winning 5 games})$

$= 1 - \left[\binom{5}{0}\left(\frac{2}{3}\right)^5\right]$

$= 1 - \left(\frac{2}{3}\right)^5$

c. $P(\text{winning no games}) = \binom{5}{5}\left(\frac{1}{3}\right)^5$

$= \left(\frac{1}{3}\right)^5$

$= \frac{1}{243}$ or 0.004

3.06 Let p = probability of American League winning $= \frac{1}{2}$

q = probability of American League losing $= 1 - \frac{1}{2} = \frac{1}{2}$

a. $P(\text{American League will win 4 games}) = \left(\frac{1}{2}\right)\left(\frac{1}{2}\right)\left(\frac{1}{2}\right)\left(\frac{1}{2}\right)$

$= \left(\frac{1}{2}\right)^4$

$= \frac{1}{16}$ or 0.06

b. The American League must win the fifth game. Therefore, the National League can win any of the other four games.

Sample space (A = American League wins; N = National League wins):

First Game	Second Game	Third Game	Fourth Game	Fifth Game	P
A	A	A	N	A	$= \left(\frac{1}{2}\right)^5 = \frac{1}{32}$
A	A	N	A	A	$= \left(\frac{1}{2}\right)^5 = \frac{1}{32}$
A	N	A	A	A	$= \left(\frac{1}{2}\right)^5 = \frac{1}{32}$
N	A	A	A	A	$= \left(\frac{1}{2}\right)^5 = \frac{1}{32}$

$P(\text{American League will win in 5 games})$

$= \frac{1}{32} + \frac{1}{32} + \frac{1}{32} + \frac{1}{32}$

$= \frac{4}{32}$

$= \frac{1}{8}$ or 0.125

3.07   Let p = probability of a
       girl = $\frac{1}{2}$
       q = probability of a
       boy = $\frac{1}{2}$
$$(p + q)^6 = \binom{6}{0}(\tfrac{1}{2})^6 +$$
$$\binom{6}{1}(\tfrac{1}{2})^5(\tfrac{1}{2})^1 +$$
$$\binom{6}{2}(\tfrac{1}{2})^4(\tfrac{1}{2})^2 +$$
$$\binom{6}{3}(\tfrac{1}{2})^3(\tfrac{1}{2})^3 +$$
$$\binom{6}{4}(\tfrac{1}{2})^2(\tfrac{1}{2})^4 +$$
$$\binom{6}{5}(\tfrac{1}{2})^1(\tfrac{1}{2})^5 +$$
$$\binom{6}{6}(\tfrac{1}{2})^6$$

a. P(4 girls and
    2 boys) = $\binom{6}{2}(\tfrac{1}{2})^4(\tfrac{1}{2})^2$
    $= 15(\tfrac{1}{16})(\tfrac{1}{4})$
    $= \tfrac{15}{64}$ or 0.23

b. P(3 boys and
    3 girls) = $\binom{6}{3}(\tfrac{1}{2})^3(\tfrac{1}{2})^3$
    $= 20(\tfrac{1}{8})(\tfrac{1}{8})$
    $= \tfrac{20}{64}$
    $= \tfrac{5}{16}$ or 0.31

3.08 $10 \cdot 10 = 100$

3.09   a. ${}_5C_3 \cdot {}_4C_2 = \dfrac{5!}{3!2!} \cdot \dfrac{4!}{2!2!}$
       $= \dfrac{5 \cdot 4 \cdot 3!}{2 \cdot 1 \cdot 3!} \cdot \dfrac{4 \cdot 3 \cdot 2!}{2 \cdot 1 \cdot 2!}$
       $= 10 \cdot 6$
       $= 60$

b. 3 Democrats and 2
    Republicans = 60 (from a.)
    4 Democrats and 1
    Republican:
$${}_5C_4 \cdot {}_4C_1 = \frac{5!}{4!1!} \cdot \frac{4!}{1!3!}$$
$$= \frac{5 \cdot 4!}{1 \cdot 4!} \cdot \frac{4 \cdot 3!}{1 \cdot 3!}$$
$$= 5 \cdot 4$$
$$= 20$$
    5 Democrats and
    0 Republicans:
$${}_5C_5 \cdot {}_4C_0 = \frac{5!}{5!0!} \cdot \frac{4!}{0!4!}$$
$$= \frac{5!}{5!} \cdot \frac{4!}{4!}$$
$$= 1 \cdot 1$$
$$= 1$$

    $60 + 20 + 1 = 81$ ways

3.010 a. $E(x) = 2(\tfrac{1}{6})$
           $= \tfrac{1}{3}$ or 0.33
       b. $P(x \neq 1) = \tfrac{1}{6} + \tfrac{1}{3} + \tfrac{1}{4}$
           $= \tfrac{2}{12} + \tfrac{4}{12} + \tfrac{3}{12}$
           $= \tfrac{9}{12}$
           $= \tfrac{3}{4}$ or 0.75
       c. $P(x < 3) = \tfrac{1}{4} + \tfrac{1}{6}$
           $= \tfrac{3}{12} + \tfrac{2}{12}$
           $= \tfrac{5}{12}$ or 0.42

3.011 P(red) = $\tfrac{3}{9}$
       $= \tfrac{1}{3}$ or 0.33

MATHEMATICS 1210
SELF TEST
SOLUTION KEY

SELF TEST 1

1.01 $\displaystyle\sum_{i=1}^{5} 3i + 1 = (3\cdot 1 + 1) +$
$(3\cdot 2 + 1) +$
$(3\cdot 3 + 1) +$
$(3\cdot 4 + 1) +$
$(3\cdot 5 + 1)$
$= (3 + 1) +$
$(6 + 1) +$
$(9 + 1) +$
$(12 + 1) +$
$(15 + 1)$
$= 4 + 7 + 10 +$
$13 + 16$
$= 50$

1.02 $\displaystyle\sum_{i=1}^{10} 1^i = 1^1 + 1^2 + 1^3 + 1^4 +$
$1^5 + 1^6 + 1^7 + 1^8 +$
$1^9 + 1^{10}$
$= 1 + 1 + 1 + 1 + 1 +$
$1 + 1 + 1 + 1 + 1$
$= 10$

1.03 $\displaystyle\sum_{i=1}^{5} 6i = 6(1) + 6(2) + 6(3) +$
$6(4) + 6(5)$
$= 6 + 12 + 18 + 24 + 30$
$= 90$

1.04 $\displaystyle\sum_{i=1}^{6} i^2 - 1 = (1^2 - 1) +$
$(2^2 - 1) +$
$(3^2 - 1) +$
$(4^2 - 1) +$
$(5^2 - 1) +$
$(6^2 - 1)$
$= (1 - 1) +$
$(4 - 1) +$
$(9 - 1) +$
$(16 - 1) +$
$(25 - 1) +$
$(36 - 1)$
$= 0 + 3 + 8 + 15 +$
$24 + 35$
$= 85$

1.05 a. When $n = 1$, $1^2 =$
$\dfrac{1(1 + 1)(2\cdot 1 + 1)}{6} = \dfrac{1\cdot 2\cdot 3}{6} =$
1. Summation is true.

b. Assume $\displaystyle\sum_{i=1}^{k} i^2 =$
$\dfrac{k(k + 1)(2k + 1)}{6}$.

c. Then $\displaystyle\sum_{i=1}^{k} i^2 + (k + 1)^2 =$
$\dfrac{k(k + 1)(2k + 1)}{6} +$
$(k + 1)^2 =$
$\dfrac{k(k + 1)(2k + 1)}{6} + \dfrac{6(k + 1)^2}{6}$
$\displaystyle\sum_{i=1}^{k + 1} i^2 = \dfrac{k + 1}{6}$.
$[k(2k + 1) + 6(k + 1)]$
(factor out $\dfrac{k + 1}{6}$ from
the preceding equation) =
$\dfrac{k + 1}{6}[2k^2 + k + 6k + 6] =$
$\dfrac{(k + 1)}{6}[2k^2 + 7k + 6] =$
$\dfrac{(k + 1)}{6}[(k + 2)(2k + 3)] =$
$\dfrac{k + 1}{6}\cdot[(k + 1 + 1)\cdot$
$[2(k + 1) + 1)]$

SELF TEST 2

2.01 $\displaystyle\sum_{i=1}^{7} 4i + 4 = (4\cdot 1 + 4) +$
$(4\cdot 2 + 4) +$
$(4\cdot 3 + 4) +$
$(4\cdot 4 + 4) +$
$(4\cdot 5 + 4) +$
$(4\cdot 6 + 4) +$
$(4\cdot 7 + 4)$
$= (4 + 4) +$
$(8 + 4) +$
$(12 + 4) +$
$(16 + 4) +$
$(20 + 4) +$
$(24 + 4) +$
$(28 + 4)$
$= 8 + 12 + 16 + 20 +$
$24 + 28 + 32$
$= 140$

2.02

$$\sum_{i=0}^{4} 7 - i = (7 - 0) + (7 - 1) + (7 - 2) + (7 - 3) + (7 - 4)$$
$$= 7 + 6 + 5 + 4 + 3$$
$$= 25$$

2.03

$$\sum_{i=1}^{n} a = a + a + a + \ldots = na$$

2.04

$$\sum_{i=1}^{5} \left(\tfrac{1}{2}\right)^{i} = \left(\tfrac{1}{2}\right)^{1} + \left(\tfrac{1}{2}\right)^{2} + \left(\tfrac{1}{2}\right)^{3} + \left(\tfrac{1}{2}\right)^{4} + \left(\tfrac{1}{2}\right)^{5}$$
$$= \tfrac{1}{2} + \tfrac{1}{4} + \tfrac{1}{8} + \tfrac{1}{16} + \tfrac{1}{32}$$
$$= \tfrac{16}{32} + \tfrac{8}{32} + \tfrac{4}{32} + \tfrac{2}{32} + \tfrac{1}{32}$$
$$= \tfrac{31}{32}$$

2.05

$$f(2) = 2^2 - 1$$
$$= 4 - 1$$
$$= 3$$

2.06

$$f(P) = P^2 - 1$$

2.07

$$\frac{f(x + h) - f(x)}{h} =$$
$$\frac{(x + h)^2 - 1 - (x^2 - 1)}{h} =$$
$$\frac{\cancel{x^2} + 2hx + h^2 - \cancel{1} - \cancel{x^2} + \cancel{1}}{h} =$$
$$\frac{2\cancel{h}x + h^{\cancel{2}}}{\cancel{h}} =$$
$$2x + h$$

2.08

a. When $n = 1$,
$$\frac{1}{1 \cdot 2} = \frac{1}{1 + 1} = \frac{1}{2}.$$

b. Assume $\sum_{i=1}^{k} \frac{1}{i(i + 1)} = \frac{k}{k + 1}.$

c. Then $\sum_{i=1}^{k} \frac{1}{i(i + 1)} +$
$$\frac{1}{(k + 1)(k + 2)} = \frac{k}{k + 1} +$$
$$\frac{1}{(k + 1)(k + 2)}$$

LCD $= (k + 1)(k + 2)$

$$\frac{k}{k + 1} + \frac{1}{(k + 1)(k + 2)} =$$
$$\frac{k(k + 2)}{(k + 1)(k + 2)} + \frac{1}{(k + 1)(k + 2)} =$$
$$\frac{k(k + 2) + 1}{(k + 1)(k + 2)} = \frac{k^2 + 2k + 1}{(k + 1)(k + 2)} =$$
$$\frac{\cancel{(k + 1)}(k + 1)}{\cancel{(k + 1)}(k + 2)} = \frac{k + 1}{(k + 1) + 1}$$

2.09

$$\lim_{x \to -4} x^2 - 1 = \lim_{x \to -4} x^2 - \lim_{x \to -4} 1$$
$$= \lim_{x \to -4} x \cdot \lim_{x \to -4} x - \lim_{x \to -4} 1$$
$$= -4(-4) - 1$$
$$= 16 - 1$$
$$= 15$$

2.010 0

2.011 Divide the numerator and the denominator by x.

$$\lim_{x \to \infty} \frac{x - 4}{x} = \lim_{x \to \infty} \frac{1 - \dfrac{4}{x}}{1}$$
$$= \frac{\lim_{x \to \infty} 1 - \lim_{x \to \infty} \dfrac{4}{x}}{\lim_{x \to \infty} 1}$$
$$= \frac{1 - 0}{1}$$
$$= 1$$

2.012 $6k$

2.013

$$\frac{5(a + h) - 5a}{h} =$$
$$\frac{\cancel{5a} + 5h - \cancel{5a}}{h} =$$
$$\frac{5\cancel{h}}{\cancel{h}} = 5$$

2.014

$$\frac{2(a + h)^2 - 3 - (2a^2 - 3)}{h} =$$
$$\frac{2(a^2 + 2ah + h^2) - 3 - 2a^2 + 3}{h} =$$
$$\frac{2\cancel{a^2} + 4ah + 2h^2 - \cancel{3} - 2\cancel{a^2} + \cancel{3}}{h} =$$
$$\frac{4a\cancel{h} + 2h^{\cancel{2}}}{\cancel{h}} =$$
$$4a + 2h$$

2.015 $\dfrac{\dfrac{7 + 3(a + h) - (7 + 3a)}{4}}{h} =$

$\dfrac{\cancel{7} + \cancel{3a} + 3h - \cancel{7} - \cancel{3a}}{4h} =$

$\dfrac{3\cancel{h}}{4\cancel{h}} =$

$\dfrac{3}{4}$

SELF TEST 3

3.01   a.   When $n = 1$, $(2\cdot1 - 1)^3 =$
$1^2(2\cdot1^2 - 1) = 1$.

b.   Assume $\displaystyle\sum_{i=1}^{k} (2i - 1)^3 =$
$k^2(2k^2 - 1)$.

c.   Then $\displaystyle\sum_{i=1}^{k} (2i - 1)^3 +$
$(2k + 1)^3 = k^2(2k^2 - 1) +$
$(2k + 1)^3$.
$\displaystyle\sum_{i=1}^{k+1} (2i - 1)^3 =$
$2k^4 - k^2 + 8k^3 + 3(2k)^2 +$
$\quad 3(2k) + 1 =$
$2k^4 + 8k^3 + 11k^2 + 6k + 1$

Use synthetic division to factor.
$2k^4 + 8k^3 + 11k^2 + 6k + 1 =$
$(k + 1)^2(2k^2 + 4k + 1) =$
$(k + 1)^2(2k^2 + 4k + 2 - 1) =$
$(k + 1)^2[2(k + 1)^2 - 1]$

3.02 $\displaystyle\sum_{i=1}^{3} i^3 - i = (1^3 - 1) +$
$\qquad\qquad (2^3 - 2) +$
$\qquad\qquad (3^3 - 3)$
$\qquad = (1 + 1) + (8 - 2) +$
$\qquad\quad (27 - 3)$
$\qquad = 0 + 6 + 24$
$\qquad = 30$

3.03 $\displaystyle\sum_{i=1}^{6} i^2 + 2i + 1 =$
$(1^2 + 2\cdot1 + 1) +$
$(2^2 + 2\cdot2 + 1) +$
$(3^2 + 2\cdot3 + 1) +$
$(4^2 + 2\cdot4 + 1) +$
$(5^2 + 2\cdot5 + 1) +$
$(6^2 + 2\cdot6 + 1) \quad =$
$(1 + 2 + 1) +$
$(4 + 4 + 1) +$
$(9 + 6 + 1) +$
$(16 + 8 + 1) +$
$(25 + 10 + 1) +$
$(36 + 12 + 1) \quad =$
$4 + 9 + 16 + 25 +$
$36 + 49 \qquad = 139$

3.04 $f(-2) = (-2)^2 - 5(-2) + 6$
$\qquad = 4 + 10 + 6$
$\qquad = 20$

3.05 $f(6) = 6^2 - 5(6) + 6$
$\qquad = 36 - 30 + 6$
$\qquad = 12$

3.06 $\dfrac{f(a + b) - f(a)}{b} =$
$\dfrac{(a + b)^2 - 5(a + b) +}{b} \ldots$
$\dfrac{6 - (a^2 - 5a + 6)}{b} =$
$\dfrac{\cancel{a^2} + 2ab + b^2 - \cancel{5a} -}{b} \ldots$
$\dfrac{5b + \cancel{6} - \cancel{a^2} + \cancel{5a} - \cancel{6}}{b} =$
$\dfrac{2a\cancel{b} + b^{\cancel{2}} - 5\cancel{b}}{\cancel{b}} =$
$2a + b - 5$

3.07 $\dfrac{6(a + h) - 6a}{h} = \dfrac{\cancel{6a} + 6h - \cancel{6a}}{h}$
$\qquad\qquad = \dfrac{6\cancel{h}}{\cancel{h}}$
$\qquad\qquad = 6$

3.08

$$\frac{5(a+h)^2 - 9 - (5a^2 - 9)}{h} =$$

$$\frac{5(a^2 + 2ah + h^2) -}{h} \ldots$$

$$\frac{9 - 5a^2 + 9}{h} =$$

$$\frac{5a^2 + 10ah + 5h^2 - 5a^2}{h} =$$

$$\frac{10ah + 5h^2}{h} =$$

$$10a + 5h$$

3.09

$$\frac{\dfrac{4(a+h) - 3}{9} - \dfrac{4a - 3}{9}}{h} =$$

$$\frac{4a + 4h - 3 - 4a + 3}{9h} =$$

$$\frac{4h}{9h} = \frac{4}{9}$$

3.010

$$\lim_{x \to 2} \frac{1}{x^2} = \frac{1}{2^2}$$

$$= \frac{1}{4}$$

3.011

$$\lim_{x \to -1} x^2 + 3x - 4 = \lim_{x \to -1} x^2 +$$
$$\lim_{x \to -1} 3x -$$
$$\lim_{x \to -1} 4$$
$$= \lim_{x \to -1} x \cdot \lim_{x \to -1} x +$$
$$\lim_{x \to -1} 3 \cdot \lim_{x \to -1} x -$$
$$\lim_{x \to -1} 4$$
$$= -1(-1) +$$
$$3(-1) - 4$$
$$= 1 - 3 - 4$$
$$= -6$$

3.012

$$\lim_{x \to 0} \frac{5x + 6}{x} = \frac{\lim_{x \to 0} 5 \cdot \lim_{x \to 0} x + \lim_{x \to 0} 6}{\lim_{x \to 0} x}$$

$$= \frac{5 \cdot 0 + 6}{0}$$

$$= \frac{6}{0}$$

$$= \text{undefined}$$

3.013

$$m = \lim_{h \to 0} \frac{f(x + h) - f(x)}{h}$$

$$= \lim_{h \to 0} \frac{\sqrt{5(x + h)} - \sqrt{5x}}{h}$$

$$= \lim_{h \to 0} \frac{\sqrt{5(x + h)} - \sqrt{5x}}{h} \cdot \frac{\sqrt{5(x + h)} + \sqrt{5x}}{\sqrt{5(x + h)} + \sqrt{5x}}$$

$$= \lim_{h \to 0} \frac{5(x + h) - 5x}{h(\sqrt{5(x + h)} + \sqrt{5x})}$$

$$= \lim_{h \to 0} \frac{5x + 5h - 5x}{h(\sqrt{5(x + h)} + \sqrt{5x})}$$

$$= \lim_{h \to 0} \frac{5h}{h(\sqrt{5x + 5h} + \sqrt{5x})}$$

$$= \lim_{h \to 0} \frac{5}{\sqrt{5x} + \sqrt{5x}}$$

$$= \lim_{h \to 0} \frac{5}{2\sqrt{5x}}$$

$$= \frac{5}{2\sqrt{5x}}$$

The slope at $x = 5$ is

$$m = \frac{5}{2\sqrt{5(5)}} = \frac{5}{2\sqrt{25}} = \frac{5}{2(5)} = \frac{1}{2}$$

3.014

$$m = \lim_{h \to 0} \frac{f(x + h) - f(x)}{h}$$

$$= \lim_{x \to 0} \frac{(x + h)^3 + 3(x + h)^2 +}{h} \ldots$$
$$\frac{3(x + h) + 1 - (x^3 +}{h} \ldots$$
$$\frac{3x^2 + 3x + 1)}{h}$$

$$= \lim_{h \to 0} \frac{(x + h)^3 + 3(x^2 +}{h} \ldots$$
$$\frac{2xh + h^2) + 3x + 3h +}{h} \ldots$$
$$\frac{1 - x^3 - 3x^2 - 3x - 1}{h}$$

$$= \lim_{h \to 0} \frac{x^3 + 3x^2h + 3xh^2 +}{h}$$
$$\frac{h^3 + 3x^2 + 6xh +}{h}$$
$$\frac{3h^2 + 3h - x^3 - 3x^2}{h}$$

$$= \lim_{h \to 0} \frac{3x^2\not{h} + 3xh^2 + h^{\not{2}} + \dots}{6x\not{h} + 3h^2 + 3\not{h}}$$

$$= \lim_{h \to 0} 3x^2 + 3xh + h^2 + 6x + 3h + 3$$

$$= \lim_{h \to 0} 3x^2 + 6x + 3$$

$$= 3x^2 + 6x + 3$$

The slope at $x = 0$ is
$m = 3(0)^2 + 6(0) + 3 = 0 + 0 + 3 = 3$

3.015   Let m_2 = slope of $f(x)$
        m_1 = slope of $g(x)$

$$m_2 = \lim_{h \to 0} \frac{(x + h)^2 + 2(x + h) + \dots}{h} \\ \frac{1 - (x^2 + 2x + 1)}{h}$$

$$= \lim_{h \to 0} \frac{\not{x^2} + 2xh + h^2 + \not{2x} + \dots}{h} \\ \frac{2h + \not{x} - \not{x^2} - \not{2x} - \not{1}}{h}$$

$$= \lim_{h \to 0} \frac{2x\not{h} + h^{\not{2}} + 2\not{h}}{\not{h}}$$

$$= \lim_{h \to 0} 2x + h + 2$$

$$= \lim_{h \to 0} 2x + 2$$

$$= 2x + 2$$

$$m_1 = \lim_{h \to 0} 1$$

$$= 1$$

Points of intersection:
$$x^2 + 2x + 1 = 1$$
$$x^2 + 2x + 1 - 1 = 0$$
$$x^2 + 2x = 0$$
$$x(x + 2) = 0$$
$$x = 0$$
$$x + 2 = 0$$
$$x = -2$$

$x = 0$: $y = x^2 + 2x + 1$
        $= 0^2 + 2(0) + 1$
        $= 0 + 0 + 1$
        $= 1$

$x = -2$: $y = x^2 + 2x + 1$
         $= (-2)^2 + 2(-2) + 1$
         $= 4 - 4 + 1$
         $= 1$

Points of intersection are
(0, 1) and (-2, 1).

Points to graph $f(x) = x^2 + 2x + 1$ are (0, 1), (-1, 0), (-2, 1), (2, 9), (-3, 4), (-4, 9).
Points to graph $g(x) = 1$ are any points such that $y = 1$.

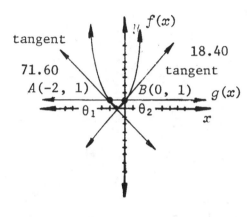

For point A:
$m_2 = 2(-2) + 2 = -4 + 2 = -2$
$m_1 = 1$

$$\tan \theta_1 = \frac{m_2 - m_1}{1 + m_2 m_1}$$

$$= \frac{-2 - 1}{1 + (-2)(1)}$$

$$= \frac{-3}{1 - 2}$$

$$= \frac{-3}{-1}$$

$$= 3$$

θ_1 = arc tan 3 = 71.6° approximately

For point B:
$m_2 = 2(0) + 2 = 2$
$m_1 = 1$

$$\tan \theta_2 = \frac{2 - 1}{1 + 2(1)}$$

$$= \frac{1}{1 + 2}$$

$$= \frac{1}{3}$$

$$= 0.\overline{3}$$

θ_2 = arc tan $0.\overline{3}$ = 18.4° approximately

SELF TEST 4

4.01 a. When $n = 1$,

$$\sum_{j=1}^{1} 2^j = 2^1 = 2(2^1 - 1) = 2.$$

b. Assume $\sum_{j=1}^{k} 2^j = 2(2^k - 1).$

c. Then $\sum_{j=1}^{k} 2^j + 2^{k+1} =$

$$2(2^k - 1) + 2^{k+1}$$

$$\sum_{j=1}^{k+1} 2^j =$$

$$2^{k+1} - 2 + 2^{k+1} =$$

$$2(2^{k+1} - 1)$$

4.02 $\sum_{i=1}^{n} 7 = 7 + 7 + 7 + \ldots = 7n$

4.03 $\sum_{i=1}^{5} 3^{-i} = 3^{-1} + 3^{-2} + 3^{-3} +$

$$3^{-4} + 3^{-5}$$

$$= \frac{1}{3^1} + \frac{1}{3^2} + \frac{1}{3^3} + \frac{1}{3^4} +$$

$$\frac{1}{3^5}$$

$$= \frac{1}{3} + \frac{1}{9} + \frac{1}{27} + \frac{1}{81} + \frac{1}{243}$$

$$= \frac{81}{243} + \frac{27}{243} + \frac{9}{243} +$$

$$\frac{3}{243} + \frac{1}{243}$$

$$= \frac{121}{243}$$

4.04 $f(\tfrac{1}{2}) = (\tfrac{1}{2})^2 - 5(\tfrac{1}{2}) + 6$

$$= \tfrac{1}{4} - \tfrac{5}{2} + 6$$

$$= \tfrac{1}{4} - \tfrac{10}{4} + \tfrac{24}{4}$$

$$= \tfrac{15}{4}$$

4.05 $\dfrac{f(x + h) - f(x)}{h} =$

$$\frac{(x + h)^2 - 5(x + h) +}{h} \ldots$$

$$\frac{6 - (x^2 - 5x + 6)}{h} =$$

$$\frac{\cancel{x^2} + 2xh + h^2 - \cancel{5x} -}{h} \ldots$$

$$\frac{5h + \cancel{6} - \cancel{x^2} + \cancel{5x} - \cancel{6}}{h} =$$

$$\frac{2x\cancel{h} + h^{\cancel{2}} - 5\cancel{h}}{\cancel{h}} =$$

$$2x + h - 5$$

4.06 $\dfrac{(a + h)^2 - 3(a + h) -}{h} \ldots$

$$\frac{(a^2 - 3a)}{h} =$$

$$\frac{\cancel{a^2} + 2ah + h^2 - \cancel{3a} -}{h} \ldots$$

$$\frac{3h - \cancel{a^2} + \cancel{3a}}{h} =$$

$$\frac{2a\cancel{h} + h^{\cancel{2}} - 3\cancel{h}}{\cancel{h}} =$$

$$2a + h - 3$$

4.07 $\dfrac{\dfrac{7(a + h) + 1}{2} - \dfrac{7a + 1}{2}}{h} =$

$$\frac{\cancel{7a} + 7h + \cancel{1} - \cancel{7a} - \cancel{1}}{2h} =$$

$$\frac{7\cancel{h}}{2\cancel{h}} =$$

$$\frac{7}{2} =$$

4.08 $\lim_{x \to 5} x^2 = \lim_{x \to 5} x \cdot \lim_{x \to 5} x$

$$= -5(-5)$$

$$= 25$$

4.09 Divide the numerator and the denominator by x.

$$\lim_{x \to \infty} \frac{2x - 1}{x} = \lim_{x \to \infty} \frac{2 - \dfrac{1}{x}}{1}$$

$$= \frac{\displaystyle\lim_{x \to \infty} 2 - \lim_{x \to \infty} \dfrac{1}{x}}{\displaystyle\lim_{x \to \infty} 1}$$

$$= \frac{2 - 0}{1}$$

$$= 2$$

4.010 $m = \lim_{h \to 0} \dfrac{f(x + h) - f(x)}{h}$

$= \lim_{h \to 0} \dfrac{5(x + h) - 5 - (5x - 5)}{h}$

$= \lim_{h \to 0} \dfrac{\cancel{5x} + 5h - \cancel{5} - \cancel{5x} + \cancel{5}}{h}$

$= \lim_{h \to 0} \dfrac{5\cancel{h}}{\cancel{h}}$

$= \lim_{h \to 0} 5$

$= 5$

4.011 $m = \lim_{h \to 0} \dfrac{f(x + h) - f(x)}{h}$

$= \lim_{h \to 0} \dfrac{(x + h)^3 - x^3}{h}$

$= \lim_{h \to 0} \dfrac{\cancel{x^3} + 3x^2 h + 3xh^2 + \quad \cdots}{h}$
$\dfrac{h^3 - \cancel{x^3}}{h}$

$= \lim_{h \to 0} \dfrac{3x^2 \cancel{h} + 3xh^{\cancel{2}} + h^{\cancel{3}2}}{\cancel{h}}$

$= \lim_{h \to 0} 3x^2 + 3xh + h^2$

$= \lim_{h \to 0} 3x^2$

$= 3x^2$

The slope at $x = -3$ is
$m = 3(-3)^2 = 3(9) = 27$.

4.012 Let $m_2 =$ slope of $f(x)$
$m_1 =$ slope of $g(x)$

$m_2 = \lim_{h \to 0} \dfrac{4(x + h) - 5 - (4x - 5)}{h}$

$= \lim_{h \to 0} \dfrac{\cancel{4x} + 4h - \cancel{5} - \cancel{4x} + \cancel{5}}{h}$

$= \lim_{h \to 0} \dfrac{4\cancel{h}}{\cancel{h}}$

$= \lim_{h \to 0} 4$

$= 4$

$m_1 = \lim_{h \to 0} \dfrac{2(x + h)^2 - 5 - \quad \cdots}{h}$
$\dfrac{(2x^2 - 5)}{h}$

$= \lim_{h \to 0} \dfrac{2(x^2 + 2xh + h^2) - \quad \cdots}{h}$
$\dfrac{\cancel{5} - 2x^2 + \cancel{5}}{h}$

$= \lim_{h \to 0} \dfrac{\cancel{2x^2} + 4xh + 2h^2 - \cancel{2x^2}}{h}$

$= \lim_{h \to 0} \dfrac{4x\cancel{h} + 2h^{\cancel{2}}}{\cancel{h}}$

$= \lim_{h \to 0} 4x + 2h$

$= \lim_{h \to 0} 4x$

$= 4x$

Points of intersection:
$4x - 5 = 2x^2 - 5$
$0 = 2x^2 - \cancel{5} - 4x + \cancel{5}$
$0 = 2x^2 - 4x$
$2x(x - 2) = 0$
$2x = 0$
$\dfrac{2x}{2} = \dfrac{0}{2}$
$x = 0$
$x - 2 = 0$
$x = 2$

$x = 0:$ $y = 4x - 5$
$\quad\quad = 4(0) - 5$
$\quad\quad = -5$

$x = 2:$ $y = 4x - 5$
$\quad\quad = 4(2) - 5$
$\quad\quad = 8 - 5$
$\quad\quad = 3$

Points of intersection are
$(0, -5)$ and $(2, 3)$.
Points to graph $f(x) = 4x - 5$
are $(-1, -9)$, $(0, -5)$, $(\frac{5}{4}, 0)$.
Points to graph $g(x) = 2x^2 - 5$
are $(0, -5)$, $(\pm 2, 3)$, $(\pm 3, 13)$.

4.012 cont.

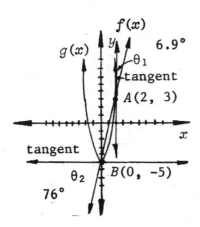

For point A:
$m_2 = 4$
$m_1 = 4x$
$\quad = 4(2)$
$\quad = 8$

$$\tan \theta_1 = \frac{m_2 - m_1}{1 + m_2 m_1}$$

$$= \frac{4 - 8}{1 + 4(8)}$$

$$= \frac{-4}{1 + 32}$$

$$= \frac{4}{33}$$

$$= -0.1212$$

$\theta_1 = $ arc tan $(-0.1212) = $ 6.9° approximately

For point B:
$m_2 = 4$
$m_1 = 4x$
$\quad = 4(0)$
$\quad = 0$

$$\tan \theta_2 = \frac{4 - 0}{1 + 4(0)}$$

$$= \frac{4}{1}$$

$$= 4$$

$\theta_2 = $ arc tan $4 = 76°$ approximately

4.013 all real numbers; $x \in R$

4.014 For x equals any real negative number, y will always be negative. For x equals 0, y will always be 0. For x equals any real positive number, y will always be positive. Therefore, the range is all real numbers; $y \in R$.

4.015 $f(x) + g(x) = 4x + 2 + x^2 - 1$
$\qquad\qquad\quad = x^2 + 4x + 1$

4.016 $f[g(x)] = 4(x^2 - 1) + 2$
$\qquad\qquad = 4x^2 - 4 + 2$
$\qquad\qquad = 4x^2 - 2$

4.017 $(2x + 3)(x - 8) = 0$
$\qquad\quad 2x + 3 = 0$
$\qquad\qquad\quad 2x = -3$
$\qquad\qquad\quad \frac{2x}{2} = \frac{-3}{2}$
$\qquad\qquad\qquad x = -\frac{3}{2}$
$\qquad\quad x - 8 = 0$
$\qquad\qquad\quad x = 8$
The zeros are $x = -\frac{3}{2}$, 8.

4.018 $f^{-1}(x) = 6^x$

4.019 $\sin^2 30° \cdot \cos 180° +$
$\tan 0° - \cot (-45°) =$
$(\frac{1}{2})^2 (-1) + 0 - (-1) =$
$-\frac{1}{4} - (-1) =$
$-\frac{1}{4} + 1 =$
$\frac{3}{4}$

4.020

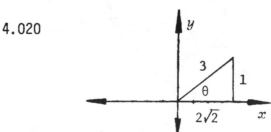

a. $\cos \theta = \dfrac{2\sqrt{2}}{3}$

b. $\tan \theta = \dfrac{1}{2\sqrt{2}}$

$\qquad\qquad = \dfrac{1}{2\sqrt{2}} \cdot \dfrac{\sqrt{2}}{\sqrt{2}}$

$\qquad\qquad = \dfrac{\sqrt{2}}{2 \cdot 2}$

$\qquad\qquad = \dfrac{\sqrt{2}}{4}$

c. $\cot \theta = \dfrac{2\sqrt{2}}{1}$

$\qquad = 2\sqrt{2}$

d. $\csc \theta = \dfrac{1}{\frac{1}{3}}$

$\qquad = 3$

e. $\sec \theta = \dfrac{1}{\frac{2\sqrt{2}}{3}}$

$\qquad = \dfrac{3}{2\sqrt{2}}$

$\qquad = \dfrac{3}{2\sqrt{2}} \cdot \dfrac{\sqrt{2}}{\sqrt{2}}$

$\qquad = \dfrac{3\sqrt{2}}{2 \cdot 2}$

$\qquad = \dfrac{3\sqrt{2}}{4}$

4.021 $G(x) = 4 \tan \left(3x + \dfrac{\pi}{6}\right)$

$\qquad = 4 \tan 3\left(x + \dfrac{\pi}{18}\right)$

Phase shift $= \dfrac{\pi}{18}$ to the left.

4.022 $8(10\pi) = 80\pi$ feet per second

4.023 $2 \cos \theta + 1 = 0$

$\qquad 2 \cos \theta = -1$

$\qquad \dfrac{2 \cos \theta}{2} = \dfrac{-1}{2}$

$\qquad \cos \theta = -\dfrac{1}{2}$

$\theta = 120°, 240°$

4.024 $\cos \theta = \dfrac{-4}{5}$

$\sin \dfrac{1}{2}\theta = \pm\sqrt{\dfrac{1 - \cos \theta}{2}}$

$\qquad = \pm\sqrt{\dfrac{1 - \left(-\frac{4}{5}\right)}{2}}$

$\qquad = \pm\sqrt{\dfrac{1 + \frac{4}{5}}{2}}$

$\qquad = \pm\sqrt{\dfrac{\frac{9}{5}}{2}}$

$\qquad = \pm\sqrt{\dfrac{9}{10}}$

$\qquad = \pm\dfrac{\sqrt{9}}{\sqrt{10}}$

$\qquad = \pm\dfrac{3}{\sqrt{10}}$

$\qquad = \pm\dfrac{3}{\sqrt{10}} \cdot \dfrac{\sqrt{10}}{\sqrt{10}}$

$\qquad = \pm\dfrac{3\sqrt{10}}{10}$

4.025

$\angle\theta = 180° - 55°$

$\qquad = 125°$

$x^2 = 16^2 + 18^2 - 2(16)(18)$
$\qquad\quad \cos 125°$

$\qquad = 256 + 324 + 330$

$\qquad = 910$

$\sqrt{x^2} = \sqrt{910}$

$\qquad x = 30$ na. mi. (rounded)

4.026 a. $\angle A = 180° - 90° - 45°$

$\qquad\quad = 45°$

b. Since $\triangle ABC$ is a 45°-45°-90° triangle, $\overline{AC} = 3\sqrt{2}$.

c. $\sin \angle A = \sin 45°$

$\qquad = \dfrac{3}{3\sqrt{2}}$

$\qquad = \dfrac{1}{\sqrt{2}}$

$\qquad = \dfrac{1}{\sqrt{2}} \cdot \dfrac{\sqrt{2}}{\sqrt{2}}$

$\qquad = \dfrac{\sqrt{2}}{2}$

$\cos \angle A = \dfrac{3}{3\sqrt{2}}$

$= \dfrac{1}{\sqrt{2}}$

$= \dfrac{1}{\sqrt{2}} \cdot \dfrac{\sqrt{2}}{\sqrt{2}}$

$= \dfrac{\sqrt{2}}{2}$

$\tan \angle A = \dfrac{3}{3}$

$= 1$

d. $\csc \angle C = \csc 45°$

$= \dfrac{3\sqrt{2}}{3}$

$= \sqrt{2}$

$\sec \angle C = \dfrac{3\sqrt{2}}{3}$

$= \sqrt{2}$

$\cot \angle C = \dfrac{3}{3}$

$= 1$

4.027 $x = r \cos \theta$
$= 2 \cos 60°$
$= 2(\tfrac{1}{2})$
$= 1$

$y = r \sin \theta$
$= 2 \sin 60°$
$= 2(\dfrac{\sqrt{3}}{2})$
$= \sqrt{3}$

$(1, \sqrt{3})$

4.028 The point is on the positive y-axis.

$\theta = \tan^{-1}(\dfrac{y}{x})$

$= \tan^{-1}(\dfrac{6}{0})$

$=$ undefined

$\tan \theta$ is undefined and

$\theta = 90°$ or $\dfrac{\pi}{2}$

$r = \sqrt{x^2 + y^2}$
$= \sqrt{0^2 + 6^2}$
$= \sqrt{36}$
$= 6$

$(6, \dfrac{\pi}{2})$

4.029

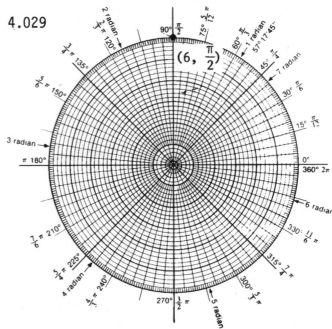

$(6, \dfrac{\pi}{2})$

4.030 $x^2 + y^2 + 10x - 4y - 7 = 0$
$x^2 + 10x + y^2 - 4y = 7$
$(x^2 + 10x + 25) +$
$\qquad (y^2 - 4y + 4) = 7 +$
$\qquad\qquad\qquad\qquad 25 + 4$
$(x + 5)^2 + (y - 2)^2 = 36$

Circle
Center $= (-5, 2)$
Radius $= \sqrt{36}$
$\qquad = 6$
Domain: $-11 \le x \le 1$
Range: $-4 \le y \le 8$

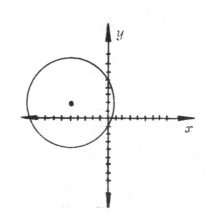

4.031 $x^2 = 6y$
Parabola
Position II
Vertex = $(0, 0)$
Focus: $4p = 6$

$$\frac{4p}{4} = \frac{6}{4}$$

$$p = \frac{3}{2}$$

$$(0, \frac{3}{2})$$

L.R. $= |4p|$
    $= 6$
Directrix: $y = -p$

$$y = -\frac{3}{2}$$

Domain: all real numbers;
    $x \in R$
Range: For x equals any
    real number, y will
    always be greater than
    or equal to zero; $y \geq 0$.

x	±5	±4	±3	±2	±1	0
y	$\frac{25}{6}$	$\frac{8}{3}$	$\frac{3}{2}$	$\frac{2}{3}$	$\frac{1}{6}$	0

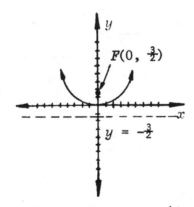

$F(0, \frac{3}{2})$

$y = -\frac{3}{2}$

4.032 Since the center is at $(4, 2)$
and the vertex is at $(0, 2)$,
then $a = |4 - 0| = 4$.
Also, since $e = \frac{c}{a} = \frac{c}{4} = \frac{1}{2}$, then

$c = 2.$
$b^2 = a^2 - c^2$; therefore,
$b^2 = 4^2 - 2^2$
    $= 16 - 4$
    $= 12$

$$\frac{(x - 4)^2}{16} + \frac{(y - 2)^2}{12} = 1$$

4.033 a. The hundreds' digit has 6
    possibilities, the tens'
    digit has 5 possibilities,
    and the units' digit has 4
    possibilities.

b. $6 \cdot 5 \cdot 4 = 120$
    $\overline{6 \cdot 5 \cdot 4} \cdot 3 \cdot 2 = 720$
c. Sample space $= \{6, 12, 18\}$.

$$P = \frac{3}{6}$$

$$= \frac{1}{2} \text{ or } 0.5$$

d. Sample space $= \{3, 6, 9,$
    $12, 15, 18\}$.

$$P = \frac{6}{6}$$

$$= 1$$

4.034 $_8P_2 = 8 \cdot 7 = 56$

4.035 $_{100}P_2 = 100 \cdot 99 = 9{,}900$

4.036 $_5C_4 = \frac{5!}{4!1!}$

$$= \frac{5 \cdot \cancel{4!}}{1 \cdot \cancel{4!}}$$

$$= 5$$

4.037 $\binom{12}{8} - \binom{12}{9} =$

$$\frac{12!}{8!4!} - \frac{12!}{9!3!} =$$

$$\frac{12 \cdot 11 \cdot \cancel{10}^5 \cdot 9 \cdot \cancel{8!}}{\cancel{4} \cdot \cancel{3} \cdot \cancel{2} \cdot \cancel{1} \cdot \cancel{8!}} - \frac{\cancel{12}^2 \cdot 11 \cdot 10 \cdot \cancel{9!}}{\cancel{3} \cdot \cancel{2} \cdot \cancel{1} \cdot \cancel{9!}} =$$

$495 - 220 = 275$

T
E
S
T

K
E
Y
S

MATHEMATICS 1201
LIFEPAC TEST
SOLUTION KEY

1. $\{x:\ x \in R,\ x \neq -4,\ x \neq 7\}$

2. $(\sqrt{3},\ -4),\ (-\sqrt{3},\ 4)$

3. $\{(-2, 2),\ (-1, 0),\ (0, 2),$
   $(1, 4),\ (2, 6)\}$

4. no

5. set of all real numbers

6. $f(x) = x^2 + 2$

7. $g(x) = 2x - 1$; then $y = 2x - 1$
   or $x = \dfrac{y + 1}{2}$. Interchanging
   x and y results in $y = \dfrac{x + 1}{2}$;
   $g^{-1}(x) = \dfrac{x + 1}{2}$.

8. $F(-2) = 3(-2)^2 + 1$
   $= 3(4) + 1$
   $= 13$

9. $F(x) + G(x) = (3x^2 + 1)$
   $+ (2x - 3) = 3x^2 + 2x - 2$

10. $F \circ G = F[G(x)] = F(2x - 3)$
    $= 3(2x - 3)^2 + 1$
    $= 3(4x^2 - 12x + 9) + 1$
    $= 12x^2 - 36x + 27 + 1$
    $= 12x^2 - 36x + 28$

11. Let $y = G(x)$; $y = 2x - 3$.

    Solve for x: $x = \dfrac{y + 3}{2}$.

    Interchange the variables:

    $y = \dfrac{x + 3}{2}$. $\therefore G^{-1}(x) = \dfrac{x + 3}{2}$.

12. Let $y = H(x)$; $y = x$ or $x = y$.
    $H^{-1}(x) = x$.

13. $F(3) + G(4) - 2H(5)$
    $= 3(3)^2 + 1 + 2(4) - 3 - 2(5)$
    $= 27 + 1 + 8 - 3 - 10$
    $= 23$

14. Let $y = F(x)$; $y = 3x^2 + 1$.

    Solve for x: $x = \pm\sqrt{\dfrac{y - 1}{3}}$.

    Interchange the variables:

    $y = \pm\sqrt{\dfrac{x - 1}{3}}$. $\therefore F^{-1}(x)$
    $= \pm\sqrt{\dfrac{x - 1}{3}}$.

15. no, for each value of x
    in the domain of F^{-1}, two
    function values occur.

16. $F[G(x)] = F(x - 4)$
    $= 5(x - 4) - 6$
    $= 5x - 20 - 6$
    $= 5x - 26$
    Let $y = 5x - 26$. Then
    $x = \dfrac{y + 26}{5}$. Then
    $(F \circ G)^{-1} = \dfrac{x + 26}{5}$.

17. $G^{-1} = x + 4$ and $F^{-1} = \dfrac{x + 6}{5}$.
    $G^{-1}(F^{-1}) = G^{-1}(\dfrac{x + 6}{5})$
    $= \dfrac{x + 6}{5} + 4 = \dfrac{x + 6 + 20}{5}$
    $= \dfrac{x + 26}{5}$.

18. $(F + G)(x) = (2x) + (x^2 + 2)$
    $= x^2 + 2x + 2$

19. $(F - G)(x) = (x^2 + 2) - (2x)$
    $= x^2 - 2x + 2$

20. $(\dfrac{F}{G})(x) = \dfrac{2x}{x^2 + 2}$

MATHEMATICS 1202
LIFEPAC TEST
SOLUTION KEY

1. a. $F(0) = 3(0)^2 - 4 = -4$
    b. $F(-3) = 3(-3)^2 - 4 = 27 - 4$
       $= 23$
    c. $8 = 3x^2 - 4$, $3x^2 = 12$, $x^2 = 4$,
       $x = \pm 2$
    d. $5 = 3x^2 - 4$, $3x^2 = 9$, $x^2 = 3$,
       $x = \pm\sqrt{3}$

2. $y = \dfrac{5x}{2} + 2$

3. $F(x) = 2x$ and $G(x) = \log x$
    $F[G(x)] = F(\log x) = 2 \log x$
    or $\log x^2$

4. $F(x) = 3 \log x$ and $G(x) = x^2 + 1$
    $G[F(x)] = G(3 \log x)$
    $= (3 \log x)^2 + 1$

5. $F(x) = \log_5 2x$; let $y = F(x)$
    $y = \log_5 2x$ and $5^y = 2x$
    Interchange the variables:
    $5^x = 2y$ and $y = \dfrac{5^x}{2}$ or $y = \dfrac{1}{2} \cdot 5^x$
    and $F^{-1}(x) = \dfrac{1}{2} \cdot 5^x$

6. $P(x) = 4x^4 + 8x^3 - 7x^2 - 21x - 9$
    Try all elements of the subset
    of factors of $\pm\frac{9}{4}$.

    $-\frac{3}{2}$ | $4 + 8 - 7 - 21 - 9$
                   | $\underline{0 - 6 - 3 + 15 + 9}$
    $-\frac{3}{2}$ | $4 + 2 - 10 - 6 + 0$
                   | $\underline{0 - 6 + 6 + 6}$
                   | $4 - 4 - 4 + 0$

    $4x^2 - 4x - 4 = 0$ or
    $\quad x^2 - x - 1 = 0$

6. cont.
   Use the quadratic formula
   to find the irrational
   roots.

   $x = \dfrac{1 \pm \sqrt{1 + 4}}{2}$

   $x = \dfrac{1 \pm \sqrt{5}}{2}$

   $\{-\dfrac{3}{2}, \dfrac{1 \pm \sqrt{5}}{2}\}$

7. $P(x) = 4x^4 + 8x^3 - 7x^2 - 21x$
             $- 9$
    Let $r = 1, 2, 3, \ldots$

    2 | $4 + 8 - 7 - 21 - 9$
        | $\underline{0 + 8 + 32 + 50 + 58}$
        | $4 + 16 + 25 + 29 + 49$

    $r = 2$ is an upper limit
    since the signs in the
    third row are all positive.
    Let $r = -1, -2, -3, \ldots$

    -3 | $4 + 8 - 7 - 21 + 9$
         | $\underline{0 - 12 + 12 - 15 + 108}$
         | $4 - 4 + 5 - 36 + 99$

    $r = -3$ is a lower limit
    since the signs in the
    third row alternate.

8. $y = x^2 - 2x$
    $y = x^2 - 2x + 1 - 1$
    $y = (x - 1)^2 - 1$
    Turning point $= (1, -1)$;
    axis of symmetry is $x = 1$;
    curve is a parabola,
    concave up.

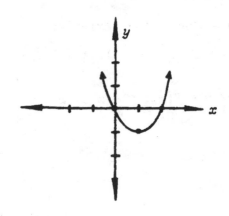

9. For $x \leq 0$, graph $y = -1$; a constant line.
    For $0 < x < 2$, graph greatest integer x (step function).
    For $x \geq 2$, graph $y = x$; identity line.

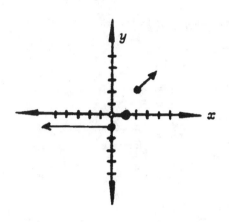

11. $y = e^x + 1$; graph the exponential e^x; then add 1 to each y value.

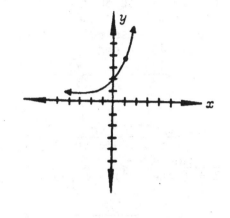

10. $G(x) = \dfrac{x^2 - 16}{x + 4} = \dfrac{(x - 4)(x + 4)}{x + 4}$
    $= x - 4$ for $x \neq -4$
    Graph the line $y = x - 4$, except for $x = -4$.

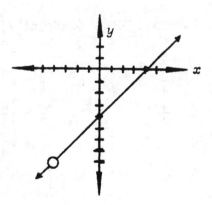

MATHEMATICS 1203
LIFEPAC TEST
SOLUTION KEY

1. cos 90° + csc 300° -
    tan 225° - sec 150° =
    cos 90° - csc 60° -
    tan 45° + sec 30° =
    $0 - \frac{2\sqrt{3}}{3} - 1 + \frac{2\sqrt{3}}{3} =$
    -1

2. $\dfrac{\tan 210° + \cot 240°}{1 + \tan 300° \cot(-60°)} =$

    $\dfrac{\tan 30° + \cot 60°}{1 + (-\tan 60°)(-\cot 60°)} =$

    $\dfrac{\frac{\sqrt{3}}{3} + \frac{\sqrt{3}}{3}}{1 + (-\sqrt{3})(-\frac{\sqrt{3}}{3})} =$

    $\dfrac{\frac{2\sqrt{3}}{3}}{1 + 1} =$

    $\dfrac{\frac{2\sqrt{3}}{3}}{2} =$

    $\dfrac{\sqrt{3}}{3}$

3. sin 270° + tan 180°cos 90° =
    $-1 + 0 \cdot 0 =$
    -1

4. sin 150°tan 210° +
    cos 135°cot 240° =
    sin 30°tan 30° +
    (-cos 45°)cos 60° =
    $\frac{1}{2} \cdot \frac{\sqrt{3}}{3} - \frac{\sqrt{2}}{2} \cdot \frac{\sqrt{3}}{3} =$
    $\frac{\sqrt{3}}{6} - \frac{\sqrt{6}}{6} =$
    $\frac{\sqrt{3} - \sqrt{6}}{6}$

5. cos 155° = cos(180° - 25°)
    = -cos 25°

6. sin 200° = sin(180° + 20°)
    = -sin 20°

7. cos(-150°) = cos 210°
    = cos(180° + 30°)
    = -cos 30°

8. tan(-50°) = tan 310°
    = tan(360° - 50°)
    = -tan 50°

9. sin 31.7°

10. a. $\sin \theta = \frac{3}{5}$
        $v = 3$
        $r = 5$
        $u = \sqrt{5^2 - 3^2}$
        $= \sqrt{25 - 9}$
        $= \sqrt{16}$
        $= \pm 4$

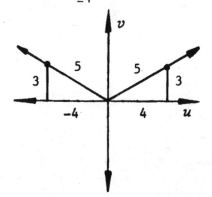

Quadrant I		Quadrant II	
b. $\frac{4}{5}$		g. $\frac{-4}{5} = -\frac{4}{5}$	
c. $\frac{3}{4}$		h. $\frac{3}{-4} = -\frac{3}{4}$	
d. $\frac{4}{3}$		i. $\frac{-4}{3} = -\frac{4}{3}$	
e. $\frac{5}{4}$		j. $\frac{5}{-4} = -\frac{5}{4}$	
f. $\frac{5}{3}$		k. $\frac{5}{3}$	

11. $\sin \theta = -\frac{1}{2}$

$v = -1$

$r = 2$

$u = \sqrt{2^2 - (-1)^2}$

$= \sqrt{4 - 1}$

$= \sqrt{3}$

a. $\frac{\sqrt{3}}{2}$

b. $\frac{-1}{\sqrt{3}} = -\frac{\sqrt{3}}{3}$

c. $\frac{\sqrt{3}}{-1} = -\sqrt{3}$

d. $\frac{2}{\sqrt{3}} = \frac{2\sqrt{3}}{3}$

e. $\frac{2}{-1} = -2$

12. $\tan 332° 30' = \tan(360° - 27° 30')$

$= -\tan 27° 30'$

$= -.5206$

13. $\cos 229° 47' = \cos(180° + 49° 47')$

$= -\cos 49° 47'$

$10\left\{ 7\left\{ \begin{matrix} \cos \\ 49° 47' = .6472 \\ \cos \\ 49° 47' = \end{matrix} \right\}x \atop \begin{matrix} \cos \\ 49° 50' = .6450 \end{matrix} \right\}.0022$

$\frac{7}{10} = \frac{x}{.0022}$

$10x = .0154$

$x = .00154 = .0015$

$\cos 49° 47' = -(.6472 - .0015)$

$= -.6457$

14. $\sec(-38° 22') = \sec 38° 22'$

$10\left\{ 2\left\{ \begin{matrix} \sec \\ 38° 20' = 1.275 \\ \sec \\ 38° 22' = \end{matrix} \right\}x \atop \begin{matrix} \sec \\ 38° 30' = 1.278 \end{matrix} \right\}.003$

$\frac{2}{10} = \frac{x}{.003}$

$10x = .006$

$x = .0006$

$\sec 38° 22' = 1.275 + .0006 =$

$= 1.2756$

15. $10\left\{ x\left\{ \begin{matrix} \cos \\ 62° 30' = .4617 \\ \cos \theta = .4600 \end{matrix} \right\}.0017 \atop \begin{matrix} \cos \\ 62° 40' = .4592 \end{matrix} \right\}.0025$

$\frac{x}{10} = \frac{.0017}{.0025}$

$.0025x = .017$

$x = 6.8 \doteq 7'$

$\theta = 62° 30' + 7' = 62° 37'$

16. $10\left\{ x\left\{ \begin{matrix} \sin \\ 29° 20' = .4899 \\ \sin \theta = .4910 \end{matrix} \right\}.0011 \atop \begin{matrix} \sin \\ 29° 30' = .4924 \end{matrix} \right\}.0025$

$\frac{x}{10} = \frac{.0011}{.0025}$

$.0025x = .011$

$x = 4.4 \doteq 4'$

$\theta = 29° 20' + 4' = 29° 24'$

17. $[4 \sin 270° \cdot \cos 180°]^4 =$

$[4(-1) \cdot (-1)]^4 =$

$4^4 =$

256

18. $(\sin 180°)^{10} = 0^{10} = 0$

19. $(\sin 270° + \cos 180°)^2 -$

$(\tan 0°)^3 =$

$[-1 + (-1)]^2 - 0 =$

$4 - 0 =$

4

20. $2 \sin 90° \cdot \cos 180° +$

$\tan 180° \cdot \sec 180° =$

$2(1) \cdot (-1) + 0 \cdot (-1) =$

$-2 + 0 =$

-2

21. a. $15° = 15° \cdot \frac{\pi}{180°} = \frac{\pi}{12}$

b. I

22. a. $\frac{2\pi}{3} = \frac{2\pi}{3} \cdot \frac{180°}{\pi} = 2 \cdot 60° = 120°$

b. II

23.   a. $45° = 45° \cdot \dfrac{\pi}{180°} = \dfrac{\pi}{4}$

        b.   I

24.   a. $240° = 240° \cdot \dfrac{\pi}{180°} = \dfrac{4\pi}{3}$

        b.   III

25.   a. $\dfrac{5\pi}{4} = \dfrac{5\pi}{4} \cdot \dfrac{180°}{\pi} = 5 \cdot 45° = 225°$

        b.   III

MATHEMATICS 1204
LIFEPAC TEST
SOLUTION KEY

1.

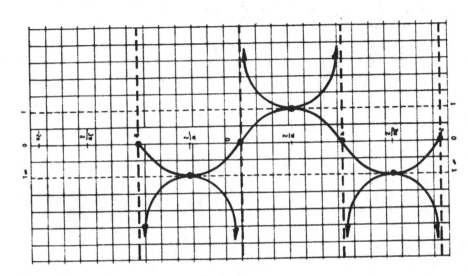

2.

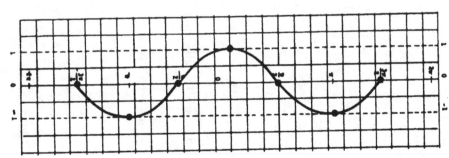

3. $A = 2$, $P = \dfrac{2\pi}{2} = \pi$, $p = -\dfrac{\pi}{2}$

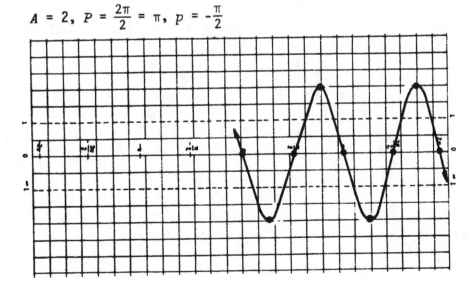

4. $A = 2$, $P = \dfrac{2\pi}{2} = \pi$, $p = -\dfrac{\pi}{2}$

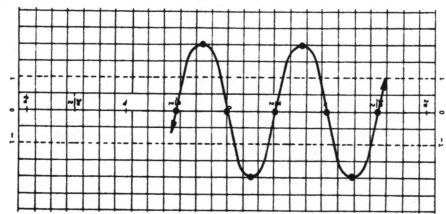

5. $v = r\omega = 12(15\pi)$
        $= 180\div \doteq 565$ feet per second

6. $\omega = \dfrac{v}{r} = \dfrac{100}{4} = 25$ radians per second

7. $C = 2\pi r$
        $r = \dfrac{C}{2\pi}$
        $r = \dfrac{425}{32}$
        $r = \dfrac{425}{2\pi(32)}$
        $= 2.11$ feet
     diameter $= 4.22 \doteq 4$ feet

8.   II; $\dfrac{\pi}{2} < \dfrac{3\pi}{5} < \pi$

9.   a.   IV
        b. $\dfrac{-4}{5} = -\dfrac{4}{5}$
        c. $\dfrac{3}{5}$
        d. $\dfrac{-4}{3} = -\dfrac{4}{3}$
        e. $\dfrac{5}{-4} = -\dfrac{5}{4}$
        f. $\dfrac{5}{3}$
        g. $\dfrac{3}{-4} = -\dfrac{3}{4}$

10.   a.   III; $r = \sqrt{(-20)^2 + (-21)^2}$
               $= \sqrt{400 + 441}$
                $= \sqrt{844}$
                $= 29$
        b. $\dfrac{-21}{29} = -\dfrac{21}{29}$
        c. $\dfrac{-20}{29} = -\dfrac{20}{29}$
        d. $\dfrac{-21}{-20} = +\dfrac{21}{20}$
        e. $\dfrac{29}{-21} = -\dfrac{29}{21}$
        f. $\dfrac{29}{-20} = -\dfrac{29}{20}$
        g. $\dfrac{-20}{-21} = +\dfrac{20}{21}$

11. $\dfrac{1,800}{60 \text{ sec.}}\ 2\pi = 60\pi$ radians per second

12.   amplitude $= |3| = 3$
     period $= \dfrac{2\pi}{2} = \pi$

13. $F(x) = 3\sin(2x - 2)$
            $= 3\sin 2(x - 1)$
     $p = 1$ unit to the right

14.

$$\frac{\tan 210° + \cot 240°}{1 + \tan 300° \cot(-60°)} =$$

$$\frac{\tan 30° + \cot 60°}{1 + (-\tan 60°)(-\cot 60°)} =$$

$$\frac{\frac{\sqrt{3}}{3} + \frac{\sqrt{3}}{3}}{1 + (\sqrt{3})(-\frac{1}{\sqrt{3}})} =$$

$$\frac{\frac{2\sqrt{3}}{3}}{1 + 1} =$$

$$\frac{\frac{2\sqrt{3}}{3}}{2} =$$

$$\frac{\sqrt{3}}{3}$$

15.   Use $y = A \cos B(x - p)$.

$A = -2$, $B = \dfrac{2\pi}{\frac{\pi}{4}} = 8$, $p = -\dfrac{\pi}{2}$

$y = -2\cos 8(x + \pi/2)$

16.   false

17.   true

18.   true

19.   true

20.   false

MATHEMATICS 1205
LIFEPAC TEST
SOLUTION KEY

1.　a.　$2 \sin x - \sqrt{3} = 0$
$$2 \sin x = \sqrt{3}$$
$$\sin x = \frac{\sqrt{3}}{2}$$
$$x = \{\frac{\pi}{3}, \frac{2\pi}{3}\}$$

　　b.　$\frac{1}{\sin^2 x} = 4$
$$\sin^2 x = \frac{1}{4}$$
$$\sqrt{\sin^2 x} + \pm\sqrt{\frac{1}{4}}$$
$$\sin x = \pm\frac{1}{2}$$
$$x = \{\frac{\pi}{6}, \frac{5\pi}{6}, \frac{7\pi}{6}, \frac{11\pi}{6}\}$$

2.　$\tan \frac{x}{2} = \frac{1 - \cos x}{\sin x}$
$$\tan \frac{60°}{2} = \frac{1 - \cos 60°}{\sin 60°}$$
$$\tan 30° = \frac{1 - \cos 60°}{\sin 60°}$$
$$\frac{\sqrt{3}}{3} = \frac{1 - \frac{1}{2}}{\frac{\sqrt{3}}{2}} = \frac{\frac{1}{2}}{\frac{\sqrt{3}}{2}} = \frac{1}{\sqrt{3}} = \frac{\sqrt{3}}{3}$$

3.
$$\cos 2x = 1 - 2 \sin^2 x$$
$$\cos 2(-135°) = 1 - 2 \sin^2 (-135°)$$
$$\cos (-270°) = 1 - 2(-\sin 225°)^2$$
$$\cos 90° = 1 - 2(-\sin 45°)^2$$
$$0 = 1 - 2(-\frac{\sqrt{2}}{2})^2$$
$$= 1 - 2 \cdot \frac{2}{4}$$
$$= 1 - 1$$
$$= 0$$

4.
$$\cos 2x + \cos^2 x = 1$$
$$2 \cos^2 x - 1 + \cos^2 x = 1$$
$$3 \cos^2 x - 1 = 1$$
$$3 \cos^2 x = 2$$
$$\cos^2 x = \frac{2}{3}$$
$$\sqrt{\cos^2 x} = \pm\sqrt{\frac{2}{3}}$$
$$\cos x = \pm\sqrt{\frac{2}{3}}$$
$$= \pm\frac{\sqrt{6}}{3}$$
$$\pm \pm\frac{2.4495}{3}$$
$$\doteq \pm.8165$$
$$x = 35°, 145°, 215°, 325°$$

5.　$\tan x$　$\Big|$　$\dfrac{1}{\cos x \csc x}$

　　$\dfrac{\sin x}{\cos x}$　$\Big|$　$\dfrac{1}{\cos x} \cdot \dfrac{1}{\csc x}$

　　　　　$\Big|$　$\dfrac{1}{\cos x} \cdot \sin x$

　　$\dfrac{\sin x}{\cos x}$　$\Big|$　$\dfrac{\sin x}{\cos x}$

6.　$\sin x = \frac{1}{3}$, $\cos x = \frac{2\sqrt{2}}{3}$
$$\cos 2x = 2 \cos^2 x - 1$$
$$= 2(\frac{2\sqrt{2}}{3})^2 - 1$$
$$= 2(\frac{8}{9}) - 1$$
$$= \frac{16}{9} - 1$$
$$= \frac{7}{9}$$

7.　$\dfrac{\sin^2 x}{1 + \cos x} = \dfrac{1 - \cos^2 x}{1 + \cos x}$
$$= \frac{(1 - \cos x)(1 + \cos x)}{1 + \cos x}$$
$$= 1 - \cos x$$

8. $\tan x = \dfrac{\sin x}{\cos x} = \dfrac{\sin x}{\sqrt{1 - \sin^2 x}}$

9. $\sin^2 x(\sec^2 x + \csc^2 x) =$

$\sin^2 x(\dfrac{1}{\cos^2 x} + \dfrac{1}{\sin^2 x}) =$

$\sin^2 x(\dfrac{\sin^2 x + \cos^2 x}{\cos^2 x \sin^2 x}) =$

$\cancel{\sin^2 x}(\dfrac{1}{\cos^2 x \cancel{\sin^2 x}}) =$

$\dfrac{1}{\cos^2 x} =$

$\sec^2 x$

10. through 19.

$\sin \theta = \dfrac{4}{5}$ $\qquad \cos \phi = -\dfrac{5}{13}$

$\cos \theta = \dfrac{3}{5}$ $\qquad \sin \phi = \dfrac{12}{13}$

$\tan \theta = \dfrac{4}{3}$ $\qquad \tan \phi = -\dfrac{12}{5}$

10. $\sin (\theta + \phi) = \sin \theta \cos \phi + \cos \theta \sin \phi$

$= \dfrac{4}{5}(-\dfrac{5}{13}) + (\dfrac{3}{5})(\dfrac{12}{13})$

$= -\dfrac{20}{65} + \dfrac{36}{65}$

$= \dfrac{16}{65}$

11. $\cos (\theta - \phi) = \cos \theta \cos \phi + \sin \theta \sin \phi$

$= \dfrac{3}{5}(-\dfrac{5}{13}) + \dfrac{4}{5}(\dfrac{12}{13})$

$= -\dfrac{15}{65} + \dfrac{48}{65}$

$= \dfrac{33}{65}$

12. $\tan (\theta + \phi) = \dfrac{\tan \theta + \tan \phi}{1 - \tan \theta \tan \phi}$

$= \dfrac{\dfrac{4}{3} + (-\dfrac{12}{5})}{1 - \dfrac{4}{3}(-\dfrac{12}{5})}$

$= \dfrac{\dfrac{4}{3} - \dfrac{12}{5}}{1 + \dfrac{48}{15}}$ Multiply by 15.

12. cont.

$= \dfrac{20 - 36}{15 + 48}$

$= -\dfrac{16}{63}$

13. $\sin 2\theta = 2 \sin \theta \cos \theta$

$= 2(\dfrac{4}{5})(\dfrac{3}{5})$

$= \dfrac{24}{25}$

14. $\cos 2\phi = 2 \cos^2 \phi - 1$

$= 2(-\dfrac{5}{13})^2 - 1$

$= 2(\dfrac{25}{169}) - 1$

$= \dfrac{50}{169} - 1$

$= -\dfrac{119}{169}$

15. $\tan 2\theta = \dfrac{2 \tan \theta}{1 - \tan^2 \theta}$

$= \dfrac{2(\dfrac{4}{3})}{1 - (\dfrac{4}{3})^2}$

$= \dfrac{\dfrac{8}{3}}{1 - (\dfrac{16}{9})}$ Multiply by 9.

$= \dfrac{24}{9 - 16}$

$= \dfrac{24}{-7}$

$= -\dfrac{24}{7}$

16. $\sin \frac{1}{2}\theta = \sqrt{\dfrac{1 - \cos \theta}{2}}$

$= \sqrt{\dfrac{1 - \dfrac{3}{5}}{2}}$

$= \sqrt{\dfrac{\dfrac{2}{5}}{\dfrac{10}{5}}}$

$= \sqrt{\dfrac{2}{10}}$

$= \sqrt{\dfrac{1}{5}}$

16. cont.

$$= \frac{1}{\sqrt{5}}$$

$$= \frac{\sqrt{5}}{5}$$

17. $\cos \frac{1}{2}\theta = \sqrt{\frac{1 + \cos \theta}{2}}$

$$= \sqrt{\frac{1 + \frac{3}{5}}{2}}$$

$$= \sqrt{\frac{\frac{8}{5}}{\frac{10}{5}}}$$

$$= \sqrt{\frac{8}{10}}$$

$$= \sqrt{\frac{4}{5}}$$

$$= \frac{2}{\sqrt{5}}$$

$$= \frac{2\sqrt{5}}{5}$$

18. $\tan \frac{1}{2}\phi = \sqrt{\frac{1 - \cos \phi}{1 + \cos \phi}}$

$$= \sqrt{\frac{1 - (-\frac{5}{13})}{1 + (-\frac{5}{13})}}$$

$$= \sqrt{\frac{\frac{18}{13}}{\frac{8}{13}}}$$

$$= \sqrt{\frac{18}{8}}$$

$$= \sqrt{\frac{9}{4}}$$

$$= \frac{3}{2}$$

19. $\sin 3\theta = 3 \sin \theta - 4 \sin^3 \theta$

$$= 3 \cdot \frac{4}{5} - 4\left(\frac{4}{5}\right)^3$$

$$= \frac{12}{5} - 4\left(\frac{64}{125}\right)$$

$$= \frac{12}{5} - \frac{256}{125}$$

$$= \frac{300 - 256}{125}$$

$$= \frac{44}{125}$$

20.

$2 \cos 2x$

$2(2 \cos^2 x - 1)$

$4 \cos^2 x - 2$

$\sin 2x \cot x - 2 \sin^2 x$

$2 \sin x \cos x \cdot \frac{\cos x}{\sin x} - 2 \sin^2 x$

$2 \cos^2 x - 2(1 - \cos^2 x)$

$2 \cos^2 x - 2 + 2 \cos^2 x$

$4 \cos^2 x - 2$

MATHEMATICS 1206
LIFEPAC TEST
SOLUTION KEY

1.

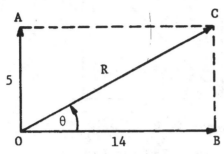

a. $R^2 = 5^2 + 14^2$
    $R^2 = 25 + 196$
    $R^2 = 221$
    $\sqrt{R^2} = \sqrt{221}$
    $R = 14.8$ or 15 (rounded)

b. $\tan \theta = \frac{5}{14}$
    $\tan \theta = .357$
    $\theta = 20°$

2.

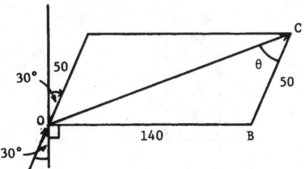

a. $\angle B = 120°$

    $R^2 = 50^2 + 140^2 - 2(50) \cdot (140)\cos 120°$
    $R^2 = 2{,}500 + 19{,}600 - 14{,}000(-.5)$
    $R^2 = 2{,}500 + 19{,}600 + 7{,}000$
    $R^2 = 29{,}100$
    $\sqrt{R^2} = \sqrt{29{,}100}$
    $R = 171$
    $R = \overrightarrow{OC}$
    $\overrightarrow{OC} = 171$ mph (rounded)

2. cont.

b. $\frac{140}{\sin \theta} = \frac{171}{\sin 120°}$

    $\sin \theta = \frac{140 \sin 120°}{171}$

    $\sin \theta = \frac{140(.866)}{171}$

    $\sin \theta = .709$
    $= 45°$

    direction of R = 30° + 45°
    $= 75°$
    $= N\ 75°\ E$

3.

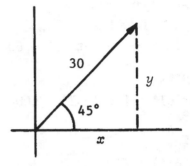

$\sin 45° = \frac{y}{30}$
    $y = 30 \sin 45°$
    $y = \frac{30\sqrt{2}}{2}$
    $y = 15\sqrt{2}$

$\cos 45° = \frac{x}{30}$
    $x = 30 \cos 45°$
    $x = \frac{30\sqrt{2}}{2}$
    $x = 15\sqrt{2}$

4.

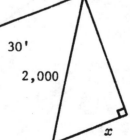

$\sin 20°\ 30' = \frac{x}{2{,}000}$
    $x = 2{,}000 \sin 20°\ 30'$
    $x = 2{,}000(.350)$
    $x = 700$ lbs.

5.

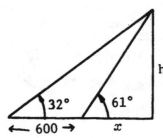

$$\cot 61° = \frac{x}{h}$$
$$x = h \cot 61°$$

Also, $\cot 32° = \frac{600 + x}{h}$ and

$h \cot 32° = 600 + x$ and
$$x = h \cot 32° - 600$$

Therefore,

$h \cot 61° = h \cot 32° - 600$
$h \cot 32° -$
$\quad h \cot 61° = 600$
$h(\cot 32° -$
$\quad \cot 61°) = 600$

$$h = \frac{600}{\cot 32° - \cot 61°}$$
$$h = \frac{600}{1.6 - .55}$$
$$h = \frac{600}{1.05}$$
$$h = 571 \text{ ft. (rounded)}$$

6.

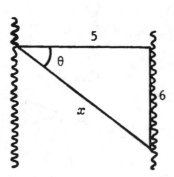

a. $\tan \theta = \frac{6}{5}$
$\tan \theta = 1.2$
$\quad \theta = 50°$

b. $x^2 = 5^2 + 6^2$
$x^2 = 25 + 36$
$\underline{x^2 = 61}$
$\sqrt{x^2} = \sqrt{61}$
$\quad x = 7.8 \text{ or } 8 \text{ mph (rounded)}$

7.

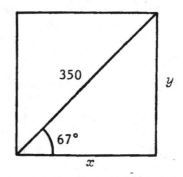

$$\sin 67° = \frac{y}{350}$$
$$y = 350 \sin 67°$$
$$y = 350(.9205)$$
$$y = 322 \text{ lbs.}$$

$$\cos 67° = \frac{x}{350}$$
$$x = 350 \cos 67°$$
$$x = 350(.3907)$$
$$x = 137 \text{ lbs.}$$

8.

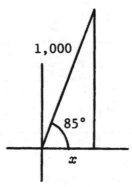

$$\cos 85° = \frac{x}{1,000}$$
$$x = 1,000 \cos 85°$$
$$x = 1,000(.0872)$$
$$x = 87.2 \text{ mph}$$

$$\text{velocity} = \frac{87.2}{60}$$
$$= 1.45 \text{ miles per minute}$$

9.

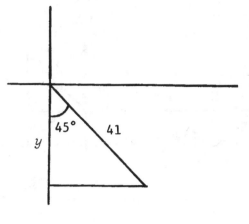

$\cos 45° = \frac{y}{41}$

$\quad y = 41 \cos 45°$

$\quad y = 41(\frac{\sqrt{2}}{2})$

$\quad y = 29$ miles

10. $\quad v = -\sqrt{17^2 - (-8)^2}$

$\qquad = -\sqrt{289 - 64}$

$\qquad = -\sqrt{225}$

$\qquad = -15$

a. $\sin \theta = \frac{-15}{17} = -\frac{15}{17}$

b. $\cos \theta = \frac{-8}{17} = -\frac{8}{17}$

c. $\tan \theta = \frac{-15}{-8} = \frac{15}{8}$

d. $\csc \theta = \frac{17}{-15} = -\frac{17}{15}$

e. $\sec \theta = \frac{17}{-8} = -\frac{17}{8}$

f. $\cot \theta = \frac{-8}{-15} = \frac{8}{15}$

MATHEMATICS 1207
LIFEPAC TEST
SOLUTION KEY

5. cont.

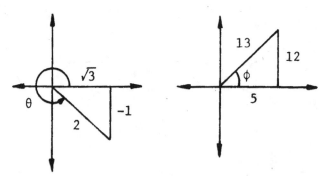

1. $y = \arcsin \frac{\sqrt{3}}{2}$, $\sin y = \frac{\sqrt{3}}{2}$

The reference angle $y = \frac{\pi}{3}$.

Therefore, the general solution

is $y = \frac{\pi}{3} \pm 2\pi K$ or $\frac{2\pi}{3} \pm 2\pi K$

2. $y = \arctan(-1)$, $\tan y = -1$
y is in the second or fourth
quadrant with reference angle of
$\frac{\pi}{4}$; $y = \frac{3\pi}{4} \pm 2\pi K$ or $\frac{7\pi}{4} \pm 2\pi K$.

3.   Let $x = \arcsin 1$; $\sin x = 1$.
Therefore, $\sin(\arcsin 1) =$
$\sin x = 1$.

4.   Let $x = \sin 50°$.
Let $y = \arccos x$ or $\cos y = x$.
Therefore, $y = 40°$.

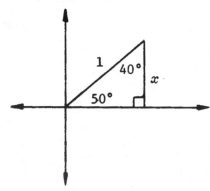

6.

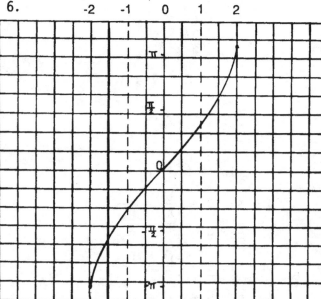

5.   Let $\theta = \arcsin\left(-\frac{1}{2}\right)$ and $\phi =$

arccos $\frac{5}{13}$.   Find $\cos(\theta + \phi)$.
$\cos(\theta + \phi) = \cos\theta\cos\phi -$
$\qquad\qquad\quad \sin\theta\sin\phi$
$\qquad = \frac{\sqrt{3}}{2} \cdot \frac{5}{13} - \left(-\frac{1}{2}\right) \cdot \frac{12}{13}$
$\qquad = \frac{5\sqrt{3}}{26} + \frac{12}{26}$
$\qquad = \frac{5\sqrt{3} + 12}{26}$

7.

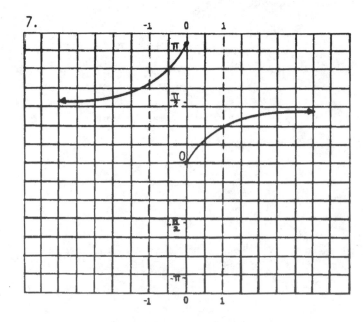

8. $F(x) = 2 \arcsin x$. Let $y = F(x)$. Then $y = 2 \arcsin x$ and $\frac{y}{2} = \arcsin x$; $\sin \frac{y}{2} = x$. Now interchange the variables and $y = \sin \frac{x}{2}$ or $F^{-1}(x) = \sin \frac{x}{2}$.

9. Let $\theta = \arccos x$; then $\cos \theta = x$.
$$\csc \theta = \frac{1}{\sqrt{1 - x^2}}$$

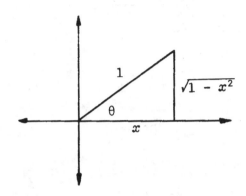

10. Domain: $-1 \leq x \leq 1$
Range: $-\frac{\pi}{2} \leq F(x) \leq \frac{\pi}{2}$

11. through 15.

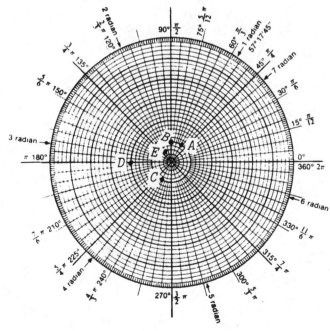

16. $x = r \cos \theta$
$x = 2 \cos 3\pi$
$x = 2 \cos \pi$
$x = 2(-1)$
$x = -2$

$y = r \sin \theta$
$y = 2 \sin 3\pi$
$y = 2 \sin \pi$
$y = 2(0)$
$y = 0$

$(x, y) = (-2, 0)$

17. $x = r \cos \theta$
$x = -3 \cos (-\frac{\pi}{3})$
$x = -3 \cos \frac{\pi}{3}$
$x = -3(\frac{1}{2})$
$x = -\frac{3}{2}$

$y = r \sin \theta$
$y = -3 \sin (-\frac{\pi}{3})$
$y = 3 \sin \frac{\pi}{3}$
$y = 3(\frac{\sqrt{3}}{2})$
$y = \frac{3\sqrt{3}}{2}$

$(x, y) = (-\frac{3}{2}, \frac{3\sqrt{3}}{2})$

18. $x = r \cos \theta$
$x = -1 \cos (-\pi)$
$x = -1 \cos \pi$
$x = -1(-1)$
$x = 1$

$y = r \sin \theta$
$y = -1 \sin (-\pi)$
$y = \sin \pi$
$y = 0$

$(x, y) = (1, 0)$

19.

$x = r \cos \theta$

$x = 3 \cos \frac{\pi}{2}$

$x = 3(0)$

$x = 0$

$y = r \sin \theta$

$y = 3 \sin \frac{\pi}{2}$

$y = 3(1)$

$y = 3$

$(x, y) = (0, 3)$

20.

$x = r \cos \theta$

$x = \pi \cos \pi$

$x = \pi(-1)$

$x = -\pi$

$y = r \sin \theta$

$y = \pi \sin \pi$

$y = \pi(0)$

$y = 0$

$(x, y) = (-\pi, 0)$

21.

$r = \sqrt{x^2 + y^2}$

$r = \sqrt{0^2 + 1^2}$

$r = 1$

$\tan \theta = \frac{y}{x} = \frac{1}{0} = $ undefined

$\theta = 90°$

$(r, \theta) = (1, 90°)$ or $(1, \frac{\pi}{2})$

22.

$r = \sqrt{x^2 + y^2}$

$r = \sqrt{(-3)^2 + 0^2}$

$r = 3$

$\tan \theta = \frac{y}{x} = \frac{0}{-3}$

$\theta = 0°, 180°$

$\theta = 180°$

$(r, \theta) = (3, 180°)$ or $(3, \pi)$

23.

$r = \sqrt{x^2 + y^2}$

$r = \sqrt{2^2 + (-2)^2}$

$r = \sqrt{4 + 4}$

$r = \sqrt{8}$

$r = 2\sqrt{2}$

$\tan \theta = \frac{y}{x} = \frac{2}{-2} = -1$

$\theta = -45° = 315°$

$(r, \theta) = (2\sqrt{2}, 315°)$ or

$(2\sqrt{2}, \frac{7\pi}{4})$

24.

$r = \sqrt{x^2 + y^2}$

$r = \sqrt{(4\sqrt{3})^2 + 4^2}$

$r = \sqrt{48 + 16}$

$r = \sqrt{64}$

$r = 8$

$\tan \theta = \frac{y}{x} = \frac{4}{4\sqrt{3}} = \frac{1}{\sqrt{3}} = \frac{\sqrt{3}}{3}$

$\theta = 30°$ or $\frac{\pi}{6}$

$(r, \theta) = (8, 30°)$ or $(8, \frac{\pi}{6})$

25.

$r = \sqrt{x^2 + y^2}$

$r = \sqrt{\left(\frac{\sqrt{2}}{2}\right)^2 + \left(\frac{\sqrt{2}}{2}\right)^2}$

$r = \sqrt{\frac{2}{4} + \frac{2}{4}}$

$r = \sqrt{1}$

$r = 1$

$\tan \theta = \frac{y}{x} = \frac{\frac{\sqrt{2}}{2}}{\frac{\sqrt{2}}{2}} = 1$

$\theta = 45°$

$(r, \theta) = (1, 45°)$ or $(1, \frac{\pi}{4})$

26.　　$2xy = 1$
　　　$x = r \cos \theta$ and $y = r \sin \theta$
　　　$2r \cos \theta\, r \sin \theta = 1$
　　　　$2r^2 \cos \theta \sin \theta = 1$
　　　　　　$r^2 \sin 2\theta = 1$

27.　　$x^2 + y^2 + ax = a\sqrt{x^2 + y^2}$
　　　$r^2 = x^2 + y^2$
　　　$x = r \cos \theta$

　　　　　$r^2 + ar \cos \theta = ar$
　　　$r^2 + ar \cos \theta - ar = 0$
　　　$r^2 + (a \cos \theta - a)r = 0$
　　　　$r + a \cos \theta - a = 0$
　　　　　　　　　$r = -a \cos \theta + a$
　　　　　　　　　$r = a(1 - \cos \theta)$

28.　　$r \sin \theta = 4$
　　　　$y = r \sin \theta$
　　　　$y = 4$

29.　　$r = \dfrac{2}{1 - \cos \theta}$
　　　$r = \sqrt{x^2 + y^2}$
　　　$x = r \cos \theta$

　　　$r - r \cos \theta = 2$
　　　$\sqrt{x^2 + y^2} - x = 2$
　　　　$\sqrt{x^2 + y^2} = x + 2$
　　　$(\sqrt{x^2 + y^2})^2 = (x + 2)^2$
　　　$\cancel{x^2} + y^2 = \cancel{x^2} + 4x + 4$
　　　　$y^2 = 4x + 4$
　　　　$y^2 = 4(x + 1)$

31.　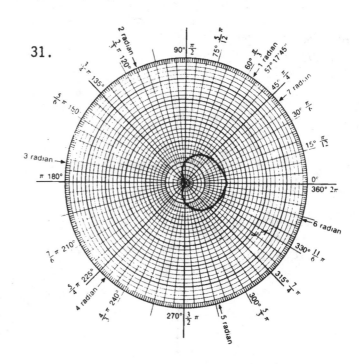

30.　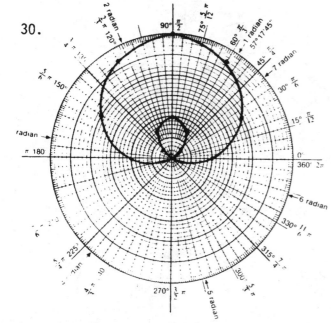

401

MATHEMATICS 1208
LIFEPAC TEST
SOLUTION KEY

1. $$x^2 + y^2 + 4x + 6y - 12 = 0$$
$$x^2 + 4x + y^2 + 6y = 12$$
$$(x + 4x + 4) +$$
$$(y^2 + 6y + 9) = 12 + 4 + 9$$
$$(x + 2)^2 + (y + 3)^2 = 25$$

Center = $(-2, -3)$
Radius = $\sqrt{25} = 5$
Domain: $-7 \le x \le 3$
Range: $-8 \le y \le 2$

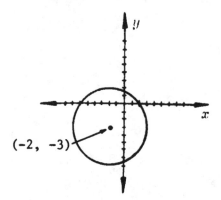

2. $$x^2 - 3y^2 - 8x + 12y + 16 = 0$$
$$x^2 - 8x - 3y^2 + 12y = -16$$
$$(x^2 - 8x + 16) -$$
$$3(y^2 - 4y + 4) = -16 + 16 - 12$$
$$(x - 4)^2 - 3(y - 2)^2 = -12$$
$$\frac{(x - 4)^2}{-12} - \frac{3(y - 2)^2}{-12} = \frac{-12}{-12}$$
$$\frac{(y - 2)^2}{4} - \frac{(x - 4)^2}{12} = 1$$

Position II
Center = $(4, 2)$
$a = \sqrt{4} = 2$
$b = \sqrt{12} = 2\sqrt{3}$
$c = \sqrt{2^2 + (2\sqrt{3})^2} = \sqrt{4 + 12}$
$= \sqrt{16} = 4$
Foci = $(4, 6)$ and $(4, -2)$
L.R. $= \frac{2(2\sqrt{3})^2}{2} = (2\sqrt{3})^2 = 12$
$e = \frac{4}{2} = 2$

2. cont.

Domain: all real x
Range: $y \ge 4$ or $y \le 0$

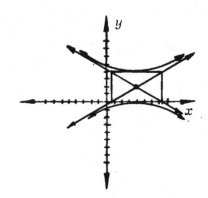

3. $$3y^2 - 2y + x + 1 = 0$$
$$3y^2 - 2y = -x - 1$$
$$3(y^2 - \frac{2}{3}y + \frac{1}{9}) = -x - 1 + \frac{1}{3}$$
$$3(y - \frac{1}{3})^2 = -(x + \frac{2}{3})$$

Parabola
Position I
Center = $(-\frac{2}{3}, \frac{1}{3})$
Focus = $4p = -\frac{1}{3}$
$p = -\frac{1}{12}$

Focus $= -\frac{2}{3} - \frac{1}{12} = \frac{-8}{12} - \frac{1}{12}$
$= \frac{-9}{12} = -\frac{3}{4}; \ (-\frac{3}{4}, \frac{1}{3})$

L.R. $= \frac{1}{3}$

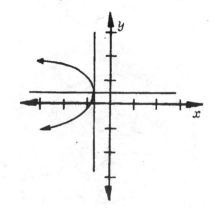

4.

$$9x^2 + 16y^2 -$$
$$36x + 96y + 36 = 0$$
$$9x^2 - 36x + 16y^2 + 96y = -36$$
$$9(x^2 - 4x + 4) +$$
$$16(y^2 + 6y + 9) = -36 +$$
$$36 + 144$$
$$9(x - 2)^2 + 16(y + 3)^2 = 144$$
$$\frac{(x - 2)^2}{16} + \frac{(y + 3)^2}{9} = 1$$

Ellipse
Position I
Center = (2, -3)
$a = \sqrt{16} = 4$
$b = \sqrt{9} = 3$
$c = \sqrt{4^2 - 3^2} = \sqrt{16 - 9} = \sqrt{7}$
Major axis = 2(4) = 8
Minor axis = 2(3) = 6

L.R. $= \frac{2(3)^2}{4} = \frac{2(9)}{4} = \frac{9}{2}$

$e = \frac{\sqrt{7}}{4}$

Domain: $-2 \le x \le 6$
Range: $-6 \le y \le 0$

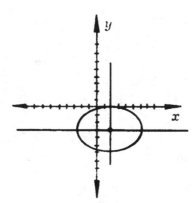

5. $2xy - x - y + 4 = 0$
$x = x' + h$ and $y = y' + k$

$$2(x' + h)(y' + k) -$$
$$(x' + h) - (y' + k) + 4 = 0$$
$$2(x'y') + 2kx' + 2hy' +$$
$$2hk - x' - h - y' - k + 4 = 0$$
$$2(x'y') + (2k - 1)x' +$$
$$(2h - 1)y' + 2hk - h - k + 4 = 0$$

Set $(2k - 1) = 0$ and $(2h - 1) = 0$.
$$2k = 1 \qquad\qquad 2h = 1$$
$$k = \tfrac{1}{2} \quad \text{and} \quad h = \tfrac{1}{2}$$

5. cont.

$$2x'y' + 2(\tfrac{1}{2})(\tfrac{1}{2}) - \tfrac{1}{2} - \tfrac{1}{2} + 4 = 0$$
$$2x'y' + \tfrac{1}{2} - \tfrac{1}{2} - \tfrac{1}{2} + 4 = 0$$
$$4x'y' + 1 - 1 - 1 + 8 = 0$$
$$4x'y' + 7 = 0$$

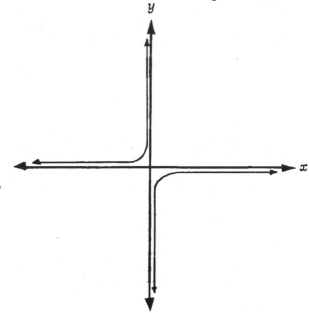

6. $7x^2 - 6\sqrt{3}xy + 13y^2 = 16$

$$\tan 2\theta = \frac{B}{A - C} = \frac{-6\sqrt{3}}{7 - 13}$$
$$= \frac{-6\sqrt{3}}{-6} = \sqrt{3}$$

$2\theta = 60°; \ \theta = 30°$

$\sin \theta = \sin 30° = \tfrac{1}{2}$

$\cos \theta = \cos 30° = \dfrac{\sqrt{3}}{2}$

$x = x' \cos \theta - y' \sin \theta$
$$= \frac{\sqrt{3}}{2}x' - \frac{1}{2}y' = \frac{1}{2}(\sqrt{3}x' - y')$$

$y = x' \sin \theta + y' \cos \theta$
$$= \frac{1}{2}x' + \frac{\sqrt{3}}{2}y' = \frac{1}{2}(x' + \sqrt{3}y')$$

6. cont.

$$7\left[\tfrac{1}{2}(\sqrt{3}x' - y')\right]^2 - 6\sqrt{3}\left[\tfrac{1}{2}(\sqrt{3}x' - y')\right]\left[\tfrac{1}{2}(x' + \sqrt{3}y')\right] + 13\left[\tfrac{1}{2}(x' + \sqrt{3}y')\right]^2 = 16$$

$$\tfrac{7}{4}\left[3(x')^2 - 2\sqrt{3}x'y' + (y')^2\right] - \tfrac{6\sqrt{3}}{4}\left[\sqrt{3}(x')^2 + 3x'y' - x'y' - \sqrt{3}(y')^2\right] +$$

$$\tfrac{13}{4}\left[(x')^2 + 2\sqrt{3}x'y' + 3(y')^2\right] = 16$$

$$\tfrac{21}{4}(x')^2 - \tfrac{14\sqrt{3}}{4}x'y' + \tfrac{7}{4}(y')^2 - \tfrac{18}{4}(x')^2 - \tfrac{12\sqrt{3}}{4}x'y' +$$

$$\tfrac{18}{4}(y')^2 + \tfrac{13}{4}(x')^2 + \tfrac{26\sqrt{3}}{4}x'y' + \tfrac{39}{4}(y')^2 = 16$$

$$4(x')^2 + 16(y')^2 = 16$$

$$\frac{(x')^2}{4} + \frac{(y')^2}{1} = 1$$

$$a = \sqrt{4} = 2$$
$$b = \sqrt{1} = 1$$

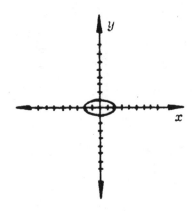

7.

$$5x^2 + 9y^2 - 80x + 54y + 221 = 0$$
$$5x^2 - 80x + 9y^2 + 54y = -221$$
$$5(x^2 - 16x + 64) + 9(y^2 + 6y + 9) = -221 + 320 + 81$$
$$5(x - 8)^2 + 9(y + 3)^2 = 180$$
$$\frac{(x - 8)^2}{36} + \frac{(y + 3)^2}{20} = 1$$

Ellipse
Center = (8, -3)
Let $x - 8 = x'$ and $y + 3 = y'$:
$$\frac{(x')^2}{36} + \frac{(y')^2}{20} = 1$$

8.

$$y^2 + dx + ey + f = 0$$

(1, 0):
$$0 + d + f = 0$$
$$d + f = 0$$

(2, 3):
$$3^2 + 2d + 3e + f = 0$$
$$9 + 2d + 3e + f = 0$$
$$2d + 3e + f = -9$$

(2, -3):
$$(-3)^2 + 2d - 3e + f = 0$$
$$9 + 2d - 3e + f = 0$$
$$2d - 3e + f = -9$$

Subtract:
$$\begin{array}{r} d + f = 0 \\ 2d + 3e + f = -9 \\ \hline -d - 3e = 9 \\ d + 3e = -9 \end{array}$$

Subtract:
$$\begin{array}{r} 2d + 3e + f = -9 \\ 2d - 3e + f = -9 \\ \hline 6e = 0 \\ e = 0 \end{array}$$

$$d + 3(0) = -9$$
$$d = -9$$

$$-9 + f = 0$$
$$f = 9$$

$$y^2 + (-9)x + 0y + 9 = 0$$
$$y^2 - 9x + 9 = 0$$

9. $\dfrac{x^2}{16} + \dfrac{y^2}{25} = 1$

    $a = \sqrt{25} = 5$

    $b = \sqrt{16} = 4$

    $c^2 = a^2 - b^2$

    $c^2 = 5^2 - 4^2 = 25 - 16 = 9$

    $\sqrt{c^2} = \sqrt{9}$

    $c = 3$

    Position II

    Foci $= (0, \pm3)$

10. $y^2 - x^2 = 1$

    $a = 1, \ b = 1$

    $b^2 = c^2 - a^2$ (note: $b^2 = c^2 - a^2$ used rather

    $1^2 = c^2 - 1^2$ than $b^2 = a^2 - c^2$ because the x^2

    $1 = c^2 - 1$ is a negative rather than a positive

    $c^2 = 2$ for which the formula on page 18

    $\sqrt{c^2} = \sqrt{2}$ was developed.)

    $c = \sqrt{2}$

    $e = \dfrac{c}{a} = \dfrac{\sqrt{2}}{1} = \sqrt{2}$

MATHEMATICS 1209
LIFEPAC TEST
SOLUTION KEY

1. a. $6! = 6 \cdot 5 \cdot 4 \cdot 3 \cdot 2 \cdot 1$
   $= 720$

   b. $\dfrac{(n+1)!}{n!}$

   $= \dfrac{(n+1)(n)(n-1)(n-2) \ldots 1}{n(n-1)(n-2) \ldots 1}$

   $= \dfrac{(n+1)(\cancel{n})(\cancel{n-1})(\cancel{n-2}) \ldots \cancel{1}}{\cancel{n}(\cancel{n-1})(\cancel{n-2}) \ldots \cancel{1}}$

   $= n + 1$

   c. $_6P_2 = 6 \cdot 5$
   $= 30$

   d. $\binom{10}{6} = \dfrac{10!}{6!4!}$

   $= \dfrac{10 \cdot 9 \cdot \overset{3}{8} \cdot 7 \cdot \cancel{6!}}{\cancel{4 \cdot 3 \cdot 2 \cdot 1} \cdot \cancel{6!}}$

   $= 210$

   e. $(n-1)! = (4-1)!$
   $= 3!$
   $= 3 \cdot 2 \cdot 1$
   $= 6$

   f. $\binom{4}{2}\left(\frac{1}{4}\right)^2\left(\frac{3}{4}\right)^2 = 6\left(\frac{1}{16}\right)\left(\frac{9}{16}\right)$
   $= \frac{54}{256}$
   $= \frac{27}{128}$ or 0.21

   g. $2^n - 1 = 2^7 - 1$
   $= 128 - 1$
   $= 127$

   h. $_5P_3 \cdot {}_6C_4 = (5 \cdot 4 \cdot 3)\left(\dfrac{6!}{4!2!}\right)$

   $= 60\left(\dfrac{\overset{3}{6} \cdot 5 \cdot \cancel{4!}}{2 \cdot 1 \cdot \cancel{4!}}\right)$

   $= 900$

2. $\binom{8}{3} = \dfrac{8!}{3!5!}$

   $= \dfrac{8 \cdot 7 \cdot \cancel{6} \cdot \cancel{5!}}{\cancel{3} \cdot 2 \cdot 1 \cdot \cancel{5!}}$

   $= 56$

3. The number of possible letters is 23. The number of possible digits is 9 for the first digit and 10 for each of the remaining three digits.

   $\underline{23} \cdot \underline{23} \cdot \underline{9} \cdot \underline{10} \cdot \underline{10} \cdot \underline{10} = 4{,}761{,}000$

4. a. $P(\text{white in Bag } A) = \frac{3}{5}$ or 0.6
   b. Sample space = 9 white marbles and 5 red marbles. Using combinations (finding combinations of 2 possibilities),

   $P = \dfrac{\binom{9}{2}}{\binom{14}{2}}$

   $= \dfrac{\frac{9!}{2!7!}}{\frac{14!}{2!12!}}$

   $= \dfrac{\dfrac{9 \cdot \overset{4}{8} \cdot \cancel{7!}}{\cancel{2} \cdot \cancel{2} \cdot \cancel{7!}}}{\dfrac{\overset{7}{14} \cdot 13 \cdot \cancel{12!}}{\cancel{2} \cdot \cancel{1} \cdot \cancel{12!}}}$

   $= \frac{36}{91}$ or 0.4

   Or, considering that the two marbles are drawn one after the other without replacement,

   $P = \dfrac{9}{\cancel{14}} \cdot \dfrac{\overset{4}{\cancel{8}}}{13}$

   $= \frac{36}{91}$ or 0.4

5. a. $P(\text{both}) = \dfrac{\overset{1}{\cancel{2}} \cdot \overset{1}{\cancel{2}}}{\underset{1}{\cancel{4}} \cdot \cancel{2}}$

   $= \frac{1}{2}$ or 0.5

   b. $P(\text{neither}) = \left(1 - \frac{3}{4}\right)\left(1 - \frac{2}{3}\right)$
   $= \frac{1}{4} \cdot \frac{1}{3}$
   $= \frac{1}{12}$ or 0.083

c. First boy   Second boy
    Solve: $\frac{3}{4}$ Not solve: $\frac{1}{3}$
    Not solve: $\frac{1}{4}$ Solve: $\frac{2}{3}$
    Solve: $\frac{3}{4}$ Solve: $\frac{2}{3}$

$\frac{3}{4} \cdot \frac{1}{3} = \frac{3}{12}$

$\frac{1}{4} \cdot \frac{2}{3} = \frac{2}{12}$

$\frac{3}{4} \cdot \frac{2}{3} = \frac{6}{12}$

$\qquad \frac{11}{12}$ or 0.92

6. Let x = number of bulbs tested to determine the second bad bulb.

$\binom{10}{2} = \frac{10!}{2!8!}$

$= \frac{\overset{5}{\cancel{10}} \cdot 9 \cdot \cancel{8!}}{\cancel{2} \cdot \cancel{1} \cdot \cancel{8!}}$

= 45 elements

The values of the random variable are x = 2, 3, 4, 5, 6, 7, 8.

Probability distribution:

x	$P(x)$	
2	$\binom{1}{1}\binom{1}{1}$	$= \frac{1}{45}$
3	$\binom{2}{1}\binom{1}{1}$	$= \frac{2}{45}$
4	$\binom{3}{1}\binom{1}{1}$	$= \frac{3}{45}$
5	$\binom{4}{1}\binom{1}{1}$	$= \frac{4}{45}$
6	$\binom{5}{1}\binom{1}{1}$	$= \frac{5}{45}$
7	$\binom{6}{1}\binom{1}{1}$	$= \frac{6}{45}$
8	$\binom{7}{1}\binom{1}{1}$	$= \frac{7}{45}$
9	$\binom{8}{1}\binom{1}{1}$	$= \frac{8}{45}$
10	$\binom{9}{1}\binom{1}{1}$	$= \frac{9}{45}$

$E(x) = 2(\frac{1}{45}) + 3(\frac{2}{45}) + 4(\frac{3}{45}) +$
$\qquad 5(\frac{4}{45}) + 6(\frac{5}{45}) + 7(\frac{6}{45}) +$
$\qquad 8(\frac{7}{45}) + 9(\frac{8}{45}) + 10(\frac{9}{45})$
$\quad = \frac{2}{45} + \frac{6}{45} + \frac{12}{45} + \frac{20}{45} +$
$\qquad \frac{30}{45} + \frac{42}{45} + \frac{56}{45} + \frac{72}{45} + \frac{90}{45}$
$\quad = \frac{330}{45}$ or 7.33

7. a. P(correct guess) = $\frac{1}{5}$ or 0.2
   b. P(incorrect guess) = $1 - \frac{1}{5}$
$\qquad\qquad\qquad\qquad\qquad = \frac{4}{5}$ or 0.8
   c. Let p = probability of getting correct answer = $\frac{1}{5}$
$\qquad$ q = probability of getting incorrect answer = $1 - \frac{1}{5}$

$(p + q)^5 = \binom{5}{0}(\frac{1}{5})^5 +$
$\qquad\qquad \binom{5}{1}(\frac{1}{5})^4(\frac{4}{5})^1 +$
$\qquad\qquad \binom{5}{2}(\frac{1}{5})^3(\frac{4}{5})^2 +$
$\qquad\qquad \binom{5}{3}(\frac{1}{5})^2(\frac{4}{5})^3 +$
$\qquad\qquad \binom{5}{4}(\frac{1}{5})^1(\frac{4}{5})^4 +$
$\qquad\qquad \binom{5}{5}(\frac{4}{5})^5$

P(3 correct answers) $= \binom{5}{2}(\frac{1}{5})^3(\frac{4}{5})^2$
$\qquad\qquad\qquad = 10(\frac{1}{125})(\frac{16}{25})$
$\qquad\qquad\qquad = \frac{160}{3,125}$
$\qquad\qquad\qquad = \frac{32}{625}$ or 0.05

d. From the equation in (c), P(at least 4 correct answers) $= \binom{5}{0}(\frac{1}{5})^5 +$
$\qquad\qquad\qquad \binom{5}{1}(\frac{1}{5})^4(\frac{4}{5})$
$\qquad\qquad = \frac{1}{3,125} + 5(\frac{1}{625}) \cdot$
$\qquad\qquad\qquad (\frac{4}{5})$
$\qquad\qquad = \frac{1}{3,125} + \frac{20}{3,125}$
$\qquad\qquad = \frac{21}{3,125}$ or 0.01

e. From the equation in (c), P(no correct answers) $= \binom{5}{5}(\frac{4}{5})^5$
$\qquad\qquad\qquad = \frac{1,024}{3,125}$ or 0.33

8. $(n - 1)! = (4 - 1)!$
$\qquad\qquad = 3!$
$\qquad\qquad = 3 \cdot 2 \cdot 1$
$\qquad\qquad = 6$

9. Sample space = {2, 4, 6, 8, 10, 12, 14, 16, 18, 20, 22, 24, 26, 28, 30, 32, 34, 36, 38, 40, 42, 44, 46, 48, 50}.
Let A = numbers divisible by 5.
Sample space (A) = {10, 20, 30, 40, 50}.
$P(A) = \frac{5}{25}$
$\qquad = \frac{1}{5}$

Let B = numbers divisible by 8.
Sample space (B) = {8, 16, 24, 32, 40, 48}.
$P(B) = \frac{6}{25}$

$A \cap B$ = {40}
$P(A \cap B) = \frac{1}{25}$

$P(A \cup B) = P(A) + P(B) -$
$\qquad\qquad P(A \cap B)$
$\qquad = \frac{5}{25} + \frac{6}{25} - \frac{1}{25}$
$\qquad = \frac{10}{25}$
$\qquad = \frac{2}{5}$ or 0.4

MATHEMATICS 1210
LIFEPAC TEST
SOLUTION KEY

1. a. When $n = 1$,

$$3(1) - 1 = \frac{1(3 \cdot 1 + 1)}{2}$$

$$2 = \frac{4}{2} = 2$$

b. Assume $\displaystyle\sum_{i=1}^{k} 3i - 1 =$

$$\frac{k(3k + 1)}{2}.$$

c. Then $\displaystyle\sum_{i=1}^{k} 3i - 1 + 3k + 2 =$

$$\frac{k(3k + 1)}{2} + 3k + 2.$$

$$\sum_{i=1}^{k+1} 3i - 1 =$$

$$\frac{3k^2 + k + 6k + 4}{2} =$$

$$\frac{1}{2}(3k^2 + 7k + 4) =$$

$$\frac{(k + 1)(3k + 4)}{2} =$$

$$\frac{k + 1}{2}[3(k + 1) + 1]$$

2. $\displaystyle\sum_{i=1}^{5} (2i - 1)^2 = (2 \cdot 1 - 1)^2 +$
$(2 \cdot 2 - 1)^2 +$
$(2 \cdot 3 - 1)^2 +$
$(2 \cdot 4 - 1)^2 +$
$(2 \cdot 5 - 1)^2$

$$= (2 - 1)^2 +$$
$$(4 - 1)^2 +$$
$$(6 - 1)^2 +$$
$$(8 - 1)^2 +$$
$$(10 - 1)^2$$

$$= 1^2 + 3^2 + 5^2 +$$
$$7^2 + 9^2$$

$$= 1 + 9 + 25 +$$
$$49 + 81$$

$$= 165$$

3. $f(-2) = 3(-2)^3 + (-2) - 1$
$= 3(-8) - 2 - 1$
$= -24 - 3$
$= -27$

4. $$\frac{(a + h)^2 + 4(a + h) - }{h} \cdots$$

$$\frac{5 - (a^2 + 4a - 5)}{h} =$$

$$\frac{\cancel{a^2} + 2ah + h^2 + \cancel{4a} + }{h} \cdots$$

$$\frac{4h - \cancel{5} - \cancel{a^2} - \cancel{4a} + \cancel{5}}{h} =$$

$$\frac{2a\cancel{h} + h^{\cancel{2}} + 4\cancel{h}}{\cancel{h}} =$$

$$2a + h + 4$$

5. $$\lim_{x \to -2} \frac{1}{x^3} = \lim_{x \to -2} \frac{1}{x} \cdot \lim_{x \to -2} \frac{1}{x} \cdot \lim_{x \to -2} \frac{1}{x}$$

$$= \frac{1}{-2} \cdot \frac{1}{-2} \cdot \frac{1}{-2}$$

$$= \frac{1}{8}$$

6. Divide the numerator and the denominator by x.

$$\lim_{x \to \infty} = \frac{3x - 2}{x} = \lim_{x \to \infty} \frac{3 - \frac{2}{x}}{1}$$

$$= \frac{\displaystyle\lim_{x \to \infty} 3 - \lim_{x \to \infty} \frac{2}{x}}{\displaystyle\lim_{x \to \infty} 1}$$

$$= \frac{3 - 0}{1}$$

$$= 3$$

7. $$m = \lim_{h \to 0} \frac{f(x + h) - f(x)}{h}$$

$$= \lim_{h \to 0} \frac{7 - 3(x + h) - (7 - 3x)}{h}$$

$$= \lim_{h \to 0} \frac{\cancel{7} - \cancel{3x} - 3h - \cancel{7} + \cancel{3x}}{h}$$

$$= \lim_{h \to 0} \frac{-3\cancel{h}}{\cancel{h}}$$

$$= \lim_{h \to 0} -3$$

$$= -3$$

8.　Let m_1 = slope of $f(x)$
　　m_2 = slope of $g(x)$

$m_1 = \lim\limits_{h \to 0} \dfrac{3(x + h) - 3x}{h}$

　　$= \lim\limits_{h \to 0} \dfrac{3x + 3h - 3x}{h}$

　　$= \lim\limits_{h \to 0} \dfrac{3h}{h}$

　　$= \lim\limits_{h \to 0} 3$

　　$= 3$

$m_2 = \lim\limits_{h \to 0} \dfrac{4 - (x + h)^2 - (4 - x^2)}{h}$

　　$= \lim\limits_{h \to 0} \dfrac{4 - (x^2 + 2xh + h^2) -}{h} \cdots$
　　　　$\dfrac{4 + x^2}{h}$

　　$= \lim\limits_{h \to 0} \dfrac{-x^2 - 2xh - h^2 + x^2}{h}$

　　$= \lim\limits_{h \to 0} \dfrac{-2xh - h^2}{h}$

　　$= \lim\limits_{h \to 0} -2x - h$

　　$= \lim\limits_{h \to 0} -2x$

　　$= -2x$

Points of intersection:
$$3x = 4 - x^2$$
$$3x - 4 + x^2 = 0$$
$$x^2 + 3x - 4 = 0$$
$$(x + 4)(x - 1) = 0$$
$$x + 4 = 0$$
$$x = -4$$
$$x - 1 = 0$$
$$x = 1$$

$x = -4$:　$y = 3x$
　　　　　$= 3(-4)$
　　　　　$= -12$

$x = 1$:　$y = 3x$
　　　　　$= 3(1)$
　　　　　$= 3$

Points of intersection are
$(-4, -12)$ and $(1, 3)$. Point
$(1, 3)$ is the only point in
Quadrant I. Points to graph
$f(x) = 3x$ are $(-3, -9)$, $(0, 0)$,
$(2, 6)$. Points to graph $g(x) =$
$4 - x^2$ are $(\pm 3, -5)$, $(\pm 2, 0)$,
$(\pm 1, 3)$, $(0, 4)$.

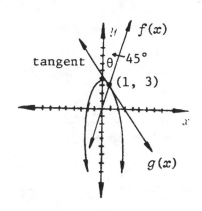

For point $(1, 3)$:
$m_1 = 3$
$m_2 = -2x$
　　$= -2(1)$
　　$= -2$

$\tan \theta = \dfrac{m_2 - m_1}{1 + m_2 m_1}$

　　　$= \dfrac{-2 - 3}{1 + 3(-2)}$

　　　$= \dfrac{-5}{1 - 6}$

　　　$= \dfrac{-5}{-5}$

　　　$= 1$

$\theta = \arctan 1 = 45°$

9.　all real numbers; $x \in R$

10.　For x equals any real number,
　　y will always be any real
　　number; $y \geq 0$.

11.　$g[h(x)] = 4(2x^2) - 1$
　　　　　$= 8x^2 - 1$

12.　$$3x^2 + x - 10 \leq 0$$
　　$$(3x - 5)(x + 2) \leq 0$$
　　　$3x - 5 \geq 0$ and $x + 2 \leq 0$
　　　　$3x \geq 5$　　　　$x \leq -2$
　　　　$\dfrac{3x}{3} \geq \dfrac{5}{3}$

　　　　$x \geq \dfrac{5}{3}$
　　　empty set
　　　or
　　$3x - 5 \leq 0$ and $x + 2 \geq 0$
　　　$3x \leq 5$　　　　$x \geq -2$
　　　$\dfrac{3x}{3} \leq \dfrac{5}{3}$

$$x \le \frac{5}{3}$$

$$-2 \le x \le \frac{5}{3}$$

13.

$$3\overline{\smash{\big)}\ 3 + 4 - 1 + 8}$$
$$\ 0 + 9 + 39 + 114$$
$$\ \overline{3 + 13 + 38 + 122}$$

14. From the trigonometric table, csc 77° 30' = 1.024.

15. $63° = 63° \cdot \dfrac{\pi}{180°}$

$$= \frac{\overset{7}{\cancel{63}}\pi}{\underset{20}{\cancel{180}}}$$

$$= \frac{7\pi}{20}$$

16. $y = 3 \cos 3x$
amplitude = 3
period = $\dfrac{2\pi}{3}$

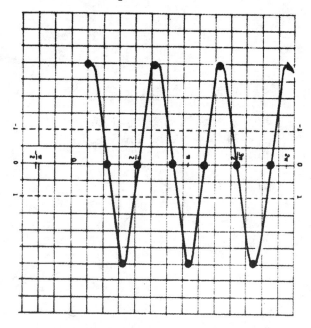

17. $120° = 120° \cdot \dfrac{\pi}{180°}$

$$= \frac{\overset{2}{\cancel{120}}\pi}{\underset{3}{\cancel{180}}}$$

$$= \frac{2\pi}{3}$$

$$\frac{2\pi}{\cancel{3}} \cdot \cancel{24}^{8} = 16\pi \text{ radians}$$

18. $2 \sin \theta - \sqrt{3} = 0$
$$2 \sin \theta = \sqrt{3}$$
$$\frac{2 \sin \theta}{2} = \frac{\sqrt{3}}{2}$$
$$\sin \theta = \frac{\sqrt{3}}{2}$$
$\theta = 60°,\ 120°$

19. $\sin(\theta - \phi) = \sin \theta \cos \phi - \cos \theta \sin \phi$

$\sin \theta = \dfrac{\sqrt{2}}{2}$ $\qquad$ $\sin \phi = -\dfrac{4}{5}$

$\cos \theta = -\dfrac{\sqrt{2}}{2}$ $\qquad$ $\cos \phi = -\dfrac{3}{5}$

$$\sin(\theta - \phi) = \frac{\sqrt{2}}{2}\left(-\frac{3}{5}\right) - \left(\frac{\sqrt{2}}{2}\right)\left(-\frac{4}{5}\right)$$

$$= -\frac{3\sqrt{2}}{10} - \frac{4\sqrt{2}}{10}$$

$$= -\frac{7\sqrt{2}}{10}$$

20.

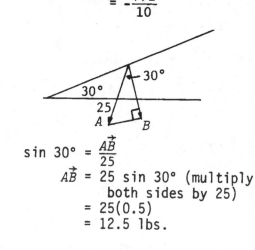

$\sin 30° = \dfrac{\vec{AB}}{25}$

$\vec{AB} = 25 \sin 30°$ (multiply both sides by 25)

$= 25(0.5)$

$= 12.5$ lbs.

21.

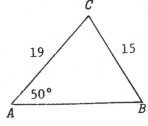

$$\frac{\sin 50°}{15} = \frac{\sin \angle B}{19}$$

$$\sin \angle B = \frac{19 \sin 50°}{15} \text{ (multiply}$$

both sides by 19)

$$= \frac{19(0.7660)}{15}$$

$$= 0.9703$$

$\angle B = $ arc sin $0.9703 = 76°$

22.

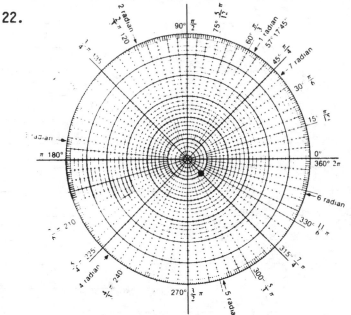

23. $x = r \cos \theta$
$y = r \sin \theta$
$2(r \cos \theta) - 3(r \sin \theta) + 4 = 0$
$\quad 2r \cos \theta - 3r \sin \theta + 4 = 0$
$\quad r(2 \cos \theta - 3 \sin \theta) + 4 = 0$

24.

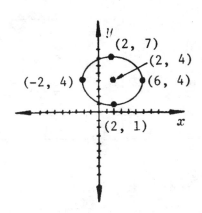

From the graph, the center is at (2, 4), the length of $a = |6 - 2| = 4$, and the length of $b = |7 - 4| = 3$. Therefore, the equation is $\frac{(x - 2)^2}{16} + \frac{(y - 4)^2}{9} = 1$.

25. $(n - 1)! = (6 - 1)!$
$= 5!$
$= 5 \cdot 4 \cdot 3 \cdot 2 \cdot 1$
$= 120$

26. Let $p = $ probability of winning $= \frac{3}{4}$
$q = $ probability of losing $= 1 - \frac{3}{4}$
$= \frac{1}{4}$

$$P(x) = \binom{n}{x} q^{n-x} p^{x}$$
$n = 5, \ x = 4$

$$P(x) = \binom{5}{4}\left(\frac{1}{4}\right)^1 \left(\frac{3}{4}\right)^4$$

$$= 5\left(\frac{1}{4}\right)\left(\frac{81}{256}\right)$$

$$= \frac{405}{1,024} \text{ or } 0.4$$

411

1. $\{y: \quad y = \sqrt[3]{7}, \sqrt[3]{9}, \sqrt[3]{11}\}$

2. H is not a function because two of the given x-values are the same.

3. $y = -2$: $\quad x = |4(-2) + 1| =$
   $$|-8 + 1| =$$
   $$|-7| = 7$$
   $$(7, -2)$$

   $y = -1$: $\quad x = |4(-1) + 1| =$
   $$|-4 + 1| =$$
   $$|-3| = 3$$
   $$(3, -1)$$

   $y = 0$: $\quad x = |4 \cdot 0 + 1| =$
   $$|0 + 1| =$$
   $$|1| = 1$$
   $$(1, 0)$$

   $y = 1$: $\quad x = |4 \cdot 1 + 1| =$
   $$|4 + 1| =$$
   $$|5| = 5$$
   $$(5, 1)$$

   $y = 2$: $\quad x = |4 \cdot 2 + 1| =$
   $$|8 + 1| =$$
   $$|9| = 9$$
   $$(9, 2)$$
   $\{(7, -2), (3, -1), (1, 0),$
   $(5, 1), (9, 2)\}$

4. a and b (c is not a function because the values for x do not have unique values).

5. set of all real numbers

6. $f(x) = \sqrt{x}$

7. $g(x) = 3x - 1$

8. $F(3) = 2(3)^2 - 2 =$
   $$2(9) - 2 = 18 - 2 = 16$$

9. $F(x) - G(x) =$
   $(2x^2 - 2) - (x + 1) =$
   $2x^2 - 2 - x - 1 =$
   $2x^2 - x - 3$

10. $F \circ G = 2(x + 1)^2 - 2$

11. Let $y = G(x)$; then $y = x + 1$.
    Interchange x and y: $x = y + 1$.

    Solve for y:
    $$x = y + 1$$
    $$x - 1 = y + 1 - 1$$
    $$x - 1 = y$$
    $$y = x - 1$$
    $$G^{-1}(x) = x - 1$$

12. $F(1) = 2(1)^2 - 2 =$
    $$2 \cdot 1 - 2 = 2 - 2 = 0$$

    $G(2) = 2 + 1 = 3$
    $3H(-1) = 3(-1) = -3$

    $F(1) + G(2) - 3H(-1) =$
    $0 + 3 - (-3) =$
    $0 + 3 + 3 = 6$

13. $(F \cdot G)(x) = F(x) \cdot G(x) =$
    $(2x^2 - 2)(x + 1) =$
    $2x^3 + 2x^2 - 2x - 2$

14. $\left(\dfrac{F}{G}\right)(x) = \dfrac{2x^2 - 2}{x + 1} = \dfrac{2(x^2 - 1)}{x + 1} =$
    $$\dfrac{2(x + 1)(x - 1)}{x + 1} = 2(x - 1)$$

15. $G \circ H = x + 1$

16. To find G^{-1}, let $y = G(x)$;
    then $y = x + 1$. Interchange
    x and y: $x = y + 1$.

    Solve for y:
    $$x = y + 1$$
    $$x - 1 = y + 1 - 1$$
    $$x - 1 = y$$
    $$y = x - 1$$
    $$G^{-1} = x - 1$$

    To find H^{-1}, let $y = H(x)$; then
    $y = x$. Interchange x and y.
    $$y = x$$
    $$x = y$$

    Solve for y: $y = x$
    $$H^{-1} = x$$

    $$G^{-1} \circ H^{-1} = x - 1$$

17. $(F + G)(x) = F(x) + G(x) =$
    $(2x^2 - 2) + (x + 1) =$
    $2x^2 + x - 1$

18. $(G + H)(x) = G(x) + H(x) =$
    $(x + 1) + (x) = 2x + 1$

19. $(G \cdot H)(x) = G(x) \cdot H(x) =$
    $(x + 1)(x) = x^2 + x$

20. To find $F^{-1}(x)$, let $y = F(x)$;
    then $y = 2x^2 - 2$.
    Interchange x and y:
    $x = 2y^2 - 2$.

    Solve for y:
    $$x = 2y^2 - 2$$
    $$x + 2 = 2y^2 - 2 + 2$$
    $$x + 2 = 2y^2$$
    $$\frac{x + 2}{2} = \frac{2y^2}{2}$$
    $$\frac{x + 2}{2} = y^2$$
    $$\pm\sqrt{\frac{x + 2}{2}} = \sqrt{y^2}$$
    $$\pm\sqrt{\frac{x + 2}{2}} = y$$
    $$y = \pm\sqrt{\frac{x + 2}{2}}$$

    Since y is double valued,
    $F^{-1}(x)$ is also double valued
    and is therefore not a function.

1. $F(x) = x - 3$
    a. $F(x) = 0 - 3 = -3$
    b. $F(x) = 0.1 - 3 = -2.9$
    c. $F(x) = -\frac{1}{2} - 3 = -3\frac{1}{2}$
    d. $3 = x - 3$
        $3 + 3 = x - 3 + 3$
        $6 = x$
        $x = 6$

2. $m = \frac{\Delta y}{\Delta x} = \frac{3 - (-5)}{6 - 2} = \frac{8}{4} = 2$

3. $2x - y + 4 > 0$

x	y
0	4
-2	0
2	8

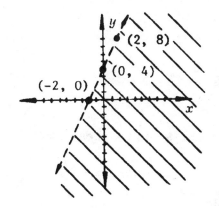

4. $P(x) = x^3 - 2x^2 + 1$
    $P(2) = 2^3 - 2(2)^2 + 1 =$
    $\qquad 8 - 8 + 1 = 1$
    remainder = 1

5. $G(x) = \frac{4x^2 - 25}{2x + 5} =$

    $\qquad \frac{(2x + 5)(2x - 5)}{2x + 5} =$

    $\qquad 2x - 5$

    $\qquad 2x - 5 = 0$
    $2x - 5 + 5 = 0 + 5$
    $\qquad 2x = 5$
    $\qquad \frac{2x}{2} = \frac{5}{2}$

5. cont.

$$x = \frac{5}{2}$$

The zero is $\frac{5}{2}$.

6. $f(x) = x^4 - x^3 - 14x^2 + 5x + 12$
    $f(4) = 4^4 - 4^3 - 14(4)^2 + 5(4) + 12$
    $\qquad 256 - 64 - 224 + 20 + 12 =$
    $\qquad 288 - 288 = 0$
    Yes, $x - 4$ is a factor.

7. $G^{-1}(x) = 4^x$

8. $f(x) = 2^x + 2^{-x}$

x	y
0	2
-1	$2\frac{1}{2}$
1	$2\frac{1}{2}$
-2	$4\frac{1}{4}$
2	$4\frac{1}{4}$

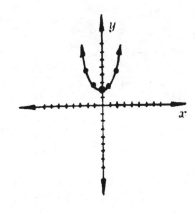

9. $f(x) = x^3 - 1$

x	y
-2	-9
-1	-2
0	-1
1	0
2	7

9. cont.

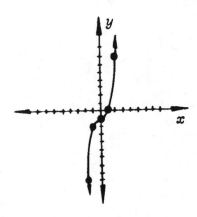

10. $f(x) = x^2 - 2$

$g(x) = -\frac{1}{2}x + 1$

$(f + g)(x) = f(x) + g(x) =$

$(x^2 - 2) + (-\frac{1}{2}x + 1) =$

$x^2 - 2 - \frac{1}{2}x + 1 =$

$x^2 - \frac{1}{2}x - 1$

x	y
-2	4
-1	$\frac{1}{2}$
0	-1
1	$-\frac{1}{2}$
2	2

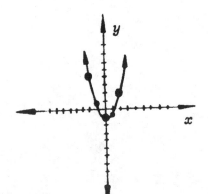

11. $f(x) = \dfrac{x^2}{1 - x^2}$

$x \neq 1$ or -1 since these values result in a 0 denominator.

x	y
$\pm\frac{8}{9}$	$\frac{64}{17}$
$\pm\frac{3}{4}$	$\frac{9}{7}$
$\pm\frac{1}{2}$	$\frac{1}{3}$
0	0
$\pm\frac{3}{2}$	$-\frac{9}{5}$
±2	$-\frac{4}{3}$
±3	$-\frac{9}{8}$
±4	$-\frac{16}{15}$

As x gets larger, y approaches -1.

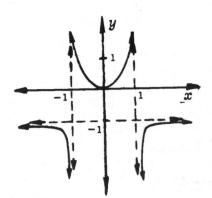

1. $\sin 90° + \cos 120° + \tan 225° +$
    $\cos 180° = 1 + (-\frac{1}{2}) + 1 + (-1) =$
    $1 - \frac{1}{2} + 1 - 1 = \frac{1}{2}$

2. $(\sin 315°)(\cos 150°) -$
    $(\sin 60°)(\cos 45°) =$
    $(-\frac{\sqrt{2}}{2})(-\frac{\sqrt{3}}{2}) - (\frac{\sqrt{3}}{2})(\frac{\sqrt{2}}{2}) =$
    $\frac{\sqrt{6}}{4} - \frac{\sqrt{6}}{4} = 0$

3. $(\sin 330°)(\tan 135°) -$
    $(\sin 210°)(\cos 300°) \cdot$
    $(\tan 180°) =$
    $(-\frac{1}{2})(-1) - (-\frac{1}{2})(\frac{1}{2})(0) =$
    $\frac{1}{2} - 0 = \frac{1}{2}$

4. $\cot 270°$
    $$\frac{\tan (-180°)}{(\sec 240°)[\sec (-180°)](\sin 90°)} =$$
    $$0 - \frac{0}{(-2)(-1)(1)} = 0$$

5. $\sec 105° = \csc (105° - 90°) =$
    $\csc 15°$

6. $\tan (-70°) = \cot (90° - 70°) =$
    $\cot 20°$

7. $\sin 237° = \cos (270° - 237°) =$
    $\cos 33°$

8. $\cos (-325°) = \cos (360° - 325°) =$
    $\cos 35°$

9. $\cos 49° \ 10' = \cos 49° \ 10'$

10. a.

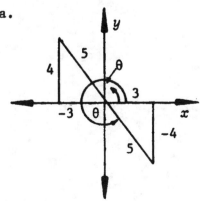

10. cont.

Quadrant 2

b. $\frac{4}{5}$

c. $-\frac{3}{5}$

d. $-\frac{3}{4}$

e. $-\frac{5}{3}$

f. $\frac{5}{4}$

Quadrant 4

g. $-\frac{4}{5}$

h. $\frac{3}{5}$

i. $-\frac{3}{4}$

j. $\frac{5}{3}$

k. $-\frac{5}{4}$

11.

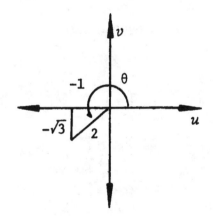

a. $-\frac{\sqrt{3}}{2}$

b. $\frac{-\sqrt{3}}{-1} = \sqrt{3}$

c. $\frac{-1}{-\sqrt{3}} = \frac{1}{\sqrt{3}} = \frac{1}{\sqrt{3}} \cdot \frac{\sqrt{3}}{\sqrt{3}} = \frac{\sqrt{3}}{3}$

d. $\frac{1}{-\frac{1}{2}} = -2$

e. $\frac{1}{-\frac{\sqrt{3}}{2}} = -\frac{2}{\sqrt{3}} = -\frac{2}{\sqrt{3}} \cdot \frac{\sqrt{3}}{\sqrt{3}} = -\frac{2\sqrt{3}}{3}$

12. csc 217° 40' =
csc (180° + 37° 40') =
−csc 37° 40° = −1.636

13. sin 98° 23' =
sin (180° − 98° 23') =
sin 81° 37'
Interpolate to find
sin 81° 37':

$$10\left\{7\left\{\begin{array}{l}\sin 81° 30' = \\ \quad 0.9890 \\ \sin 81° 37' = \\ \sin 81° 40' = \\ \quad 0.9894\end{array}\right\}x\right\}0.0004$$

$$\frac{7}{10} = \frac{x}{0.0004}$$
7(0.0004) = 10x
10x = 0.0028
$$\frac{10x}{10} = \frac{0.0028}{10}$$
x = 0.00028 =
0.0003 rounded
to the fourth
decimal place

sin 81° 37' = 0.9890 + 0.0003 =
0.9893

14. cot (−12° 35') = −cot 12° 35'
Interpolate to find
cot 12° 35':

$$10\left\{5\left\{\begin{array}{l}\cot 12° 30' = \\ \quad 4.511 \\ \cot 12° 35' = \\ \cot 12° 40' = \\ \quad 4.449\end{array}\right\}x\right\}0.062$$

$$\frac{5}{10} = \frac{x}{0.062}$$
5(0.062) = 10x
10x = 0.310
$$\frac{10x}{10} = \frac{0.310}{10}$$
x = 0.031

cot 12° 35' = 4.511 − 0.031 =
4.480
cot (−12° 35') = −4.480

15. sin θ = 0.7396
sin θ lies between sin
47° 40' and sin 47° 50'.

$$10\left\{x\left\{\begin{array}{l}\sin 47° 40' = \\ \quad 0.7392 \\ \sin θ \quad = \\ \quad 0.7396 \\ \sin 47° 50' = \\ \quad 0.7412\end{array}\right\}0.0004\right\}0.0020$$

$$\frac{x}{10} = \frac{0.0004}{0.0020}$$
0.0020x = 10(0.0004)
0.0020x = 0.004
$$\frac{0.0020x}{0.0020} = \frac{0.004}{0.0020}$$
x = 2 minutes

θ = 47° 40' + 2' = 47° 42'

16. cot θ = 0.2905
cot θ lies between
cot 73° 40' and cot 73° 50'.

$$10\left\{x\left\{\begin{array}{l}\cot 73° 40' = \\ \quad 0.2931 \\ \cot θ \quad = \\ \quad 0.2905 \\ \cot 73° 50' = \\ \quad 0.2899\end{array}\right\}0.0026\right\}0.0032$$

$$\frac{x}{10} = \frac{0.0026}{0.0032}$$
0.0032x = 10(0.0026)
0.0032x = 0.026
$$\frac{0.0032x}{0.0032} = \frac{0.026}{0.0032}$$
x = 8.125 or 8 minutes

θ = 73° 40' + 8' = 73° 48'

17. $(\cos 180°)^6 = (-1)^6 = 1$

18. $(\tan 180° - \sec 0°)^3 +$
$\sin 270° = (0 - 1)^3 + (-1) =$
$-1 - 1 = -2$

19. $(\cos 0° \cdot 3 \sin 90°)^4 =$
$[1 \cdot 3(1)]^4 = 3^4 = 81$

20. csc 270°·sin (-90°) +
    4 tan 225° - cot² 90° =
    (-1)(-1) + 4(1) - 0² =
    1 + 4 - 0 = 5

21. a. $75° = 75° \cdot \frac{\pi}{180°} =$

    $\frac{\overset{5}{\cancel{75}}\pi}{\underset{12}{\cancel{180}}} = \frac{5\pi}{12}$ radians

    b. I

22. a. $\frac{7\pi}{4}$ radians =

    $\frac{7\pi}{4} \cdot \frac{180°}{\pi} =$

    $\frac{7\cancel{\pi}}{\cancel{4}} \cdot \frac{\overset{45}{\cancel{180}}}{\underset{1}{\cancel{\pi}}} = 315°$

    b. IV

23. a. $225° = 225° \cdot \frac{\pi}{180°} =$

    $\frac{\overset{5}{\cancel{225}}\pi}{\underset{4}{\cancel{180}}} = \frac{5\pi}{4}$ radians

    b. III

24. a. $150° = 150° \cdot \frac{\pi}{180°} =$

    $\frac{\overset{5}{\cancel{150}}\pi}{\underset{6}{\cancel{180}}} \quad \frac{5\pi}{6}$ radians

    b. II

25. a. $\frac{\pi}{3}$ radians $= \frac{\pi}{3} \cdot \frac{180°}{\pi} =$

    $\frac{\cancel{\pi}}{\cancel{3}} \cdot \frac{\overset{60}{\cancel{180}}}{\cancel{\pi}} = 60°$

    b. I

1.

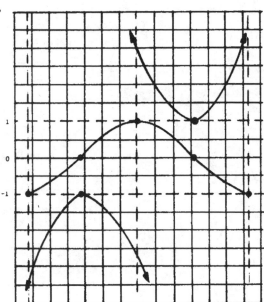

2.

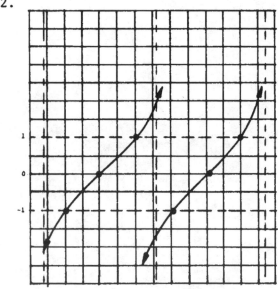

3.

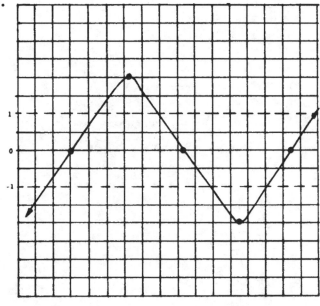

4.

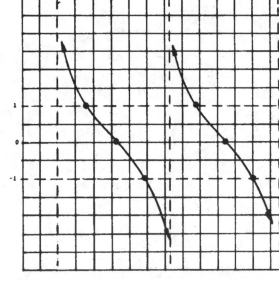

5. $v = r\omega$

$75 = 4\omega$

$\dfrac{75}{4} = \dfrac{4\omega}{4}$

$\omega = 18\tfrac{3}{4} = 19$ to the nearest whole number

6. $v = r\omega$
    $180 = 12\omega$
    $\dfrac{180}{12} = \dfrac{12\omega}{12}$
    $\omega = 15$ inches

7. 33 r.p.m. = $33(2\pi)$ =
    66π radians per minute

8. $\cot \dfrac{\pi}{4} + \sin 2\pi - \cos \dfrac{3\pi}{2}$ =
    $\cot 45° + \sin 360°$ –
    $\cos 270° = 1 + 0 - 0 = 1$

9. $2 \cos \dfrac{5\pi}{2} = 2 \cos 90°$ =
    $2(0) = 0$

10. $P = \dfrac{2\pi}{B}$
    $B = \dfrac{1}{4}$
    $P = \dfrac{2\pi}{\frac{1}{4}} = 2\pi(4) = 8\pi$

11. a. $\dfrac{3\pi}{4}$ lies between $\dfrac{\pi}{2}$ and π;
        therefore, $\dfrac{3\pi}{4}$ is located
        in Quadrant II.
    b. $\dfrac{6\pi}{5}$ lies between π and $\dfrac{3\pi}{2}$;
        therefore, $\dfrac{6\pi}{5}$ is located
        in Quadrant III.
    c. $\dfrac{2\pi}{3}$ lies between $\dfrac{\pi}{2}$ and π;
        therefore, $\dfrac{2\pi}{3}$ is located
        in Quadrant II.
    d. $\dfrac{10\pi}{6}$ lies between π and $\dfrac{3\pi}{2}$;
        therefore, $\dfrac{10\pi}{6}$ is located
        in Quadrant III.
    e. $\dfrac{\pi}{5}$ lies between 0 and $\dfrac{\pi}{2}$;
        therefore, $\dfrac{\pi}{5}$ is located
        in Quadrant I.
    f. $\dfrac{11\pi}{6}$ lies between $\dfrac{3\pi}{2}$ and 2π;
        therefore, $\dfrac{11\pi}{6}$ is located
        in Quadrant IV.

12. a.

    b.

    c.

    d.

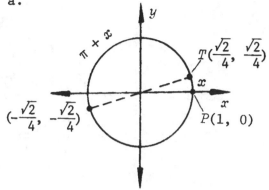

12. cont.

e.

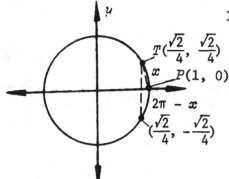

f.

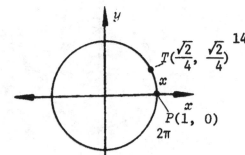

g.

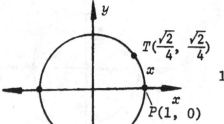

h.

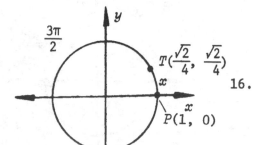

13. a. $y = 3 \sin (2x + 4)$
$y = 3 \sin 2(x + 2)$
$p = -2$; the phase shift is 2 units to the left

b. $y = \cos (4x - 8)$
$y = \cos 4(x - 2)$
$p = 2$; the phase shift is 2 units to the right

c. $y = 4 \sin (3x - 15)$
$y = 4 \sin 3(x - 5)$
$p = 5$; the phase shift is 5 units to the right

14. a. amplitude $= A = |2| = 2$
period $= P = \dfrac{2\pi}{B}$
$B = 3$
$P = \dfrac{2\pi}{3}$

b. amplitude $= A = |3| = 3$
period $= P = \dfrac{2\pi}{B}$
$B = \dfrac{1}{2}$
$P = \dfrac{2\pi}{\frac{1}{2}} = 2\pi(2) = 4\pi$

15. $y = -\sin 3(x + \dfrac{\pi}{2})$
$A = |-1| = 1$
$P = \dfrac{2\pi}{B}$
$B = 3$
$P = \dfrac{2\pi}{3}$
$P = -\dfrac{\pi}{2}$
true

16. false; $\sin (-\dfrac{\pi}{2}) = \sin 270° = -1$
and $\sin \dfrac{\pi}{2} = \sin 90° = 1$.
$y = \sin x$ for $-1 \le x \le 1$; the maximum value for $y = \sin x$ is 1.

1. $\dfrac{1}{\cos \theta} - \cos \theta = \tan \theta \cdot \sin \theta$

$$\dfrac{1}{\cos \theta} - \cos \theta = \dfrac{1}{\cos \theta} - \dfrac{\cos^2 \theta}{\cos \theta}$$

$$= \dfrac{1 - \cos^2 \theta}{\cos \theta}$$

$$= \dfrac{\sin^2 \theta}{\cos \theta}$$

$$= \dfrac{\sin \theta}{\cos \theta} \cdot \sin \theta$$

$$= \tan \theta \cdot \sin \theta$$

2. $(1 - \sin \theta) \cdot (1 + \sin \theta) = \dfrac{1}{1 + \tan^2 \theta}$

$(1 - \sin \theta) \cdot (1 + \sin \theta) = 1 - \sin^2 \theta$

$$= \cos^2 \theta$$

$$= \dfrac{1}{\sec^2 \theta}$$

$$= \dfrac{1}{1 + \tan^2 \theta}$$

3. yes; $\tan \dfrac{x}{2} = \dfrac{\sin x}{1 + \cos x}$

$$\tan \dfrac{90°}{2} = \dfrac{\sin 90°}{1 + \cos 90°}$$

$$\tan 45° = \dfrac{\sin 90°}{1 + \cos 90°}$$

$$1 = \dfrac{1}{1 + 0}$$

$$1 = 1$$

4. yes; $\cos \dfrac{\pi}{12} = \dfrac{\sqrt{2} + \sqrt{6}}{4}$

$\dfrac{\pi}{12} = \dfrac{\pi}{3} - \dfrac{\pi}{4}$: $\dfrac{4\pi}{12} - \dfrac{3\pi}{12} = \dfrac{\pi}{12}$

$$\cos \dfrac{\pi}{12} = \cos \left(\dfrac{\pi}{3} - \dfrac{\pi}{4}\right)$$

$$= \left(\cos \dfrac{\pi}{3}\right)\left(\cos \dfrac{\pi}{4}\right) +$$

$$\left(\sin \dfrac{\pi}{3}\right)\left(\sin \dfrac{\pi}{4}\right)$$

$$= \dfrac{1}{2} \cdot \dfrac{\sqrt{2}}{2} + \dfrac{\sqrt{3}}{2} \cdot \dfrac{\sqrt{2}}{2}$$

$$= \dfrac{\sqrt{2}}{4} + \dfrac{\sqrt{6}}{4}$$

$$= \dfrac{\sqrt{2} + \sqrt{6}}{4}$$

5. $\sin 2\alpha = \sin (\alpha + \alpha)$

$$= \sin \alpha \cos \alpha +$$
$$\sin \alpha \cos \alpha$$
$$= 2 \sin \alpha \cos \alpha$$

6. $\tan \left(\theta - \dfrac{\pi}{4}\right) = \dfrac{\tan \theta - \tan \dfrac{\pi}{4}}{1 + \tan \theta \tan \dfrac{\pi}{4}}$

$$\dfrac{\tan \theta - 1}{1 + \tan \theta \cdot (1)} = \dfrac{\dfrac{\sin \theta}{\cos \theta} - \dfrac{\cos \theta}{\cos \theta}}{\dfrac{\cos \theta}{\cos \theta} + \dfrac{\sin \theta}{\cos \theta}} =$$

$$\dfrac{\dfrac{\sin \theta - \cos \theta}{\cos \theta}}{\dfrac{\cos \theta + \sin \theta}{\cos \theta}} = \dfrac{\sin \theta - \cos \theta}{\sin \theta + \cos \theta}$$

7. $\dfrac{\csc^2 \theta - 1}{\csc^2 \theta} = \dfrac{\csc^2 \theta}{\csc^2 \theta} - \dfrac{1}{\csc^2 \theta}$

$$= 1 - \dfrac{1}{\csc^2 \theta}$$

$$= 1 - \sin^2 \theta$$

$$= \cos^2 \theta$$

8. $\dfrac{1 - \tan^2 x}{1 + \tan^2 x} = \dfrac{1 - \dfrac{\sin^2 x}{\cos^2 x}}{1 + \dfrac{\sin^2 x}{\cos^2 x}}$

$$= \dfrac{\dfrac{\cos^2 x}{\cos^2 x} - \dfrac{\sin^2 x}{\cos^2 x}}{\dfrac{\cos^2 x}{\cos^2 x} + \dfrac{\sin^2 x}{\cos^2 x}}$$

$$= \dfrac{\dfrac{\cos^2 x - \sin^2 x}{\cos^2 x}}{\dfrac{\cos^2 x + \sin^2 x}{\cos^2 x}}$$

$$= \dfrac{\cos^2 x - \sin^2 x}{1}$$

$$= \cos^2 x - \sin^2 x$$

9. $\cos (\alpha - \beta) = \cos \alpha \cos \beta +$
$$\sin \alpha \sin \beta$$

9. cont.

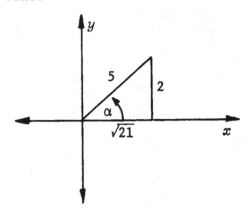

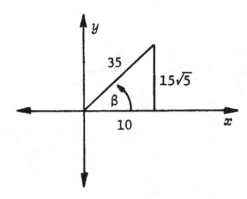

$$\cos \alpha = \frac{\sqrt{21}}{5} \qquad \sin \alpha = \frac{2}{5}$$

$$\cos \beta = \frac{10}{35} \qquad \sin \beta = \frac{15\sqrt{5}}{35}$$

$$\cos \alpha \cos \beta + \sin \alpha \sin \beta =$$

$$\left(\frac{\sqrt{21}}{5}\right)\left(\frac{10}{35}\right)^{2} + \left(\frac{2}{5}\right)\left(\frac{15\sqrt{5}}{35}\right)^{3} =$$

$$\frac{2\sqrt{21}}{35} + \frac{6\sqrt{5}}{35} = \frac{2\sqrt{21} + 6\sqrt{5}}{35}$$

10. $\sin (\theta - \phi) =$
$\sin \theta \cos \phi - \cos \theta \sin \phi$

$$\sin \theta = \frac{12}{15} \qquad \cos \theta = \frac{9}{15}$$

$$\sin \phi = \frac{4}{5} \qquad \cos \phi = -\frac{3}{5}$$

$$\sin \theta \cos \phi - \cos \theta \sin \phi =$$

$$\left(\frac{12}{15}\right)\left(-\frac{3}{5}\right) - \left(\frac{9}{15}\right)\left(\frac{4}{5}\right) =$$

$$-\frac{12}{25} - \frac{4}{25} = -\frac{16}{25}$$

11. $\sin (\theta + \phi) =$
$\sin \theta \cos \phi + \cos \theta \sin \phi$

$$\sin \theta = \frac{12}{15} \qquad \cos \theta = \frac{9}{15}$$

$$\sin \phi = \frac{4}{5} \qquad \cos \phi = -\frac{3}{5}$$

$$\sin \theta \cos \phi + \cos \theta \sin \phi =$$

$$\left(\frac{12}{15}\right)\left(-\frac{3}{5}\right) + \left(\frac{9}{15}\right)\left(\frac{4}{5}\right) =$$

$$-\frac{12}{25} + \frac{12}{25} = 0$$

12. $\cos (\theta - \phi) =$
$\cos \theta \cos \phi + \sin \theta \sin \phi$

$$\sin \theta = \frac{12}{15} \qquad \cos \theta = \frac{9}{15}$$

$$\sin \phi = \frac{4}{5} \qquad \cos \phi = -\frac{3}{5}$$

$$\cos \theta \cos \phi + \sin \theta \sin \phi =$$

$$\left(\frac{9}{15}\right)\left(-\frac{3}{5}\right) + \left(\frac{12}{15}\right)\left(\frac{4}{5}\right) =$$

$$-\frac{9}{25} + \frac{16}{25} = \frac{7}{25}$$

13. $\cos (\theta - \phi) =$
$\cos \theta \cos \phi - \sin \theta \sin \phi$

$$\sin \theta = \frac{12}{15} \qquad \cos \theta = \frac{9}{15}$$

$$\sin \phi = \frac{4}{5} \qquad \cos \phi = -\frac{3}{5}$$

$$\cos \theta \cos \phi - \sin \theta \sin \phi =$$

$$\left(\frac{9}{15}\right)\left(-\frac{3}{5}\right) - \left(\frac{12}{15}\right)\left(\frac{4}{5}\right) =$$

$$-\frac{9}{25} - \frac{16}{25} = -\frac{25}{25} = -1$$

14. $\tan(\theta + \phi) = \dfrac{\tan\theta + \tan\phi}{1 - \tan\theta\tan\phi}$

$\tan\theta = \dfrac{12}{9} = \dfrac{4}{3}$

$\tan\phi = -\dfrac{4}{3}$

$\dfrac{\tan\theta + \tan\phi}{1 - \tan\theta\tan\phi} = \dfrac{\dfrac{4}{3} + \left(-\dfrac{4}{3}\right)}{1 - \left(\dfrac{4}{3}\right)\left(-\dfrac{4}{3}\right)} =$

$\dfrac{\dfrac{4}{3} - \dfrac{4}{3}}{1 + \dfrac{16}{9}} = \dfrac{0}{\dfrac{25}{9}} = 0$

15. $\sin\dfrac{1}{2}\theta = \pm\sqrt{\dfrac{1 - \cos\theta}{2}}$

$\cos\theta = \dfrac{9}{15} = \dfrac{3}{5}$

$\pm\sqrt{\dfrac{1 - \cos\theta}{2}} = \pm\sqrt{\dfrac{1 - \dfrac{3}{5}}{2}} =$

$\pm\sqrt{\dfrac{\dfrac{5}{5} - \dfrac{3}{5}}{2}} = \pm\sqrt{\dfrac{\dfrac{2}{5}}{2}} =$

$\pm\sqrt{\dfrac{2}{5}\cdot\dfrac{1}{2}} = \pm\sqrt{\dfrac{1}{5}} =$

$\pm\dfrac{\sqrt{1}}{\sqrt{5}} = \pm\dfrac{1}{\sqrt{5}}\cdot\dfrac{\sqrt{5}}{\sqrt{5}} = \pm\dfrac{\sqrt{5}}{5}$

16. $\cos 2\phi = \cos^2\phi - \sin^2\phi$

$\sin\phi = \dfrac{4}{5} \qquad \cos\phi = -\dfrac{3}{5}$

$\cos^2\phi - \sin^2\phi =$

$\left(-\dfrac{3}{5}\right)^2 - \left(\dfrac{4}{5}\right)^2 =$

$\dfrac{9}{25} - \dfrac{16}{25} = -\dfrac{7}{25}$

17. $\tan 2\theta = \dfrac{2\tan\theta}{1 - \tan^2\theta}$

$\tan\theta = \dfrac{12}{9} = \dfrac{4}{3}$

$\dfrac{2\tan\theta}{1 - \tan^2\theta} = \dfrac{2\left(\dfrac{4}{3}\right)}{1 - \left(\dfrac{4}{3}\right)^2} =$

17. cont.

$\dfrac{\dfrac{8}{3}}{1 - \dfrac{16}{9}} = \dfrac{\dfrac{24}{9}}{\dfrac{9}{9} - \dfrac{16}{9}} =$

$\dfrac{24}{9 - 16} = \dfrac{24}{-7} = -\dfrac{24}{7}$

18. $\cos 4\theta = 8\cos^4\theta - 8\cos^2\theta + 1$

$\cos\theta = \dfrac{9}{15} = \dfrac{3}{5}$

$8\cos^4\theta - 8\cos^2\theta + 1 =$

$8\left(\dfrac{3}{5}\right)^4 - 8\left(\dfrac{3}{5}\right)^2 + 1 =$

$8\left(\dfrac{81}{625}\right) - 8\left(\dfrac{9}{25}\right) + 1 =$

$\dfrac{648}{625} - \dfrac{72}{25} + 1 =$

$\dfrac{648}{625} - \left(\dfrac{25}{25}\right)\left(\dfrac{72}{25}\right) + \dfrac{625}{625} =$

$\dfrac{648}{625} - \dfrac{1{,}800}{625} + \dfrac{625}{625} = -\dfrac{527}{625}$

19. $\cos 3\phi = 4\cos^3\phi - 3\cos\phi$

$\cos\phi = -\dfrac{3}{5}$

$4\cos^3\phi - 3\cos\phi =$

$4\left(-\dfrac{3}{5}\right)^3 - 3\left(-\dfrac{3}{5}\right) =$

$4\left(-\dfrac{27}{125}\right) + \dfrac{9}{5} =$

$-\dfrac{108}{125} + \left(\dfrac{25}{25}\right)\left(\dfrac{9}{5}\right) =$

$-\dfrac{108}{125} + \dfrac{225}{125} = \dfrac{117}{125}$

20. $\tan\left(\dfrac{\pi}{2} - \theta\right) = \dfrac{\sin\left(\dfrac{\pi}{2} - \theta\right)}{\cos\left(\dfrac{\pi}{2} - \theta\right)}$

$= \dfrac{\cos\theta}{\sin\theta}$

$= \cot\theta$

1.

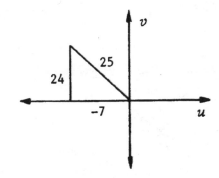

a. $\sin\theta = \dfrac{24}{25}$

b. $\cos\theta = -\dfrac{7}{25}$

c. $\tan\theta = -\dfrac{24}{7}$

d. $\csc\theta = \dfrac{1}{\frac{24}{25}} = \dfrac{25}{24}$

e. $\sec\theta = \dfrac{1}{-\frac{7}{25}} = -\dfrac{25}{7}$

f. $\cot\theta = \dfrac{1}{-\frac{24}{7}} = -\dfrac{7}{24}$

2.

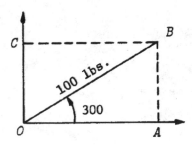

Find $\overrightarrow{OA}$.

$\overrightarrow{OA} = \overrightarrow{OB}\cos 30° =$
100 $\cos 30° =$
100(0.8660) =
86.6 lbs.

3. a. $F_1 = 450\cos 25° =$
450(0.9063) =
407.84 lbs.

$F_2 = 450\sin 25° =$
450(0.4226) =
190.17 lbs.

b. Since $F_3 = F_2$ (the horizontal component) and F_3 is in the opposite direction of F_2, $F_3 = -190.17$ lbs.

4.

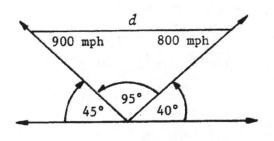

$d^2 = 900^2 + 800^2 - 2(900)(800)\cdot$
$\quad \cos 105°$
$d^2 = 810{,}000 + 640{,}000 -$
$\quad 1{,}440{,}000(-0.2588)$
$d^2 = 810{,}000 + 640{,}000 +$
$\quad 372{,}672$
$d^2 = 1{,}822{,}672$
$d^2 = 1{,}350$ mi. (rounded)

5.

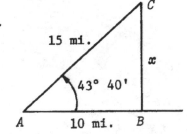

5. cont.

$$\sin 43° \ 40' = \frac{x}{15}$$

$$15 \sin 43° \ 40' = x$$

$$x = 15(0.6905) =$$
$$10.3575 \text{ or } 10.4 \text{ mi.}$$

$$d = rt$$

$$10 + 10.4 + 15 = 45t$$
$$35.4 = 45t$$
$$\frac{35.4}{45} = \frac{45t}{45}$$
$$0.786 = t$$
$$t = 0.786 \text{ hr. or}$$
$$47.16 \text{ min.}$$

6.

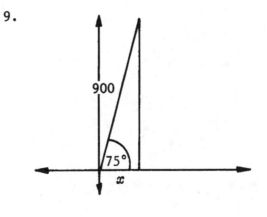

$$\angle \theta = 90° - 80° = 10°$$
$$\angle \phi = 180° - 10° = 170°$$

$$d^2 = 20^2 + 12^2 - 2(20)(16) \cdot$$
$$\cos 170°$$
$$d^2 = 400 + 144 - 640 \cdot$$
$$(-0.9848)$$
$$d^2 = 544 - (-630.272)$$
$$d^2 = 1,174.272$$
$$d = 34 \text{ na. mi. (rounded)}$$

7.

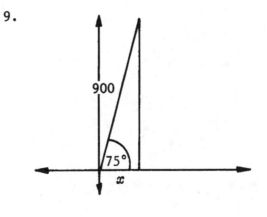

7.

$$\frac{75}{\sin \angle BCA} = \frac{65}{\sin 45°}$$
$$\sin \angle BCA (65) = 75 \sin 45°$$
$$\sin \angle BCA = \frac{75 \sin 45°}{65}$$
$$\sin \angle BCA = \frac{75(0.7071)}{65} =$$
$$0.8159$$
$$\angle BCA = 180° - 55°$$
$$\angle BCA = 125°$$

$$\angle ACD = 180° - \angle BCA$$
$$\angle ACD = 180° - 125°$$
$$\angle ACD = 55°$$

8.

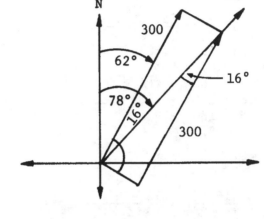

$$x^2 = 270^2 + 300^2 -$$
$$2(270)(300)\cos 16°$$
$$x^2 = 72,900 + 90,000 -$$
$$162,000(0.9613)$$
$$x^2 = 162,900 - 155,730.6$$
$$x^2 = 7,169.4$$
$$x = 84.7 \text{ or } 85 \text{ mph}$$

9.

9. cont.

$$\cos 75° = \frac{x}{90}$$

$$90 \cos 75° = x$$

$$x = 90(0.2588)$$

$$x = 23.292 \text{ mph}$$

$$\text{velocity} = \frac{23.292}{60} =$$

$$0.3882 \text{ or}$$

$$0.39 \text{ mi./min.}$$

10. a. $$\frac{\sin 40°}{12} = \frac{\sin \angle C}{15}$$

$$\sin \angle C = \frac{15 \sin 40°}{12}$$

$$\sin \angle C = \frac{15(0.6428)}{12}$$

$$\sin \angle C = 0.8035$$

$$\angle C \doteq 53°$$

   b. $$\angle B = 180° - (\angle A + \angle C)$$

$$\angle B = 180° - (40° + 53°)$$

$$\angle B = 180° - 93°$$

$$\angle B = 87°$$

   c. $$\frac{\sin 40°}{12} = \frac{\sin 87°}{b}$$

$$\frac{b \sin 40°}{\sin 40°} = \frac{12 \sin 87°}{\sin 40°}$$

$$b = \frac{12 \sin 87°}{\sin 40°}$$

$$b = \frac{12(0.9986)}{0.6428}$$

$$b = 18.642 \text{ or } 18.6$$

1. Let $x = \sin^{-1}\left(-\dfrac{1}{\sqrt{2}}\right)$.

   Then $\sin x = -\dfrac{1}{\sqrt{2}}$

   $x = -\dfrac{\pi}{4}$

2. $\tan \dfrac{2\pi}{3} = -\sqrt{3}$

   Let $x = \arctan(-\sqrt{3})$.
   Then $\tan x = -\sqrt{3}$
   $x = \dfrac{\pi}{3}$

3. $\sin\left(-\dfrac{5\pi}{6}\right) = -\dfrac{1}{2}$

   Let $x = \arccos\left(-\dfrac{1}{2}\right)$.
   Then $\cos x = -\dfrac{1}{2}$.
   $x = \dfrac{2\pi}{3}$

4. Let $x = \arcsin \dfrac{\sqrt{3}}{2}$

   Then $\sin x = \dfrac{\sqrt{3}}{2}$.
   $x = \dfrac{\pi}{3}$

5. Let $x = \arccos 0.8888$.
   Then $\cos x = 0.8888$.
   $x = 27°\ 17'$

6.

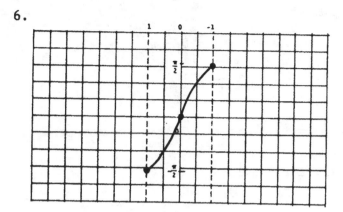

7.

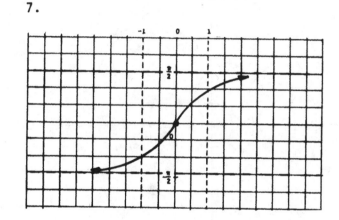

8. $F(x) = 3 \cos^{-1} x$
   Let $y = F(x)$. Then $y = 3 \cos^{-1} x$ and
   $\dfrac{y}{3} = \cos^{-1} x$; $\cos \dfrac{y}{3} = x$
   Now interchange the variables and
   $y = \cos \dfrac{x}{3}$ or $F^{-1}(x) = \cos \dfrac{x}{3}$.

9. Domain: $-1 \le x \le 1$
   Range: $0 \le F(x) \le \pi$

10. $\arcsin(2x^2 - 2x) = -\dfrac{\pi}{6}$

    $\sin\left(-\dfrac{\pi}{6}\right) = -\dfrac{1}{2}$

    $2x^2 - 2x = -\dfrac{1}{2}$

    $4x^2 - 4x = -1$ (multiply by 2)
    $4x^2 - 4x + 1 = -1 + 1$
    $4x^2 - 4x + 1 = 0$
    $(2x - 1)(2x - 1) = 0$
    $2x - 1 = 0$

10. cont.

$$2x - 1 + 1 = 0 + 1$$
$$2x = 1$$
$$\frac{2x}{2} = \frac{1}{2}$$
$$x = \frac{1}{2}$$

11. through 15.

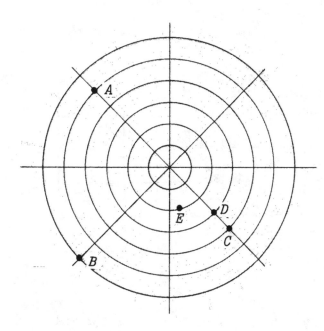

16. $x = r \cos \theta$
$x = 2 \cos 315° =$
$2 \cos 45° =$

$2\left(\frac{\sqrt{2}}{2}\right) =$

$\sqrt{2}$

$y = r \sin \theta$
$y = 2 \sin 315° =$
$2 \sin (-45°) =$

$2\left(-\frac{\sqrt{2}}{2}\right) =$

$-\sqrt{2}$

$(x, y) = (\sqrt{2}, -\sqrt{2})$

17. $x = r \cos \theta$
$x = 5 \cos 135° =$
$\quad 5 (-\cos 45°) =$

$5\left(-\frac{\sqrt{2}}{2}\right) =$

$-\frac{5\sqrt{2}}{2}$

$y = r \sin \theta$
$y = 5 \sin 135°$
$\quad 5 \sin 45°$

$5\left(\frac{\sqrt{2}}{2}\right) =$

$\frac{5\sqrt{2}}{2}$

$(x, y) = \left(-\frac{5\sqrt{2}}{2}, \frac{5\sqrt{2}}{2}\right)$

18. $x = r \cos \theta$
$x = 3 \cos 90° =$
$\quad 3(0) =$
$\quad 0$

$y = r \sin \theta$
$y = 3 \sin 90°$
$\quad 3(1) =$
$\quad 3$

$(x, y) = (0, 3)$

19. $x = r \cos \theta$
$x = 6 \cos 225° =$
$\quad 6(-\cos 45°) =$

$6\left(-\frac{\sqrt{2}}{2}\right) =$

$-3\sqrt{2}$

$y = r \sin \theta$
$y = 6 \sin 225°$
$\quad 6(-\sin 45°)$

$6\left(-\frac{\sqrt{2}}{2}\right)$

$\left(y = -3\sqrt{2}\right)$

$(x, y) = (-3\sqrt{2}, -3\sqrt{2})$

20. $x = r \cos \theta$
   $x = 4 \cos 120° =$
       $4(-\cos 60°) =$
       $4 \left(-\dfrac{1}{2}\right) =$
       -2

   $y = r \sin \theta$
   $y = 4 \sin 120°$
       $4 \sin 60°$
       $4 \left(\dfrac{\sqrt{3}}{2}\right) =$

       $2\sqrt{3}$

       $(x, y) = (-2, \ 2\sqrt{3})$

21. $r = \sqrt{x^2 + y^2}$

   $r = \sqrt{2^2 + (-1)^2} =$

       $\sqrt{4 + 1} =$
       $\sqrt{5}$

   $\tan \theta = \dfrac{y}{x} = \dfrac{-1}{2} = -\dfrac{1}{2}$

       $\theta = 333° \ 29'$

       $(r, \theta) = (\sqrt{5}, \ 333° \ 29')$

22. $r = \sqrt{x^2 + y^2}$

   $r = \sqrt{(-4)^2 + (4\sqrt{3})^2} =$

       $\sqrt{16 + 48} =$

       $\sqrt{64} =$
       8

   $\tan \theta = \dfrac{y}{x} = \dfrac{4\sqrt{3}}{-4} = -\sqrt{3}$
       $\theta = 120°$

       $(r, \theta) = (8, \ 120°)$

23. $r = \sqrt{x^2 + y^2}$

   $r = \sqrt{\left(-\dfrac{\sqrt{2}}{2}\right)^2 + \left(-\dfrac{\sqrt{2}}{2}\right)^2} =$

23. cont.

       $\sqrt{\dfrac{2}{4} + \dfrac{2}{4}} =$

       $\sqrt{1} =$
       1

   $\tan \theta = \dfrac{y}{x} = \dfrac{-\dfrac{\sqrt{2}}{2}}{-\dfrac{\sqrt{2}}{2}} = 1$

       $\theta = 225°$
       $(r, \theta) = (1, \ 225°)$

24. $r = \sqrt{x^2 + y^2}$

   $r = \sqrt{0^2 + 3^2} =$

       $\sqrt{9} =$
       3

   $\tan \theta = \dfrac{y}{x} = \dfrac{3}{0} = \text{undefined}$

       $\theta = 90°$

       $(r, \theta) = (3, \ 90°)$

25. $r = \sqrt{x^2 + y^2} =$

   $r = \sqrt{(-2)^2 + 2^2} =$

       $\sqrt{4 + 4} =$
       $\sqrt{8} =$
       $2\sqrt{2}$

   $\tan \theta = \dfrac{y}{x} = \dfrac{2}{-2} = 1$
       $\theta = 135°$

       $(r, \theta) = (2\sqrt{2}, \ 135°)$

26. $x^2 + y^2 - 2x = 0$
   $x = r \cos \theta, \ y = r \sin \theta$
   $r^2 \cos^2 \theta + r^2 \sin^2 \theta - 2r \cos \theta = 0$

431

26. cont.

$$r^2(\cos^2 \theta + \sin^2 \theta) - 2r \cos \theta = 0$$

$$r^2(1) - 2r \cos \theta = 0$$
$$r^2 - 2r \cos \theta = 0 \text{ or (dividing by } r)$$
$$r - 2 \cos \theta = 0 \text{ or } r = 2 \cos \theta$$

27. $x^2 + y^2 = 9y$
$x = r \cos \theta, \ y = r \sin \theta$
$$r^2 \cos^2 \theta + r^2 \sin^2 \theta = 9r \sin \theta$$
$$r^2(\cos^2 \theta + \sin^2 \theta) = 9r \sin \theta$$
$$r^2(1) = 9r \sin \theta$$
$$r^2 = 9r \sin \theta$$
$$r = 9 \sin \theta \text{ (divide by } r)$$

28. $r^2 = 6 \cos 2x$
$$r^2 = 6(\cos^2 x - \sin^2 x)$$
$$r^2 = 6 \cos^2 x - 6 \sin^2 x$$
$$r^2 = x^2 + y^2, \ \sin x = \frac{y}{r}, \ \cos x = \frac{x}{r}$$
$$x^2 + y^2 = 6\left(\frac{x^2}{r^2} - \frac{y^2}{r^2}\right)$$
$$x^2 + y^2 = \frac{6(x^2 - y^2)}{r^2}$$
$$x^2 + y^2 = \frac{6(x^2 - y^2)}{x^2 + y^2}$$
$$(x^2 + y^2)^2 = 6(x^2 - y^2)$$

29. $r^2 = 4 \tan 2\theta$
$$r^2 = 4\left(\frac{2 \tan \theta}{1 - \tan^2 \theta}\right)$$
$$r^2 = x^2 + y^2, \ \tan \theta = \frac{y}{x}$$
$$x^2 + y^2 = 4\left(\frac{\frac{2y}{x}}{1 - \frac{y^2}{x^2}}\right)$$
$$x^2 + y^2 = \frac{\frac{8xy}{x^2}}{\frac{x^2}{x^2} - \frac{y^2}{x^2}}$$

29. cont.

$$x^2 + y^2 = \frac{8xy}{x^2 - y^2}$$
$$(x^2 + y^2)(x^2 - y^2) = 8xy$$

30. $r = 1 + 2 \cos \theta$

θ	0	$\frac{\pi}{6}$	$\frac{\pi}{3}$	$\frac{\pi}{2}$	$\frac{2\pi}{3}$	$\frac{3\pi}{4}$	$\frac{5\pi}{6}$	π
r	3	2.7	2	1	0	-0.4	-0.7	-1

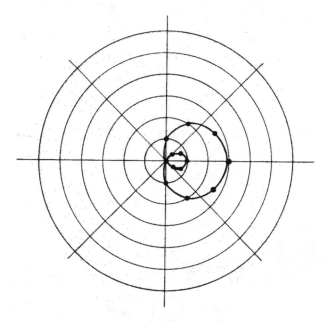

31. $r = \theta$
A few solutions are
$(0.\ 0)$, $(\frac{\pi}{2}, \frac{\pi}{2})$, and (π, π).

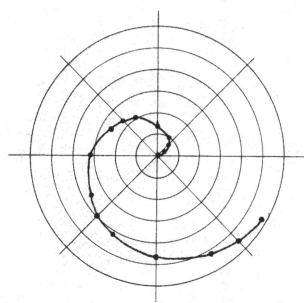

1. $x^2 + y^2 - 6x + 4y - 87 = 0$
   $$x^2 - 6x + y^2 + 4y = 87$$
   $$(x^2 - 6x + 9) +$$
   $$(y^2 + 4y + 4) = 87 +$$
   $$9 + 4$$
   $$(x - 3)^2 + (y + 2)^2 = 100$$
   The graph is a circle with center at (3, -2) and radius of 10.

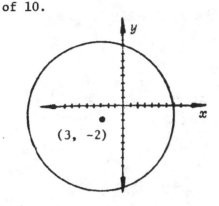

2. $9x^2 + 36y^2 = 324$
   $$\frac{9x^2}{324} + \frac{36y^2}{324} = \frac{324}{324}$$
   $$\frac{x^2}{36} + \frac{y^2}{9} = 1$$
   The graph is an ellipse in Position I with center at (0, 0).
   $a = \sqrt{36} = 6$
   $b = \sqrt{9} = 3$
   $c = \sqrt{a^2 - b^2} = \sqrt{36 - 9} =$
   $\sqrt{27} = 3\sqrt{3}$
   Major axis = $2a = 2(6) = 12$
   Minor axis = $2b = 2(3) = 6$
   L. R. = $\frac{2b^2}{a} = \frac{2(9)}{6} = \frac{18}{6} = 3$
   $e = \frac{c}{a} = \frac{3\sqrt{3}}{6} = \frac{\sqrt{3}}{2}$
   Domain: $-6 \leq x \leq 6$
   Range: $-3 < y < 3$

2. cont.

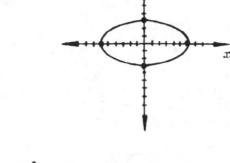

3. $x^2 - 10x - 20y - 15 = 0$
   $$x^2 - 10x = 20y + 15 \text{ (add}$$
   $$20y + 15 \text{ to both sides)}$$
   $$x^2 - 10x + 25 = 20y + 15 + 25$$
   $$(x - 5)(x - 5) = 20y + 40$$
   $$(x - 5)^2 = 20(y + 2)$$
   The graph is a parabola in Position I with vertex at (5, -2).

   Focus: $4p = 20$
   $$\frac{4p}{4} = \frac{20}{4}$$
   $$p = 5, \ (3, 5)$$

   L. R. = $4p = 20$
   Directrix: $y = -7$
   Domain: all real x
   Range: $y \geq -2$

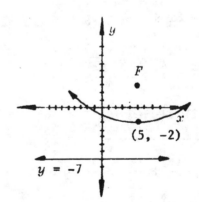

4. $4x^2 - 49y^2 = 196$

$$\frac{4x^2}{196} - \frac{49y^2}{196} = \frac{196}{196}$$

$$\frac{x^2}{49} - \frac{y^2}{4} = 1$$

The graph is a hyperbola in Position I with center at $(0, 0)$.

$a = \sqrt{49} = 7$

$b = \sqrt{4} = 2$

$c = \sqrt{a^2 + b^2} = \sqrt{49 + 4} = \sqrt{53}$

Foci $= (\pm c, 0) = (\pm\sqrt{53}, 0)$

L. R. $= \dfrac{2b^2}{a} = \dfrac{2(4)}{49} = \dfrac{8}{49}$

$e = \dfrac{c}{a^2} = \dfrac{\sqrt{53}}{49}$

Domain: $-7 \geq x \geq 7$

Range: all real y

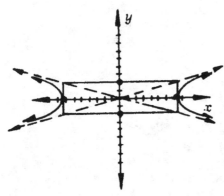

5. $2x^2 + 3y^2 - 8x + 6y - 7 = 0$

$$2x^2 - 8x + 3y^2 + 6y = 7$$

$$2(x^2 - 4x + \_\_) +$$
$$3(y^2 + 2y + \_\_) = 7$$

$$2(x^2 - 4x + 4) +$$
$$3(y^2 + 2y + 1) = 7 +$$
$$8 + 3$$

$$2(x - 2)^2 + 3(y + 1)^2 = 18$$

$$\frac{2(x - 2)^2}{18} + \frac{3(y + 1)^2}{18} = \frac{18}{18}$$

$$\frac{(x - 2)^2}{9} + \frac{(y + 1)^2}{6} = 1$$

Center $(h, k) = (2, -1)$

Let $x' = x - 2$ and $y' = y + 1$.

Then $\dfrac{(x')^2}{9} + \dfrac{(y')^2}{6} = 1$.

The graph is an ellipse with center (x', y') at $(0, 0)$.

$a = \sqrt{9} = 3$

$b = \sqrt{6}$

5. cont.

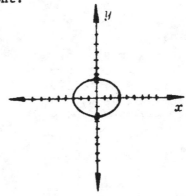

6. $9x^2 - 3\sqrt{3}xy + 6y^2 = 94.5$

$\tan 2\theta = \dfrac{B}{A - C} =$

$$\dfrac{-3\sqrt{3}}{9 - 6} =$$

$$\dfrac{-3\sqrt{3}}{3} =$$

$$-\sqrt{3}$$

$2\theta = 120°, \ \theta = 60°$

$\sin \theta = \dfrac{\sqrt{3}}{2}, \ \cos \theta = \dfrac{1}{2}$

$x = x' \cos \theta - y' \sin \theta =$
$$x'(\tfrac{1}{2}) - y'(\tfrac{\sqrt{3}}{2}) = \tfrac{1}{2}(x' - \sqrt{3}y')$$

$y = x' \sin \theta + y' \cos \theta =$
$$x'(\tfrac{\sqrt{3}}{2}) + y'(\tfrac{1}{2}) = \tfrac{1}{2}(\sqrt{3}x' + y')$$

$9[\tfrac{1}{2}(x' - \sqrt{3}y')]^2 - 3\sqrt{3}[\tfrac{1}{2}(x' -$
$$\sqrt{3}y')][\tfrac{1}{2}(\sqrt{3}x' + y')] +$$
$$6[\tfrac{1}{2}(\sqrt{3}x' + y')]^2 = 94.5$$

$\tfrac{9}{4}[(x')^2 - 2\sqrt{3}x'y' + 3(y')^2] -$
$$\tfrac{3\sqrt{3}}{4}[\sqrt{3}(x')^2 - 3x'y' + x'y' -$$
$$\sqrt{3}(y')^2] + \tfrac{3}{2}[3(x')^2 + 2\sqrt{3}x'y' +$$
$$(y')^2] = 94.5$$

6. cont.

$$\frac{9}{4}(x')^2 - \frac{9\sqrt{3}}{2}x'y' + \frac{27}{4}(y')^2 -$$

$$\frac{9}{4}(x')^2 + \frac{9\sqrt{3}}{4}x'y' - \frac{3\sqrt{3}}{4}x'y' +$$

$$\frac{9}{4}(y')^2 + \frac{9}{2}(x')^2 + 3\sqrt{3}x'y' +$$

$$\frac{3}{2}(y')^2 = 94.5$$

$$\frac{9}{2}(x')^2 + \frac{21}{2}(y')^2 = 94.5$$

$$9(x')^2 + 21(y')^2 = 189$$

$$\frac{(x')^2}{21} + \frac{(y')^2}{9} = 1$$

The graph is an ellipse with center at $(0, 0)$, $a = \sqrt{21}$, and $b = 3$.

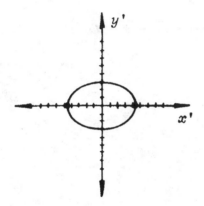

7. $x^2 + 4xy + y^2 = 16$

$$\tan 2\theta = \frac{B}{A - C} = \frac{4}{1 - 1} = \frac{4}{0} =$$
undefined

$$2\theta = 90° \text{ and } \theta = 45°$$

Therefore, $\sin \theta = \frac{\sqrt{2}}{2}$ and $\cos \theta = \frac{\sqrt{2}}{2}$.

$$x = x' \cos \theta - y' \sin \theta$$
$$y = x' \sin \theta + y' \cos \theta$$

$$x = \frac{\sqrt{2}}{2}x' - \frac{\sqrt{2}}{2}y'; \quad x = \frac{x'}{\sqrt{2}} - \frac{y'}{\sqrt{2}};$$

$$x = \left(\frac{x' - y'}{\sqrt{2}}\right)$$

7. cont.

$$y = \frac{\sqrt{2}}{2}x' + \frac{\sqrt{2}}{2}y'; \quad y = \frac{x'}{\sqrt{2}} + \frac{y'}{\sqrt{2}};$$

$$y = \left(\frac{x' + y'}{\sqrt{2}}\right)$$

Substitute these values of x and y into the given equation:

$$\left(\frac{x' - y'}{\sqrt{2}}\right)^2 + 4\left(\frac{x' - y'}{\sqrt{2}}\right)\left(\frac{x' + y'}{\sqrt{2}}\right) +$$

$$\left(\frac{x' + y'}{\sqrt{2}}\right)^2 = 16$$

$$\frac{(x')^2 - 2x'y' + (y')^2}{2} + 2(x')^2 -$$

$$2(y')^2 + \frac{(x')^2 + 2x'y' + (y')^2}{2} =$$

16

Multiply both sides of the equation by 2:

$$(x')^2 - 2x'y' + (y')^2 + 4(x')^2 - 4(y')^2 + (x')^2 + 2x'y' + (y')^2 =$$
32

$$6(x')^2 - 2(y')^2 = 32$$

Divide both sides of the equation by 2:

$$3(x')^2 - (y')^2 = 16$$

Divide both sides of the equation by 16:

$$\frac{3(x')^2}{16} - \frac{(y')^2}{16} = 1$$

$$\frac{(x')^2}{\frac{16}{3}} - \frac{(y')^2}{16} = 1$$

8. Use the standard equation of the circle $x^2 + y^2 + Dx + Ey + F = 0$.

For point $(4, 5)$:
$$4^2 + 5^2 + 4d + 5e + f = 0$$
$$16 + 25 + 4d + 5e + f = 0$$
$$41 + 4d + 5e + f = 0$$
$$4d + 5e + f = -41$$

8. cont.

For point $(3, -2)$:
$$3^2 + (-2)^2 + 3d - 2e + f = 0$$
$$9 + 4 + 3d - 2e + f = 0$$
$$13 + 3d - 2e + f = 0$$
$$3d - 2e + f = -13$$

For point $(1, -4)$:
$$1^2 + (-4)^2 + d - 4e + f = 0$$
$$1 + 16 + d - 4e + f = 0$$
$$17 + d - 4e + f = 0$$
$$d - 4e + f = -17$$

Subtracting $3d - 2e + f = -13$ from $4d + 5e + f = -41$ equals $d + 7e = -28$.

Subtracting $d - 4e + f = -17$ from $4d + 5e + f = -41$ equals $3d + 9e = -24$ or, dividing by 3, $d + 3e = -8$.

Solve for e:
$$d + 7e = -28$$
$$d + 3e = -8$$
$$\overline{\hspace{1cm} 4e = -20}$$

$$\frac{4e}{4} = \frac{-20}{4}$$
$$e = -5$$

Solve for d:
$$d + 3e = -8$$
$$d + 3(-5) = -8$$
$$d - 15 = -8$$
$$d - 15 + 15 = -8 + 15$$
$$d = 7$$

Solve for f:
$$d - 4e + f = -17$$
$$7 - 4(-5) + f = -17$$
$$7 + 20 + f = -17$$
$$27 + f = -17$$
$$27 - 27 + f = -17 - 27$$
$$f = -44$$

Therefore, the equation is
$$x^2 + y^2 + 7x - 5y - 44 = 0.$$

9.
$$x^2 + y^2 + 8x - 10y + 1 = 0$$
$$x^2 + 8x + y^2 - 10y = -1$$
$$(x^2 + 8x + 16) + (y^2 - 10y + 25) =$$
$$-1 + 16 + 25$$
$$(x + 4)^2 + (y - 5)^2 = 40$$

Center $(h, k) = (-4, 5)$
$r = \sqrt{40} = 2\sqrt{10}$

10.
$$3x^2 - 4y^2 + 12x + 8y - 4 = 0$$
$$3x^2 + 12x - 4y^2 + 8y = 4$$
$$3(x^2 + 4x + 4) - 4(y^2 - 2y + 1) =$$
$$4 + 12 - 4$$
$$3(x + 2)^2 - 4(y - 1)^2 = 12$$

$$\frac{3(x + 2)^2}{12} - \frac{4(y - 1)^2}{12} = \frac{12}{12}$$
$$\frac{(x + 2)^2}{4} - \frac{(y - 1)^2}{3} = 1$$

$a = \sqrt{4} = 2$
$b = \sqrt{3}$
$c = \sqrt{a^2 + b^2} = \sqrt{4 + 3} = \sqrt{7}$
$e = \dfrac{c}{a} = \dfrac{\sqrt{7}}{2}$

1. a. $6^P4 = 6 \cdot 5 \cdot 4 \cdot 3 = 360$

   b. $5! = 5 \cdot 4 \cdot 3 \cdot 2 \cdot 1 = 120$

   c. $\binom{8}{4} = \dfrac{8 \cdot 7 \cdot 6 \cdot 5 \cdot 4!}{4 \cdot 3 \cdot 2 \cdot 1 \cdot 4!} =$

   $\dfrac{8 \cdot 7 \cdot \overset{2}{6} \cdot 5}{4 \cdot 3 \cdot 2 \cdot 1} = 70$

   d. $7^C2 = \dfrac{7!}{2!5!} = \dfrac{7 \cdot 6 \cdot 5!}{2 \cdot 1 \cdot 5!} =$

   $\dfrac{7 \cdot \overset{3}{6}}{2 \cdot 1} = 21$

2. $(n - 1)! = (5 - 1)! = 4! =$
   $4 \cdot 3 \cdot 2 \cdot 1 = 24$

3. a. Sample space = (H, H), (H, T), (T, H), (T, T).

   $P(1 \text{ head}) = \dfrac{1}{2}$

   b. $P(x) = \binom{n}{x} q^{n-x} p^x$

   Let p = probability of heads $\left(\dfrac{1}{2}\right)$

   q = probability of tails $\left(\dfrac{1}{2}\right)$

   $x = 1, 2$

   $P(x) = \left(\dfrac{1}{2} + \dfrac{1}{2}\right)^2 =$

   $\binom{2}{1}\left(\dfrac{1}{2}\right)^1 \left(\dfrac{1}{2}\right)^1 +$

   $\binom{2}{2}\left(\dfrac{1}{2}\right)^2 = 2\left(\dfrac{1}{4}\right) +$

   $1\left(\dfrac{1}{4}\right) = \dfrac{2}{4} + \dfrac{1}{4} = \dfrac{3}{4}$

   c. $P(1 \text{ head}) = \dfrac{1}{2}$

   $P(2 \text{ heads}) = \dfrac{1}{2} \cdot \dfrac{1}{2} = \dfrac{1}{4}$

   d. $P(\text{no heads}) = P(2 \text{ tails})$

   $P(1 \text{ tail}) = \dfrac{1}{2}$

   $P(2 \text{ tails}) = \dfrac{1}{2} \cdot \dfrac{1}{2} = \dfrac{1}{4}$

   $P(\text{no heads}) = \dfrac{1}{4}$

4. a. $P(\text{red}) = 30\%$
   $P(\text{blue}) = 20\%$
   $P(\text{red or blue}) = 30\% + 20\% = 50\%$

   b. $P(\text{yellow}) = 40\%$
   $P(\text{any color except yellow}) = 100\% - 40\% = 60\%$

   c. $P(\text{red}) = 30\%$
   $P(\text{white}) = 10\%$
   $P(\text{blue}) = 20\%$
   $P(\text{red, white, or blue}) = 30\% + 10\% + 20\% = 60\%$

5. a. $P(\text{exactly 6 correct answers}) =$
   $\left(\dfrac{1}{5}\right)^6 = \dfrac{1}{5} \cdot \dfrac{1}{5} \cdot \dfrac{1}{5} \cdot \dfrac{1}{5} \cdot \dfrac{1}{5} \cdot \dfrac{1}{5} = \dfrac{1}{15{,}625}$

   b. Let p = probability of getting a correct answer $\left(\dfrac{1}{5}\right)$.

   q = probability of getting an incorrect answer $\left(\dfrac{4}{5}\right)$.

   $(p + q)^{10} = p^{10} + 10p^9 q +$
   $45p^8 q^2 + 120p^7 q^3 + 210p^6 q^4 +$
   $252p^5 q^5 + 210p^4 q^6 + 120p^3 q^7 +$
   $45p^2 q^8 + 10pq^9 + q^{10}$

   $P(\text{at least 6 correct answers}) =$
   $\left(\dfrac{1}{5}\right)^{10} + 10\left(\dfrac{1}{5}\right)^9 \left(\dfrac{4}{5}\right) + 45\left(\dfrac{1}{5}\right)^8 \left(\dfrac{4}{5}\right)^2 +$
   $120\left(\dfrac{1}{5}\right)^7 \left(\dfrac{4}{5}\right)^3 + 210\left(\dfrac{1}{5}\right)^6 \left(\dfrac{4}{5}\right)^4$

6. $7^C4 = \dfrac{7!}{4!3!} = \dfrac{7 \cdot 6 \cdot 5 \cdot 4!}{4! \cdot 3 \cdot 2 \cdot 1} = \dfrac{7 \cdot 6 \cdot 5}{3 \cdot 2 \cdot 1} =$
   35 ways

7. $10^P3 = 10 \cdot 9 \cdot 8 = 720$

8. $P(A) = \dfrac{30}{75}$

   $P(B) = \dfrac{13}{75}$

   $P(A \text{ or } B) = \dfrac{30}{75} + \dfrac{13}{75} = \dfrac{43}{75}$ or 0.57

9. Sample space = {1, 3, 5, 7, 9, 11, 13, 15, 17, 19, 21, 23, 25, 27, 29, 31, 33, 35, 37, 39, 41, 43, 45, 47, 49}

Let A = multiple of 3. Sample space = {3, 9, 15, 21, 27, 33, 39, 45}

$P(A) = \dfrac{8}{25}$

Let B = multiple of 5. Sample space = {5, 15, 25, 35, 45}

$P(B) = \dfrac{5}{25}$ or $\dfrac{1}{5}$

Sample space of $A \cap B$ = {15, 45}

$P(A \cap B) = \dfrac{2}{25}$

$P(A \text{ or } B) = P(A) + P(B) -$

$P(A \cap B) = \dfrac{8}{25} + \dfrac{1}{5} - \dfrac{2}{25} =$

$\dfrac{13}{25} - \dfrac{2}{25} = \dfrac{11}{25}$

10. Let p = probability of
success $\left(\dfrac{10}{50} = \dfrac{1}{5}\right)$
q = probability of
failure $(1 - \dfrac{1}{5} = \dfrac{4}{5})$

$(p + q)^{10} = p^{10} + 10p^9q +$
$45p^8q^2 + 120p^7q^3 + 210p^6q^4 +$
$252p^5q^5 + 210p^4q^6 + 120p^3q^7 +$
$45p^2q^8 + 10pq^9 + q^{10}$

a. P(4 successes out of 10) =
$210p^4q^6 = 210\left(\dfrac{1}{5}\right)^4\left(\dfrac{4}{5}\right)^6 =$
$210\left(\dfrac{1}{625}\right)\left(\dfrac{4,096}{15,625}\right) =$
$\dfrac{860,160}{9,765,625} = \dfrac{172,032}{1,953,125}$ or
0.09

10. b. P(7 successes out of 10) =
$120p^7q^3 = 120\left(\dfrac{1}{5}\right)^7\left(\dfrac{4}{5}\right)^3 =$
$120\left(\dfrac{1}{78,125}\right)\left(\dfrac{64}{125}\right) = \dfrac{7,680}{9,765,625} =$
$\dfrac{1,536}{1,953,125}$ or 0.0008

c. $(p + q)^5 = p^5 + 5p^4q +$
$10p^3q^2 + 10p^2q^3 + 5pq^4 + q^5$
$P(\dfrac{1}{5}$ success out of 5) =
$P(1$ success out of 5) =
$5pq^4 = 5\left(\dfrac{1}{5}\right)\left(\dfrac{4}{5}\right)^4 = 5\left(\dfrac{1}{5}\right)\left(\dfrac{256}{625}\right) =$
$\dfrac{256}{625}$ or 0.4

d. $P(\dfrac{3}{5}$ success out of 5) =
$P(3$ successes out of 5) =
$10p^3q^2 = 10\left(\dfrac{1}{5}\right)^3\left(\dfrac{4}{5}\right)^2 =$
$10\left(\dfrac{1}{125}\right)\left(\dfrac{16}{25}\right) = \dfrac{160}{3,125} =$
$\dfrac{32}{625}$ or 0.05

1. a. When $n = 1$, $\dfrac{1(1 + 1)}{2} =$ $\dfrac{2}{2} = 1.$

   b. Assume $\displaystyle\sum_{i = 1}^{k} i = \dfrac{k(k + 1)}{2}$

   c. Then $\displaystyle\sum_{i = 1}^{k} i + (k + 1) =$

   $\dfrac{k(k + 1)}{2} + k + 1.$

   $\displaystyle\sum_{i = 1}^{k + 1} i =$

   $\dfrac{k(k + 1) + 2(k + 1)}{2} =$

   $\dfrac{k + 1}{2}(k + 2) =$

   $\dfrac{k + 1}{2}[(k + 1) + 1]$

2. $\displaystyle\sum_{i = 1}^{3} i^i = 1^1 + 2^2 + 3^3 =$
   $1 + 4 + 27 = 32$

3. $f(-1) = 2(-1)^2 - 6(-1) - 1 =$
   $2 + 6 - 1 = 8 - 1 = 7$

4. $f(x) = 8x^2 + 7$
   $\dfrac{f(a + h) - f(a)}{h} =$

   $\dfrac{8(a + h)^2 + 7 - (8a^2 + 7)}{h} =$

   $\dfrac{8(a^2 + 2ah + h^2) + 7 - 8a^2 - 7}{h} =$

   $\dfrac{8a^2 + 16ah + 8h^2 + 7 - 8a^2 - 7}{h} =$

   $\dfrac{16ah + 8h^2}{h} = 16a + 8h$

5. $\displaystyle\lim_{x \to 4} 3x^2 = 3(4)^2 = 3(16) = 48$

6. $\displaystyle\lim_{x \to \infty} \dfrac{x^2 + 2x}{3} = \infty$

7. $m = \displaystyle\lim_{h \to 0} \dfrac{f(x + h) - f(x)}{h} =$

   $\displaystyle\lim_{h \to 0} \dfrac{4(x + h) - 6 - (4x - 6)}{h} =$

   $\displaystyle\lim_{h \to 0} \dfrac{4x + 4h - 6 - 4x + 6}{h} =$

   $\displaystyle\lim_{h \to 0} \dfrac{4h}{h} =$

   $\displaystyle\lim_{h \to 0} 4 = 4$

8. Intersection: $x^2 = 4$; $\sqrt{x^2} = \sqrt{4}$; $x = 2$

   Let $m_2 =$ slope of $f(x)$.
   $m_2 = \displaystyle\lim_{h \to 0} \dfrac{f(x + h) - f(x)}{h} =$

   $m_2 = \displaystyle\lim_{h \to 0} \dfrac{(x + h)^2 - x^2}{h} =$

   $\displaystyle\lim_{h \to 0} \dfrac{x^2 + 2xh + h^2 - x^2}{h} =$

   $\displaystyle\lim_{h \to 0} \dfrac{2xh + h^2}{h} =$

   $\displaystyle\lim_{h \to 0} 2x + h = 2x$

   m at $x = 2 = 2(2) = 4$

   Let $m_1 =$ slope of $g(x) = 0$.
   $\tan \theta = \dfrac{m_2 - m_1}{1 + m_2 m_1} = \dfrac{4 - 0}{1 + 4(0)} =$

   $\dfrac{4}{1} = 4$

   $\theta = \arctan 4 = 76°$
   approximately

8. cont.

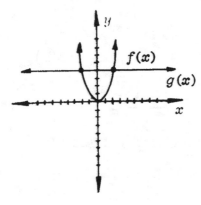

9. Domain: all real numbers;
   $x \in R$

10. Some values of x and y are
    $(\pm 3, -3)$, $(\pm 2, -\frac{4}{3})$, $(\pm 1, -\frac{1}{3})$,
    and $(0, 0)$. Values for y will
    never be greater than zero.
    Therefore, the range is all
    real numbers less than or
    equal to zero; $y \leq 0$.

11. $f(x) + g(x) =$
    $3x^2 + 1 + 5x - 3 =$
    $3x^2 + 5x - 2$

12. $\quad 8x^2 + 2x - 3 \leq 0$
    $(4x + 3)(2x - 1) \leq 0$
    $\quad\quad 4x + 3 \leq 0$
    $4x + 3 - 3 \leq 0 - 3$
    $\quad\quad\quad 4x \leq -3$
    $\quad\quad\quad \frac{4x}{4} \leq \frac{-3}{4}$
    $\quad\quad\quad\quad x \leq -\frac{3}{4}$ and

    $\quad\quad 2x - 1 \leq 0$
    $2x - 1 + 1 \leq 0 + 1$
    $\quad\quad\quad 2x \leq 1$
    $\quad\quad\quad \frac{2x}{2} \leq \frac{1}{2}$
    $\quad\quad\quad\quad x \leq \frac{1}{2}$

    $-\frac{3}{4} \leq x \leq \frac{1}{2}$

13. $\begin{array}{r} 4 \quad\; 2 - 5 + \;8 \\ 0 + 8 + 12 \\ \hline 2 + 3 + 20 \end{array}$

    $P(4) = 20$

14. From the table of trigonometric
    functions, sec 24° 20' = 1.097.

15. $95° = 95° \cdot \frac{\pi}{180°} = \frac{19\pi}{36}$

16.

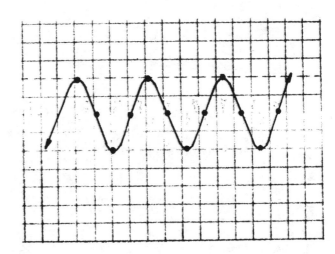

17. $60° = 60° \cdot \frac{\pi}{180°} = \frac{\pi}{3}$

    $\frac{\pi}{3}(24) = 8\pi$

18. $\quad\quad\quad\quad \sin 2\theta = 2 \sin \theta$
    $\quad 2 \sin \theta \cos \theta = 2 \sin \theta$
    $\dfrac{2 \sin \theta \cos \theta}{2 \sin \theta} = \dfrac{2 \sin \theta}{2 \sin \theta}$
    $\quad\quad\quad\quad \cos \theta = 1$
    $\quad\quad\quad\quad\quad \theta = 0°, 180°, 360°$

19. $\sin \theta = \frac{1}{2}$, $\cos \theta = \frac{\sqrt{3}}{2}$

    $\sin \phi = -\frac{\sqrt{3}}{2}$, $\cos \phi = -\frac{1}{2}$

    $\cos (\theta + \phi) = \cos \theta \cos \phi$
    $\quad\quad\quad\quad\quad \sin \theta \sin \phi$

    $\cos (\theta + \phi) = \left(\frac{\sqrt{3}}{2}\right)\left(-\frac{1}{2}\right) -$
    $\quad\quad\quad \left(\frac{1}{2}\right)\left(-\frac{\sqrt{3}}{2}\right) =$
    $\quad\quad -\frac{\sqrt{3}}{4} + \frac{\sqrt{3}}{4} = 0$

20.

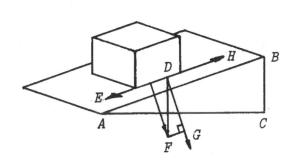

The weight of the ice is represented by $\overrightarrow{DF}$, which is $\perp$ to $\overline{AC}$. $\angle FGD = 90°$ and $\overrightarrow{GD} \perp \overline{AD}$.

$$\sin 15° = \frac{\overrightarrow{GF}}{75}$$
$$\overrightarrow{GF} = 75 \sin 15° =$$
$$75(0.2588) =$$
$$19.41 \text{ or } 19.4)$$

Since the magnitude of $\overrightarrow{DE} = \overrightarrow{GF} = \overrightarrow{DH}$, $\overrightarrow{DH} = 19.4$ lbs.

21.

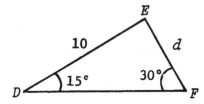

Using the Law of Sines,
$$\frac{\sin 30°}{10} = \frac{\sin 15°}{d}$$

$$d \sin 30° = 10 \sin 15°$$
$$\frac{d \sin 30°}{\sin 30°} = \frac{10 \sin 15°}{\sin 30°}$$
$$d = \frac{10(0.2588)}{\frac{1}{2}}$$
$$2.588(2) = 5.176 \text{ or } 5$$

22.

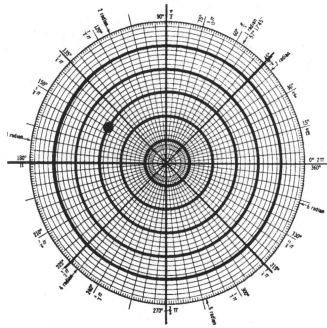

23. $x = r \cos \theta$
$y = r \sin \theta$

$$x^2 + 3y^2 - 6 = 0$$
$$(r \cos \theta)^2 + 3(r \sin \theta)^2 - 6 = 0$$
$$r^2 \cos^2 \theta + 3r^2 \sin^2 \theta - 6 = 0$$
$$r^2(\cos^2 \theta + 3 \sin^2 \theta) - 6 = 0$$

24. $y^2 = 4px$ is the general equation for a parabola in Position I. The focus = $p = 2$.
$$y^2 = 4(2)x$$
$$y^2 = 8x$$

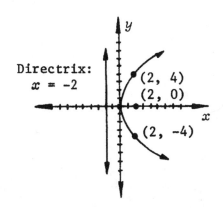

Directrix: $x = -2$

(2, 4)
(2, 0)
(2, -4)

25. $_8C_6 = \dfrac{8!}{6!2!} = \dfrac{8 \cdot 7 \cdot 6!}{6! \cdot 2 \cdot 1} = \dfrac{\overset{4}{\cancel{8}} \cdot 7}{\cancel{2} \cdot \cancel{1}} = 28$

26. $n = 7, \; q = \dfrac{3}{4}, \; p = \dfrac{1}{4}$

$(q + p)^7 = \dbinom{7}{0}\left(\dfrac{3}{4}\right)^7 +$

$\dbinom{7}{1}\left(\dfrac{3}{4}\right)^6\left(\dfrac{1}{4}\right) +$

$\dbinom{7}{2}\left(\dfrac{3}{4}\right)^5\left(\dfrac{1}{4}\right)^2 +$

$\dbinom{7}{3}\left(\dfrac{3}{4}\right)^4\left(\dfrac{1}{4}\right)^3 +$

$\dbinom{7}{4}\left(\dfrac{3}{4}\right)^3\left(\dfrac{1}{4}\right)^4 +$

$\dbinom{7}{5}\left(\dfrac{3}{4}\right)^2\left(\dfrac{1}{4}\right)^5 +$

$\dbinom{7}{6}\left(\dfrac{3}{4}\right)\left(\dfrac{1}{4}\right)^6 + \dbinom{7}{7}\left(\dfrac{1}{4}\right)^7$

Since we are interested
only in the probability
of 3 days of rain, figure
$\dbinom{7}{3}\left(\dfrac{3}{4}\right)^4\left(\dfrac{1}{4}\right)^3$.

$_7C_3 = \dfrac{7!}{3!4!} = \dfrac{7 \cdot 6 \cdot 5 \cdot 4!}{3 \cdot 2 \cdot 1 \cdot 4!} =$

$\dfrac{7 \cdot \cancel{6} \cdot 5}{\cancel{3} \cdot \cancel{2} \cdot \cancel{1}} = 35$

$\dbinom{7}{3}\left(\dfrac{3}{4}\right)^4\left(\dfrac{1}{4}\right)^3 =$

$35\left(\dfrac{81}{256}\right)\left(\dfrac{1}{64}\right) = \dfrac{2{,}835}{16{,}384} = 0.17$